*probabilistic reliability:*

*an engineering approach*

## brooklyn polytechnic institute series

## mcgraw-hill electrical and electronic engineering series

# probabilistic reliability: an engineering approach

MARTIN L. SHOOMAN
Associate Professor of Electrical Engineering
Polytechnic Institute of Brooklyn

McGraw-Hill Book Company
New York   St. Louis   San Francisco   Toronto   London   Sydney

# *probabilistic reliability:*
# *an engineering approach*

*Library of Congress Catalog Card Number* 68-13099

57015

234567890 MAMM 754321069

*To Sylvia, Andy, and Alice*

# *preface*

This book is written as a text for college and industrial courses in reliability, which are rapidly multiplying in number, and is intended for an engineering audience at the level of first-year graduate school or senior undergraduate. The material should also appeal to an industrial reader who has not had formal training in the reliability field. The approach is one of carefully (although not always rigorously) relating reliability concepts and approaches to the basic probability mathematics on which they are based.

The author was first introduced to the subject of reliability in 1956 while working in a control-system research group at the Sperry Gyroscope Co., Great Neck, N.Y. His interest was rekindled in 1962, when he developed a graduate Reliability Analysis course at the Polytechnic Institute of Brooklyn, the notes for which served as the draft for this book. The Poly course is jointly sponsored by the department of Electrical Engineering and the division of Operations Research and Industrial Engineering, which in part accounts for the interdepartmental nature of the course enrollment: 40 percent electrical engineering, 40 percent industrial engineering, and the remaining 20 percent from mathematics, mechanical engineering, aeronautical engineering, and system science. It is anticipated that reliability will become a popular undergraduate senior elective course in the future and will become a required course in system-science curricula.

The need for reliable equipment and reliability analysis became apparent at the close of World War II.   The field came to a focus and began to develop in the early 1950s, when people agreed that the proper definition of reliability was in terms of the probability of success.   This decision marshaled all the powerful techniques of modern probability theory behind the growing field of reliability.   The main theme of this book is the formulation and interpretation of probabilistic reliability models in analysis and the utilization of these techniques for reliability design.   Thus, the probability background of the reader of this book is a matter of prime importance.   The graduate Reliability Analysis course at Poly assumes elementary differential equations and introductory probability as prerequisites.   Occasionally a student has taken this course without the probability prerequisite and is able to keep up with the course by background reading.   Chapter 2 contains a summary of probability and differential equations to serve such a purpose, but in addition it can be used to teach probability as a prelude to reliability if the students have not had such material as a prerequisite, and it can also serve as a review for the student whose probability background needs refreshing.   The reader with a good probability background should thumb through Chapter 2 and begin reading Chapter 3.   The author recommends that when probability and reliability are to be taught in the same course, the material be alternated.   The material in Chapter 2 has been organized to facilitate just such a presentation.   For example, all the material in Chapter 3 can be taught after studying Sections 2.1 to 2.5.   This allows the reader to alternate mathematical background and applications as he progresses through the book.   The author has found this approach far superior to the conventional technique of teaching all probability and then all reliability.   The coverage of a "limited packet" of theory immediately followed by application is highly successful in terms of student interest and absorption.

The author has several suggestions on the organization of material for a course.   If the material in Chapter 2 is to be taught, the book contains adequate material for a two-semester 2-hr-per-week course or, with a little supplementary material, a two-semester 3-hr-per-week course. The author's present graduate course, a 2-hr per-week two-semester course for students with a probability background, covers in entirety Chapters 1 and 3 to 5, reviews the material in Chapter 2 briefly, and selects material from Chapter 6 for the first term.   The second term covers Chapters 7 and 8 and class notes on reliability apportionment, optimization, and statistical reliability tests.   The problems at the end of each chapter are divided into three classes: reinforcement of the material discussed in the text, extension of the theory (denoted by an asterisk), and applications of the underlying principles to allied areas (denoted by a dagger). The selected references listed in the bibliography for each chapter include a brief discussion of the material cited to allow the reader to delve into the source material himself or to read more deeply in an area of particular interest. A Teacher's Manual, available from the publisher, includes solution and discussion of the problems at the end of each chapter. The author also hopes to prepare at some future time recorded television lectures and programmed text material to correlate with this book.

The author would like to point out some specific material and approaches to the reader who is already active in the field of reliability. The material on general combinatorial approaches in Sec. 3.6.5 summarizes some of the recent literature in the field, including some new approximate approaches. In Section 4.4 the concepts of failure density and hazard rate are related to basic probability in a straightforward manner via either of two alternate derivations. The discussions in Sections 5.8 and 5.9 of how and where to apply the joint-density-function method, joint probabilities, or Markov models should help the reader to model simple problems easily and to enumerate the difficulties in complex and difficult problems. The discussion which follows (Section 5.10) on Monte Carlo methods presents the most promising computer solution methods for truly large and complicated problems. The material on digital-computer reliability (Section 6.9) and on renewal theory (Section 6.11) is self-contained and does not assume prior knowledge in the area. Much of the material in Chapter 7 on marginal failures appears for the first time as a cohesive discussion in a reliability book. Some of the physical-failure models presented in Section 8.3 are to the author's knowledge new results.

The author would like to thank all his friends and colleagues for their help and suggestions. Specifically many thanks are due: Professors John Truxal and Mischa Schwartz for their interest and encouragement. In addition the author is deeply indebted to the reviewers: Mr. Leonard Doyon of the Raytheon Co., Professors John Truxal and Robert Boorstyn and Dr. Martin Messinger of Polytechnic Institute of Brooklyn. Although the author accepts all responsibility for any errors or weaknesses in the text, his reviewers' suggestions have been of great help in rewriting the final draft into a completed manuscript. The clarification of probability fundamentals by Professors Boorstyn and Papoulis, comments on network sensitivity by Professor Belove, and Dr. Messinger's contribution of new ideas (many developed in conjunction with his Ph.D. dissertation) were of great help. Some of the reliability research which the author has engaged in was supported by the Air Force Office of Scientific Research of the Office of Aerospace Research under contract

No. AF-(648)-1402.   A large number of typists and illustrators worked on the manuscript in its various stages; in order to avoid an inadvertent omission the author thanks them as a group.   He would like to thank Mr. Max Bashoff for his patient proofreading help.   Lastly, he wishes to thank his wife for her constant encouragement and proofreading help.

Martin L. Shooman

# contents

## chapter 6   reliability improvement    267

## chapter 7   drift failures, component tolerances, and parameter variations    364

# *1*

# *introduction*

## 1.1 INTRODUCTION

Reliability is a relatively new field whose conception is primarily due to the complexity, sophistication, and automation inherent in modern technology. The problems of maintenance, repair, and field failures became severe for the military equipment used in World War II. In the late 1940s and early 1950s reliability engineering appeared on the scene. The fields of communication and transportation were perhaps the first to witness rapid growth in complexity as advances in electronics and control systems spurred equipment manufacturers.

The 5-tube superheterodyne table radio is a fairly complex device but is much simpler and more trouble-free than the early 30-tube television receivers. The addition of the video channel greatly increased not only the number of components but also the complexity and thereby the realm of possible malfunctions. In the early days of television, standard antenna and transmission line designs were inadequate for fringe reception. Horizontal and vertical synchronizing (hold) circuits were too temperamental, and the small performance latitude provided by some of the circuits necessitated frequent adjustment (generally by skilled servicemen) as parts aged. The present black and white television receiver has reached a refined level of design, and most service problems

| Year | No. of sets | No. Sylvania tubes tested | No. Sylvania tubes failed | Percent failure |
|---|---|---|---|---|
| July 1954 – 1955 | 120 | 2300 | 209 | 9.1 |
| July 1955 – 1956 | 157 | 3244 | 205 | 6.3 |
| July 1956 – 1957 | 89 | 1291 | 58 | 4.5 |

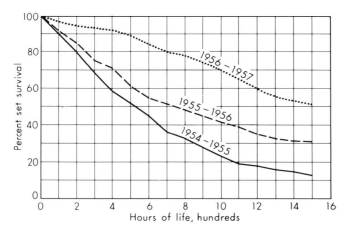

**Fig. 1.1**   Percent television-set survival for transformer-powered sets with Sylvania tubes.   (*E. H. Boden, IRE Trans. Reliability Quality Control, vol. PGRQC*-13, *July,* 1958.)

can be handled by the owner by replacement of failed vacuum tubes with the aid of the corner-drugstore tube checker.

The results of Fig. 1.1 substantiate the improvement in television-set reliability as a function of better tubes.   This trend has probably continued for more modern receivers.   The article by Boden cited in Fig. 1.1 reveals an interesting sidelight.   In order to reduce test time many sets were operated at 130 volts rather than 117 volts.   The failure rate of the 130-volt test group was 2.4 times that of the 117-volt control group.

As transistorized and integrated circuitry gradually replaces vacuum-tube versions, the longer life of the solid-state devices will improve reliability.   There are indications that the color television set and the stereophonic high-fidelity receiver are undergoing a shorter transition time from the early commercial product to the trouble-free refined version. There are many similar examples in the field of military communication equipment, but they are harder to document.

An interesting compilation of military-system reliability is given in

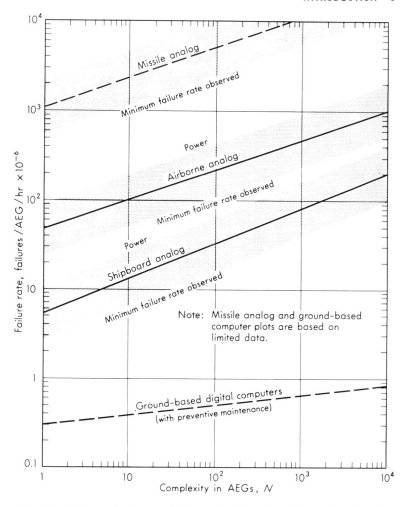

**Fig. 1.2** Failure rates for reliability estimation when the number of active elements is known. (*From "Handbook of Reliability Engineering," Bureau of Naval Weapons Handbook, NAVWEPS 100-65-502, 1964.*)

Fig. 1.2. The analog systems are actually analog-type systems, as contrasted with the ground-based digital computers. The data are plotted as a function of the number of active element groups (AEG) in the system. As intuition would predict, the failure rate (failures per hour) increases with the severity of the environment. Thus, a missile component is subject to much greater vibration, temperature extremes, changes in pressure, etc., than a ground-based computer. The shaded areas indicate the band of observed values, with power-handling falling at the upper extreme.

One can correlate the information of Figs. 1.1 and 1.2 in a simple manner. The simplest and most common reliability function is an exponential, $R(t) = e^{-\lambda t}$. (The derivation of this function appears in Chap. 4.) The parameter $\lambda$ is the failure rate in failures per hour. The curves in Fig. 1.1 are roughly exponential, and the parameter $\lambda$ for the 1956–1957 data can be estimated[1] as $0.5 \times 10^{-3}$. Assuming that a television set has 30 active element groups and using the shipboard analog curve in Fig. 1.2, we obtain a failure rate of $20 \times 10^{-6}$ failures per hr. Multiplying this by the 30 active element groups, we obtain another estimate for $\lambda = 30 \times 20 \times 10^{-6} = 0.6 \times 10^{-3}$ failures per hr. A more convenient way to express this result is to use the mean time to failure (MTTF) as a figure of merit. A careful derivation of the MTTF is given in Chap. 4. We may explain MTTF simply as the average failure time for a large number of items placed on life test. For the case where $R(t) = e^{-\lambda t}$, the MTTF is $1/\lambda$. Thus, for a television set we estimate that the MTTF is approximately 2,000 hr. Many families watch television extensively, say, for an average of 12 hr per day. This would predict about two television-set failures per year. If the owner tests his own tubes, it might cost him $3 per year for the two tubes, whereas a repair man might charge $20 for the two tube replacements. Even in the latter case the repairs would run only about 10 percent of the initial cost per year for a $200 television set.

The automobile and truck are not only a cornerstone of our modern economy but are the most used transportation vehicles. From the beginning repair and replacement have been a key factor in the use of an automobile. With the advent of automatic transmissions, power-assist equipment, and air conditioning, the automobile has grown in complexity. The rise in sales of a more complex and expensive product has required a concomitant gain in quality control of the product. The rising cost of skilled labor has greatly increased the cost of automobile repairs, and the lack of emphasis on skill and thoroughness has compounded the problem. In response to consumer dissatisfaction automobile manufacturers have increased the length of their service warranties up to 5 years or 50,000 miles on certain subsystems. The following calculation is instructive in that it relates 50,000 miles of driving to an equivalent number of operating hours.

If we assume that a vehicle is driven a total of 50 miles to and from work for 5 days per week and 150 miles for pleasure over the weekend,

---

[1] The value $1/\lambda$ is taken as the time at which the percent survival drops to 0.368, which is by extrapolation about 2,000 hr.

a total of about 10,000 miles per year is accumulated.    If the average speed driving to work is 20 mph and weekend cruising is at an average of 50 mph, the car is used 5.5 hr per week.    For 5 years of 50 weeks each, the total operating time is 1,375 hr.    Thus, 5 years' automobile usage amounts to about 0.16 years of time.    Although the accumulated aging process after 5 years is of great importance in the deterioration of an automobile, the reliability is primarily a function of miles traveled. Thus, although we have no statistical data, experience with automobiles predicts an MTTF of a few thousand operating hours.    Whenever the reliability of a product affects human life, the reliability problem usually becomes part of a large issue called safety.    Although the transportation industry has many accomplishments in this area, there is still much to be done.

The viewpoint of this book is that reliability considerations are an important factor in any engineering design.    This means that in evaluating system usefulness or goodness, reliability must take its proper place among performance, cost, size, weight, etc.    The technique for optimizing system goodness subject to various constraints is properly a topic covered in operations research or value analysis.    Some of the problems in the text will deal with such engineering compromises.    The following two examples illustrate how reliability must be viewed as one of the cornerstones of any well-balanced design.

Reliability engineering has been stressed for several years in the field of military-aircraft design and is becoming increasingly important to commercial-aircraft manufacturers.    One can divide an aircraft into three basic subsystems, the structure, the propulsion, and the avionics (aircraft electronics).    The avionics subsystem has grown increasingly important as the complexity of aircraft has increased (see Fig. 1.3).    The reliability of aircraft structures has in most cases been satisfactory, probably due in good part to the safety-factor technique used in structural design and to the routine inspection and test system for aircraft.

In the case of jet engines, the MTTF is greater than $10^4$ hr, because engines are torn down for overhaul every few thousand hours.    Also there is inherent redundancy since a four-engine plane needs only two engines to perform critical functions.    Thus, if only two out of four engines are needed for a 20-hr mission with an engine MTTF of $10^4$ hr, the probability of aircraft failure is $3.2 \times 10^{-8}$.†

Because avionics systems are newer devices and very complex, and since electronic designers tend to be less conservative than their mechanical counterparts, the mean time between failures (MTBF) for commercial avionics systems containing about $10^4$ parts is under 100 hr (see Fig. 1.4).

---

† See the example in Sec. 5.5.4 for the details of this computation.

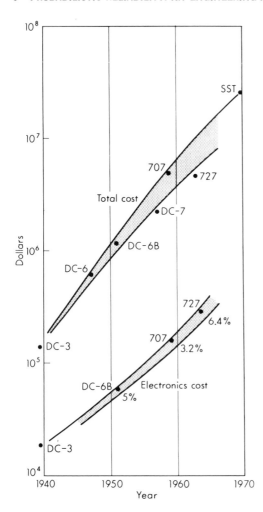

**Fig. 1.3** Dollar cost of commercial avionics for various aircraft produced by the Boeing and Douglas companies. (*E. J. Nalos and R. B. Schultz, Reliability and Cost of Avionics, IEEE Trans. Reliability, October, 1965.*)

Even though not all parts of the avionics system are crucial to flight safety, it is clear that avionics reliability must be greatly improved to make it compatible with engine reliability. (The $3.2 \times 10^{-8}$ failure probability is for a 20-hr mission.) This formidable task could be done by raising the MTBF of an avionics system to approximately $10^5$ hr and using two parallel systems operating redundantly.[1] Alternately, with an MTBF of approximately $10^4$ hr for a single system, one can use three parallel systems in a redundant configuration to increase the reliability to the desired level. Of course either scheme calls for an increase in basic system reliability by a factor of $10^2$ or more.

[1] In Chap. 6 we shall study more efficient schemes for employing redundancy than this one.

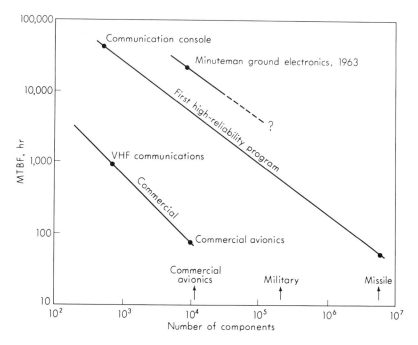

**Fig. 1.4**  Comparison of mean time between failures for commercial equipment and high-reliability military equipment.  (*E. J. Nalos and R. B. Schultz, Reliability and Cost of Avionics, IEEE Trans. Reliability, October,* 1965.)

The Minuteman missile program included a reliability program running into hundreds of millions of dollars.  Part of this program was the development of a line of high-reliability, premium-quality, and premium-cost parts, which were designed to be used with sizable safety factors. Figure 1.4 illustrates what sort of gains in system reliability might be expected using such parts.

The first high-reliability program, shown in Fig. 1.4 (Minuteman), used component-circuit-card techniques.  The best reliability depicted by the top curve was achieved by Minuteman components using microelectronic technology.  The reliability gains achieved by using high-reliability parts such as those described are about two or three orders of magnitude for systems with parts counts of $10^4$.  Of course to sell such a system to the conservative airline industry, volume, weight, and cost must be kept to a minimum.  Figures 1.5 to 1.7 illustrate what sort of trends we may expect.  The conclusion that Nalos and Schultz[1] reach is that by 1970

[1] E. J. Nalos and R. B. Schulz, Reliability and Cost of Avionics, *IEEE Trans. Reliability*, October, 1965.

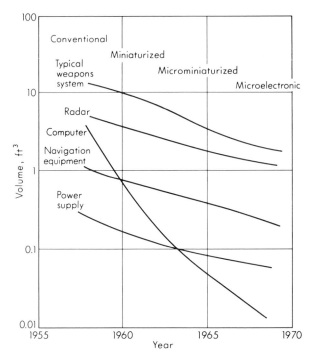

**Fig. 1.5** Volume trends of military avionic equipment. (*E. J. Nalos and R. B. Schultz, Reliability and Cost of Avionics, IEEE Trans. Reliability, October,* 1965.)

redundant, highly reliable microelectronic avionics systems will be feasible for commercial aircraft at attractive weight, size, and cost figures.[1]

Another area of modern technology intimately involved with reliability is our space program. Even the casual observer realizes that the percentage of successful space launchings has increased dramatically since the early days of our space program. For example, in the short period from 1961 to 1964 the percentage of successful missions performed by NASA increased from 62 to 83 percent.[2] A striking example of the cost penalty for low-reliability equipment is given in a paper by Myers,[3] which describes a satellite communications system using four active-

[1] This assumes that we are talking about a 1970 commercial version of a 1965 advanced avionics system. The increases in complexity of avionics by 1970 may outweigh the gains made possible by perfected integrated circuits.

[2] W. M. Redler, Parts Reliability Problems in Aerospace Systems, *IEEE, New York Conf. Electron. Reliability,* May, 1965.

[3] R. H. Myers, Which Road to Satellite Reliability, *Ann. Conv. Trans. Am. Soc. Quality Control,* 1961.

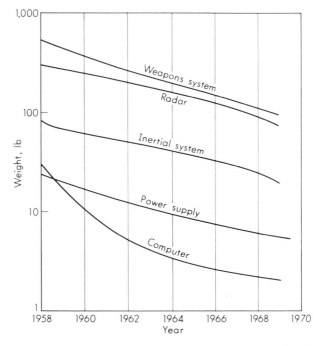

**Fig. 1.6**  Weight trends of military avionic equipment.  (*E. J. Nalos and R. B. Schultz, Reliability and Cost of Avionics, IEEE Trans. Reliability, October,* 1965.)

relay orbiting satellites.  Assuming a missile reliability of 0.8 and a guidance reliability of 0.8 yields a probability of 0.64 of successful orbiting.  (This figure is somewhat lower than the previously quoted NASA figures.)  The cost per launching is $6 million.  These figures are combined with the satellite reliability to yield Fig. 1.8.  The operating costs for a four-satellite system decreases with increased reliability.  At an MTTF of about 30,000 hr, or about $4\frac{1}{2}$ years, the cost is about $50 million per year.  To estimate the reliability of a communications satellite, we can compare it with the parts count and estimated MTTF for other space vehicles given in Table 1.1.  A 40,000-hr MTBF is seen to be about the best figure one can expect.  If the reliability were at the level of the Mariner or USSR Venus probe, the operating costs would be nearly $1 billion per year.  The message of the example is clear: in space programs reliability engineering is not a costly extra but the only possible way to try and keep the tremendous costs within bounds by making every rocket shot count.

One of the foremost problems facing our modern urban society is transportation.  Experience has shown that in and around a major metro-

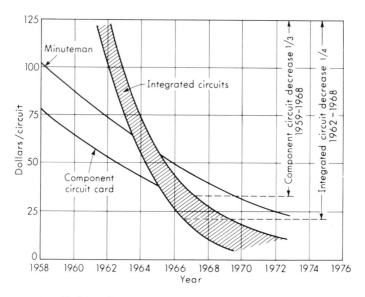

**Fig. 1.7** Estimated costs of microavionics and printed-circuit constructions. (*E. J. Nalos and R. B. Schultz, Reliability and Cost of Avionics, IEEE Trans. Reliability, October, 1965.*)

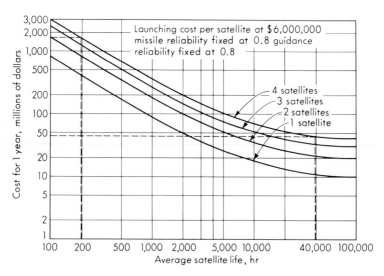

**Fig. 1.8** Operating cost vs. satellite reliability levels. (*R. H. Myers, Ann. Conv. Trans. Am. Soc. Quality Control, 1961.*)

**Table 1.1  Parts count and estimated reliability**

| System | Total No. of parts | Part failure rate per hr | Estimated MTTF, hr† |
|---|---|---|---|
| DOD spacecraft (four units) | 25,800 | $1.0 \times 10^{-9}$ | $3.9 \times 10^4$ |
| DOD spacecraft (four units) | 4,700–13,400 | $4.5 \times 10^{-9}$ | $1.7$–$4.7 \times 10^4$ |
| Tiros (six units) | 5,000 | $80 \times 10^{-9}$ | $0.25 \times 10^4$ |
| Syncom (one unit) | 3,500 | $38 \times 10^{-9}$ | $0.75 \times 10^4$ |
| Mariner Venus probe | (25,000) 7,500 crit. | $4 \times 10^{-7}$ | 330 |
| USSR Venus probe | ? | ? | Probe failed after 360 hr |
| Mariner 4 | 30,000 | $20 \times 10^{-9}$‡ | $0.17 \times 10^4$ |

† MTTF is calculated as the reciprocal of the product of the number of parts and the failure rate per part.

‡ April, 1965.

SOURCE: W. M. Redler, Parts Reliability Problems in Aerospace Systems, *IEEE New York Conf. Electron. Reliability*, May, 1965.

politan area, the growth in modern highway building has been badly outdistanced by the increase in automobile ownership and usage.    High-speed high-passenger-density rail transportation seems to be the appropriate solution for the 1970s and 1980s.    High reliability is important in such systems, not only from the safety standpoint, but as a vital necessity if passengers are to abandon their passenger cars and ride public transportation.

As an example consider the Bay Area Rapid Transit (BART) System[1] which is to begin operation in the San Francisco, California, area in 1969. A typical commuting ride of 25 miles, which takes about 1 hr by automobile, is to be replaced by a quiet, air-conditioned, high-speed railroad ride of about 30 min.    Trains will leave about every 3 min during rush hours and *average* 50 mph, including 20-sec stops.    The maximum rush-hour traffic density will be roughly 1,500 passengers per train, or 30,000 passengers per hour.

A train breakdown results not only in railroad repair costs but also in passenger delays, which are intangible but of great importance in terms of human costs.    We might place a tangible value on human time wasted by assessing it at $1.50 per hour (certainly the Bay Area commuters would think this a very conservative figure).    Thus, a $\frac{1}{2}$-hr delay of one train load of 1,500 passengers would be valued at $1,125.    If the breakdown of the one train actually delayed successive trains $\frac{1}{2}$ hr each over a period

[1] Getting to Work and Back, *Consumer Rept.*, February, 1965.

of 1 hr, 30,000 passengers would be involved, and the cost would rise to $22,500.   If delays were frequent enough to turn the commuter back to his automobile, he would pay back the $4.75 per day he gained by riding the railroad.   Such a reduction in passenger load would also adversely affect the railroad profit structure, adding more losses.

These examples represent just a few areas in which reliability must play an important engineering role.   The reader can no doubt add many more.   One might well ponder the costs of a central-computer failure in a totally automated factory or reflect on the fact that failure of an electronic heart pacemaker is truly a matter of life and death.


## 1.2  HISTORY OF RELIABILITY

Reliability was first recognized as a pressing need during World War II. The preliminary steps taken were to establish joint Army and Navy (JAN) parts standards and to set up the Vacuum Tube Development Committee (VTDC) in June, 1943.   At the close of the war, between 1945 and 1950, several studies revealed some startling results:

1  A Navy study made during maneuvers showed that the electronic equipment was operative only 30 percent of the time.
2  An Army study revealed that between two-thirds and three-fourths of their equipment was out of commission or under repairs.
3  An Air Force study conducted over a 5-year period disclosed that repair and maintenance costs were about 10 times the original cost.
4  A study uncovered the fact that for every tube in use there were one on the shelf and seven in transit.
5  Approximately one electronics technician was required for every 250 tubes.
6  In 1937 a destroyer had 60 tubes; in 1952 the number had risen to 3,200.

These findings served as an impetus for further investigations.

One focal point of trouble appeared to be the vacuum tube.   Following the VTDC, an airlines group set up a study in 1946 aimed at development of better electronic tubes.   This was followed by parallel studies conducted by Aeronautical Radio, Inc. and Cornell University, in which, respectively, 45,000 and 100,000 defective tubes were examined.   Between 1949 and 1953 Vitro Laboratories and Bell Laboratories pursued similar studies on the failure of parts other than vacuum tubes, such as resistors, capacitors, transformers, relays, etc.   In 1950 the Department of Defense established an ad hoc committee on reliability, which in 1952 became a permanent group called the Advisory Group on the Reliability of Electronic Equipment (AGREE).    An AGREE report was published in 1957, which was shortly followed by a specification on the reliability of military electronic equipment.

Since the mid-1950s much work has been done on reliability analysis. The titles *reliability engineer* and *reliability group* have been born.    Several texts have appeared on the subject of reliability, and college and industrial courses on reliability have been initiated.    Many bibliographies have been published in various sources.[1]    NASA currently publishes a monthly digest entitled Reliability Abstracts and Technical Reviews, containing about 50 one-page reviews.    Research results are printed in many different journals and presented at a large number of conferences. Three research publications of particular interest are *The IEEE Transactions on Reliability; The Proceedings of the Annual Symposium on Reliability*, a symposium sponsored by the IEEE and the ASQC; and *The Proceedings of the Annual Reliability and Maintainability Conference*, sponsored by the SAE, ASME, and AIAA.

## 1.3  SCOPE OF THE TEXT

The approach used in reliability work varies with the individual and the organization.    In a field as young as this, few established schools or doctrines are prevalent.    Thus, the mathematician faced with a reliability problem often treats it as an exercise in applied probability or statistics.    A manager attempts to organize a reliability group, which often turns out to be a staff organization.    The quality-control expert views reliability as an extension of his efforts.    The components engineer tries to buy the best and most reliable parts.    The system engineer looks for an inherently simple scheme which will lead to a reliable design.

In actuality no single approach is satisfactory, and the problem must be approached at all levels and at each step of the industrial process. Thus, reliability is essentially a birth-to-death problem, involving such areas as raw material and parts quality, conceptual design, detailed engineering design, production, test and quality control, product shipment, warehouse storage, operator skill and technique, maintenance, and product use.

Since it is impossible to treat such a broad spectrum of topics in one

[1] Two selected bibliographies which are of interest are G. H. Weiss, A Survey of Mathematical Models in the Theory of Reliability, in M. Zelen (ed.), "Statistical Theory of Reliability," The University of Wisconsin Press, Madison, Wis., 1963, with 85 references listed; and H. S. Balaban, A Selected Bibliography on Reliability and Quality Control, *IRE Trans. Reliability Quality Control*, July, 1962.

volume, several of the fundamental areas of interest to the engineer are developed in an integrated fashion.   The viewpoint is that each system engineer need not be a reliability expert but must be cognizant of the available techniques of reliability analysis, reliability design, and reliability improvement.   Reliability must be considered in evaluation of the system along with performance, weight, cost, volume, etc.

Certain topics, such as field-failure reporting schemes, are not covered in this text, since the author believes that reading a detailed case study on such a topic is often more instructive than a textbook discussion would be.   Other topics, such as acceptance testing and design of experiments, are of considerable interest but are excluded on the basis of space limitations.

## PROBLEMS

1.1   Try to estimate on the basis of your own experience and reading, the reliability of:

| | |
|---|---|
| (a)   Your TV set | (b)   Your automobile |
| (c)   Your washing machine | (d)   Your home heating unit |
| (e)   A satellite rocket booster | (f)   Your wristwatch |
| (g)   A telephone | |

Clearly state your assumptions concerning the usage factor of each device. Compute the mean time between failures.

1.2   The news sign on the old Times tower in Times Square contained about 13,000 light bulbs.   Assume that the average light bulb burns for 1,000 hr before failure and is governed by the exponential reliability law, $R(t) = e^{-\lambda t}$.   If each bulb failure is independent, the system $\lambda$ is the sum of the component $\lambda$'s.   How long would you expect to wait for the first failure?   Do the results make sense?   Do you think the assumptions are valid?

1.3   The following data are taken from an article by G. J. Levenback (see the Bibliography for Chap. 1): The oldest transatlantic telephone cable was put into service in 1956, and by 1965 no failures had occurred.   The connection is actually composed of a pair of 2,000-mile cables each carrying a one-way transmission. Amplifiers are spaced at 40-mile intervals, and each contains about 60 parts. Assume independent parts with identical failure rates equal to $\lambda$.   What must the system reliability be if we require only one amplifier failure in 20 years? Assuming an exponential failure law and that the system $\lambda$ is the sum of the part $\lambda$'s, what must be the part $\lambda$'s?

1.4   The cable in Prob. 1.3 is capable of carrying 36 conversations.   Assume that transatlantic call time averages $10 per 3 min.   The cost of a repair ship is about $500,000, and it takes about 1 week to reach and repair a break.   How much extra could you pay for each amplifier component if one could increase the system reliability to 1 failure per 30 years?

# *mathematical background*

## 2.1 INTRODUCTION

Most modern engineering disciplines are based on applied mathematics, and reliability leans heavily on probability for its underlying support. A good working knowledge of probability theory is necessary for any real appreciation of reliability. The reader who is familiar with the details of modern probability at the level covered in undergraduate texts such as Wadsworth and Bryan[1] or Freund[2] will need to refer to this chapter only occasionally. It is suggested that he scan the material and skip to Chap. 3. This chapter serves best the needs of a reader with an elementary knowledge of probability theory who needs review and extension of his background before he begins. For a reader with this background it is suggested that Secs. 2.2 to 2.4 be read with care before skipping to Chap. 3. An attempt has been made to compartmentalize Chap. 2 so that each following chapter is built upon the background in a few sections of Chap. 2. This should enable the reader to skip back and forth between the background material in this chapter and later chapters.

[1] G. P. A. Wadsworth and J. P. Bryan, "Introduction to Probability and Random Variables," McGraw Hill Book Company, New York, 1960.

[2] John E. Freund, "Mathematical Statistics," Prentice-Hall, Inc., Englewood Cliffs, N.J., 1962.

The introduction to each following chapter refers the reader to the appropriate background section in Chap. 2, thus allowing the reader to progress into the text without having to digest all of Chap. 2 first. If the reader has no background in probability, a detailed study of Chap. 2 along with some of the selected references listed for Chap. 2 in the bibliography is indicated.

The analysis of complicated reliability problems often becomes lengthy or difficult, and transform methods or computer solutions are often necessary to complete the problem. Since the topic of reliability appeals to a rather broad group of people with various backgrounds, sections on matrices and Laplace transforms are included. Analog computation and digital computation are discussed in Appendixes A and B, in the event the reader is unfamiliar with the details of these techniques.

For these reasons, the material in Chap. 2 is organized in a functional fashion, which may conflict occasionally with the order of theoretical development one generally finds in a probability text. Also, in an attempt to be concise, the examples and problems used deal almost wholly with reliability and its engineering applications. This principle of adhering to examples and problems within the realm of reliability is followed only in Chap. 2. In subsequent chapters problems and examples are inserted from other allied fields in order to show that the application of probability to reliability is not particularly unique, the point being that once the reader has learned how to apply probability to one engineering field, the application to others is much easier. One of the clearest examples of this is the unity between the material in Sec. 2.3, the contents of Chap. 3, and digital-computer logic.

## 2.2  PROBABILITY THEORY

"Probability had its beginnings in the 17th century when the Chevalier de Méré, supposedly an ardent gambler, became puzzled over how to divide the winnings in a game of chance. He consulted the French mathematician Blaise Pascal (1623–1662), who in turn wrote about this matter to Pierre Fermat (1601–1665); it is this correspondence which is generally considered the origin of modern probability theory."[1] In the eighteenth century Karl Gauss (1777–1855) and Pierre Laplace (1749–1827) further developed probability theory and applied it to fields other than games of chance.

The solution of an engineering problem involving probability is divided into three phases:

1  Transition of the physical problem into a mathematical statement, often called *modeling* of the problem.

[1] *Ibid.*

2 Application of the laws of probability theory in order to solve the probabilistic model.

3 Interpretation of the mathematical results in terms of engineering principles.

Chapter 2 of this book is primarily concerned with phase 2, a brief study of the laws of probability theory.  Section 2.10 discusses some topics in estimation theory which deal with measurement of the parameters of the probability model from test data.  This topic really relates to phases 1 and 2 listed above.  Some of the illustrative problems of this chapter and the rest of the book deal with how phases 1 and 3 apply to reliability problems.

Today probability theory is viewed in three different ways:[1] the a priori, or equally-likely-events approach, the relative-frequency approach, and the axiomatic definition.  It is perhaps intuitive to state that the probability of obtaining the number 2 on a single roll of a die is $\frac{1}{6}$.  Assuming each of the six faces is equally likely and that there is one favorable outcome, we merely take the ratio.  This is a convenient approach; however, it falls down in the case of a loaded die, where all events are not equally likely, and also in the case of compound events, where the definition of "equally likely" is not at all obvious.  The relative-frequency approach begins with a discussion of an experiment such as the rolling of a die.  The experiment is repeated $n$ times (or $n$ *identical* dice are all rolled at the same time in *identical* fashion).  If $n_2$ represents the number of times that two dots face up, then the ratio $n_2/n$ is said to approach the probability of rolling a 2 as $n$ approaches infinity.  The requirement that the experiment be repeated an infinite number of times and that the probability be defined as the limit of the frequency ratio can cause theoretical problems unless stated with care.  The newest and most generally accepted approach is to base probability theory on three fundamental axioms.  The entire theory is built in a deductive manner on these axioms in much the same way plane geometry is developed in an axiomatic manner.  This approach has the advantage that if it is followed carefully, there are no loopholes, and all properties are well defined.  As with any other theory or abstract model, the engineering usefulness of the technique is measured by how well it describes problems in the physical world.  In order to evaluate the parameters in the axiomatic model one may perform an experiment and utilize the relative-frequency interpretation or evoke a hypothesis on the basis of equally likely events.  In fact a good portion of mathematical statistics is devoted to sophisticated techniques for determining probability values from an experiment.

---

[1] A. Papoulis, "Probability, Random Variables, and Stochastic Processes," McGraw Hill Book Company, New York, 1965.

The axiomatic approach begins with a statement of the three fundamental axioms of probability:

1  The probability that an event $A$ occurs is a number between zero
   and unity:

$$0 \leq P(A) \leq 1 \tag{2.1}$$

2  The probability of a certain event (also called the *entire sample space*
   or the *universal set*) is unity:

$$P(S) = 1 \tag{2.2}$$

3  The probability of the *union* (also called sum) of two *disjoint* (also
   called *mutually exclusive*) events is the sum of the probabilities:

$$P(A_1 + A_2) = P(A_1) + P(A_2) \tag{2.3}$$

In order to appreciate the meaning of these three statements, one must
learn a few basic definitions and results from the theory of sets.   The
next section introduces these results and presents a discussion of the
development of probability theory.

## 2.3   SET THEORY

### 2.3.1   DEFINITIONS

Since axiomatic probability is based on set theory, we shall briefly
discuss a few concepts of sets.   The same concept often appears in set
theory and in probability theory, with different notation and nomenclature being used for the same ideas.   A *set* is simply a collection or
enumeration of objects.   The order in which the objects of the set are
enumerated is not significant.   Typical sets are the numbers 1, 2, 3, all
100 cars in the parking lot, and the 52 cards in a deck.   Each item in the
collection is an *element* of the set.   Thus, in the examples given there are
3, 100, and 52 elements, respectively.   Each set (except the trivial one
composed of only one element) contains a number of *subsets*.   The subsets are defined by a smaller number of elements selected from the original
set.   To be more specific one first defines the largest set of any interest
in the problem and calls this the *universal set* $U$.   The universal set contains all possible elements in the problem.   Thus, a universal set of $n$
elements has a maximum of $2^n$ distinct subsets.   The universal set might
be all cars in the United States, all red convertibles in New York, or all
cars in the parking lot.   This is a chosen collection which is fixed throughout a problem.   In probability theory, the type of sets one is interested

in are those which can, at least in theory, be viewed as outcomes of an experiment. These sets are generally called *events*. It is often more convenient if the events are defined so that they cannot be subdivided; i.e., each event contains only one element. For example, in some card games of chance only the numbers on the cards may count, and 13 events are necessary, 1, 2, 3, 4, 5, 6, 7, 8, 9, 10, J, Q, K. In other games only the suits count, and spades, hearts, diamonds, and clubs would represent the four events. When the game of chance involves a single draw of a card from a deck, one can construct a universal set composed of 52 elements, where one element is associated with each card in the deck.

When the concept of universal set is used in probability theory, the term *sample space S* is generally applied. Thus, one could say the sample space corresponds to all the cards in the deck and that there are 52 distinct events each corresponding to the draw of a particular card. If we consider a game of two consecutive draws with replacement and shuffle between draws, the sample space would contain $52 \times 52 = 2,704$ events. It is often convenient to associate a geometric picture, called a *Venn diagram*, with these ideas of sample space and event (or set and subset). In Fig. 2.1$a$ the area inside the rectangle corresponds to the sample space. In Fig. 2.1$b$ all 52 events corresponding to each card in the deck are

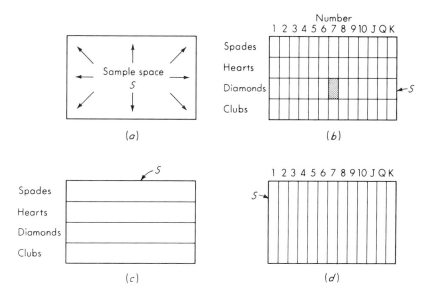

**Fig. 2.1** Venn diagrams indicating sample spaces and events associated with a deck of cards. (*a*) Sample space; (*b*) sample space and events for a deck of cards; (*c*) the four events spades, hearts, diamonds, clubs; (*d*) the thirteen events 1, 2, 3, 4, 5, 6, 7, 8, 9, 10, J, Q, K.

shown.   The shaded box represents the event seven of diamonds.   In Fig. 2.1c the four events corresponding to the four suits are shown, and in Fig. 2.1d the thirteen events corresponding to the thirteen card values are depicted.

### 2.3.2  AXIOMATIC PROBABILITY

With the above background one can intelligently discuss the meaning of probability axioms 1 and 2 given in Eqs. (2.1) and (2.2).   Equation (2.1) implies that the probability of an event $A$ is a positive number between zero and one.   From the relative-frequency interpretation we know that the probability of a certain event is unity and the probability of an impossible event is zero.   All other events have probabilities between zero and unity.   In Eq. (2.2) we let the event $A$ be the entire sample space $S$, and not too surprisingly we find that this is a certain event.   This is true because we say that $S$ occurs if at least one element of $S$ occurs.   In terms of our card-deck example, when we draw a card, we must get one of the cards in the deck; therefore this is a certain event.

### 2.3.3  UNION AND INTERSECTION

Inspection of Fig. 2.1c and d immediately suggests that one should be able to obtain the event spades or the event jack by some combination of the more basic card events given in Fig. 2.1b.   The reader must take care not to jump to any hasty conclusions about combinatorial operations or probabilities.   To place the discussion on a firm basis one must define certain set-theory operations and then proceed to the probability interpretation.

The union of sets $A_1$ and $A_2$ is a third set $B$.   Set $B$ contains all the elements which are in set $A_1$ or in set $A_2$ or in both sets $A_1$ and $A_2$. Symbolically,

$$B = A_1 \cup A_2 \qquad \text{or} \qquad B = A_1 + A_2 \tag{2.4}$$

The $\cup$ notation is more common in mathematical work, whereas the $+$ notation is commonly used in applied work.   The union operation is most easily explained in terms of the Venn diagram of Fig. 2.2a.   Set $A_1$ is composed of disjoint subsets $C_1$ and $C_2$ and set $A_2$ of disjoint subsets $C_2$ and $C_3$.   Subset $C_2$ represents points common to $A_1$ and $A_2$, whereas $C_1$ represents points in $A_1$ but not in $A_2$, and $C_3$ represents points that are in $A_2$ but not $A_1$.   When the two sets have no common elements, the areas do not overlap (Fig. 2.2b), and they are said to be *disjoint* or *mutually exclusive*.   The intersection of events $A_1$ and $A_2$ is defined as a third set $D$ which is composed of all elements which are contained in both $A_1$ and $A_2$.   The notation is:

$$D = A_1 \cap A_2 \qquad \text{or} \qquad D = A_1 A_2 \tag{2.5}$$

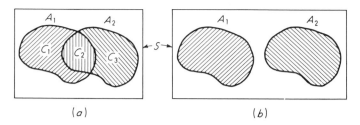

**Fig. 2.2**    Venn diagram illustrating the union of sets $A_1$ and $A_2$.
(*a*) Ordinary sets; (*b*) disjoint sets.

As before, the former symbol is more common in mathematical literature and the latter more common in applied work. In Fig. 2.2*a*, $A_1A_2 = C_2$, and in Fig. 2.2*b*, $A_1A_2 = 0$. If two sets are disjoint, they contain no common elements, and their intersection is zero. (A set with no elements is called a *null set.*)

### 2.3.4 PROBABILITY OF A DISJOINT UNION

We can now interpret the third probability axiom given in Eq. (2.3). In terms of the card-deck example we see immediately that the events in the sample space of Fig. 2.1*b* are disjoint and

$$P(\text{spades}) = P(S_1 + S_2 + \cdots + S_Q + S_K)$$

Since all events are disjoint,

$$P(\text{spades}) = P(S_1) + P(S_2) + \cdots + P(S_Q) + P(S_K) \qquad (2.6)$$

From the equally-likely-events hypothesis one would expect that for a fair deck (without nicks, spots, bumps, torn corners, or other marking)

$$P(\text{spades}) = \tfrac{1}{52} + \tfrac{1}{52} + \cdots + \tfrac{1}{52} + \tfrac{1}{52} = \tfrac{13}{52} = \tfrac{1}{4}$$

Similarly the probability of event jack is

$$P(\text{jack}) = P(S_J + H_J + D_J + C_J) = P(S_J) + P(H_J) \\ + P(D_J) + P(C_J) \quad (2.7)$$

Again hypothesizing equally likely events gives

$$P(\text{jack}) = \tfrac{1}{52} + \tfrac{1}{52} + \tfrac{1}{52} + \tfrac{1}{52} = \tfrac{4}{52} = \tfrac{1}{13}$$

These computations are particularly easy since all the events are mutually exclusive. The probability of a union of events which are not disjoint and other combinatorial properties are discussed in the following section.

## 2.4  COMBINATORIAL PROPERTIES

### 2.4.1  COMPLEMENT

The concepts of union and intersection defined in the previous section are basic to a fundamental understanding of the three axioms of probability.   This section will introduce the *complement* property and continue the discussion of combinatorial probability properties.   The complement of set $A$, written as $\bar{A}$, is another set $B$.   Set $B = \bar{A}$ is composed of all the elements of the universal set which are not in set $A$.   (The term $A$ *not* is often used in engineering circles instead of $A$ *complement*.)   By definition the union of $A$ and $\bar{A}$ is the universal set (see Fig. 2.3.)

$$A + \bar{A} = U \tag{2.8}$$

Applying axioms 2 and 3 from Eqs. (2.3) and (2.2) to Eq. (2.8) yields

$$P(A + \bar{A}) = P(A) + P(\bar{A}) = P(S) = 1$$

This is valid since $A$ and $\bar{A}$ are obviously disjoint events (we have substituted the notation $S$ for $U$, since the former is more common in probability work).   Because probabilities are merely numbers, the above algebraic equation can be written in three ways

$$\begin{aligned} P(A) + P(\bar{A}) &= 1 \\ P(A) &= 1 - P(\bar{A}) \\ P(\bar{A}) &= 1 - P(A) \end{aligned} \tag{2.9}$$

The operations of union, intersection, and complement, along with the three probability axioms, make it possible to develop probability theory in a deductive fashion.

### 2.4.2  PROBABILITY OF A UNION

Perhaps the first basic relationship to be deduced is the probability of a union of two events which are not mutually exclusive.   We begin by extending the axiom of Eq. (2.3) to three or more events.   Assuming that event $A_2$ is the union of two other disjoint events $B_1 + B_2$, we obtain

$$A_2 = B_1 + B_2$$
$$P(A_1 + A_2) = P(A_1) + P(B_1 + B_2) = P(A_1) + P(B_1) + P(B_2)$$

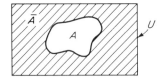

**Fig. 2.3**   Venn diagram showing set $A$ and its complement.

By successive application of this stratagem of splitting events into unions of other mutually exclusive events, we obtain the general result by induction

$$P(A_1 + A_2 + \cdots + A_n) = P(A_1) + P(A_2) + \cdots + P(A_n)$$
$$\text{for disjoint } A\text{'s} \quad (2.10)$$

If we consider the case of two events $A_1$ and $A_2$ which are not disjoint, we can divide each event into the union of two subevents. This is most easily discussed with reference to the Venn diagram shown in Fig. 2.2a. The event (set) $A_1$ is divided into those elements (1) which are contained in $A_1$ and not in $A_2$, $C_1$ and (2) which are common to $A_1$ and $A_2$, $C_2$. Then $A_1 = C_1 + C_2$. Similarly we define $A_2 = C_3 + C_2$. We have now broken $A_1$ and $A_2$ into disjoint events and can apply Eq. (2.10)

$$P(A_1 + A_2) = P(C_1 + C_2 + C_2 + C_3) = P[C_1 + C_3 + (C_2 + C_2)]$$

By definition, the union of $C_2$ with itself is $C_2$; therefore

$$P(A_1 + A_2) = P(C_1 + C_2 + C_3) = P(C_1) + P(C_2) + P(C_3)$$

We can manipulate this result into a more useful form if we add and subtract the number $P(C_2)$ and apply Eq. (2.3) in reverse

$$P(A_1 + A_2) = [P(C_1) + P(C_2)] + [P(C_2) + P(C_3)] - P(C_2)$$
$$= P(A_1) + P(A_2) - P(A_1A_2) \quad (2.11)$$

Thus, when events $A_1$ and $A_2$ are not disjoint, we must subtract the probability of the union of $A_1$ and $A_2$ from the sum of the probabilities. Note that Eq. (2.11) reduces to Eq. (2.3) if events $A_1$ and $A_2$ are disjoint since $P(A_1A_2) = 0$ for disjoint events.

We can illustrate the combinatorial properties discussed above by returning to the deck of cards. The probability of drawing a spade from a deck is clearly $13/52$. The probability of the complement of this event is the probability of not drawing a spade (the probability of drawing a heart or diamond or club), which is $39/52$. Obviously

$$\tfrac{13}{52} + \tfrac{39}{52} = 1$$

To illustrate Eq. (2.11) we can define event $A_1$ as the probability of drawing a club and event $A_2$ as the probability of drawing a four. These events are not disjoint, since there is a common element to each set, i.e., the four of clubs. Applying Eq. (2.11) gives

$$P(C \text{ or } 4) = P(C) + P(4) - P(C \text{ and } 4)$$
$$= \tfrac{13}{52} + \tfrac{4}{52} - \tfrac{1}{52} = \tfrac{4}{13}$$

We can check this result by enumerating all possible elements which belong to the event a club or a four. These events are $C_1$, $C_2$, $C_3$, $C_4$, $C_5$,

$C_6$, $C_7$, $C_8$, $C_9$, $C_{10}$, $C_J$, $C_Q$, $C_K$, $D_4$, $H_4$, $S_4$.   Since these events number 16, the probability (using the equally-likely-events hypothesis) is

$\frac{16}{52} = \frac{4}{13}$

If we change the problem and ask the probability of drawing a queen or a four, we are dealing with disjoint events.

$P(\text{Q or 4}) = P(\text{Q}) + P(4) - P(\text{Q and 4})$

Since one card being both a queen and a four is logically impossible, the two events are mutually exclusive, and the probability of their intersection is zero; therefore

$P(\text{Q or 4}) = \frac{4}{52} + \frac{4}{52} - 0 = \frac{2}{13}$

Equation (2.11) can be extended to apply to three or more events, using the same technique which was used to derive Eq. (2.10).   The detailed proof is developed in the problems at the end of the chapter.   The result is

$P(A_1 + A_2 + \cdots + A_n)$

$= [P(A_1) + P(A_2) + \cdots + P(A_n)] \qquad \leftarrow \binom{n}{1} = n \text{ terms}$

$\quad - [P(A_1A_2) + P(A_1A_3) + \cdots + \underset{i \neq j}{P(A_iA_j)}] \qquad \leftarrow \binom{n}{2} \text{ terms}$

$\quad + [P(A_1A_2A_3) + P(A_1A_2A_4) + \cdots + \underset{i \neq j \neq k}{P(A_iA_jA_k)}] \qquad \leftarrow \binom{n}{3} \text{ terms}$

$\cdots \cdots \cdots \cdots \cdots \cdots \cdots \cdots \cdots \cdots \cdots \cdots \cdots$

$\qquad (-1)^{n-1}[P(A_1A_2 \cdots A_n)] \qquad \leftarrow \binom{n}{n} = 1 \text{ term} \quad (2.12)\dagger$

This states that the probability of the union of $n$ events is given by $n$ sets of terms (shown in brackets).   The first term is plus the sum of the probabilities of the events taken one at a time, the second is minus the sum of the probabilities of the events taken two at a time, etc.   The algebraic signs of the sets of terms alternate.   Thus, the complete expansion of Eq. (2.12) involves

$\binom{n}{1} + \binom{n}{2} + \binom{n}{3} + \cdots + \binom{n}{n-1} + \binom{n}{n} = 2^n - 1$

$\dagger$ The notation $\underset{i \neq j}{P(A_iA_j)}$ means the probability of all combinations of events taken two at a time.   For example, if there are four events $A_1$, $A_2$, $A_3$, $A_4$, the second term of Eq. (2.12) is

$-[P(A_1A_2) + P(A_1A_3) + P(A_1A_4) + P(A_2A_3) + P(A_2A_4) + P(A_3A_4)]$

terms.  In the special case of mutually exclusive events all terms except the $n$ terms in the first bracket of Eq. (2.12) are identically zero, and Eq. (2.12) reduces to Eq. (2.10).  Note that if the events $A_1$, $A_2$, . . . , $A_n$ are pairwise disjoint, $P(A_1A_2) = P(A_1A_3) = \cdots P(A_iA_j) = 0$, then the events are mutually disjoint; i.e., all possible intersections are zero.

### 2.4.3  CONDITIONAL PROBABILITIES AND INDEPENDENCE

It is important to study in more detail the probability of an intersection of two events, that is, $P(A_1A_2)$.  We are especially interested in how $P(A_1A_2)$ is related to $P(A_1)$ and $P(A_2)$.

Before proceeding further we must define conditional probability and introduce a new notation.  Suppose we want the probability of obtaining the four of clubs on one draw from a deck of cards.  The answer is of course $1/52$, which can be written: $P(C_4) = 1/52$.  Let us change the problem so it reads: What is the probability of drawing the four of clubs *given that a club is drawn?*  The answer is $1/13$.  Obviously by restating the problem we have essentially changed our sample space from the 52 cards in the deck to the 13 clubs.  The additional piece of information "given that a club is drawn" radically changes the problem.  In such a situation we call the probability statement a *conditional probability*.  The notation $P(C_4|C) = 1/13$ is used to represent the conditional probability of drawing a four of clubs given that a club is drawn.  We read $P(A_2|A_1)$ as the probability of $A_2$ occurring conditioned on the previous occurrence of $A_1$, or more simply as the probability of $A_2$ given $A_1$.  Conditional probabilities can of course be zero; e.g., the probability of drawing a four of clubs given that a heart is drawn is $P(C_4|H) = 0$.

We are now able to define $P(A_1A_2)$ in terms of conditional probabilities

$$P(A_1A_2) = P(A_1)P(A_2|A_1) \tag{2.13a}$$
$$P(A_1A_2) = P(A_2)P(A_1|A_2) \tag{2.13b}$$

We can interpret Eq. (2.13) in terms of the Venn diagram.  From Fig. 2.2a we see by inspection that $P(A_1A_2) = P(C_2)$.  We assume that the Venn diagram represents a uniform sheet with a given mass density.  If we let the total mass of the sample space $M_S$ be equal to unity, the probability of any subset $X$ is equal to $M_X/M_S = M_X$.  Using this model, we can write $P(A_1) = P(C_1 + C_2) = (M_{C_1} + M_{C_2})/M_S = M_{C_1} + M_{C_2}$. Thus, Eq. (2.13a) becomes

$$P(A_1A_2) = (M_{C_1} + M_{C_2}) \frac{M_{C_2}}{M_{C_1} + M_{C_2}} = M_{C_2} = P(C_2)$$

which is, of course, the correct result.  It is clear that for $P(A_2|A_1)$ the new sample space is $C_1 + C_2$ rather than $S$ and the $P(A_2|A_1)$ is $P(C_2)/$

$P(C_1 + C_2)$.  Similarly for Eq. (2.13$b$)

$$P(A_1A_2) = (M_{C_2} + M_{C_3}) \frac{M_{C_2}}{M_{C_2} + M_{C_3}} = M_{C_2} = P(C_2)$$

Thus, both Eqs. (2.13$a$) and (2.13$b$) yield identical results.

There is a special case of Eqs. (2.13$a$) and (2.13$b$) which is worthy of separate discussion.  If $A_1$ and $A_2$ are disjoint, $P(A_1A_2) = 0$.  If $P(A_1) \neq 0$ and $P(A_2) \neq 0$, from Eqs. (2.13$a$) and (2.13$b$) we see that for disjoint events $P(A_2|A_1) = P(A_1|A_2) = 0$ (see Fig. 2.2$b$).

Intuition tells us that there must be many cases in which

$$P(A_2|A_1) = P(A_2)$$

In other words, the probability of occurrence of event $A_2$ is independent of the occurrence of event $A_1$.  From Eq. (2.13$a$) we see that this implies $P(A_1A_2) = P(A_1)P(A_2)$, and this latter result in turn implies

$$P(A_1|A_2) = P(A_1)$$

Thus we define independence by any one of the three equivalent relations

$$P(A_1A_2) = P(A_1)P(A_2) \tag{2.14a}$$

or

$$P(A_1|A_2) = P(A_1) \tag{2.14b}$$

or

$$P(A_2|A_1) = P(A_2) \tag{2.14c}$$

Because of Eqs. (2.14$b$) and (2.14$c$) conditional probabilities are sometimes called *dependent probabilities*, and the term will be used frequently in this book since it suggests physical interpretations in reliability problems.  We shall return to the discussion of independence in Sec. 2.9 and interpret Eqs. (2.14) in terms of random variables.

We can easily illustrate conditional probabilities, independence, and dependence by discussing the drawing of cards from a deck with and without replacement.  Let event $A$ be the first draw of an ace and event $B$ be the second draw of an ace without replacement.  The probabilities are

$$P(AB) = P(A)P(B|A) = \tfrac{4}{52}(\tfrac{3}{51}) = \tfrac{1}{221}$$

The conditional probability $P(B|A)$ is obviously conditioned on the occurrence of $A$.

If we now use the same example but replace the first card and shuffle, we obtain independence

$$P(AB) = P(A)P(B) = \tfrac{4}{52}(\tfrac{4}{52}) = \tfrac{1}{169}$$

It is important to clarify the differences between the general property of dependence and the more restrictive disjoint property. Let us define two dependent events. Event $A$ is the probability of drawing an ace of spades from a deck on the first draw, and event $B$ is the probability of drawing a second ace of spades from the deck on the second draw without replacement. Since we specify drawing without replacement, the events are dependent; and if the deck is a fair one, there is only one ace of spades, and events $A$ and $B$ are mutually exclusive

$$P(AB) = P(A)P(B|A) = \tfrac{1}{52}(\tfrac{0}{51}) = 0$$

One can define conditional probabilities for three events by splitting event $B$ into the intersection of events $A_2$ and $A_3$. Then letting $A = A_1$ and $B = A_2A_3$, we have

$$P(AB) = P(A)P(B|A) = P(A_1)P(A_2A_3|A_1)$$
$$= P(A_1)P(A_2|A_1)P(A_3|A_1A_2)$$

Successive application of this technique leads to the general result

$$P(A_1A_2 \cdots A_n) = P(A_1)P(A_2|A_1)P(A_3|A_1A_2) \cdots$$
$$P(A_n|A_1A_2 \cdots A_{n-1}) \quad (2.15)$$

Thus, the probability of the union of $n$ terms is expressed as the joint product of one independent probability and $n - 1$ dependent probabilities. Evaluation of dependent probabilities can become quite cumbersome; e.g., in the evaluation of Eq. (2.12) there are $2^n - (n + 1)$ dependent probabilities involved.[1]

In addition to the basic probability relations discussed above, one special relationship will be of value in computing system probabilities. The reliability expression for a system is a complex probability expression which can be evaluated by successive application of the rules of unions, intersections, and complements. One shortcut in this evaluation is to locate one keystone event $A_K$ in the group $A_1, A_2, \ldots, A_n$. Then use the following identity

$$P(G) = P(A_K)P(G|A_K) + P(\bar{A}_K)P(G|\bar{A}_K)$$
$$= P(A_KG) + P(\bar{A}_KG) \quad (2.16)$$

where $G \equiv$ system is good
$A_K \equiv$ element $K$ is good
$\bar{A}_K \equiv$ element $K$ is bad

The validity of Eq. (2.16) is obvious upon inspection of the Venn diagram in Fig. 2.4. Event $G$ is the dotted plus the ruled area, and event $A_K$ is the dotted plus the black area. The intersection of $A_K$ and $G$ is the

---

[1] Equation (2.12) contains $2^n - 1$ terms. The first $n$ terms are independent probabilities, and the remainder are dependent probabilities.

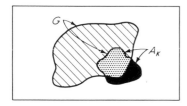

**Fig. 2.4** Venn diagram for Eq. (2.16).

dotted area, and the intersection of $\bar{A}_K$ and $G$ is the ruled area. The identity is valid, since the ruled area and the dotted area are disjoint and make up event $G$.

### 2.4.4 SUMMARY

A summary of the basic probability properties discussed so far appears in Table 2.1.

**Table 2.1   Summary of basic probability properties**

| Property | Comment |
|---|---|
| $0 \le P(A) \le 1$ | Basic axiom |
| $P(S) = 1$ | Basic axiom |
| $P(\bar{S}) = 0$ | Null set, has no elements |
| $\begin{aligned} P(A_1 + A_2 + \cdots + A_n) &= [P(A_1) + P(A_2) + \cdots + P(A_n)] \\ &\quad - [P(A_1 A_2) + P(A_1 A_3) + \cdots + P(A_i A_j)] \cdots \\ &\qquad\qquad\qquad {\scriptstyle i \ne j} \\ &\quad + (-1)^{n-1}[P(A_1 A_2 \cdots A_n)] \end{aligned}$ | Probability of a union of $n$ events |
| $P(A_1 + A_2 + \cdots + A_n) = P(A_1) + P(A_2) + \cdots + P(A_n)$ <br> all events *disjoint* | Probability of a union of $n$ *disjoint* events |
| $P(A + \bar{A}) = P(S) = 1$ | Complement property |
| $P(A) = 1 - P(\bar{A})$ | Complement property |
| $P(A_1 A_2 \cdots A_n) = P(A_1)P(A_2\mid A_1) \cdots P(A_n \mid A_1 A_2 \cdots A_{n-1})$ | Probability of an intersection of $n$ events |
| $P(A_1 A_2 \cdots A_n) = P(A_1)P(A_2) \cdots P(A_n)$ <br> all events *independent* | Probability of an intersection of $n$ *independent* events |

## 2.5 DISCRETE RANDOM VARIABLES

### 2.5.1 DEFINITION

One can define a sample space $S$ and an event $A$ defined on the sample space. If the elements of $A$ are $x_1, x_2, \ldots, x_n$ then

$$P(A) = P(x_1 + x_2 + \cdots + x_n)$$

and since the events $x_1, x_2, \ldots, x_n$ are disjoint,

$$P(A) = P(x_1) + P(x_2) + \cdots + P(x_n)$$

In order to describe $P(A)$, we can tabulate $P(x_i)$. Thus, if we describe another event $B$ which is a subset of $A$, we can write down $P(B)$ by just summing the probabilities associated with each element of $B$ as read from the table. The concepts of a random variable, density function, and distribution function merely constitute a formal procedure for accomplishing the above probability description.

### 2.5.2 DENSITY FUNCTION

We can define $\mathbf{x}$ as a random variable if we associate each value of $\mathbf{x}$ with an element in event $A$ defined on sample space $S$. If the random variable $\mathbf{x}$ assumes a finite number of values, then $\mathbf{x}$ is called a *discrete random variable*. In the case of a discrete random variable, we associate with each value of $\mathbf{x}$ a number $x_i$ and a probability of occurrence $P(x_i)$. We could describe the probabilities associated with the random variable by a table of values, but it is easier to write a formula that permits calculation of $P(x_i)$ by substitution of the appropriate value of $x_i$. Such a formula is called a *probability function* for the random variable $\mathbf{x}$. More exactly, we use the notation $f(x)$ to mean a discrete probability density function[1] associated with the discrete random variable $\mathbf{x}$. (The reason for the inclusion of the word "density" will be clear once the parallel development for continuous random variables is completed.) Thus,

$$P(\mathbf{x} = x_i) = P(x_i) = f(x_i) \tag{2.17}$$

In general we use the sequence of positive integers $0, 1, 2, \ldots, n$ to represent the subscripts of the $n + 1$ discrete values of $\mathbf{x}$. Thus, the random variable is denoted by $\mathbf{x}$ and particular values of the random variable by $x_1, x_2, \ldots, x_n$. The term *domain of* $\mathbf{x}$ is generally used to describe the interval of values of $\mathbf{x}$ to be considered; i.e., we write

$$f(x) \quad \text{for } x = 0, 1, 2, \ldots, n$$

---

[1] Some authors prefer to call this a discrete probability *mass* function to indicate the differences between discrete and continuous random variables.

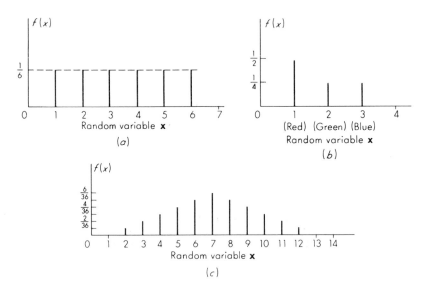

**Fig. 2.5**   Line diagrams depicting discrete density functions.   (a) For the throw of one die; (b) for a pick of colored balls from a hat; (c) for the throw of two dice.

The sequence of values which $f(x)$ takes on is called the *range* of $f(x)$. If the random variable under consideration is not a numerical quantity, e.g., the colors of the spectrum, red, orange, yellow, green, blue, indigo, violet, then the colors (or other quantity) would first be coded by associating a number 1 to 7 with each one.   If the random variable $\mathbf{x}$ is defined over the entire sample space $S$, $P(A)$ is given by

$$P(A) = \underset{\substack{\text{for all } x_i \\ \text{values which} \\ \text{are elements of } A}}{\Sigma P(x_i)} = \underset{\substack{\text{for all } x_i \\ \text{in } A}}{\Sigma f(x_i)} \tag{2.18}$$

The probability of the sample space is

$$P(S) = \underset{\substack{\text{over all} \\ i}}{\Sigma f(x_i)} = 1 \tag{2.19}$$

As an example of the above concepts we shall consider the throw of one die.   The random variable $\mathbf{x}$ is the number of spots which face up on any throw.   The domain of the random variable is $x = 1, 2, 3, 4, 5, 6$. Using the equally-likely-event hypothesis, we conclude that

$$P(x = 1) = P(x = 2) = \cdot\cdot\cdot = \tfrac{1}{6}$$

Thus, $f(x) = 1/6$, a constant density function.   This can also be depicted graphically as in Fig. 2.5a.   The probability of an even roll is

$$P(\text{even}) = \sum_{i=2,4,6} f(x_i) = \tfrac{1}{6} + \tfrac{1}{6} + \tfrac{1}{6} = \tfrac{1}{2}$$

Of course the probability of the certain event is 1.

$$P(S) = \sum_{i=1}^{6} f(x_i) = \tfrac{1}{6} + \tfrac{1}{6} + \tfrac{1}{6} + \tfrac{1}{6} + \tfrac{1}{6} + \tfrac{1}{6} = 1$$

As a second example consider a hat with two red, one green, and one blue ball in it. The random variable is associated with the color of the ball drawn on one pick from the hat. We let red = 1, green = 2, and blue = 3. Then the density function is given by

$$f(x) = \begin{cases} \tfrac{1}{2} & x = 1 \text{ (red)} \\ \tfrac{1}{4} & x = 2 \text{ (green)} \\ \tfrac{1}{4} & x = 3 \text{ (blue)} \end{cases} \tag{2.20}$$

This is also shown in Fig. 2.5b. The probability of green is, of course, $f(x = 2) = 1/4$ and the probability of $S$ is

$$\sum_{i=1,2,3} f(x_i) = \tfrac{1}{2} + \tfrac{1}{4} + \tfrac{1}{4} = 1$$

A slightly more complicated example is the throw of two dice. The random variable $\mathbf{x}$ is the total number of spots facing up on the two dice. The density function is

$$f(x) = \begin{cases} \dfrac{x-1}{36} & \text{for } x = 2, 3, \ldots, 7 \\ \dfrac{13-x}{36} & \text{for } x = 8, 9, \ldots, 13 \end{cases} \tag{2.21}$$

The validity of this density function can be verified by tabulating all possible outcomes and using the equally-likely-events hypothesis. The density function is graphed in Fig. 2.5c. The probability of a throw of seven or higher is

$$P(\mathbf{x} \geq 7) = \sum_{i=7}^{12} f(x_i) = \tfrac{6}{36} + \tfrac{5}{36} + \tfrac{4}{36} + \tfrac{3}{36} + \tfrac{2}{36} = \tfrac{5}{9}$$

Obviously the sum of all possible outcomes for this example is unity.

### 2.5.3  DISTRIBUTION FUNCTION

It is often convenient to deal with another, related function rather than the density function itself. The *distribution function* is defined in terms of the probability that $\mathbf{x} \leq x$

$$P(\mathbf{x} \leq x) \equiv F(x) = \sum_{\mathbf{x} \leq x} f(x) \tag{2.22}$$

The distribution function is a cumulative probability and is often called the *cumulative distribution function*. The analytical form of $F(x)$ for

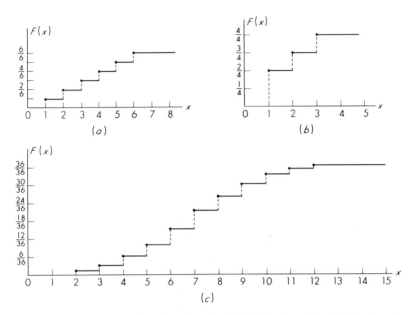

**Fig. 2.6**   Step diagrams depicting discrete distribution functions for the density functions given in Fig. 2.5.   (a) For the throw of one die; (b) for a pick of colored balls from a hat; (c) for the throw of two dice.

each of the examples in Fig. 2.5 is

Fig. 2.5a:   $F(x) = \dfrac{x}{6}$     for $1 \leq x \leq 6$     (2.23)

Fig. 2.5b:   $F(x) = \begin{cases} 0 & -\infty \leq x < 1 \\ \frac{1}{2} & 1 \leq x < 2 \\ \frac{3}{4} & 2 \leq x < 3 \\ 1 & 3 \leq x \leq +\infty \end{cases}$     (2.24)

Fig. 2.5c:   $F(x) = \begin{cases} \dfrac{n(n-1)}{72} & 2 \leq x < 8 \\ \frac{26}{36} & 8 \leq x < 9 \\ \frac{30}{36} & 9 \leq x < 10 \\ \frac{33}{36} & 10 \leq x < 11 \\ \frac{35}{36} & 11 \leq x < 12 \\ \frac{36}{36} & 12 \leq x \end{cases}$     (2.25)

The cumulative distribution function is more clearly illustrated graphically, as shown in Fig. 2.6.   The summation of the line diagrams given in Fig. 2.5 of course results in the step diagrams of Fig. 2.6.   Equation (2.22) relates $F(x)$ to $f(x)$ by a process of summation.   One can write an inverse relation[1] defining $f(x)$ in terms of the difference between two values of $F(x)$

$$f(x) = F(x^+) - F(x^-) \tag{2.26}$$

In other words, $f(x)$ is equal to the value of the discontinuity at $x$ in the step diagram of $F(x)$.  There are a few basic properties of density and distribution functions which are of importance.  They can be proved from the basic definitions but are almost obvious after consideration of Figs. 2.5 and 2.6.

1   Since $f(x)$ is a probability,

   $$0 \le f(x) \le 1$$

2   Because $P(S) = 1$,

   $$\sum_{\substack{\text{all} \\ x}} f(x) = 1$$

3   If the domain of $\mathbf{x}$ is $n_1 \le \mathbf{x} \le n_2$,

   $$F(x) = \begin{cases} 0 & \mathbf{x} < n_1 \\ 1 & \mathbf{x} \ge n_2 \end{cases}$$

4   Since $F(x)$ is a summation of positive numbers $f(x)$, the function $F(x)$ is a nondecreasing function.

Although there is some redundancy in these four properties, it is clear that any density function which violates property 1 or 2 or any distribution function which violates property 3 or 4 is not a valid probability function.   These conditions are useful in checking to see that reliability models proposed from data or conjecture are valid.

### 2.5.4   BINOMIAL DISTRIBUTION

Many discrete probability models are used in applications, the foremost being the binomial distribution and the Poisson distribution.   The *binomial distribution* (sometimes called the *Bernoulli distribution*) applies to a situation in which an event can either occur or not occur (the more common terms are *success* or *failure*, a legacy from the days when probability theory centered around games of chance).   The terms success and failure, of course, are ideally suited to reliability applications.   The probability of success on any one trial is $p$, and that of failure is $1 - p$.

---

[1] The notation $F(x^+)$ means $\lim_{\epsilon \to 0} F(x + \epsilon)$ and $F(x^-)$ means $\lim_{\epsilon \to 0} F(x - \epsilon)$.   In other words the limits as approached from the right and the left, respectively.   From Eq. (2.22) we see that $F(x^+) = F(x)$.

The number of independent trials is denoted by $n$, and the number of successes by $r$. Thus, the probability of $r$ successes in $n$ trials with the probability of one success being $p$ is

$$B(r;n,p) = \binom{n}{r} p^r (1-p)^{n-r} \qquad \text{for } r = 0, 1, 2, \ldots , n \qquad (2.27)$$

This equation is easily derived. One way of achieving $r$ favorable outcomes is to have $r$ consecutive successes followed by $n-r$ consecutive failures. Since each success and failure is independent, the probability of the above sequence is obviously $(p)^r(1-p)^{n-r}$. Of course, this is only one possible sequence that leads to $r$ out of $n$ successes. In general, the number of possible sequences leading to the desired result is equal to the number of combinations of $n$ things taken $r$ at a time, which is given by $\binom{n}{r} = n!/r!(n-r)!$. All the possible sequences are independent events, and the desired probability is the probability of the union of these events. Therefore, $B(r;n,p)$ is the sum of the $\binom{n}{r}$ identical probabilities $p^r(1-p)^{n-r}$, which is of course Eq. (2.27).

A number of line diagrams for the binomial density function[1] are given in Figs. 2.7 and 2.8. In Fig. 2.7 the number of trials is fixed at nine, and the probability of success on each trial is changed from 0.2 to 0.5 to 0.8. Intuition tells us that the most probable number of successes is $np$, which is 1.8, 4.5, and 7.2, respectively. (It is shown in Sec. 2.7 that intuition has predicted the mean value.) Note that the peaks of the density function occur near these values and fall off on each side. The falloff is symmetrical for $p = 0.5$ and asymmetrical for $p = 0.2$ and 0.8. In Fig. 2.8, $p$ is fixed at 0.2, and $n$ is allowed to vary. Again the product $np$ occurs near the peak of the density function.

[1] We use the notation $B(r;n,p)$ rather than the conventional and less descriptive notation $f(x)$.

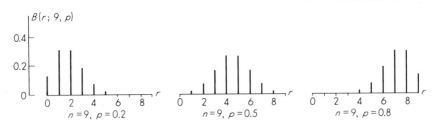

**Fig. 2.7**  Binomial density function for fixed $n$. (*Adapted from G. A. Wadsworth and J. G. Bryan, "Introduction to Probability and Random Variables," Fig. 3.5. Copyright 1960. McGraw-Hill Book Company. Used by permission.*)

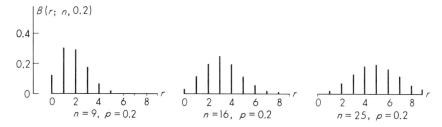

**Fig. 2.8** Binomial density function for fixed $p$. (*Adapted from G. A. Wadsworth and J. G. Bryan, "Introduction to Probability and Random Variables," Fig. 3.6. Copyright* 1960. *McGraw-Hill Book Company. Used by permission.*)

Clearly, we could use the binomial distribution to predict the probability of twice obtaining a three, in six throws of a die

$$r = 2 \qquad n = 6 \qquad p = \tfrac{1}{6}$$

$$B\,(2;6,\tfrac{1}{6}) = \binom{6}{2}(\tfrac{1}{6})^2\,(1 - \tfrac{1}{6})^{6-2} = 15 \times 0.0131 = 0.196$$

The computation of $\binom{6}{2}$ can be done by evaluating $6!/2!4!$ or by using Pascal's triangle (Fig. 2.9), which is a convenient self-generating table for the binomial coefficients.[1]   We can also use the binomial distribution to evaluate the probability of picking three aces on ten draws with

[1] Extensive tables of the binomial distribution were published in 1950 by the National Bureau of Standards under the title "Tables of the Binomial Probability Distribution."

```
n   r
0   0. . . . . . . . . . . . . . . . . . . . . . . . . 1
1   0, 1 . . . . . . . . . . . . . . . . . . . . . . 1      1
2   0, 1, 2. . . . . . . . . . . . . . . . . . . 1      2      1
3   0, 1, 2, 3. . . . . . . . . . . . . . . . 1      3      3      1
4   0, 1, 2, 3, 4. . . . . . . . . . . . . . 1      4      6      4      1
5   0, 1, 2, 3, 4, 5. . . . . . . . . . . 1      5     10     10      5      1
6   0 through 6 . . . . . . . . . . . 1      6     15     20     15      6      1
7   0 through 7 . . . . . . . . . . 1      7     21     35     35     21      7      1
8   0 through 8 . . . . . . . . . 1      8     28     56     70     56     28      8      1
9   0 through 9 . . . . . . . 1      9     36     84    126    126     84     36      9      1
10  0 through 10. . . . . . 1     10     45    120    210    252    210    120     45     10      1
```

ANY NUMBER IN THE TRIANGLE IS THE SUM OF THE TWO NUMBERS IMMEDIATELY ABOVE IT TO THE LEFT AND TO THE RIGHT.

**Fig. 2.9** Pascal's triangle for the computation of

$$\binom{n}{r} = \frac{n!}{r!(n - r)!} \qquad \text{for } 0 \le n \le 10$$

replacement from a deck; however, if we do not replace the drawn cards after each pick, the binomial model will no longer hold, since the parameter $p$ will change with each draw.[1]  The binomial distribution does not hold when draws are made without replacement, because the trials are no longer independent.

It is easy to see that the binomial distribution can be used to compute the probability that a bridge will be successful if the success depends on the fact that $r$ out of $n$ support cables are necessary to support the suspended roadway.  In this problem there is more than one way to succeed.  The minimum number of support cables is $r$, but obviously the bridge stands if $r + 1, r + 2, \ldots, n - 1$, or $n$ cables are good. The probability of bridge success is the sum of all these probabilities. If $p$ represents the probability of one cable succeeding, then the system probability of success is given by a summation of binomial probabilities. Letting **k** be the number of successes,

$$P_s = P(r \leq \mathbf{k} \leq n) = \sum_{k=r}^{n} B(k;n,p) = \sum_{k=r}^{n} \binom{n}{k} p^k (1 - p)^{n-k} \qquad (2.28)$$

This is related to the cumulative distribution function given in Eq. (2.22) by

$$P_s = P(r \leq \mathbf{x} \leq n) = 1 - P(0 \leq \mathbf{x} < r) = 1 - F(x) \qquad (2.29)$$

This illustrates the point that the sum of probabilities involved in the definition of the cumulative distribution function plays an important practical role.

### 2.5.5  MULTINOMIAL DISTRIBUTION

When more than two system states are present, the binomial distribution does not hold, and a similar distribution, called the *multinomial*, must be used, as shown in the following example.  An interesting problem which relates to the multinomial distribution is that of power transmission over several lines between two cities.  We assume that $n$ lines connect the cities and that the total power load is $T$.  If the power-transmission capacity of each line is somewhat greater than $T/n$, the system has some redundancy, and not all lines need survive if the system is to survive. Failure of one line merely redistributes the load among the other lines, which have reserve capacity, and the system still operates.  If the maximum capacity of each line is $T/r > T/n$, then Eq. (2.28) predicts the probability of success (assuming that the failures are independent, e.g., that the lines are sufficiently separated so that one toppling tree or one

---

[1] The proper distribution to use in such a case is the hypergeometric distribution, Wadsworth and Bryan, *op. cit.*, p. 59.

lightning bolt will not fell more than one line). Deeper thought reveals a more complicated situation. An open circuit of a line will behave as discussed above, but a short circuit on even one line might overload the system so as to trip out several circuit breakers and disable the entire system. This type of situation cannot be modeled by a binomial distribution, since three rather than two states are involved, and is governed by the multinomial distribution. The multinomial distribution applies to a set of mutually exclusive results $R_1, R_2, \ldots, R_n$. The $P(R_i) = p_i$, and $\sum\limits_{i=1}^{n} p_i = 1$. In $n$ trials $R_1$ occurs $x_1$ times, $R_2$ occurs $x_2$ times, etc., such that $x_1 + x_2 + \cdots + x_n = n$. The density function for the multinomial distribution is

$$f(x_1, x_2, \ldots, x_n) = \frac{n!}{x_1! x_2! \cdots x_n!} p_1^{x_1} p_2^{x_2} \cdots p_n^{x_n} \tag{2.30}$$

For our power-transmission problem

$R_1$ = good line $\qquad P(R_1) = p_1$
$R_2$ = open line $\qquad P(R_2) = p_2$
$R_3$ = shorted line $\qquad P(R_3) = p_3$
$x_1 + x_2 + x_3 = n$

The probability of a successful system is given by the probability that all lines are good ($x_1 = n$, $x_2 = x_3 = 0$), plus the probability that one line is open and $n - 1$ lines are good ($x_1 = n - 1$, $x_2 = 1$, $x_3 = 0$), etc.

$$P_s = f(n,0,0) + f(n - 1, 1, 0) + f(n - 2, 2, 0) + \cdots + f(r, n - r, 0)$$

$$= \frac{n!}{n!0!0!} p_1^n p_2^0 p_3^0 + \frac{n!}{(n - 1)!1!0!} p_1^{n-1} p_2^1 p_3^0 + \cdots$$

$$+ \frac{n!}{r!(n - r)!0!} p_1^r p_2^{n-r} p_3^0 \tag{2.31}$$

### 2.5.6 POISSON DISTRIBUTION

Another discrete distribution of great importance is the *Poisson distribution*, which can be derived in a number of ways. One derivation will be given in this section and a second derivation in Sec. 2.8. If $p$ is very small and $n$ is very large, the binomial density, Eq. (2.27), takes on a special limiting form, which is the Poisson law of probability. Starting with Eq. (2.27), we let $np$, the most probable number of occurrences, be some number $\mu$

$$\mu = np \qquad \therefore \; p = \frac{\mu}{n}$$

$$B\left(r; n, \frac{\mu}{n}\right) = \frac{n!}{r!(n - r)!} \left(\frac{\mu}{n}\right)^r \left(1 - \frac{\mu}{n}\right)^{n-r}$$

Now if we let $n \to \infty$ and keep $r$ finite,

$$\lim_{n \to \infty} \left(1 - \frac{\mu}{n}\right)^{n-r} \to \lim_{n \to \infty} \left(1 - \frac{\mu}{n}\right)^{n} = 1 - \frac{n!}{1!(n-1)!} \frac{\mu}{n} + \frac{n!}{2!(n-2)!} \left(\frac{\mu}{n}\right)^{2} + \cdots$$

As $n \to \infty$, $\mu/n \to 0$, and we may approximate the series by the first two terms, $1 - \mu$. If $\mu$ is small, then $e^{-\mu} \approx 1 - \mu$, and thus we conclude that the term $(1 - \mu/n)^{n-r} \to e^{-\mu}$. The ratio $n!/(n-r)!$ is given by the product $n(n-1)(n-2) \cdots (n-r+1)$. If $n \gg r$, this product becomes $n^r$ in the limit. The limiting form called the Poisson distribution is

$$f(r;\mu) = \frac{\mu^r e^{-\mu}}{r!} \tag{2.32}$$

The Poisson distribution can be written in a second form, which is very useful for our purposes. If we are interested in events which occur in time, we can define the rate of occurrence as the constant $\lambda$ = occurrences per unit time. In a small time period $\Delta t$, the expected number of occurrences is $p = \lambda \Delta t$. Substitution in Eq. (2.27) yields

$$B(r;n,\lambda \Delta t) = \frac{n!}{r!(n-r)!} (\lambda \Delta t)^r (1 - \lambda \Delta t)^{n-r}$$

As before, we fix $r$ and let $n \to \infty$

$$\lim_{n \to \infty} B(r;n,\lambda \Delta t) \to \frac{n^r}{r!} (\lambda \Delta t)^r e^{-n\lambda \Delta t}$$

If we now let $t = n \Delta t$, then $\Delta t = t/n$ and

$$B\left(r;n, \frac{\lambda t}{n}\right) = \frac{n^r}{r!} \left(\frac{\lambda t}{n}\right)^r e^{-\lambda t}$$

Thus, the alternate form of the Poisson distribution is

$$f(r;\lambda,t) = \frac{(\lambda t)^r e^{-\lambda t}}{r!} \tag{2.33}$$

Equation (2.32) was derived from the binomial distribution as a limiting form for $n$ large and $p$ small.[1] To illustrate how closely Eqs. (2.27) and (2.32) agree for large $n$ and small $p$ the reader can examine Table 2.2, which was prepared for $n = 500$, $p = 1/500$, $\mu = np = 1$. Although

---

[1] The usual rule of thumb is that the approximation is *satisfactory* for $n \geq 20$ and $p \leq 0.05$ and *excellent* for $n \geq 100$ and $np \leq 10$. See I. Miller and J. Freund, "Probability and Statistics for Engineers," p. 50, Prentice-Hall, Inc., Englewood Cliffs, N.J. 1965.

the Poisson distribution was derived as a limiting form of the binomial, it should be considered as a distribution in its own right.  The derivation in Sec. 2.8 points this out most clearly.  Thus, the binomial and Poisson are two different distributions which happen to give similar numerical results for large $n$ and small $\mu = np$.  Line diagrams for the Poisson density function given in Eq. (2.32) are shown in Fig. 2.10 for various values of $\mu$.  Note that the peak of the distribution is near $\mu$ and that symmetry about the peak begins to develop for larger values of $\mu$.  The Poisson probabilities can be calculated, obtained from tables,[1] or read simply from the chart in Fig. 2.11.

To illustrate the use of the Poisson distribution and how it differs from the binomial, the following problem will be solved.  A satellite-tracking station is supplied with three identical radar units.  Only one is needed in tracking, the other two being spares to ensure continuous operation. If all units were operated with power on, we could assume the failures to be independent and governed by the binomial distribution.  In this case the probability of success would be

$$P_s = B(3;3,p) + B(2;3,p) + B(1;3,p) = p^3 + 3p^2(1 - p)$$
$$+ 3p(1 - p)^2 = p^3 - 3p^2 + 3p \quad (2.34)$$

where $p$ is the probability of each radar-system success.  To improve

[1] E. C. Molina, "Poisson's Exponential Binomial Limit," D. Van Nostrand Company, Inc., Princeton, N.J., 1942.

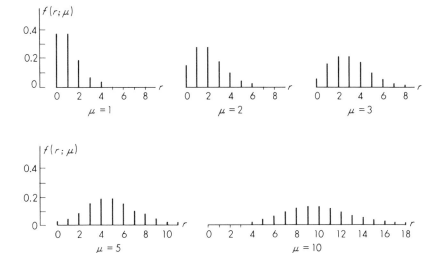

**Fig. 2.10**  Poisson density function for several values of $\mu$.

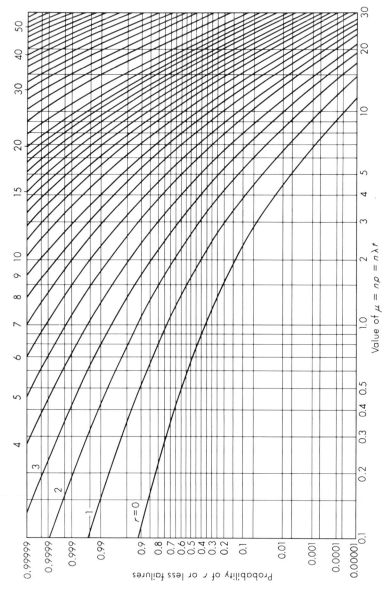

**Fig. 2.11** Poisson cumulative probabilities. ("*Handbook of Reliability Engineering,*" *Bureau of Naval Weapons Handbook,* 00-65-502, 1964.)

Table 2.2 Comparison of density functions of binomial distribution with $n = 500$, $p = 1/500$ and Poisson distribution with $\mu = np = 1$

| $x$ | Binomial | Poisson |
|---|---|---|
| 0 | 0.3675 | 0.3679 |
| 1 | 0.3682 | 0.3679 |
| 2 | 0.1841 | 0.1839 |
| 3 | 0.0612 | 0.0613 |
| 4 | 0.0153 | 0.0153 |
| 5 | 0.00303 | 0.00307 |
| 6 | 0.00050 | 0.00051 |
| 7 | 0.000071 | 0.000073 |

SOURCE: G. A. Wadsworth and J. G. Bryan, "Introduction to Probability and Random Variables," table 3-18. Copyright 1960. McGraw-Hill Book Company. Used by permission.

the probability of at least one good operating system the units not in use have their power turned off (are kept on standby) and are turned on in succession only when the on-line unit fails. Assuming that the warm-up and acquisition period is short enough so that tracking is not seriously interrupted and that the units do not deteriorate while on standby, the probability of success should improve. The binomial distribution does not apply, since the probabilities of success are dependent on the failure of the preceding element. In Sec. 2.8 we shall prove that the Poisson distribution holds for this problem. The occurrences in question must have a small probability; therefore we let $\mu$ be the expected number of failures. In this case the system succeeds if there are zero, one, or two failures and

$$P_s = f(0,\mu) + f(1,\mu) + f(2,\mu) = e^{-\mu} + \mu e^{-\mu} + \frac{\mu^2 e^{-\mu}}{2} \tag{2.35}$$

In order to compare Eqs. (2.34) and (2.35) we let the probability of success for a single parallel element $p$ be 0.9 and equate this to the probability of success for a single standby unit (zero failures) $e^{-\mu}$. Thus $p = 0.9$, $e^{-\mu} = 0.9$, and $\mu = 0.10536$. Substitution into Eqs. (2.34) and (2.35) yields for the parallel system $P_s = 0.99900$ and the standby system $P_s = 0.99982$. Restatement of the results in terms of the probability of failure is more dramatic. In the parallel case the probability of failure is $100 \times 10^{-5}$ and in the standby case $18 \times 10^{-5}$, about a 5:1 improvement. Among the many discrete distributions commonly used, the binomial and Poisson play the key roles in reliability work.

## 2.6  CONTINUOUS RANDOM VARIABLES

### 2.6.1  DENSITY AND DISTRIBUTION FUNCTIONS

The preceding section introduced the concept of a discrete random variable and its associated density and distribution functions. A similar development will be pursued in this section for continuous variables. Examples of some continuous random variables are the length of a manufactured part, the failure time of a system, and the value of a circuit resistance. In each of these examples there is no reason to believe that the random variable takes on discrete values. On the contrary, the variable is continuous over some range of definition. In a manner analogous to the development of the discrete variable, we define a continuous density function and a continuous distribution function. We shall start with the cumulative distribution function.

The cumulative distribution function for the discrete case was defined in Eq. (2.22) as a summation. If the spacings between the discrete values of the random variable $\mathbf{x}$ are $\Delta x$ and we let $\Delta x \to 0$, then the discrete variable becomes a continuous variable, and the summation becomes an integration. Thus, the cumulative distribution function of a continuous random variable is given by

$$F(x) = \int_{\substack{\text{over the} \\ \text{domain of } \mathbf{x}}} f(x)\, dx \tag{2.36}$$

If we let $\mathbf{x}$ take on all values between points $a$ and $b$ and choose $\mathbf{x}$ such that $a < \mathbf{x} \leq b$, then[1]

$$P(\mathbf{x} \leq x) = F(x) = \int_a^x f(x)\, dx \tag{2.37}$$

The density function $f(x)$ is given by the derivative of the distribution function. This is easily seen from Eq. (2.36) and the fact that the derivative of the integral of a function is the function itself.[2]

$$\frac{dF(x)}{dx} = f(x) \tag{2.38}$$

---

[1] We are using $\mathbf{x}$ to denote the random variable and $x$ to stand for the values assumed by the random variable. This distinction is necessary if one wishes to make careful probability statements. To avoid confusion some authors use $X$ to denote the random variable and $x$ to denote the values assumed by the random variable.

[2] If $a$ is a function of $x$, we use Leibniz's rule. See any book on advanced calculus.

The probability that **x** lies in an interval $x < \mathbf{x} < x + dx$ is given by

$$P(x < \mathbf{x} < x + dx) = P(\mathbf{x} \leq x + dx) - P(x \leq \mathbf{x})$$
$$= \int_a^{x+dx} f(x)\, dx - \int_a^x f(x)\, dx = \int_x^{x+dx} f(x)\, dx$$
$$= F(x + dx) - F(x) \qquad (2.39)\dagger$$

It is easy to see from Eq. (2.39) that if $F(x)$ is continuous and we let $dx \to 0, P(\mathbf{x} = x)$ is zero.   Thus, when we deal with continuous proability, it makes sense to talk of the probability that **x** is within an interval rather than at one point.   In fact since the $P(\mathbf{x} = x)$ is zero, we need not be very careful in the continuous case in specifying whether the interval is open or closed since

$$P(a \leq \mathbf{x} \leq b) = P(a < \mathbf{x} < b) = P(a \leq \mathbf{x} < b) = P(a < \mathbf{x} \leq b)$$

Thus the density function $f(x)$ is truly a density, and like any other density function it has a value only when integrated over some finite interval.[1]   The basic properties of density and distribution functions previously discussed in the discrete case hold in the continuous case. At the lower limit of **x** we have $F(a) = 0$, and at the upper limit $F(b) = 1$. These two statements, coupled with Eq. (2.36), lead to $\int_a^b f(x)\, dx = 1$. Since $f(x)$ is a probability, $f(x)$ is nonnegative, and $F(x)$, its integral, is a nondecreasing function.

### 2.6.2  SINGULARITY FUNCTIONS

Since continuous density and distribution functions form a very convenient *integrodifferential pair*, it is germane to ask why we do not treat discrete random variables as just a special case of continuous theory. The only hindrance to doing so is the fact that the discrete distribution function is a discontinuous function which can be treated as a stepwise continuous function.   Thus, the associated density function depends on the differentiation of a discontinuous function.   Precise mathematical formulation of such a problem becomes involved; however, the engineer has found that by using the singularity functions popular in signal analysis such a development is not too difficult.   (Singularity functions are also useful in formulating the hazard models discussed in Chap. 4.) The step function is defined graphically in Fig. 2.12$a$ and is denoted by[2]

$$\text{Step function of height } A \text{ beginning at } t = t_0 = \begin{cases} 0 & t < t_0 \\ A & t \geq t_0 \end{cases}$$
$$= A u_{-1}(t - t_0) \qquad (2.40)$$

† Similarly, $P(a < \mathbf{x} \leq b) = F(b) - F(a)$.
[1] The one important exception is the impulse function (see Sec. 2.6.2).
[2] The notation $u(t - t_0)$ is also commonly used.

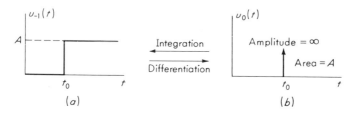

**Fig. 2.12**   Definition of (a) step function and (b) impulse function.

A staircase distribution function like that in Fig. 2.6b can be defined in terms of a sequence of steps as

$$F(x) = \tfrac{2}{4}u_{-1}(t - 1) + \tfrac{1}{4}u_{-1}(t - 2) + \tfrac{1}{4}u_{-1}(t - 3) \qquad (2.41)$$

The derivative of a step function is the impulse function shown in Fig. 2.12b.   The impulse function is defined by the properties[1]

$$
\text{Impulse function of } area = \begin{cases} \infty & t = t_0 \\ 0 & \text{elsewhere} \\ \lim\limits_{\epsilon \to 0} \int_{t_0}^{t_0+\epsilon} A u_0(\xi - t_0)f(\xi)\, d\xi = Af(t_0) \end{cases}
$$

$$= A u_0(t - t_0) \qquad (2.42)$$

The symbol $\xi$ is merely a dummy variable.   The area under the function $A u_0(t - t_0)f(t)$, where $f(t)$ is a continuous function, is simply $Af(t_0)$.   A simple limiting process showing the evolution of the impulse function is given in Fig. 2.13.   The *gradual step* in Fig. 2.13a can easily be differentiated graphically to give the pulse of Fig. 2.13b.   If we allow $\epsilon \to 0$, then in the limit the gradual step becomes a true step, and the pulse becomes an impulse.   Note that the height of the pulse $A/\epsilon$ goes to infinity as $\epsilon \to 0$; however, the area is $(A/\epsilon)\epsilon$, which equals $A$ independent of the limiting process.   Thus, it makes little sense to speak of the amplitude of an impulse, and one should always use the impulse area as a measure of the size of the impulse.   Using impulse functions it is easy to write down an expression for the density function associated with the distribution function given by Eq. (2.41)

$$f(x) = \tfrac{2}{4}u_0(t - 1) + \tfrac{1}{4}u_0(t - 2) + \tfrac{1}{4}u_0(t - 3) \qquad (2.43)$$

Thus, if we choose to deal with discrete random variables as a special case of continuous random variables, we represent distribution functions as sums of step functions and density functions as sums of impulse func-

---

[1] The notation $\delta(t - t_0)$ is often used.   In fact some authors call it the delta function.

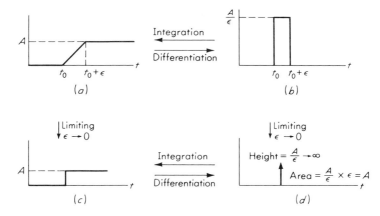

**Fig. 2.13**  Evolution of the impulse function.   (a) Gradual step; (b) high, thin pulse; (c) step function; (d) impulse function.

tions.[1]   The reader should note that since the amplitude of any impulse is infinity and its area is the parameter of primary significance, one generally makes the *length* of the arrow symbol for the impulse proportional to the area (the value) of the impulse.   Using this convention, all we need do to the line diagram in Fig. 2.5b to use the impulse notation given in Eq. (2.43) is to put arrowheads on the lines.

### 2.6.3  CHOICE OF DISTRIBUTION

In general one chooses a model for a continuous distribution function on the basis of one or more of the following criteria:

1   The physical nature of the problem fits most or all of the underlying assumptions associated with a particular distribution.
2   Data are available, and a plot of the data in terms of $f(x)$ or $F(x)$ turns the problem into one of curve fitting.  [In Chap. 3 we shall show that the hazard function $z(t)$, related to $f(x)$ *and* $F(x)$, is even more convenient for curve fitting.]
3   A convenient and simple model is chosen which approximately satisfies criterion 1 or 2.   The type of problem must justify the approximate nature of the modeling.   (Engineering judgment plays the paramount role here.)

A discussion of a number of important continuous random-variable distributions follows.

---

[1] If we have a distribution which is a mixture of continuous and discrete variables, $f(x)$ contains both continuous functions and impulses.

### 2.6.4  RECTANGULAR DISTRIBUTION

The simplest continuous variable distribution is the uniform or rectangular distribution shown in Fig. 2.14a. The two parameters of this distribution are the limits $a$ and $b$. This model predicts a uniform probability of occurrence in any interval

$$\Delta x, \ P(x < \mathbf{x} \le x + \Delta x) = \Delta x/(b - a)$$

between $a$ and $b$.† An example of a uniform random variable is the resistance value of a precision resistor which is picked out of a large batch by measurement and selection of each resistor (see Figs. 7.6 and 7.7); for

† Actually one can make good use of the singularity functions (step, impulse, and the entire family of derivatives and integrals) to write down the rectangular density and distribution functions. Using the notation $u_{-1}(x)$ for a step and $u_{-2}(x)$ for a ramp (the integral of the step) yields for the rectangular distribution

$$f(x) = \frac{1}{b-a}[u_{-1}(t-a) - u_{-1}(t-b)] \qquad F(x) = \frac{1}{b-a}[u_{-2}(t-a) - u_{-2}(t-b)]$$

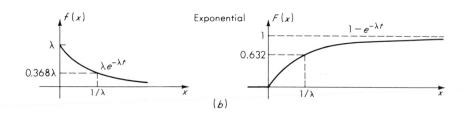

(a)

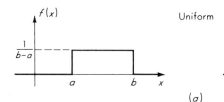

(b)

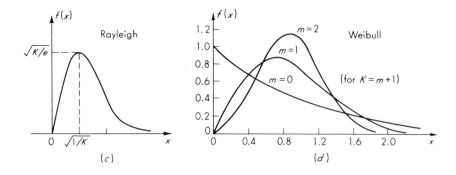

(c)          (d)

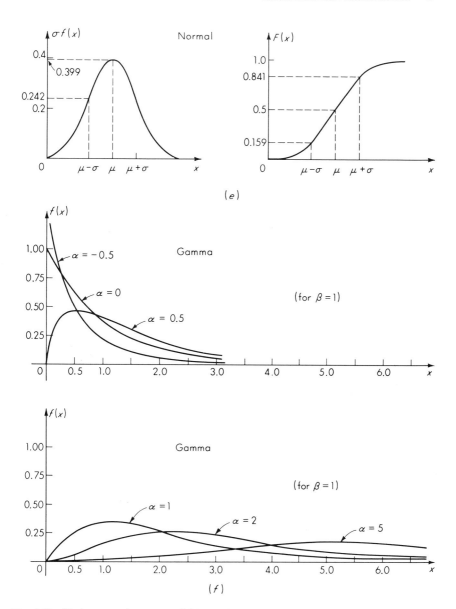

**Fig. 2.14** Various continuous variable probability distributions. (a) Uniform distribution; (b) exponential distribution; (c) Rayleigh distribution; (d) Weibull distribution; (e) normal distribution; (f) gamma distribution for unit $\beta$ and various values of $\alpha$. (Parts c and e adapted from A. Papoulis, "Probability, Random Variables, and Stochastic Processes," Copyright 1965. McGraw-Hill Book Company. Used by permission. Part d adapted from D. K. Lloyd and M. Lipow, "Reliability: Management, Methods and Mathematics," Copyright 1962. Prentice-Hall, Inc. Used by permission. Part f from G. A. Wadsworth and J. G. Bryan, "Introduction to Probability and Random Variables," Copyright 1960. McGraw-Hill Book Company. Used by permission.)

example, resistors of 1,000 ohms $\pm$ 1 percent might have an approximately rectangular distribution between 990 and 1,010 ohms.  About 50 percent of these resistors will be within $\pm 5$ ohms; i.e., the

$$P(995 < R \leq 1,005) = 0.5$$

### 2.6.5  EXPONENTIAL DISTRIBUTION

Another simple continuous variable distribution is the exponential distribution.  The exponential density function is

$$f(x) = \lambda e^{-\lambda x} \qquad 0 < x \leq +\infty \tag{2.44}$$

which is sketched in Fig. 2.14b.  This distribution recurs time and time again in reliability work.  The exponential is the distribution of the time to failure $t$ for a great number of electronic-system parts.  The parameter $\lambda$ is constant and is called the *conditional failure rate* with the units fractional failures per hour.  The distribution function yields the failure probability and $1 - F(t)$ the success probability.  Specifically, the probability of no failure (success) in the interval $0 - t$ is given by

$$P_s(t_1) = 1 - F(t_1) = e^{-\lambda t_1}$$

Thus, the shape of the probability-of-success function is the same as that of the density function $f(x)$ with only a vertical scale change, since $P_s(t_1 = 0) = 1$, whereas $f(0) = \lambda$.

As an example of the use of the exponential distribution let us assume we are dealing with an electronic part which has an exponential density for the time to failure.  The probability of the system's surviving up to $t_1 = 1/\lambda$ hr is given by

$$P_s\left(t_1 = \frac{1}{\lambda}\right) = 1 - F\left(\frac{1}{\lambda}\right) = e^{-1} = 0.368$$

### 2.6.6  RAYLEIGH DISTRIBUTION

Another single-parameter density function of considerable importance is the *Rayleigh distribution*, which is given as

$$f(x) = Axe^{-Kx^2/2} \qquad 0 < x \leq +\infty$$

Once we have stipulated the form of the distribution, the constant $A$ is fixed, and since $\int_{+\infty}^{-\infty} f(x)\, dx = 1$,

$$\int_0^{+\infty} Axe^{-Kx^2/2} = \frac{A}{K} = 1$$

(This integral, as well as many others which occur frequently in probability and reliability, can be found in Appendix C.)  Solving the above equation for $A$ yields for the Rayleigh density function

$$f(x) = Kxe^{-Kx^2/2} \tag{2.45}$$

and for the distribution function

$$F(x) = 1 - e^{-Kx^2/2} \tag{2.46}$$

The density function is sketched in Fig. 2.14c.   The Rayleigh distribution finds application in noise problems in communication systems and in reliability work.   Whereas the exponential distribution holds for time to failure of a component with a constant conditional failure rate $\lambda$, the Rayleigh distribution holds for a component with a linearly increasing conditional failure rate $Kt$.   The probability of success of such a unit is

$$P_s(t) = 1 - F(t) = e^{-Kt^2/2}$$

We compare the Rayleigh distribution with the exponential distribution.   For the exponential $P_s(1/\lambda) = 0.368$.   Solving for the time which the Rayleigh drops to 0.368, $P_s(t) = e^{-Kt^2/2} = 0.368 = e^{-1}$.   Thus, $Kt^2/2 = 1$, and $t = \sqrt{2/K}$.   We conclude that for the Rayleigh distribution $P_s(t \geq \sqrt{2/K}) \leq 0.368$ and $P_s(0 \leq t \leq \sqrt{2/K}) \geq 0.368$.

### 2.6.7  WEIBULL DISTRIBUTION

Both the exponential and the Rayleigh distributions are single-parameter distributions which can be represented as special cases of a more general two-parameter distribution called the *Weibull distribution*.   The density and distribution functions for the Weibull are

$$f(x) = Kx^m e^{-Kx^{m+1}/(m+1)} \qquad F(x) = 1 - e^{-Kx^{m+1}/(m+1)} \tag{2.47}$$

This family of functions is sketched for several values of $m$ in Fig. 2.14d. A special set of normalized Weibull curves is given in Fig. 4.19.   When $m = 0$, the distribution becomes exponential, and when $m = 1$, a Rayleigh distribution is obtained.   The parameter $m$ determines the shape of the distribution, and parameter $K$ is a scale-change parameter.   The use of the Weibull distribution as a general reliability model is discussed in Chap. 4.

### 2.6.8  NORMAL DISTRIBUTION

The best known two-parameter distribution is the *normal*, or *gaussian*, distribution.   "The normal distribution was discovered by De Moivre, whose published works as early as 1733 contained a derivation of it as the limiting form of the binomial.   It was also known to Laplace[1] no later

[1] In France the normal distribution is sometimes called the Laplacian.

than 1774, but through historical error, it has been attributed to Gauss, whose earliest published reference to it appeared in 1809. Nevertheless, the term 'Gaussian distribution' is an accepted synonym for 'normal distribution.'"[1] This distribution is very often a good fit for the size of manufactured parts, the size of a living organism, or the magnitude of certain electric signals. In Sec. 2.9 it will be shown that when a certain parameter which is a random variable is the sum of many other random variables, the parameter will have a normal distribution in most all cases.

The density function for the normal distribution is written as

$$f(x) = \frac{1}{\sigma \sqrt{2\pi}} e^{-x^2/2\sigma^2} \qquad -\infty < \mathbf{x} < +\infty$$

This function has a peak of $1/\sigma \sqrt{2\pi}$ at $x = 0$ and falls off symmetrically on either side of zero. The rate of falloff and the height of the peak at $x = 0$ are determined by the parameter $\sigma$, which is called the *standard deviation*. In general one deals with a random variable $\mathbf{x}$ which is spread about some value such that the peak of the distribution is not at zero. In this case one shifts the horizontal scale of the normal distribution so that the peak occurs at $x = \mu$

$$f(x) = \frac{1}{\sigma \sqrt{2\pi}} e^{-(x-\mu)^2/2\sigma^2} \tag{2.48}$$

The effect of changing $\sigma$ is illustrated in Fig. 2.15a, showing how a large value of $\sigma$ means a low, broad curve and a small value of $\sigma$ a thin, high curve. A change in $\mu$ merely slides the curve along the $x$ axis, as shown in Fig. 2.15b.

The distribution function is given by

$$F(x) = \frac{1}{\sigma \sqrt{2\pi}} \int_{-\infty}^{x} e^{-(\xi-\mu)^2/2\sigma^2} \, d\xi \tag{2.49}$$

where $\xi$ is a dummy variable of integration. The shapes of the normal density and distribution functions are shown in Fig. 2.14e. The distribution function given in Eq. (2.49) is left in integral form since the result cannot be expressed in closed form. This causes no particular difficulty, since because of the great importance of the normal distribution, both $f(x)$ and $F(x)$ have been extensively tabulated (a short list appears in Table 2.3). In tabulating the integral of Eq. (2.49) it is generally convenient to introduce the change of variables $\mathbf{t} = (\mathbf{x} - \mu)/\sigma$, which shifts

[1] Wadsworth and Bryan, *op. cit.*, p. 104.

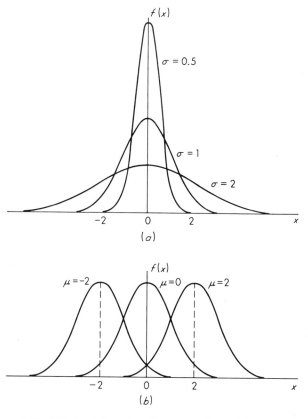

**Fig. 2.15** Effect of changing the parameters of the normal distribution. (a) Changing $\sigma$ with $\mu$ constant; (b) changing $\mu$ with $\sigma$ constant. (*Adapted from G. A. Wadsworth and J. G. Bryan, "Introduction to Probability and Random Variables." Copyright 1960. McGraw-Hill Book Company. Used by permission.*)

the distribution back to the origin and normalizes the $x$ axis in terms of $\sigma$ units.

To perform this change of variables we write

$$P(a < \mathbf{x} \le b) = F(x = b) - F(x = a)$$

$$F(x = b) = P(\mathbf{x} \le b) = \frac{1}{\sigma \sqrt{2\pi}} \int_{-\infty}^{b} e^{-(\xi-\mu)^2/2\sigma^2} \, d\xi$$

$$F(x = a) = P(\mathbf{x} \le a) = \frac{1}{\sigma \sqrt{2\pi}} \int_{-\infty}^{a} e^{-(\xi-\mu)^2/2\sigma^2} \, d\xi$$

**Table 2.3  Tabulation of the unit normal distribution** $t = \dfrac{x - \mu}{\sigma}$

| $t$ | $f(t)$ | $F(t)$ | $R(t)$ | $2R(t)$ | $W(t)$ |
|---|---|---|---|---|---|
| 0.0 | 0.3989 | 0.5000 | 0.5000 | 1.0000 | 0 |
| 0.1 | 0.3970 | 0.5398 | 0.4602 | 0.9203 | 0.0797 |
| 0.2 | 0.3910 | 0.5793 | 0.4207 | 0.8415 | 0.1585 |
| 0.3 | 0.3814 | 0.6179 | 0.3821 | 0.7642 | 0.2358 |
| 0.4 | 0.3683 | 0.6554 | 0.3446 | 0.6892 | 0.3108 |
| 0.5 | 0.3521 | 0.6915 | 0.3085 | 0.6171 | 0.3829 |
| 0.6 | 0.3332 | 0.7257 | 0.2743 | 0.5485 | 0.4515 |
| 0.7 | 0.3123 | 0.7580 | 0.2420 | 0.4839 | 0.5161 |
| 0.8 | 0.2897 | 0.7881 | 0.2119 | 0.4237 | 0.5763 |
| 0.9 | 0.2661 | 0.8159 | 0.1841 | 0.3681 | 0.6319 |
| 1.0 | 0.2420 | 0.8413 | 0.1587 | 0.3173 | 0.6827 |
| 1.1 | 0.2179 | 0.8643 | 0.1357 | 0.2713 | 0.7287 |
| 1.2 | 0.1942 | 0.8849 | 0.1151 | 0.2301 | 0.7699 |
| 1.3 | 0.1714 | 0.9032 | 0.0968 | 0.1936 | 0.8064 |
| 1.4 | 0.1497 | 0.9192 | 0.0808 | 0.1615 | 0.8385 |
| 1.5 | 0.1295 | 0.9332 | 0.0668 | 0.1336 | 0.8664 |
| 1.6 | 0.1109 | 0.9452 | 0.0548 | 0.1096 | 0.8904 |
| 1.7 | 0.0940 | 0.9554 | 0.0446 | 0.0891 | 0.9109 |
| 1.8 | 0.0790 | 0.9641 | 0.0359 | 0.0719 | 0.9281 |
| 1.9 | 0.0656 | 0.9713 | 0.0287 | 0.0574 | 0.9426 |
| 2.0 | 0.0540 | 0.9772 | 0.0228 | 0.0455 | 0.9545 |
| 2.1 | 0.0440 | 0.9821 | 0.0179 | 0.0357 | 0.9643 |
| 2.2 | 0.0355 | 0.9861 | 0.0139 | 0.0278 | 0.9722 |
| 2.3 | 0.0283 | 0.9893 | 0.0107 | 0.0214 | 0.9786 |
| 2.4 | 0.0224 | 0.9918 | 0.0082 | 0.0164 | 0.9836 |
| 2.5 | 0.0175 | 0.9938 | 0.0062 | 0.0124 | 0.9876 |
| 2.6 | 0.0136 | 0.9953 | 0.0047 | 0.0093 | 0.9907 |
| 2.7 | 0.0104 | 0.9965 | 0.0035 | 0.0069 | 0.9931 |
| 2.8 | 0.0079 | 0.9974 | 0.0026 | 0.0051 | 0.9949 |
| 2.9 | 0.0060 | 0.9981 | 0.0019 | 0.0037 | 0.9963 |
| 3.0 | 0.0044 | 0.9987 | 0.0013 | 0.0027 | 0.9973 |
| Fractiles: | | | | | |
| 1.2816 | 0.1755 | 0.9000 | 0.1000 | 0.2000 | 0.8000 |
| 1.6449 | 0.1031 | 0.9500 | 0.0500 | 0.1000 | 0.9000 |
| 1.9600 | 0.0584 | 0.9750 | 0.0250 | 0.0500 | 0.9500 |
| 2.0537 | 0.0484 | 0.9800 | 0.0200 | 0.0400 | 0.9600 |
| 2.3263 | 0.0267 | 0.9900 | 0.0100 | 0.0200 | 0.9800 |
| 2.5758 | 0.0145 | 0.9950 | 0.0050 | 0.0100 | 0.9900 |

SOURCE: Adapted with permission from G. A. Wadsworth and J. G. Bryan, "Introduction to Probability and Random Variables." Copyright 1960, McGraw-Hill Book Company, table 4-4.

Since $t = (x - \mu)/\sigma$, $dt = dx/\sigma$, and

$$P(x \leq b') = \frac{1}{\sqrt{2\pi}} \int_{-\infty}^{b'} e^{-t^2/2} \, dt$$

$$P(x \leq a') = \frac{1}{\sqrt{2\pi}} \int_{-\infty}^{a'} e^{-t^2/2} \, dt$$

where

$$b' = \frac{b - \mu}{\sigma} \qquad \text{and} \qquad a' = \frac{a - \mu}{\sigma}$$

The area under the $f(x)$ curve between $a$ and $b$ is of interest since it represents the probability that $x$ is within the interval $a < x \leq b$. The areas for $-1 < t \leq +1$, $-2 < t \leq +2$, $-3 < t \leq +3$ are shown in Fig. 2.16 and are 0.683, 0.954, and 0.997.

As an example of the use of the normal distribution let us suppose that a resistor manufacturer produces 100-ohm resistors with a tolerance of $\pm 10$ percent. We would guess that his manufacturing process produces a normal distribution of resistance values clustered about the central value $\mu = 100$ ohms. If $\sigma$ is set at about 5 ohms, the probability that any particular resistor is out of tolerance is

$$1 - P(90 < x \leq 110) = 1 - [F(110) - F(90)]$$
$$= 1 - P(-2 < t \leq +2) = 0.046$$

Thus, the resistors would be out of tolerance about 4.6 percent of the time. If the manufacturer is concerned over this, he may adjust his manufacturing controls so that $\sigma = 3.33$ ohms and reduce this percentage to 0.3 percent, or he may test each resistor to cut off the tails of the distribution.

The normal distribution can also be used as a limiting form for many other distributions. As suggested by DeMoivre's original work, the binomial distribution approaches the normal distribution for large $n$.

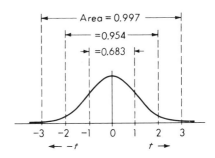

**Fig. 2.16**  Area under the normal curve.

A detailed derivation[1] shows that the approximation is good for $p \leq 0.5$ and $np \geq 5$ or $p > 0.5$ and $nq > 5$ and that one equates $\mu = np$ and $\sigma^2 = np(1 - p)$. Further exploitation of these results is left to the problems at the end of the chapter.

### 2.6.9 GAMMA DISTRIBUTION

The two-parameter distributions such as the normal and the Weibull are quite flexible in fitting a wide variety of problems. Another two-parameter distribution of use in reliability work is the *gamma distribution*, which is defined by

$$f(x) = \frac{1}{\beta^{\alpha+1}\Gamma(\alpha + 1)} \, x^\alpha e^{-x/\beta} \qquad \begin{array}{l} \alpha > -1, \beta > 0 \\ 0 < x \leq \infty \end{array} \tag{2.50}$$

[The gamma function $\Gamma(z)$ is defined in Appendix C. When $z$ is an integer, $\Gamma(z) = (z - 1)!$.] The parameter $\beta$ serves as a scale parameter and merely changes the vertical and horizontal scales, but a change in $\alpha$ changes the shape of the curve. The gamma density function is shown for several values of $\alpha$ in Fig. 2.14$f$; this distribution has been extensively tabulated.[2] The gamma distribution can be used to fit many sets of experimental data by proper choice of the two parameters $\alpha$ and $\beta$, but (as will be shown in Chap. 4) the Weibull is superior for this task in reliability work.

The gamma is the governing distribution for a standby system. If we let $t_1, t_2, \ldots, t_n$ be the failure times of the on-line component and the $n - 1$ standby components, then the failure time of the system $t_s = t_1 + t_2 + \cdots + t_n$. The most common model to choose for each time-to-failure distribution is the exponential. Note that if we let $\alpha = 0$ in Eq. (2.50), we obtain an exponential distribution with $1/\beta = \lambda$. In Sec. 2.9 we shall prove that if $t_1, t_2, \ldots, t_n$ are independent random variables and have an exponential distribution with the same $\beta$, then $t_s$ is gamma-distributed with the same $\beta$ and $\alpha = n - 1$. In our discussion of the Poisson distribution in Sec. 2.5 we found that the probability of success for a three-element standby system is

$$P_s = e^{-\lambda t}\left(1 + \frac{\lambda t}{1!} + \frac{\lambda^2 t^2}{2!}\right)$$

Using the above information, we find that $\alpha = 3 - 1 = 2$ and $\beta = \beta$; therefore

$$f(t_s = t_1 + t_2 + t_3) = \frac{1}{\beta^3\Gamma(3)} \, t_s{}^2 e^{-t_s/\beta}$$

---

[1] Wadsworth and Bryan, *op. cit.*, p. 109–111, and Paul G. Hoel, "Introduction to Mathematical Statistics," p. 87, John Wiley & Sons, Inc., New York, 1955.

[2] Karl Pearson, "Tables of the Incomplete Gamma Function," Cambridge University Press, New York, 1922.

The probability of success is given by

$$P_s = 1 - F(t_s) = 1 - \int_0^{t_s} \frac{1}{2\beta^3} z^2 e^{-z/\beta} \, dz$$

Using the integral table given in Appendix C or two integrations by parts (let $u = z^2$ the first time and $u = z$ the second time) yields

$$P_s = 1 - \left( -\frac{t_s^2}{2\beta^2} e^{-t_s/\beta} - \frac{1}{\beta} t_s e^{-t_s/\beta} - e^{-t_s/\beta} + 1 \right)$$

Substitution of $\lambda = 1/\beta$ checks with the previous result.

## 2.7  MOMENTS

The density or distribution function of a random variable contains all the information about the variable, i.e., the entire story.  Sometimes the entire story of the random variable is not necessary, and an excerpt which sufficiently characterizes the distribution is sufficient.  In such a case one computes a few moments (generally two) for the distribution and uses them to delineate the salient features.  The moments are weighted integrals of the density function which describe various geometrical properties of the density function.

### 2.7.1  EXPECTED VALUE

It is easy to express the various moments of a probability distribution in terms of an operator called the *expected value*.  The expected value of the continuous random variable $\mathbf{x}$ defined over the range $a < \mathbf{x} \leq b$ with density function $f(x)$ is defined by

$$E(\mathbf{x}) = \int_a^b x f(x) \, dx \tag{2.51}$$

For a discrete random variable $\mathbf{x}$ taking on values $x = x_1, x_2, \ldots, x_n$ the expected value is defined in terms of a summation

$$E(\mathbf{x}) = \sum_{i=1}^{n} x_i f(x_i) \tag{2.52}$$

We shall compute the expected values for a few simple examples in order to give some physical meaning to the operator $E(\mathbf{x})$.  Suppose we have a discrete random variable $\mathbf{x}$ which takes on 10 discrete values $1, 2, \ldots, 10$ and that each value is equally likely.  Then using the equally-likely-probability hypothesis, we would expect that $f(x) = 1/10$ for each value of $\mathbf{x}$.  Application of Eq. (2.52) yields

$$E(\mathbf{x}) = \sum_{i=1}^{10} x_i \tfrac{1}{10} = \tfrac{1}{10} + \tfrac{2}{10} + \cdots + \tfrac{10}{10} = 5.5$$

This is simply the average value of the integers 1 to 10.† Since the numbers are equally probable, the result is the arithmetic mean of the limits 1 and 10.

If we change $f(x)$, the expected value will change. Assuming that the values of $\mathbf{x}$ between 1 and 5 have identical probabilities and are only half as likely to occur as the numbers between 6 and 10, which also have identical probabilities, we can solve for $f(x)$. Setting up a simple algebraic equation and using the property that $\sum_{i=1}^{10} f(x_i) = 1$, we obtain

$$f(x) = \begin{cases} \frac{1}{15} & x = 1, 2, 3, 4, 5 \\ \frac{2}{15} & x = 6, 7, 8, 9, 10 \end{cases}$$

Computing the expected value yields

$$E(\mathbf{x}) = \sum_{i=1}^{5} x_i \tfrac{1}{15} + \sum_{i=6}^{10} x_i \tfrac{2}{15} = 7$$

Because the larger numbers have higher probabilities, the expected value is shifted upward. The expected value is the weighted average of the function.

Switching to continuous random variables, we assume a rectangular density function for $\mathbf{x}$ over the interval $a < \mathbf{x} \le b$. Computing the expected value from Eq. (2.51) gives

$$E(\mathbf{x}) = \int_a^b x \frac{1}{b-a} \, dx = \frac{b+a}{2}$$

Again because of the flatness of the density function, the expected value is the arithmetic mean of the two limits. If we let $f(x)$ increase as a ramp between $a$ and $b$, we have

$$f(x) = \frac{2}{(b-a)^2} x \qquad a < \mathbf{x} \le b$$

$$E(\mathbf{x}) = \int_a^b x \frac{2}{(b-a)^2} \, dx = \frac{b+a}{b-a}$$

The expected value for the ramp distribution is $2/(b-a)$ times the mean of the step distribution.

### 2.7.2  MOMENTS

To be more general one defines an entire set of moments. The $n$th moment of the random variable $\mathbf{x}$ computed about the origin and defined

---

† Note that if the distribution includes the additional value $x_i = 0$, then $\sum_{i=0}^{10} x_i \tfrac{1}{11} = 5.0$.

over the range $a < \mathbf{x} \le b$ is given by

$$m_r = \int_{-\infty}^{+\infty} x^r f(x)\, dx \tag{2.53}$$

The zero-order moment $m_0$ is the area under the density function, which is, of course, unity. The first-order moment is simply the expected value, which is called the *mean* and is given the symbol $\mu$

$$m_1 = E(\mathbf{x}) = \mu \tag{2.54}$$

Equation (2.53) can be rewritten in terms of the expected-value operator as

$$m_r = E(\mathbf{x}^r) \tag{2.55}\dagger$$

If the density function $f(x)$ is an even function about the origin, the 1, 3, 5, . . . moments are zero. The origin moments for a discrete random variable which takes on the values $x_1,\ x_2,\ \dots,\ x_n$ are given by

$$m_r = \sum_{i=1}^{n} x_i^r f(x_i) \tag{2.56}$$

This can also be expressed in terms of the expected-value operator, as in Eq. (2.55), but we must interpret the expected value in the discrete sense, as given in Eq. (2.52). It is often of importance to compute moments about the mean rather than the origin. The set of moments about the mean are defined as:

For continuous random variables:

$$m_r' = E[(\mathbf{x} - \mu)^r] = \int_{-\infty}^{+\infty} (x - \mu)^r f(x)\, dx \tag{2.57}$$

For discrete random variables:

$$m_r' = E[(\mathbf{x} - \mu)^r] = \sum_{i=1}^{n} (x_i - \mu)^r f(x_i) \tag{2.58}$$

The zero-order moment about the mean is the area under the density function (or in the discrete case the sum of the probabilities of all possible outcomes), which is, of course, unity. The first moment about the mean is zero, since

$$\int_{-\infty}^{+\infty} (x - \mu)f(x)\, dx = \int_{-\infty}^{+\infty} xf(x)\, dx - \mu \int_{-\infty}^{+\infty} f(x)\, dx = \mu - \mu = 0$$

The second moment about the mean, $m_2' = \int_{-\infty}^{+\infty} (x - \mu)^2 f(x)\, dx$, is called the *variance* of $\mathbf{x}$, var $\mathbf{x}$, and is a measure of the sum of the square

---

† This conclusion assumes that the $E[u(\mathbf{x})] = \int_{-\infty}^{+\infty} u(x)f(x)\, dx$, which is true but will not be formally derived until Sec. 2.9.

of the deviations from $\mu$. Generally this is expressed in terms of the standard deviation $\sigma = \sqrt{\operatorname{var} \mathbf{x}}$. One can easily express var $\mathbf{x}$ and $\sigma$ in terms of the expected-value operator

$$\sigma^2 = \operatorname{var} \mathbf{x} = \int_{-\infty}^{+\infty} (x - \mu)^2 f(x)\,dx = \int_{-\infty}^{+\infty} x^2 f(x)\,dx$$
$$- 2\mu \int_{-\infty}^{+\infty} xf(x)\,dx + \mu^2 \int_{-\infty}^{+\infty} f(x)\,dx$$

By definition, the first integral is $E(\mathbf{x}^2)$, the second $2\mu$ times the mean, and the third $\mu^2$ times unity. The result is

$$\sigma^2 = \operatorname{var} \mathbf{x} = E(\mathbf{x}^2) - \mu^2 = E(\mathbf{x}^2) - [E(\mathbf{x})]^2$$

The means and variances of the distributions discussed in Sec. 2.6 are given in Table 2.4. For a density function which is symmetrical about the mean $m_1' = m_3' = \cdots = m_{2n+1}' = 0$. Although the higher-order moments reveal extra detail about the asymmetry of $f(x)$ or how fast $f(x)$ falls off away from the mean, they are generally not calculated, since $\mu$ and $\sigma$ reveal enough about the problem for most engineering estimates.

### 2.7.3  MOMENT–GENERATING FUNCTION

A third technique for calculating moments, in addition to the integral definition or the expected-value operator, uses the *moment-generating function*, an auxiliary function which can be computed by integration. Appropriate manipulation of the moment-generating function yields all the moments of the distribution. The moment-generating function is defined by

$$M_x(\theta) = E(e^{\theta x}) \tag{2.59}$$

Interpretation of the expected-value operator in the discrete case and the continuous case yields:

Discrete case:    $$M_x(\theta) = \sum_{i=1}^{n} e^{\theta x_i} f(x_i) \tag{2.60}$$

Continuous case: $M_x(\theta) = \displaystyle\int_{-\infty}^{+\infty} e^{\theta x} f(x)\,dx \tag{2.61}$

The reader who is familiar with Laplace transforms (to be discussed in Sec. 2.11) will immediately notice that Eq. (2.61) is identical with the definition of the Laplace transform[1] if we substitute $\theta = -s$. For the case of the exponential function, $f(x) = \lambda e^{-\lambda x}, 0 < \mathbf{x} \le +\infty$, the moment-generating function becomes

$$M_x(\theta) = \int_0^{+\infty} \lambda e^{\theta x} e^{-\lambda x}\,dx = \lambda \int_0^{+\infty} e^{(\theta - \lambda)x}\,dx = \frac{\lambda e^{(\theta - \lambda)x}}{\theta - \lambda}\bigg|_0^{+\infty}$$

[1] Actually the double-sided Laplace transform, since we integrate from $-\infty$ to $+\infty$.

At the upper limit, as long as $\theta < +\lambda$, the term is $e^{-\infty}$, which of course vanishes.[1]  Substitution of the lower limit yields

$$M_x(\theta) = \frac{-\lambda}{\theta - \lambda} \tag{2.62}$$

(Note that by letting $\theta = -s$ we obtain the Laplace transform of the exponential function.)  The moment-generating functions for several distributions of interest are given in Table 2.4.  The value of the moment-generating function in computing moments is apparent when the exponential term in Eq. (2.59) is expanded in a series

$$M_x(\theta) = E(e^{\theta x}) = E\left(1 + \theta x + \frac{\theta^2 x^2}{2!} + \cdots + \frac{\theta^n x^n}{n!} + \cdots\right)$$

$$= 1 + \theta E(x) + \frac{\theta^2}{2!} E(x^2) + \cdots + \frac{\theta^n}{n!} E(x^n) + \cdots \tag{2.63}$$

We can thus view the moment-generating function as an expansion in terms of the origin moments.  If we let $\theta = 0$ in Eq. (2.63), we obtain $E(x^0) = 1$, but if we first differentiate with respect to $\theta$ and then let $\theta \to 0$, we obtain $E(x)$.  Thus, to obtain any origin moment from the moment-generating function we apply

$$m_n = \left[\frac{d^n M_x(\theta)}{d\theta^n}\right]_{\theta=0} \tag{2.64}$$

Applying this formula to the exponential-generating function given in Eq. (2.62) gives

$$E(x^0) = [M_x(\theta)]_{\theta=0} = \left[\frac{-\lambda}{\theta - \lambda}\right]_{\theta=0} = 1$$

$$E(x^1) = \left[\frac{dM_x(\theta)}{d\theta}\right]_{\theta=0} = \left[\frac{\lambda}{(\theta - \lambda)^2}\right]_{\theta=0} = \frac{1}{\lambda}$$

$$E(x^2) = \left[\frac{d^2 M_x(\theta)}{d\theta^2}\right]_{\theta=0} = \left[\frac{-2\lambda}{(\theta - \lambda)^3}\right]_{\theta=0} = \frac{2}{\lambda^2}$$

In order to compute the standard deviation, we use

$$\sigma = \sqrt{\text{var } x} = \sqrt{E(x^2) - [E(x)]^2} = \sqrt{\frac{2}{\lambda^2} - \frac{1}{\lambda^2}} = \frac{1}{\lambda}$$

The results, $\mu = 1/\lambda$ and $\sigma = 1/\lambda$, of course check with the values given in Table 2.4.  The moment-generating function is also useful in computing derived distributions [see Eq. (2.108)].

---

[1] The moment-generating function is not defined for $\theta > \lambda$. This does not inconvenience us since we are interested in the region near $\theta = 0$ [see Eq. (2.64), which is within our range of definition].

**Table 2.4  Mean, variance, and moment-generating functions of several distributions**

| *Distribution* | $f(x)$ | $E(\mathbf{x})$ | var $\mathbf{x}$ | $M_x(\theta)$ |
|---|---|---|---|---|
| Binomial | $\binom{n}{r} p^r (1-p)^{n-r}$ | $np$ | $np(1-p)$ | $[1 + p(e^\theta - 1)]^n$ |
| Poisson | $\dfrac{e^{-\mu}\mu^x}{x!}$ | $\mu$ | $\mu$ | $e^{\lambda(e^\theta - 1)}$ |
| Exponential | $\lambda e^{-\lambda x}$ | $\dfrac{1}{\lambda}$ | $\dfrac{1}{\lambda^2}$ | $-\dfrac{\lambda}{\theta - \lambda}$ |
| Rayleigh | $Kxe^{-Kx^2/2}$ | $\sqrt{\dfrac{\pi}{2K}}$ | $\dfrac{2}{K}\left(1 - \dfrac{\pi}{4}\right)$ | Complex form |
| Weibull | $Kx^m e^{-Kx^{m+1}/(m+1)}$ | $\left(\dfrac{K}{m+1}\right)^{1/(m+1)} \Gamma\left(\dfrac{m+2}{m+1}\right)$ | $\left(\dfrac{K}{m+1}\right)^{-2/(m+1)} \left[\Gamma\left(\dfrac{m+3}{m+1}\right) - \Gamma^2\left(\dfrac{m+2}{m+1}\right)\right]$ | Complex form |
| Gamma | $\dfrac{1}{\beta^{\alpha+1}\Gamma(\alpha+1)} x^\alpha e^{-x/\beta}$ | $\beta(\alpha+1)$ | $\beta^2(\alpha+1)$ | $-\dfrac{(1/\beta)^{\alpha+1}}{(\theta - 1/\beta)^{\alpha+1}}$ |
| Normal | $\dfrac{1}{\sigma\sqrt{2\pi}} e^{-(x-\mu)^2/2\sigma^2}$ | $\mu$ | $\sigma^2$ | $e^{+\mu\theta + \theta^2\sigma^2/2}$ |

## 2.8  MARKOV MODELS

### 2.8.1  PROPERTIES

There are basically four kinds of Markov probability models, one of which plays a central role in the reliability material which follows. Markov models are functions of two random variables, the state of the system **x** and the time of observation **t**.  The four kinds of models arise because both **x** and **t** may be either discrete or continuous random variables, resulting in four combinations.  As a simple example of the concepts of state and time of observation, we visualize a shoe box with two interior partitions which divide the box into four interior compartments labeled 1, 2, 3, 4.  A Ping-Pong ball is placed into one of these compartments, and the box is periodically tapped on the bottom causing the Ping-Pong ball to jump up and fall back into one of the four compartments.  (For the moment we neglect the possibility that it falls out onto the floor.)  The states of the system are the four compartments in the box.  The time of observation is immediately after each rap, when the ball has fallen back into one of the compartments.  Since we specified that the raps occur periodically, the model is discrete in both state and time.  This sort of model is generally called a *Markov chain model* or a *discrete-state discrete-time model*.  When the raps at the bottom of the box occur continuously, the model becomes a discrete-state continuous-time model, called a *Markov process*.  If we remove the partitions and call the long axis of the box the $x$ axis, we can visualize a continuum of states from $x = -l/2$ to $x = +l/2$.  If the ball is coated with rubber cement, it will stick wherever it hits when it falls back into the box.  In this manner we can visualize the other two types of models, which involve a continuous-state variable.  We shall be primarily concerned with the discrete-state continuous-time model, the Markov process.

Any Markov model is defined by a set of probabilities $p_{ij}$ which define the probability of transition from any state $i$ to any state $j$.  If in the discrete-state case we make our box compartments equal in size, it seems reasonable for all the transition probabilities to be equal.  (In the general case, where each compartment is of different size, the transition probabilities are unequal.)  One of the most important features of any Markov model is that the transition probability $p_{ij}$ depends only on states $i$ and $j$ and is completely independent of all past states except the last one, state $i$.  This seems reasonable in terms of our shoe-box model since transitions are really dependent only on the height of the wall between adjacent compartments $i$ and $j$ and the area of the compartments and not on the sequence of states the ball has occupied before arriving in state $i$.  Before delving further into the properties of Markov processes, an example of great importance, the Poisson process, will be discussed on page 62.

### 2.8.2  POISSON PROCESS

In Sec. 2.5 the Poisson distribution was introduced as a limiting form of the binomial distribution. In this section we shall derive the Poisson distribution as the governing probability law for a Poisson process, a particular kind of Markov process. In a Poisson process we are interested in the number of occurrences in time, the probability of each occurrence in a small time $\Delta t$ being a constant which is the parameter of the process. Examples of Poisson processes are the number of atoms transmuting as a function of time in the radioactive decay of a substance, the number of noise pulses as a function of time in certain types of electric systems, and the number of failures for a group of components operating in a standby mode or in an instantaneous-replacement situation. The occurrences are discrete, and time is continuous; therefore this is a discrete-state continuous-time model. The basic assumptions which are necessary in deriving a Poisson process model are as follows:

1   The probability that a transition occurs from the state of $n$ occurrences to the state of $n + 1$ occurrences in time $\Delta t$ is $\lambda \, \Delta t$. The parameter $\lambda$ is a constant and has the dimensions of occurrences per unit time.[1] The occurrences are irreversible, which means that the number of occurrences can never decrease with time.[2]

2   Each occurrence is independent of all other occurrences.

3   The transition probability of two or more occurrences in interval $\Delta t$ is negligible. Another way of saying this is to make use of the independence-of-occurrence property and write the probability of two occurrences in interval $\Delta t$ as the product of the probability of each occurrence, that is, $(\lambda \, \Delta t)(\lambda \, \Delta t)$. This is obviously an infinitesimal of second order for $\Delta t$ small and can be neglected.

We wish to solve for the probability of $n$ occurrences in time $t$, and to that end we set up a system of difference equations representing the state probabilities and transition probabilities. The probability of $n$ occurrences having taken place by time $t$ is denoted by

$$P(x = n, t) \equiv P_n(t)$$

For the case of zero occurrences at time $t + \Delta t$ we write the following difference equation

$$P_0(t + \Delta t) = (1 - \lambda \, \Delta t)P_0(t) \tag{2.65}$$

---

[1] In reliability work $\lambda$ is the failure rate, failures per hour. Cases in which the failure rate changes as a function of time are discussed in Chap. 5.

[2] Markov models in which transitions are allowed in both directions are discussed in Chap. 6, when the reliability of repairable systems is discussed.

which says that the probability of zero occurrences at time $t + \Delta t$ is $P_0(t + \Delta t)$. This probability is given by the probability of zero occurrences at time $t$, $P_0(t)$, multiplied by the probability of no occurrences in interval $\Delta t$, $1 - \lambda \Delta t$. For the case of one occurrence at time $t + \Delta t$ we write

$$P_1(t + \Delta t) = (\lambda \Delta t)P_0(t) + (1 - \lambda \Delta t)P_1(t) \qquad (2.66)$$

The probability of one occurrence at $t + \Delta t$ can arise in two ways: (1) either there was no occurrence at time $t$, $P_0(t)$, and one happened in the interval $\Delta t$, with probability $\lambda \Delta t$, or (2) there had already been one occurrence at time $t$, $P_1(t)$, and no additional ones came along, $1 - \lambda \Delta t$, in the time interval $\Delta t$. It is clear that Eq. (2.66) can be generalized, yielding

$$P_n(t + \Delta t) = (\lambda \Delta t)P_{n-1}(t) + (1 - \lambda \Delta t)P_n(t)$$
$$\text{for } n = 1, 2, \ldots \quad (2.67)$$

The difference equations (2.65) and (2.67) really describe a discrete-time system, since time is divided into intervals $\Delta t$, but by taking limits as $\Delta t \to 0$ we obtain a set of differential equations which truly describe the continuous-time Poisson process. Rearranging Eq. (2.65) and taking the limit of both sides of the equation as $\Delta t \to 0$ leads to

$$\lim_{\Delta t \to 0} \frac{P_0(t + \Delta t) - P_0(t)}{\Delta t} = \lim_{\Delta t \to 0} - \lambda P_0(t)$$

By definition the left-hand side of the equation is the time derivative of $P_0(t)$ and the right-hand side is independent of $\Delta t$; therefore

$$\frac{dP_0(t)}{dt} = \dot{P}_0(t) = -\lambda P_0(t) \qquad (2.68)$$

Similarly for Eq. (2.67)

$$\lim_{\Delta t \to 0} \frac{P_n(t + \Delta t) - P_n(t)}{\Delta t} = \lim_{\Delta t \to 0} \lambda P_{n-1}(t) - \lim_{\Delta t \to 0} \lambda P_n(t)$$
$$\frac{dP_n(t)}{dt} = \dot{P}_n(t) = \lambda P_{n-1}(t) - \lambda P_n(t)$$
$$\text{for } n = 1, 2, \ldots, n \quad (2.69)$$

Equations (2.68) and (2.69) are a complete set of differential equations which, together with a set of initial conditions, describe the process. If there are no occurrences at the start of the problem, $t = 0$, $n = 0$, and $P_0(0) = 1$, $P_1(0) = P_2(0) = \cdots = P_n(0) = 0$. If we started with three occurrences at $t = 0$, $P_0(0) = P_1(0) = P_2(0) = 0$, $P_3(0) = 1$,

$$P_4(0) = P_5(0) = \cdots = P_n(0) = 0$$

Solution of this set of equations can be performed in several ways: classical differential-equation techniques, Laplace transforms, matrix methods, etc. In this section we shall solve them using the classical technique of undetermined coefficients. (Undetermined coefficients are reviewed in Sec. 2.11, as are Laplace transforms and matrix techniques.) Equation (2.68) is homogeneous and the total solution is of the form $Ae^{st}$. Substituting

$$\frac{d}{dt} Ae^{st} = Ase^{st} = -\lambda Ae^{st} \qquad \text{and} \qquad s = -\lambda$$

gives

$$P_0(t) = Ae^{-\lambda t}$$

Substituting the initial condition $P_0(0) = 1$

$$P_0(0) = Ae^{-\lambda 0} = A = 1$$

gives

$$P_0(t) = e^{-\lambda t} \tag{2.70}$$

For $n = 1$, Eq. (2.69) becomes

$$\dot{P}_1(t) = \lambda P_0(t) - \lambda P_1(t)$$

Substitution from Eq. (2.70) and rearrangement yields

$$\dot{P}_1(t) + \lambda P_1(t) = \lambda e^{-\lambda t}$$

The homogeneous portion of this equation is the same as that for $P_0(t)$; thus, the homogeneous part of $P_1(t)$ is $Ae^{-\lambda t}$. The particular solution is generally of the same form as the right-hand side of the equation, but since the driver is the same function as the homogeneous solution, we must first multiply by $t$. Thus, the driver solution is $Bte^{-\lambda t}$. Substituting

$$\frac{d}{dt} Bte^{-\lambda t} = -\lambda Bte^{-\lambda t} + Be^{-\lambda t}$$

$$(-\lambda Bte^{-\lambda t} + Be^{-\lambda t}) + \lambda Bte^{-\lambda t} = \lambda e^{-\lambda t}$$

$$B = \lambda$$

gives

$$P_1(t) = Ae^{-\lambda t} + \lambda te^{-\lambda t}$$

Substituting the initial condition

$$P_1(0) = 0 = A$$

gives

$$P_1(t) = \lambda t e^{-\lambda t} \tag{2.71}$$

It should be clear that solving for $P_n(t)$ for $n = 2, 3, \ldots$ will generate the Poisson probability law given in Eq. (2.33).[1]

Thus, the Poisson process has been shown to be a special type of Markov process which can be derived from the three basic postulates with no mention of the binomial distribution. We can give another important interpretation to $P_0(t)$. If we let $t_0$ be the time of the first occurrence, then $P_0(t)$ is the probability of no occurrences

$$P_0(t) \equiv P(t < t_0) = 1 - P(t_0 < t)$$

Thus, $1 - P_0(t)$ is a cumulative distribution function for the random variable **t**, the time of occurrence. The density function for time of first occurrence is obtained by differentiation

$$f(t) = \frac{d}{dt}(1 - e^{-\lambda t}) = \lambda e^{-\lambda t} \tag{2.72}$$

This means that the time of first occurrence is exponentially distributed. Since each occurrence is independent of all others, it also means that the time between any two occurrences is exponentially distributed. This conclusion agrees with the previous result that the sum of exponentially distributed random variables is gamma-distributed and that for the particular values of $\alpha$ and $\beta$ the gamma distribution obtained reduces to a Poisson.

### 2.8.3  TRANSITION MATRIX

Returning to some of the basic properties of Markov processes, we find that we can specify the process by a set of differential equations and their associated initial conditions. Because of the basic Markov assumption that only the last state is involved in determining the probabilities, we always obtain a set of first-order differential equations. The constants in these equations can be specified by constructing a transition-probability matrix.[2] The rows represent the probability of being in any state $A$ at time $t$ and the columns the probability of being in state $B$ at time $t + \Delta t$. The former are called *initial states* and the latter *final states*. An example is given in Table 2.5 for a process with $n + 1$ discrete states. The transition probability $p_{ij}$ is the probability that in time $\Delta t$ the system will undergo a transition from initial state $i$ to final state $j$.

[1] $P_n(t) = (\lambda t)^n e^{-\lambda t}/n!$  This is the same expression as Eq. (2.33); however, $n$ is the number of occurrences as used in this section, whereas $r$ was previously used.

[2] In Chap. 5 a flow-graph model for a Markov process will be developed which parallels the use of the transition matrix.

**Table 2.5    A transition matrix**

|                    |         | Final states |              |              |       |              |
|--------------------|---------|--------------|--------------|--------------|-------|--------------|
| Initial states     |         | $s_0(t + \Delta t)$ | $s_1(t + \Delta t)$ | $s_2(t + \Delta t)$ | $\cdots$ | $s_n(t + \Delta t)$ |
| $s_0(t)$           | $n = 0$ | $p_{00}$     | $p_{01}$     | $p_{02}$     | $\cdots$ | $p_{0n}$     |
| $s_1(t)$           | $n = 1$ | $p_{10}$     | $p_{11}$     | $p_{12}$     | $\cdots$ | $p_{1n}$     |
| $s_2(t)$           | $n = 2$ | $p_{20}$     | $p_{21}$     | $p_{22}$     | $\cdots$ | $p_{2n}$     |
| $\cdots\cdots\cdots$ |       |              |              |              |       |              |
| $s_n(t)$           | $n = n$ | $p_{n0}$     | $p_{n1}$     | $p_{n2}$     | $\cdots$ | $p_{nn}$     |

Of course $p_{ii}$, a term on the main diagonal, is the probability that the system will remain in the same state during one transition. The sum of the $p_{ij}$ terms in any row must be unity, since this is the sum of all possible transition probabilities. In the case of a Poisson process, there are an infinite number of states. The transition matrix for the first five terms of a Poisson process is given in Table 2.6. Inspection of the Poisson example reveals that the difference equations[1] for the system can be obtained simply. The procedure is to equate the probability of any final state at the top of each column to the product of the transition probabili-

---

[1] The differential equations are obtained by taking the limit of the difference equations as $\Delta t \to 0$.

**Table 2.6    The first five rows and columns of the transition matrix for a Poisson process**

|          | $s_0(t + \Delta t)$ | $s_1(t + \Delta t)$ | $s_2(t + \Delta t)$ | $s_3(t + \Delta t)$ | $s_4(t + \Delta t)$ |
|----------|---------------------|---------------------|---------------------|---------------------|---------------------|
| $s_0(t)$ | $1 - \lambda \Delta t$ | $\lambda \Delta t$  | 0                   | 0                   | 0                   |
| $s_1(t)$ | 0                   | $1 - \lambda \Delta t$ | $\lambda \Delta t$  | 0                   | 0                   |
| $s_2(t)$ | 0                   | 0                   | $1 - \lambda \Delta t$ | $\lambda \Delta t$  | 0                   |
| $s_3(t)$ | 0                   | 0                   | 0                   | $1 - \lambda \Delta t$ | $\lambda \Delta t$  |
| $s_4(t)$ | 0                   | 0                   | 0                   | 0                   | $1 - \lambda \Delta t$ |

ties in that column and the initial probabilities in the row. Specifically for the transition matrix given in Table 2.5

$$P_{s_0}(t + \Delta t) = p_{00}P_{s_0}(t) + p_{10}P_{s_1}(t) + \cdots + p_{n0}P_{s_n}(t)$$

If the $p_{ij}$ terms are all independent of time and depend only on constants and $\Delta t$, the process is called *homogeneous*. For a homogeneous process, the resulting differential equations have constant coefficients, and the solutions are of the form $e^{-rt}$ or $t^n e^{-rt}$. If for a homogeneous process the final value of the probability of being in any state is independent of the initial conditions, the process is called *ergodic*. A finite-state homogeneous process is ergodic if every state can be reached from any other state with positive probability. Whenever it is not possible to reach any outside state from some particular state, the latter state is called an *absorbing state*. Returning to our example of the partitioned shoe box, if we occasionally allow the ball to hop completely out of the box onto the floor, the floor forms a fifth state, which is absorbing. In a transition matrix any column $j$ having only a single entry $p_{ij}$ along the main diagonal is an absorbing state. If several states taken together form an absorbing set, they can be segregated from the main problem and studied separately. The discussion of the matrix formulation and solution of a Markov model is continued in Sec. 2.11.

## 2.9  SEVERAL RANDOM VARIABLES

### 2.9.1  DENSITY AND DISTRIBUTION FUNCTIONS

Just as we developed density and distribution functions for one discrete or one continuous random variable so can we extend the development to two or more random variables. As a practical matter we shall be most concerned with the case of two continuous random variables, and therefore we develop the theory for this case only. The theories for discrete variables and three or more variables follow by analogy. We define the joint density function for the two continuous random variables $\mathbf{x}$ and $\mathbf{y}$ by

$$\phi(x,y)\,dx\,dy = P(x < \mathbf{x} \leq x + dx,\, y < \mathbf{y} \leq y + dy) \tag{2.73}$$

The cumulative distribution function associated with this density function is given by

$$\phi(x,y) = \int_{-\infty}^{x} \int_{-\infty}^{y} \phi(x,y)\,dx\,dy = P(-\infty < \mathbf{x} \leq x,\, -\infty < \mathbf{y} \leq y) \tag{2.74}$$

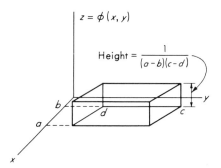

**Fig. 2.17**   Parallelepiped joint density function.

As an example, a joint density function which is a parallelepiped is given in Fig. 2.17. The probability that $b < \mathbf{x} \le (a + b)/2$ and $d < \mathbf{y} \le (c + d)/2$ is given by

$$P\left(b < \mathbf{x} \le \frac{a + b}{2}, d < \mathbf{y} \le \frac{c + d}{2}\right) = \Phi\left(\frac{a + b}{2}, \frac{c + d}{2}\right)$$

$$= \int_b^{(a+b)/2} \int_d^{(c+d)/2} \frac{1}{(a - b)(c - d)} \, dy \, dx$$

$$= \frac{1}{(a - b)(c - d)} \left(\frac{c + d}{2} - d\right)\left(\frac{a + b}{2} - b\right) = \frac{1}{4}$$

### 2.9.2   MARGINAL DENSITY FUNCTIONS

Since $\mathbf{x}$ and $\mathbf{y}$ are random variables, we can define density functions for each of them alone

$$f(x) \, dx = P(x < \mathbf{x} \le x + dx) \qquad (2.75a)$$
$$g(y) \, dy = P(y < \mathbf{y} \le y + dy) \qquad (2.75b)$$

We may now ask how Eqs. (2.75a) and (2.75b) are related to Eqs. (2.73) and (2.74). Equation (2.75a) is the density function for $\mathbf{x}$ independent of the value of $\mathbf{y}$. The only way we can obtain this is to integrate $\mathbf{y}$ out of the joint density function. A similar argument holds for $g(y)$; therefore

$$f(x) \, dx = P(x < \mathbf{x} \le x + dx, -\infty < \mathbf{y} \le +\infty)$$
$$= \left[\int_{-\infty}^{+\infty} \phi(x,y) \, dy\right] dx \quad (2.76a)$$
$$g(y) \, dy = P(-\infty < \mathbf{x} \le +\infty, y < \mathbf{y} \le y + dy)$$
$$= \left[\int_{-\infty}^{+\infty} \phi(x,y) \, dx\right] dy \quad (2.76b)$$

The density functions $f(x)$ and $g(y)$ are called the *marginal density func-*

*tions*[1] of the joint distribution of **x** and **y**.    For the example of Fig. 2.16

$$f(x) = \frac{1}{(a-b)(c-d)} \int_b^a dy = \frac{1}{c-d} \qquad c < \mathbf{x} \le d$$

$$g(y) = \frac{1}{(a-b)(c-d)} \int_b^a dx = \frac{1}{a-b} \qquad a < \mathbf{y} \le b$$

It is of course not very surprising that the parallelepiped joint distribution gives rise to rectangular marginal distributions.

### 2.9.3  CONDITIONAL DENSITY FUNCTIONS

We have previously defined events $A$ and $B$ as being independent if

$$P(AB) = P(A)P(B) \tag{2.77}$$

Now if we associate random variable **x** with $A$ and random variable **y** with $B$, then

$$
\begin{align}
P(A) &= P(x < \mathbf{x} \le x + dx) = f(x)\,dx \tag{2.78a}\\
P(B) &= P(y < \mathbf{y} \le y + dy) = g(y)\,dy \tag{2.78b}\\
P(AB) &= P(x < \mathbf{x} \le x + dx,\, y < \mathbf{y} \le y + dy) = \phi(x,y)\,dx\,dy \tag{2.78c}
\end{align}
$$

Thus, substituting Eqs. (2.78) into (2.77) one obtains

$$\phi(x,y) = f(x)g(y) \tag{2.79}$$

Equation (2.79) can now be used as the definition of independence for random variables **x** and **y**; that is, random variables **x** and **y** are independent if their joint density function is the product of the two marginal density functions.    The example given in Fig. 2.17 happens to represent two independent random variables, since

$$\frac{1}{(a-b)(c-d)} = \frac{1}{a-b} \frac{1}{c-d}$$

If events $A$ and $B$ are not independent, we must deal with *dependent* (also called *conditional*) *probabilities*.    In Sec. 2.4 the following relations were developed:

$$P(AB) = P(A)P(B|A)$$

$$P(B|A) = \frac{P(AB)}{P(A)}$$

---

[1] If we had first discussed the case of two discrete random variables, the reason for the term marginal density would be clear.    In the discrete case the x and y variables form a grid on a set of cartesian coordinates, and the value of $\phi(x_i, y_i)$ is written on each grid point.    The densities $f(x)$ and $g(y)$ are found by summation of the respective vertical or horizontal column values.    One generally writes $f(x)$ and $g(y)$ along the margins of the graph; hence the term marginal density.

We can express conditional probability in terms of the random variables **x** and **y**.

$$P(y < \mathbf{y} \leq y + dy | x < \mathbf{x} \leq x + dx)$$
$$= \frac{P(x < \mathbf{x} \leq x + dx,\ y < \mathbf{y} \leq y + dy)}{P(x < \mathbf{x} \leq x + dx)}$$

The function on the left-hand side defines the conditional density function for **y** given **x**, which is written as

$$h(y|x) = \frac{\phi(x,y)}{f(x)} \tag{2.80a}$$

Similarly, the conditional density function for **x** given **y** is

$$w(x|y) = \frac{\phi(x,y)}{g(y)} \tag{2.80b}$$

The following example illustrates how a conditional density function can be used.

The time to failure of a component is the random variable **t**.   Therefore the failure density function is defined by

$$P(t < \mathbf{t} \leq t + dt) = f(t)\ dt \tag{2.81}$$

Sometimes it is more convenient to deal with the probability of failure between time $t$ and $t + dt$, given that there were no failures up to time $t$. The probability expression becomes

$$P(t < \mathbf{t} \leq t + dt | \mathbf{t} > t) = \frac{P(t < \mathbf{t} \leq t + dt)}{P(\mathbf{t} > t)} \tag{2.82}$$

where

$$P(\mathbf{t} > t) = 1 - P(\mathbf{t} < t) = 1 - F(t) \tag{2.83}$$

The conditional probability on the left side gives rise to the conditional density function $z(t)$ defined by

$$z(t) = \lim_{dt \to 0} \frac{P(t < \mathbf{t} \leq t + dt | \mathbf{t} > t)}{dt} \tag{2.84}$$

The conditional density function is generally called the *hazard*.   Combining Eqs. (2.81) to (2.84) yields

$$z(t) = \frac{f(t)}{1 - F(t)} \tag{2.85}$$

The main reason for defining the $z(t)$ function is that it is often more convenient to work with than $f(t)$.

For example, suppose that $f(t)$ is an exponential, the most common failure density one deals with in reliability work.    Then

$$f(t) = \lambda e^{-\lambda t}$$
$$F(t) = 1 - e^{-\lambda t}$$
$$1 - F(t) = e^{-\lambda t}$$
$$z(t) = \frac{f(t)}{1 - F(t)} = \frac{\lambda e^{-\lambda t}}{e^{-\lambda t}} = \lambda$$

Thus, an exponential failure density corresponds to a constant hazard function.

### 2.9.4  MOMENTS

The moments of a function of several random variables are defined in a manner analogous to that of a single random variable.    The joint moments about the origin of the random variables $\mathbf{x}$ and $\mathbf{y}$ are given by

$$m_{kr} = E(\mathbf{x}^k \mathbf{y}^r) = \int\!\!\!\int_{-\infty}^{+\infty} x^k y^r \phi(x,y)\ dx\ dy \tag{2.86}$$

and the joint moments about the means of $\mathbf{x}$ and $\mathbf{y}$ by

$$m'_{kr} = E[(\mathbf{x} - \mu_x)^k(\mathbf{y} - \mu_y)^r] = \int\!\!\!\int_{-\infty}^{+\infty} (x - \mu_x)^k(y - \mu_y)^r \phi(x,y)\ dx\ dy \tag{2.87}$$

where

$$\mu_x = E(\mathbf{x}) \qquad \mu_y = E(\mathbf{y})$$

The entire family of moments is too large to deal with, and in general we center interest on five particular moments, just as in the single-variable case, where we were mainly interested in the mean and variance.    These five moments are

$$
\begin{aligned}
m_{10} &= E(\mathbf{x}) = \mu_x & &\text{mean of } \mathbf{x} \\
m_{01} &= E(\mathbf{y}) = \mu_y & &\text{mean of } \mathbf{y} \\
m'_{20} &= E[(\mathbf{x} - \mu_x)^2] = \sigma_x^2 & &\text{variance of } \mathbf{x} \\
m'_{02} &= E[(\mathbf{y} - \mu_y)^2 = \sigma_y^2 & &\text{variance of } \mathbf{y} \\
m'_{11} &= E[(\mathbf{x} - \mu_x)(\mathbf{y} - \mu_y)] = \text{cov } (\mathbf{x},\mathbf{y}) & &\text{covariance of } \mathbf{x} \text{ and } \mathbf{y}
\end{aligned}
\tag{2.88a}
$$

The first four moments listed can be obtained directly from the marginal distributions $f(x)$ and $g(y)$ which are associated with $\phi(x,y)$.    In fact, whenever one of the subscripts of $m_{kr}$ or $m'_{kr}$ is zero, Eq. (2.86) or (2.87) immediately reduces to an integration of $f(x)$ or $g(y)$.    The covariance moment does require integration with respect to both $\mathbf{x}$ and $\mathbf{y}$ and is a measure of how strongly the two variables are linked. The covariance can be expressed as

$$\text{cov }(\mathbf{x,y}) = E[(\mathbf{x} - \mu_x)(\mathbf{y} - \mu_y)] = E(\mathbf{xy} - \mu_x\mathbf{y} - \mu_y\mathbf{x} + \mu_x\mu_y)$$
$$= E(\mathbf{x,y}) - \mu_x E(\mathbf{y}) - \mu_y E(\mathbf{x}) + \mu_x\mu_y = E(\mathbf{xy}) - E(\mathbf{x})E(\mathbf{y})$$
$$(2.88b)$$

It is generally useful to normalize the covariance with respect to $\sigma_x$ and $\sigma_y$ and deal with the normalized variable called the *correlation coefficient* $\rho$.

$$\rho = \frac{\text{cov }(\mathbf{x,y})}{\sigma_x\sigma_y} \tag{2.89}$$

It can be shown that $-1 \leq \rho \leq +1$. Whenever $\rho = 0$ (and $\sigma_x$ and $\sigma_y$ are finite), it implies that cov $(\mathbf{x,y}) = 0$, which means that

$$E(\mathbf{xy}) = E(\mathbf{x})E(\mathbf{y})$$

When two random variables satisfy this property, they are said to be *uncorrelated*. It happens that if $\mathbf{x}$ and $\mathbf{y}$ are independent random variables, $\phi(xy) = f(x)g(y)$, and, by inspection of Eq. (2.86),

$$E(\mathbf{xy}) = E(\mathbf{x})E(\mathbf{y})$$

Therefore two independent variables are uncorrelated, but uncorrelated variables need not be independent. It will shortly be shown that if $y = ax + b$, then $\rho = +1$ and if $y = -ax + b$, then $\rho = -1$. This proof will be given after the theory of variable transformations is introduced.

### 2.9.5 TRANSFORMATIONS

Transformations of random variables play an important role in reliability work, e.g., when we talk about a simple exponential part failure model $R(t) = e^{-\lambda t}$. Suppose that we fix $t = t_1$; then $R(t_1) = e^{-\lambda t_1}$, that is, some number. However, if we choose the part at random from a bin of parts, then $\lambda$ is a random variable, and it is important to know what the distribution of $e^{-\lambda t_1}$ is, given the distribution of $\lambda$. We begin our discussion of the transformation of random variables with the following comments: the mathematical theory of transformation is fairly simple if one random variable is involved, but it becomes more complex when several random variables are involved. When the functions are multivalued, the limits must be set with care to avoid errors. In some cases the end result is an integral which cannot be reduced to elementary form.

### 2.9.6 CHANGE OF VARIABLE—ONE RANDOM VARIABLE

For a single random variable $\mathbf{x}$ we start with the following definitions: the original density and distribution functions are $f(x)$ and $F(x)$. The

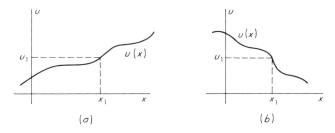

**Fig. 2.18**  The transformation function $u(x)$.  (a) Monotonically increasing; (b) monotonically decreasing.

new random variable **u** has density and distribution functions $h(u)$ and $H(u)$.  The equation relating **u** to **x** is denoted by $u(x)$ and the inverse relation by $x(u)$.  If we assume that $u(x)$ is a monotonically increasing function, it will appear as shown in Fig. 2.18a.  Since there is a one-to-one mapping between **u** and **x**, $x(u)$ is unique, and we can write

$$P(\mathbf{u} \leq u_1) = P(\mathbf{x} \leq x_1) \tag{2.90}$$

Expressing these probabilities in terms of the distribution function gives

$$H(u_1) = F(x_1)$$

Differentiating with respect to $u_1$ and using the chain rule leads to

$$\frac{dH(u_1)}{du_1} = h(u_1) = \frac{d}{du_1} F(x_1) = \frac{dF(x_1)}{dx_1} \frac{dx_1}{du_1}$$

By definition the derivative of the distribution function is the density function

$$h(u_1) = \frac{dx_1}{du_1} f(x_1)$$

Since $x_1$ and the corresponding $u_1$ were chosen arbitrarily, this relation must hold for any $x$ and its corresponding $u$, $h(u) = (dx/du)f(x)$.  Since we must make both sides of the equation a function of $u$, we substitute for $x$ in terms of $u$, that is, $x(u)$,

$$h(u) = \frac{dx}{du} f[x(u)] \tag{2.91}$$

In Fig. 2.18b we find a monotonically decreasing function $u(x)$.  In this case we write

$$P(\mathbf{u} \geq u_1) = P(\mathbf{x} \leq x_1) \qquad 1 - H(u_1) = F(x_1)$$

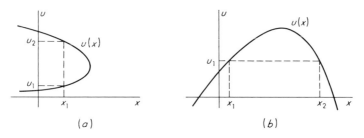

**Fig. 2.19**  The transformation $u(x)$ for double-valued functions.  (a) **u** is a double-valued function of **x**; (b) **x** is a double-valued function of **u**.

Proceeding as in the previous case, we obtain

$$h(u) = \frac{dx}{du} f[x(u)] \tag{2.92}$$

Here $dx/du$ is negative; therefore we can combine Eqs. (2.91) and (2.92) by rewriting

$$h(u) = \left| \frac{dx}{du} \right| f[x(u)] \tag{2.93a}$$

Even if **u** is a double-valued or multiple-valued function of **x**, as shown in Fig. 2.19a, Eq. (2.93a) is still valid, since the inverse function $x(u)$ is still single-valued and the absolute-value signs take care of the change in sign of the slope.  If **x** is a double-valued function of **u**, as shown in Fig. 2.19b, we have two roots to the equation $x(u_1)$, and Eq. (2.93a) must be written as the sum of each root.  Specifically for Fig. 2.19b

$$P(\mathbf{y} \le y_1) = P(\mathbf{x} \le x_1) + P(\mathbf{x} \ge x_2)$$
$$H(u_1) = F(x_1) + 1 - F(x_2) \tag{2.93b}$$

Differentiating with respect to $u_1$ and proceeding as before, we obtain

$$h(u_1) = \left| \frac{dx_1}{du_1} \right| f(x_1) + \left| \frac{dx_2}{du_2} \right| f(x_2) \tag{2.94}$$

Obviously if the equation $x(u_1)$ has $n$ roots, the right-hand side of Eq. (2.94) has $n$ terms, one for each root.

We have already used some change-of-variable theorems without proof in previous sections.  Now, using Eq. (2.93), we are able to prove the validity of the results.  In Eq. (2.55) we tacitly assumed that

$$E[u(x)] = \int_{-\infty}^{+\infty} u(x)f(x)\, dx \tag{2.95}$$

We can now prove this starting with the definition

$$E(\mathbf{x}) = \int_{-\infty}^{+\infty} xf(x)\,dx$$

which implies that

$$E(\mathbf{u}) = \int_{-\infty}^{+\infty} uh(u)\,du$$

From Eq. (2.93) we see that $h(u)\,du = f(x)\,dx$, and replacing $u$ by its equivalent $u(x)$, we obtain Eq. (2.95).

We can now use Eqs. (2.93) and (2.95) to derive some interesting transformations. Suppose $u = ax + b$ and we wish to find $h(u)$ in terms of $f(x)$

$$u = ax + b \qquad x = \frac{u - b}{a} \qquad \left|\frac{dx}{du}\right| = \frac{1}{a}$$

therefore

$$h(u) = \frac{1}{a} f\left(\frac{u - b}{a}\right) \tag{2.96}$$

Thus, we conclude that if we add a constant to a random variable ($u = x + b$, that is, $a = 1$), the new variable has the same density function shifted by the constant. If we multiply a random variable by a constant ($u = ax$, that is, $b = 0$), the abscissa and ordinate scales are multiplied by $1/a$. Equation (2.96) is just a superposition of these two effects. If we wish to compute the moments of $\mathbf{u}$ in terms of the moments of $\mathbf{x}$, we can use the result of Eq. (2.96) or use Eq. (2.95) directly

$$E(\mathbf{u}) = \int_{-\infty}^{+\infty} (ax + b)f(x)\,dx = a \int_{-\infty}^{+\infty} xf(x)\,dx + b \int_{-\infty}^{+\infty} f(x)\,dy$$
$$= aE(\mathbf{x}) + b \tag{2.97}$$

And for the var $\mathbf{u}$

$$E(\mathbf{u}^2) = \int_{-\infty}^{+\infty} (ax + b)^2 f(x)\,dx = a^2 \int_{-\infty}^{+\infty} x^2 f(x)\,dx$$
$$+ 2ab \int_{-\infty}^{+\infty} xf(x)\,dx + b^2 \int_{-\infty}^{+\infty} f(x)\,dx$$
$$= a^2 E(\mathbf{x}^2) + 2abE(\mathbf{x}) + b^2$$
$$\text{var } \mathbf{u} = E(\mathbf{u}^2) - [E(\mathbf{u})]^2 = a^2 E(\mathbf{x}^2) + 2abE(\mathbf{x}) + b^2 - [aE(\mathbf{x}) + b]^2$$
$$= a^2 \text{ var } \mathbf{x} \tag{2.98a}$$

The mean is affected by both $a$ and $b$, but the variance is affected only by $a$. We can now show that if $y = \pm ax + b$, $\rho = \pm 1$

$$\text{cov } (\mathbf{x},\mathbf{y}) = E[(\mathbf{x} - \mu_x)(\mathbf{y} - \mu_y)]$$
$$= E[(\mathbf{x} - \mu_x)(\pm ax + b - \mu_y)]$$

But from Eq. (2.97)

$$\mu_y = \pm a\mu_x + b$$
$$\text{cov } (\mathbf{x},\mathbf{y}) = E[(\mathbf{x} - \mu_x)(\pm a\mathbf{x} + b \mp a\mu_x - b)]$$
$$= \pm aE[(\mathbf{x} - \mu_x)^2] = \pm a\sigma x^2$$

From Eq. (2.98) $\sigma_y = a\sigma_x$. Substituting gives

$$\rho = \frac{\text{cov } (\mathbf{x},\mathbf{y})}{\sigma_x \sigma_y} = \frac{\pm a\sigma_x^2}{\sigma_x a\sigma_x} = \pm 1$$

Other examples of change of variables for one random variable appear in Chap. 7, with many specific results listed in Tables 7.1, 7.5, and 7.6.

### 2.9.7  CHANGE OF VARIABLES—TWO OR MORE RANDOM VARIABLES

In many cases we must deal with transformations involving more than one variable. The two most important cases are (1) where one variable $\mathbf{u}$ is a function of many random variables, that is, $u(x_1,x_2, \ldots ,x_n)$ (we encountered this situation when we found that the sum of exponentially distributed variables is gamma-distributed) and (2) where two random variables $\mathbf{x}$ and $\mathbf{y}$ are transformed to two new random variables $u(x,y)$ and $v(x,y)$. We shall use this latter case as our point of departure. We consider the initial random variables $\mathbf{x}$ and $\mathbf{y}$ to have a joint density function $\phi(x,y)$ and to be related to two final random variables $\mathbf{u}$ and $\mathbf{v}$ by $u(x,y)$ and $v(x,y)$. The density function for $\mathbf{u}$ and $\mathbf{v}$ is $\psi(u,v)$, and the inverse relations are $x(u,v)$ and $y(u,v)$. As was done with a single random variable, we can equate probabilities when there is a one-to-one correspondence[1] between points in the $xy$ plane and points in the $uv$ plane; thus we map equivalent areas from $xy$ into $uv$

$$\iint\limits_{\text{area } A} \psi(u,v) \, du \, dv = \iint\limits_{\substack{\text{equivalent} \\ \text{to area } A}} \phi(x,y) \, dx \, dy$$

A theorem from advanced calculus[2] dealing with multiple integrals states that for one-to-one transformations

$$\iint\limits_{\substack{\text{area} \\ A}} \phi(x,y) \, dx \, dy = \iint\limits_{\substack{\text{equivalent} \\ \text{to area } A}} \phi[x(u,v),y(u,v)] \, \frac{\partial(x,y)}{\partial(u,v)} \, du \, dv \qquad (2.98b)$$

[1] For a discussion of the case where the mapping is not one to one, see Papoulis, *op. cit.*, p. 201.

[2] P. Franklin, "Treatise on Advanced Calculus," p. 368, Dover Publications, Inc., New York, 1964; and R. Courant, "Differential and Integral Calculus," vol. 2, p. 247, John Wiley & Sons, Inc., New York, 1964.

where

$$\frac{\partial(x,y)}{\partial(u,v)} \equiv \begin{vmatrix} \dfrac{\partial x}{\partial u} & \dfrac{\partial x}{\partial v} \\ \dfrac{\partial y}{\partial u} & \dfrac{\partial y}{\partial v} \end{vmatrix} \equiv J \equiv \text{the Jacobian}^{1,2} \text{ (determinant)} \qquad (2.99)$$

If the integrals in Eq. (2.98) are to hold for all corresponding area elements, the integrands must be equal and

$$\psi(u,v) = \phi[x(u,v),y(u,v)]|J| \qquad (2.100)$$

The magnitude signs are added to the Jacobian to account for changes in slope of the surface, just as $|dx/du|$ accounted for changes in sign of the slope of the curve.

As our first example we shall solve for the sum or difference of two random variables, that is, $u = a_1 x + a_2 y$ (to be more precise $u$ is a linear combination of $x$ and $y$). We could now choose $v$ as the difference of two random variables, but $u$ represents sum or difference as long as we allow $a_1$ and $a_2$ to take on negative values. Thus, we have no $v$ function, but in order to apply Eq. (2.100) we need two functions. We could calculate another transformation with $v$, say $v = xy$, or to make things simple let $v$ be a dummy variable and choose it simply as $v = x$

$$u = a_1 x + a_2 y \qquad v = x$$

The inverse relations are

$$x = v \qquad y = \frac{u - a_1 v}{a_2}$$

The partial derivatives are

$$\frac{\partial x}{\partial u} = 0 \qquad \frac{\partial x}{\partial v} = 1 \qquad \frac{\partial y}{\partial u} = \frac{1}{a_2} \qquad \frac{\partial y}{\partial v} = -\frac{a_1}{a_2}$$

$$J = \begin{vmatrix} 0 & 1 \\ \dfrac{1}{a_2} & -\dfrac{a_1}{a_2} \end{vmatrix} = -\frac{1}{a_2}$$

$$|J| = \left| -\frac{1}{a_2} \right| = \frac{1}{a_2}$$

$$\psi(u,v) = \phi\left( v, \frac{u - a_1 v}{a_2} \right) \frac{1}{a_2}$$

---

[1] H. Freeman, "Introduction to Statistical Inference," p. 78, Addison-Wesley Publishing Company, Inc., Reading, Mass., 1963.

[2] Sometimes the rows and columns of the Jacobian are interchanged. This in no way changes $J$.

We are really interested only in the marginal density function $h(u)$, which is given by

$$h(u) = \int_v \psi(u,v) \, dv = \frac{1}{a_2} \int_v \phi\left(v, \frac{u - a_1 v}{a_2}\right) dv \qquad (2.101)$$

Equation (2.101) is the well-known *convolution integral*, which is more commonly written in a simplified form. If u is simply the sum of **x** and **y**, then $a_1 = a_2 = 1$, and if **x** and **y** are independent, Eq. (2.101) becomes

$$h(u) = \int_v \phi(v, u - v) \, dv = \int_v f(v)g(u - v) \, dv \qquad (2.102)$$

which is the most common form for the convolution integral.

We previously stated a theorem which said that the sum of $n$ independent exponential distributions with the same $\beta$ have a gamma distribution with parameters $\beta = \beta$ and $\alpha = n - 1$. For the case of two variables, we can use Eq. (2.102) to prove the theorem

$$f(x) = \frac{1}{\beta} e^{-x/\beta} \qquad 0 < \mathbf{x} \le +\infty \qquad (2.103)$$

$$g(y) = \frac{1}{\beta} e^{-y/\beta} \qquad 0 < \mathbf{y} \le +\infty \qquad (2.104)$$

The range of **v** in Eq. (2.102) must go from 0 to $+\infty$; however, $g(u - v)$ is defined only for $u - v$ positive (equivalent to $x$ positive). This means that the range of **v** is from 0 to $u$

$$
\begin{aligned}
h(u) &= \int_0^u \frac{1}{\beta} e^{-v/\beta} \frac{1}{\beta} e^{-(u-v)/\beta} \, dv \\
&= \frac{1}{\beta^2} \int_0^u e^{-u/\beta} \, dv \\
&= \frac{1}{\beta^2} e^{-u/\beta} \int_0^u dv \\
&= \frac{u e^{-u/\beta}}{2\beta^2} \qquad \mathbf{u} \ge 0 \qquad (2.105)
\end{aligned}
$$

which is the correct result. The substitution of limits in the convolution integral is crucial, as seen in the above example. We have just illustrated how one can perform a change of variables from two old variables to two new variables. In fact we really wanted only one new variable, but had to choose a dummy variable anyway. The generalization to the case of $n$ old variables and $m$ new variables is straightforward. If $n \ne m$, we must define sufficient dummy variables. The convolution integral given in Eq. (2.102) can also be extended to the case of a sum of $n$ independent random variables.

### 2.9.8  MOMENT–GENERATING FUNCTION

As illustrated above, the change-of-variables technique, Eq. (2.94) and especially Eq. (2.100), can be difficult to apply.    In some cases a simpler technique based on the moment-generating function can be applied.    We can express $M(\theta)$ in a different way by using Eq. (2.95)

$$E(\mathbf{u}) = E[u(x)] = \int_{-\infty}^{+\infty} u(x)f(x)\,dx \qquad (2.95)$$

Since the moment-generating function $M_x(\theta)$ is defined as $M_x(\theta) = E(e^{\theta\mathbf{x}})$, we can write $M_u(\theta)$ as

$$M_u(\theta) = E(e^{\theta u(x)}) = \int_{-\infty}^{+\infty} e^{\theta u(x)}f(x)\,dx \qquad (2.106)$$

Suppose we let $u(x) = ax$ and repeat the previous example

$$M_u(\theta) = \int_{-\infty}^{+\infty} e^{a\theta x}f(x)\,dx$$

writing this equation in terms of $u = ax$ and $x = u/a$

$$M_u(\theta) = \int_{-\infty}^{+\infty} e^{\theta u}\left[\frac{1}{a}f\left(\frac{u}{a}\right)\right] du$$

Now since we can show that each density function $f(x)$ has a unique moment-generating function,[1] we know that

$$h(u) = \frac{1}{a}f\left(\frac{u}{a}\right)$$

which of course checks with our previous result.

When one random variable is a function of two others, we can write $u(x,y)$ as the transformation relation.    The expected value of $u$ is given by

$$E[u(x,y)] = \int\!\!\!\int_{-\infty}^{+\infty} u(x,y)\phi(x,y)\,dx\,dy \qquad (2.107)$$

Thus, the moment-generating function is

$$M_u(\theta) = \int\!\!\!\int_{-\infty}^{+\infty} e^{\theta u(x,y)}\phi(x,y)\,dx\,dy \qquad (2.108)$$

We can use this result as we did for the case of a single variable.    Let us repeat the problem of finding the distribution for the sum of two independ-

---

[1] The analogous case of the inverse Laplace transform is discussed in F. B. Hildebrand, "Advanced Calculus for Engineers," p. 62, Prentice-Hall, Inc., Englewood Cliffs, N.J., 1949.    The same reasoning holds for the moment-generating function.

ent exponential variables

$$\phi(x,y) = f(x)g(y)$$
$$u(x,y) = x + y$$
$$M_u(\theta) = \int_{-\infty}^{+\infty} e^{\theta x} f(x)\, dx \int_{-\infty}^{+\infty} e^{\theta y} f(y)\, dy = M_x(\theta) M_y(\theta)$$

For

$$f(x) = \frac{1}{\beta} e^{-x/\beta} \qquad M_x(\theta) = \frac{1/\beta}{-\theta + 1/\beta}$$

$$f(y) = \frac{1}{\beta} e^{-y/\beta} \qquad M_y(\theta) = M_x(\theta)$$

therefore

$$M_u(\theta) = \frac{1/\beta^2}{(-\theta + 1/\beta)^2}$$

From Table 2.4 it can be seen that this moment-generating function corresponds to

$$f(u) = \frac{u e^{-u/\beta}}{\beta^2}$$

If the reader is familiar with Laplace transforms, Eqs. (2.106) and (2.108) lead to results which are recognizable by inspection in many cases.

## 2.10 ESTIMATION THEORY

### 2.10.1 INTRODUCTION

Estimation theory has to do with how one determines the parameters in a probabilistic model from statistical data taken on the items governed by the model. Specifically, in reliability work we place a group of components on life test and observe the sequence of failure times $t_1, t_2, \ldots, t_n$. On the basis of these data we compute time-to-failure models and hazard models, which it is hoped govern the behavior of other similar items. The model parameters are computed from certain calculations made with the data. Estimation theory provides guidelines for efficient and accurate computations.

If only a few data are available, say $n \leq 5$, the result must be questioned no matter how sophisticated the formula. If many data are available, $n \geq 100$, the results should be good as long as the formula used is sensible. (Many of the different computational schemes used converge as the number of data $n \to \infty$.) Estimation theory is probably of most help in the intermediate range $10 \leq n \leq 50$. A *point estimation* formula computes one value which represents the parameter in question. For example, if we had data representing failure times of 10, 20, 25, 35, and 40 hr, intuition would tell us to estimate the MTTF as

$(10 + 20 + 25 + 35 + 40)/5 = 26$ hr

Thus, 26 hr is a point estimate of the MTTF. Our discussion of the properties of point estimators will shed some light on how good such an estimate is. Of course, we could very properly argue that with only five data we cannot be very sure the MTTF is exactly 26 hr, and it makes more sense to quote a range of values. If we say that we are fairly sure the MTTF is between 20 and 30 hr, we are giving an *interval estimate*. Interval estimation will be discussed following point estimation.

### 2.10.2  ESTIMATOR PROPERTIES

In devising a point-estimator formula there are no hard and fast rules. The three techniques to be discussed, moment methods, maximum likelihood, and least squares, all have a number of good features. We start out by postulating from intuition what seems to be a good property of an estimator, and if it can be computed in a reasonable mathematical fashion, we adopt it as one of our criteria of goodness. Any estimator which satisfies many of the goodness criteria is probably a useful estimator. In order to systematize the notation we shall let $\mathbf{x}$ be the random variable in question, and the mean and variance of $\mathbf{x}$ will be defined by

$$\mu_x = E(\mathbf{x})$$
$$\text{var } \mathbf{x} = \sigma^2 = E(x^2) - E^2(x)$$

The estimator of $\mathbf{x}$ is $\mathbf{w}$, which is a new random variable.[1] The actual data values will be denoted by $x_1, x_2, \ldots, x_n$.

### 2.10.3  UNBIASED ESTIMATORS

One important estimator property is the *unbiased property*, by which we mean that the expected value of $\mathbf{w}$ must equal the expected value of $\mathbf{x}$, that is, $E(\mathbf{w}) = E(\mathbf{x})$. As an example of the unbiased property we shall examine the sample mean and sample variance.

We define the sample mean $\bar{x}$ as

$$\bar{x} = \frac{1}{n} \sum_{i=1}^{n} x_i \tag{2.109}$$

---

[1] The formula relating $\mathbf{w}$ to $\mathbf{x}$ is called the *estimator*. When we substitute data values $x_1, x_2, \ldots, x_n$ in $\mathbf{w}$, we obtain a value $w$ which is called the *estimate* of the parameter.

Since we may wish to estimate $x$ by $\bar{x}$, we test to see whether $\bar{x}$ is unbiased

$$E(\mathbf{w}) = E(\bar{x}) = E \frac{1}{n} \left( \sum_{i=1}^{n} x_i \right) = \frac{1}{n} E \left( \sum_{i=1}^{n} x_i \right)$$

$$= \frac{1}{n} [E(\mathbf{x}_1) + E(\mathbf{x}_2) + \cdots + E(\mathbf{x}_n)]$$

Assuming that the data $x_n$ are independent and are themselves random variables with $E(\mathbf{x}_1) = E(\mathbf{x}_2) = \cdots = E(\mathbf{x}_n)$, then

$$E(\bar{x}) = \frac{1}{n} nE(\mathbf{x}) = E(\mathbf{x})$$

Thus, we have shown that the sample mean, Eq. (2.109), is an unbiased estimator if the data represent independent samples.

We define the sample variance as

$$s^2 = \frac{1}{n} \sum_{i=1}^{n} (x_i - \bar{x})^2 \tag{2.110}$$

and of course we wish to test whether $s^2$ is an unbiased estimator

$$E(s^2) = E \left[ \frac{1}{n} \sum_{i=1}^{n} (x_i - \bar{x})^2 \right] \tag{2.111}$$

Manipulation of this equation requires some care, and as a first step the equation is rewritten in terms of the second moment about the true mean $\mu$. Therefore, adding and subtracting $\mu$,

$$E(s^2) = \frac{1}{n} E \left\{ \sum_{i=1}^{n} [(x_i - \mu) - (\bar{x} - \mu)]^2 \right\}$$

$$= \frac{1}{n} E \left\{ \sum_{i=1}^{n} [(x_i - \mu)^2 - 2(x_i - \mu)(\bar{x} - \mu) + (\bar{x} - \mu)^2] \right\} \tag{2.112}$$

The middle term may be simplified

$$\sum_{i=1}^{n} 2(\bar{x} - \mu)(x_i - \mu) = 2(\bar{x} - \mu) \left( \sum_{i=1}^{n} x_i - \sum_{i=1}^{n} \mu \right) = 2(\bar{x} - \mu)(n\bar{x} - n\mu)$$

$$= 2n(\bar{x} - \mu)^2$$

and the last term becomes

$$\sum_{i=1}^{n} (\bar{x} - \mu)^2 = n(\bar{x} - \mu)^2$$

Combining the middle and last terms, we obtain

$$E(s^2) = \frac{1}{n} E\left[ \sum_{i=1}^{n} (x_i - \mu)^2 - n(\bar{x} - \mu)^2 \right]$$

$$= \frac{1}{n} \left[ \sum_{i=1}^{n} E(x_i - \mu)^2 - nE(\bar{x} - \mu)^2 \right]$$

By definition $E(x_i - \mu)^2 = \sigma^2$. Also

$$E[(\bar{x} - \mu)^2] = E\left( \frac{1}{n} \sum_{i=1}^{n} x_i - \mu \right)^2 = E\left( \frac{x_1 - \mu}{n} + \frac{x_2 - \mu}{n} \right.$$

$$\left. + \cdots + \frac{x_n - \mu}{n} \right)^2$$

$$= E\left[ \frac{(x_1 - \mu)^2}{n^2} + \frac{(x_2 - \mu)^2}{n^2} + \cdots + \frac{(x_n - \mu)^2}{n^2} \right.$$

$$+ \frac{2(x_1 - \mu)(x_2 - \mu)}{n^2}$$

$$\left. + \frac{2(x_1 - \mu)(x_3 - \mu)}{n^2} + \cdots + \frac{2(x_i - \mu)(x_j - \mu)}{n^2} \right] \quad i \neq j$$

The squared terms are variances, and since we expect $x_1, x_2, \ldots, x_n$ all to have the same distribution, they yield $n\sigma^2/n^2 = \sigma^2/n$. The cross-product terms become covariances, and since the $x_i$'s are independent, they are zero. Substituting gives

$$E(s^2) = \frac{1}{n} \left( n\sigma^2 - \frac{n\sigma^2}{n} \right) = \frac{n-1}{n} \sigma^2 \qquad (2.113)$$

The result shows that $s^2$ is a biased statistic since $E(s^2) \neq \sigma^2$. For large $n$ the bias is small numerically. Once we know this fact, we can just use

$$\frac{n}{n-1} s^2 = \frac{1}{n-1} \sum_{i=1}^{n} (x_i - \bar{x})^2 \qquad (2.114)$$

as an unbiased estimator.

### 2.10.4 OTHER CRITERIA

If intuition or just guesswork suggests several estimator formulas, we can test to see which are unbiased. The unbiased property is not sufficient to ensure a good estimator. First there can be several unbiased estimators, and second we shall shortly see that at least one estimator in common use is a biased one. Another "good property" is to require the variance of the estimate to be small. There are several ways in which we can specify a small variance. These small-variance good properties are as follows:[1]

1 *Consistency* The estimator $\mathbf{w}$ is said to be consistent if the probability that $\mathbf{w}$ differs from $\mathbf{x}$ by more than an arbitrary constant $c$ approaches 0 when $n \to \infty$; $\lim_{n \to \infty} P(|\mathbf{w} - \mathbf{x}| > c) \to 0$. In other words, the probability of a large error goes to zero for large $n$. *Sufficient* conditions for consistency of $\mathbf{w}$ are $\mathbf{w}$ is unbiased and var $\mathbf{w} \to 0$ when $n \to \infty$.

2 *Relative efficiency* The relative efficiency of two estimators $\mathbf{w}_1$ and $\mathbf{w}_2$ can be measured by the ratio of their variances: (var $\mathbf{w}_2$)/(var $\mathbf{w}_1$). The better estimator has the smaller variance.

3 *Best unbiased* The best unbiased estimator (also called *most efficient* and *minimum variance*) is unbiased and has the smallest variance among all the possible unbiased estimators.

4 *Sufficiency* An estimator $\mathbf{w}$ is sufficient if the conditional density function $f(x_1, x_2, \ldots, x_n | w)$ does not depend on $\mathbf{x}$. A sufficient estimator utilizes all the information contained in the sample.

The mathematics associated with testing for the above properties and searching for estimators which have the above properties is quite sophisticated and will not be pursued further.[2]

In general these good properties all use some *risk function* $R$ to measure how well $\mathbf{w}$ estimates $\mathbf{x}$; unbiased estimators use expected value as a risk function, consistent estimators use $|\mathbf{w} - \mathbf{x}|$, efficient and minimum-variance estimators use var $\mathbf{w}$, and sufficient estimators use a conditional density function.

Another useful property of estimators is invariance.

5 *Invariance* An estimator $\mathbf{w}$ is invariant if $g(w) = g(x)$. For example, if $\mathbf{w}$ is an estimator for var $\mathbf{x}$, and if $\mathbf{w}$ is invariant, then $\sqrt{w}$ is an estimator for $\sigma_x$.

Rather than discussing good properties further we shall define three of the most commonly used estimator families and discuss some of the properties which make them useful.

### 2.10.5 MOMENT ESTIMATORS

The moment method[3] of point estimation is the simplest method in common use. If the numbers $x_1, x_2, \ldots, x_n$ represent a set of data,

---

[1] Freund, *op. cit.*, chap. 9.

[2] Freeman, *op. cit.*, chap. 25.

[3] This method is often attributed to Karl Pearson; however, the original work was done by Bessel, Gauss, and Thiele. See R. A. Fischer, "Contributions to Mathematical Statistics," paper 29, p. 29.318, John Wiley & Sons, Inc., New York, 1950.

then an unbiased estimator for the $k$th origin moment is

$$\breve{m}_k = \frac{1}{n} \sum_{i=1}^{n} x_i{}^k \qquad (2.115)$$

where $\breve{m}_k$ stands for the moment estimate of $m_k$. To prove that $\breve{m}_k$ is an unbiased estimate we write

$$E(\breve{m}_k) = \frac{1}{n} E \sum_{i=1}^{n} x_i{}^k = \frac{1}{n} [E(\mathbf{x}_1{}^k) + E(\mathbf{x}_2{}^k) + \cdots + E(\mathbf{x}_n{}^k)]$$

$$= \frac{1}{n} nE(\mathbf{x}^k) = E(\mathbf{x}^k)$$

Thus, using Eq. (2.115), we can generate a series of $r$ values for the first $r$ origin moments of the data. Similarly we can compute the first $r$ origin moments from the density function in question. This latter set of equations will contain several unknown parameters $\theta_1, \theta_2, \ldots, \theta_j$, which we wish to estimate. We equate the first $j$ data moments to the first $j$ theoretical moments, and solve the resulting $j$ simultaneous equations for the estimates $\breve{\theta}_1, \breve{\theta}_2, \ldots, \breve{\theta}_j$. As an example consider the estimation of the parameter $\lambda$ of the exponential distribution

$$m_1 = E(\mathbf{x}) = \int_0^{+\infty} x\lambda e^{-\lambda x}\, dx = \frac{1}{\lambda}$$

$$\breve{m}_1 = \frac{1}{n} \sum_{i=1}^{n} x_i = m_1$$

$$\frac{1}{n} \sum_{i=1}^{n} x_i = \frac{1}{\lambda}$$

$$\breve{\lambda} = \frac{n}{\displaystyle\sum_{i=1}^{n} x_i} \qquad (2.116)$$

To illustrate the procedure for a two-parameter distribution we shall estimate $\mu$ and $\sigma^2$ for a normal distribution

$$m_1 = \mu = \breve{m}_1 = \frac{1}{n} \sum_{i=1}^{n} x_i$$

$$m_2 = \sigma^2 + \mu^2 = \breve{m}_2 = \frac{1}{n} \sum_{i=1}^{n} x_i{}^2$$

Solving these two equations simultaneously,

$$\breve{\mu} = \frac{1}{n} \sum_{i=1}^{n} x_i \tag{2.117}$$

$$\breve{\sigma}^2 = \frac{1}{n} \sum_{i=1}^{n} x_i^2 - \left( \frac{1}{n} \sum_{i=1}^{n} x_i \right)^2 = \frac{1}{n} \sum_{i=1}^{n} x_i^2 - \breve{\mu}^2 \tag{2.118}†$$

Of course we might argue that it is better to match $E(\mathbf{x})$ and $E[(x - \mu)^2]$. In such a case we equate

$$\mu = \frac{1}{n} \sum_{i=1}^{n} x_i$$

and from Eq. (2.114)

$$\sigma_2 = \frac{1}{n-1} \sum_{i=1}^{n} (x_i - \bar{x})^2$$

solving simultaneously

$$\breve{\mu} = \frac{1}{n} \sum_{i=1}^{n} x_i \tag{2.119}$$

$$\breve{\sigma}^2 = \frac{1}{n-1} \sum_{i=1}^{n} (x_i - \breve{\mu})^2 \tag{2.120}$$

The set of parameters given by Eqs. (2.117) and (2.118) should yield a distribution which gives accurate results near $x = 0$, whereas Eqs. (2.119) and (2.120) should be more accurate about $x = \mu$. In reliability work we are mostly concerned with probabilities close to $t = 0$. Numerical solutions of the moment equations are sometimes necessary. The main features of moment estimates are that they are unbiased, with respect to the moments, and generally lead to a simple set of equations.

### 2.10.6 MAXIMUM–LIKELIHOOD ESTIMATORS

A different system of estimation, which is newer and is generally accepted as superior to moment estimation, is *maximum-likelihood estimation* (MLE).[1] The computation is a little more difficult than that of moment estimates; however, the philosophy behind it is somewhat more subtle and powerful. If we let each sample value be a random

---

† To avoid confusion the moment estimate of the variance is written $\breve{\sigma}^2$, whereas the square of the moment estimate of the standard deviation is written $(\breve{\sigma})^2$.

[1] See Fischer, *op. cit.*, p. 269, for a guide to Fischer's original papers, which are reprinted in that volume.

variable $\mathbf{x}_1$, $\mathbf{x}_2$, . . . , $\mathbf{x}_n$ and the particular data values obtained be $x_1$, $x_2$, . . . , $x_n$, we can write $n$ marginal density functions which represent the probability that $\mathbf{x}_i = x_i$

$$f(x_i;\theta)\, dx_i = P(\mathbf{x}_i = x_i) \tag{2.121}$$

Since the $\mathbf{x}_i$'s are independent, the joint density function can be written as the product of the marginal density functions

$$\phi(x_1,x_2,\ . \ . \ . \ ,x_n;\theta) = L(x_1,x_2,\ . \ . \ . \ ,x_n;\theta)$$
$$= f(x_1;\theta)f(x_2;\theta)\ \cdot\ \cdot\ \cdot\ f(x_n;\theta) \tag{2.122a}$$

In Eq. (2.122a) we have written each probability density as a function of $\theta$, the parameter to be estimated.   The joint density function $\phi$ is generally called the likelihood function $L$, as given in Eq. (2.122a).   We would expect that if we really knew the true value, call it $\theta_{\text{true}}$, and substituted it into the density for $x_1$, yielding $f(x_1;\theta_{\text{true}})$, then this density function would have a large value.   Similar reasoning holds for $f(x_2;\theta_{\text{true}})$, etc. This of course implies that $\phi(x_1,x_2,\ . \ . \ . \ ,x_n;\theta_{\text{true}})$ will be large.   In fact for any $\theta_1 \neq \theta_{\text{true}}$ we would expect that

$$\phi(x_1,x_2,\ . \ . \ . \ ,x_n;\theta_1) < \phi(x_1,x_2,\ . \ . \ . \ ,x_n;\theta_{\text{true}})$$

Since the integration of $\phi$ over all $n$ variables must yield unity regardless of how $\phi$ is distributed, if $\phi$ is very high at one point, it is also concentrated about that point (assuming smooth variation and no large discontinuities).   This means that the relative magnitude of the likelihood function will serve as a measure of how close to $\theta_{\text{true}}$ any estimate is. The obvious conclusion is that we shall obtain a good estimate for $\theta$ if we maximize $L$ as a function of $\theta$, that is, set $\partial L/\partial\theta = 0$.   In other words, we are trying to maximize the probability that the set of data $x_1$, $x_2$, . . . , $x_n$ represents a sample governed by the density function $f(x,\theta)$. To do this we choose the most likely value of $\theta$.

As an example we shall derive the MLE for the parameter $\lambda$ of the exponential distribution

$$f(x,\lambda) = \lambda e^{-\lambda x}$$
$$f(x_i,\lambda) = \lambda e^{-\lambda x_i}$$

$$L(x_1,x_2,\ . \ . \ . \ ;\lambda) = f(x_1,\lambda)f(x_2,\lambda)\ \cdot\ \cdot\ \cdot\ f(x_n;\lambda) = \prod_{i=1}^{n} f(x_i;\lambda)$$

$$= \lambda^n \prod_{i=1}^{n} e^{-\lambda x_i} = \lambda^n \exp\left(-\lambda \sum_{i=1}^{n} x_i\right)$$

Now to maximize we compute $\partial L/\partial\lambda$ and set it equal to zero.   At this point the computation looks a bit messy since the derivative of a product of $n$ functions leads to $n$ differentiations. A simple modification of the procedure eliminates this extra labor. Because of the one-to-one nature of the mapping, the functions max $z$ and max (log $z$) both coincide. Thus, we can deal with

$$\log L(x_1, x_2, \ldots ; \lambda) \equiv \mathcal{L}(x_1, x_2, \ldots ; \lambda)$$

where $\mathcal{L}$ represents the log of the likelihood function.

$$\mathcal{L}(x_1, x_2, \ldots ; \lambda) = \log \left[ \prod_{i=1}^{n} f(x_i; \lambda) \right] = \sum_{i=1}^{n} \log f(x_i; \lambda)$$

$$\frac{\partial \mathcal{L}}{\partial \lambda} = \frac{\partial}{\partial \lambda} \left[ \sum_{i=1}^{n} \log f(x_i; \lambda) \right] = \sum_{i=1}^{n} \left[ \frac{\partial}{\partial \lambda} \log f(x_i; \lambda) \right]$$

where we have assumed that we can interchange the order of summation and differentiation. Substituting the exponential density,

$$\frac{\partial \mathcal{L}}{\partial \lambda} = \sum_{i=1}^{n} \frac{\partial}{\partial \lambda} \log \lambda e^{-\lambda x_i} = \sum_{i=1}^{n} \frac{\partial}{\partial \lambda} (\log \lambda - \lambda x_i)$$

$$= \sum_{i=1}^{n} \left( \frac{1}{\lambda} - x_i \right) = \frac{n}{\lambda} - \sum_{i=1}^{n} x_i$$

Equating $\partial \mathcal{L}/\partial \lambda$ to zero,

$$\frac{n}{\lambda} - \sum_{i=1}^{n} x_i = 0$$

$$\hat{\lambda} = \frac{n}{\displaystyle\sum_{i=1}^{n} x_i} \tag{2.122b}$$

where $\hat{\lambda}$ means the MLE of $\lambda$. Equations (2.116) and (2.122b) are identical and the moment estimate and MLE for the parameter $\lambda$ of the exponential distribution agree. This is just a coincidence, and the moment and MLE of most functions will differ.

As an example of how the method applies to a two-parameter distribution we consider the normal distribution

$$f(x) = \frac{1}{\sigma \sqrt{2\pi}} e^{-(x-\mu^2)/2\sigma^2}$$

$$L(x_1, x_2, \ldots ; \mu, \sigma) = \left( \frac{1}{\sigma \sqrt{2\pi}} \right)^n \prod_{i=1}^{n} e^{-(x_i-\mu)^2/2\sigma^2}$$

$$= \left( \frac{1}{\sigma \sqrt{2\pi}} \right)^n \exp \left[ - \sum_{i=1}^{n} \frac{(x_i - \mu)^2}{2\sigma^2} \right]$$

$$\mathcal{L}(x_1, x_2, \ldots ; \mu, \sigma) = n \log \frac{1}{\sigma \sqrt{2\pi}} - \sum_{i=1}^{n} \frac{(x_i - \mu)^2}{2\sigma^2}$$

$$\frac{\partial \mathcal{L}}{\partial \mu} = - \sum_{i=1}^{n} \frac{\partial}{\partial \mu} \frac{(x_i - \mu)^2}{2\sigma^2} = - \sum_{i=1}^{n} \frac{2(x_i - \mu)(-1)}{2\sigma^2}$$

$$= \sum_{i=1}^{n} \frac{x_i - \mu}{\sigma} = \frac{1}{\sigma} \left( \sum_{i=1}^{n} x_i - n\mu \right)$$

Setting $\partial \mathcal{L}/\partial \mu = 0$ yields

$$\hat{\mu} = \frac{1}{n} \sum_{i=1}^{n} x_i \qquad (2.123)$$

Similarly for $\sigma$

$$\frac{\partial \mathcal{L}}{\partial \sigma} = \frac{\partial}{\partial \sigma} \left[ n \log \frac{1}{\sqrt{2\pi}} - n \log \sigma - \sum_{i=1}^{n} \frac{(x_i - \mu)^2}{2\sigma^2} \right]$$

$$= - \frac{n}{\sigma} - \sum_{i=1}^{n} \frac{(x_i - \mu)^2}{2\sigma^3} (-2)$$

$$= \frac{1}{\sigma} \left[ -n + \sum_{i=1}^{n} \frac{(x_i - \mu)^2}{\sigma^2} \right]$$

Setting $\partial \mathcal{L}/\partial \sigma = 0$ yields

$$\sigma^2 = \frac{1}{n} \sum_{i=1}^{n} (x_i - \mu)^2$$

Of course for $\mu$ we use $\hat{\mu}$ from Eq. (2.123)

$$\hat{\sigma}^2 = \frac{1}{n} \sum_{i=1}^{n} (x_i - \hat{\mu})^2 \qquad (2.124)$$

Equation (2.123) agrees with Eq. (2.109), showing that $\hat{\mu}$ is unbiased. When we compare the estimator for $\hat{\sigma}^2$ given in Eq. (2.124) with Eq. (2.114) we see that the MLE for $\sigma^2$ is biased.

The MLE has many good properties which outweigh the drawback that it sometimes yields biased estimates. The bias can be removed in many cases by multiplying by an appropriate constant, as illustrated by Eq. (2.113) and (2.114). Four good properties of the MLE are:

1  The MLE is a sufficient estimator if a sufficient estimator exists for the problem.
2  The MLE is most efficient for $n$ large.

3 The MLE possesses the invariance property.

4 One can compute the var $\hat{\theta}$ and describe its distribution in the limit as $n \to \infty$.

Properties 1 and 2 build up our confidence in the usefulness of the MLE. Property 3 is very useful. For example, if we know that

$$\widehat{\text{var } \mathbf{x}} = \frac{1}{n} \sum_{i=1}^{n} (x_i - \mu)^2$$

then it is true that

$$\hat{\sigma}_x = \sqrt{\frac{1}{n} \sum_{i=1}^{n} (x_i - \hat{\mu})^2}$$

Estimators other than MLE generally do not possess this property. Property 4 pertains to the variance of the MLE, which can be shown[1] to approach

$$\text{var } \hat{\theta} = - \cfrac{1}{nE\left[ \cfrac{\partial^2 \log f(x;\hat{\theta})}{\partial \hat{\theta}^2} \right]} \tag{2.125}$$

as $n$ becomes large. Furthermore, the distribution of $\hat{\theta}$ approaches a normal distribution for large $n$ with parameters $\mu = \hat{\theta}$ and $\sigma^2 = \text{var } \hat{\theta}$. Equation (2.125) can also be written in an equivalent form[2] which is a little simpler computationally

$$\text{var } \hat{\theta} = - \frac{1}{\partial^2 \mathcal{L}/\partial \hat{\theta}^2} \tag{2.126}$$

As an example, the var $\hat{\mu}$ and var $\hat{\sigma}^2$ are computed for the normal distribution. For $\mu$

$$\mathcal{L} = n \log \frac{1}{\sqrt{2\pi}} - n \log \sigma - \sum_{i=1}^{n} \frac{(x_i - \mu)^2}{2\sigma^2}$$

$$\frac{\partial^2 \mathcal{L}}{\partial \mu^2} = - \sum_{i=1}^{n} \frac{1}{\sigma^2} = - \frac{n}{\sigma^2}$$

$$\text{var } \hat{\mu} = \frac{\sigma^2}{n} = \frac{\hat{\sigma}^2}{n} \tag{2.127}$$

---

[1] Freeman, op. cit., p. 259.

[2] D. K. Lloyd and M. Lipow, "Reliability: Management, Methods, and Mathematics," p. 168, Prentice-Hall, Inc., Englewood Cliffs, N.J., 1962.

For $\sigma^2 \equiv v$

$$\mathcal{L} = n \log \frac{1}{\sqrt{2\pi}} - \frac{n}{2} \log v - \sum_{i=1}^{n} \frac{(x_i - \mu)^2}{2v}$$

$$\frac{\partial^2 \mathcal{L}}{\partial v^2} = \frac{n}{2} \frac{1}{v^2} - \sum_{i=1}^{n} \frac{(x_i - \mu)^2}{v^3} = \frac{n}{2} \frac{1}{v^2} - \frac{n}{v^2} = - \frac{n}{2v^2}$$

$$\text{var } \hat{\sigma}^2 = \frac{2\hat{\sigma}^4}{n} \tag{2.128}$$

MLEs are now considered superior to moment estimates by most people. This was not true during the early twentieth century, and the resulting controversy sparked a clash of personalities between Pearson and Fischer. A fascinating account of this rivalry is given in a paper by Fischer.[1]

### 2.10.7  LEAST-SQUARES ESTIMATORS

The third estimation technique we shall discuss is known as the *method of least squares*. It is so commonly applied in engineering and mathematics problems that it is often not thought of as an estimation problem. We assume that a linear law relates two variables, the independent variable $x$ and the dependent variable $y$, and write

$$y = ax + b \tag{2.129}$$

We assume that experimental data are available which link values of $y_i$ with corresponding values of $x_i$. If the experiment were perfect and Eq. (2.129) were an exact model for the physical situation, we would expect a data plot like that in Fig. 2.20a.  Notice that the data perfectly fit the perfect model.  Obviously this is an unnatural situation, and the problem should contain experimental inaccuracies and imperfections in

[1] Fischer, *op. cit.*, Professor Karl Pearson and the Method of Moments, paper 29, p. 29.302a.

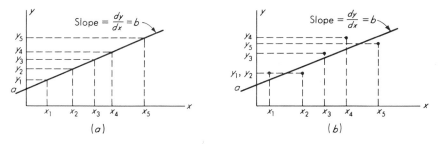

**Fig. 2.20**   Least-squares estimates.   (a) Ideal situation; (b) actual situation.

the linear fit.   To account for these effects we modify Eq. (2.129) by adding to it the random variable ε.

$$\mathbf{y} = a\mathbf{x} + b + \varepsilon \tag{2.130}$$

Since ε is a random variable, $\mathbf{y}$ is also a random variable.   A set of data which fits this model is shown in Fig. 2.20b.

One can develop the least-squares estimation formula from Eq. (2.130) or by focusing on the paired values of $x_i$ and $y_i$.   Both approaches will be used.   The former gives greater insight into the theoretical qualities of the estimate, whereas the latter is computationally simpler.   We first focus on the data values.

To define the least-squares criterion we let $y_i$ and $x_i$ represent paired outcomes of the experiment, and $y = ax_i + b$ is the value predicted by Eq. (2.129).   The difference between actual and predicted values is $y_i - y$ and represents an error.   We wish to sum up these errors for the $n$ data points in order to evaluate the total error.   Since positive and negative errors cancel, giving us invalid results, we would like to deal with $|y_i - y|$; however, absolute values are mathematically cumbersome, and we deal instead with $(y_i - y)^2$.   The sum of the squared errors is

$$\sum_{i=1}^{n} (y_i - y)^2 = \sum_{i=1}^{n} (y_i - ax_i - b)^2 \tag{2.131}$$

In order to choose $a$ and $b$ so that they best fit the data in a least-squares sense, we minimize Eq. (2.131) with respect to $a$ and $b$

$$\frac{\partial \sum_{i=1}^{n} (y_i - y)^2}{\partial a} = 0 \qquad \frac{\partial \sum_{i=1}^{n} (y_i - y)^2}{\partial b} = 0$$

Substitution for $y$ and differentiation yield

$$\frac{\partial \sum_{i=1}^{n} (y_i - ax_i - b)^2}{\partial a} = \sum_{i=1}^{n} [2(y_i - ax_i - b)(-x_i)]$$

$$\frac{\partial \sum_{i=1}^{n} (y_i - ax_i - b)^2}{\partial b} = \sum_{i=1}^{n} [2(y_i - ax_i - b)(-1)]$$

Equating these quantities to zero and rearranging yields

$$\sum_{i=1}^{n} x_i y = a \sum_{i=1}^{n} x_i^2 + b \sum_{i=1}^{n} x_i$$

$$\sum_{i=1}^{n} y_i = a \sum_{i=1}^{n} x_i + nb$$

Solution of the above equations yields

$$\tilde{a} = \frac{\sum\limits_{i=1}^{n} y_i(x_i - \bar{x})}{\sum\limits_{i=1}^{n} (x_i - \bar{x})^2} \qquad \text{where} \qquad \begin{aligned} \bar{x} &= \frac{1}{n} \sum\limits_{i=1}^{n} x_i \\ \bar{y} &= \frac{1}{n} \sum\limits_{i=1}^{n} y_i \end{aligned} \qquad (2.132)$$

$$\tilde{b} = \bar{y} - \tilde{a}\bar{x}$$

The symbol $\tilde{x}$ stands for the least squares estimate of $x$.

In order to proceed with our alternate derivation, which begins with Eq. (2.130), we must make some assumptions about the random variable $\varepsilon$.  A simple set of assumptions which allows us to proceed is that

$$E(\varepsilon) = 0 \qquad \text{and} \qquad \text{var } \varepsilon = \sigma_\varepsilon^2$$

i.e., the mean of $\varepsilon$ is zero and the variance of $\varepsilon$ is some constant *independent* of $x$.  With these assumptions we shall be able to reach Eq. (2.133) by a different path.

If we call the actual values of the random variable $\mathbf{y}_a$, then to differentiate we call the values predicted by Eq. (2.130) $\mathbf{y}_p$.  The difference is, of course, $\mathbf{y}_a - \mathbf{y}_p$, and the expected value of the square of this difference is

$$E[(\mathbf{y}_a - \mathbf{y}_p)^2] = E[(\mathbf{y}_a - a\mathbf{x} - b - \varepsilon)^2]$$

In order to minimize the expected value of the squared difference, we take $\partial/\partial a$ and $\partial/\partial b$ and equate to zero, as before.  Assuming that we can differentiate inside the expectation,

$$\frac{\partial}{\partial b} E[(\mathbf{y}_a - a\mathbf{x} - b - \varepsilon)^2] = E\left[\frac{\partial}{\partial b}(\mathbf{y}_a - a\mathbf{x} - b - \varepsilon)^2\right]$$

$$= E[2(\mathbf{y}_a - a\mathbf{x} - b - \varepsilon)(-1)]$$

Since, $E(b) = b$ and by assumption $E(\varepsilon) = 0$, we obtain

$$-2[E(\mathbf{y}_a) - aE(\mathbf{x})]$$

Equating to zero to minimize yields a solution for $b$

$$b = E(\mathbf{y}_a) - aE(\mathbf{x}) \qquad (2.133a)$$

The variables $\mathbf{y}_a$ and $\mathbf{x}$ are discrete random variables, and their expectation is given by the unbiased estimator $\bar{x}$ in Eq. (2.109).  Substituting (2.109) into (2.133a) yields the same result for $b$ as Eq. (2.132).

Now to compute $a$ we proceed similarly

$$\frac{\partial}{\partial a} E[(\mathbf{y}_a - a\mathbf{x} - b - \varepsilon)^2] = E\left[\frac{\partial}{\partial a}(\mathbf{y}_a - a\mathbf{x} - b - \varepsilon)^2\right]$$

$$= E[2(\mathbf{y}_a - a\mathbf{x} - b - \varepsilon)(-\mathbf{x})]$$

$$- 2[E(\mathbf{xy}_a) - aE(\mathbf{x}^2) - bE(\mathbf{x}) - E(\varepsilon\mathbf{x})]$$

The term $E(\epsilon \mathbf{x})$ is zero, which can be shown from Eqs. (2.88) and (2.89)

$$E(\epsilon \mathbf{x}) = \text{cov } (\epsilon, \mathbf{x}) + E(\epsilon)E(\mathbf{x}) = \rho \sigma_\epsilon \sigma_x + E(\epsilon)E(\mathbf{x})$$

since by assumption $E(\epsilon) = 0$ and because $\epsilon$ and $\mathbf{x}$ are independent, $\rho = 0$, $E(\epsilon \mathbf{x}) = 0$. Thus, equating our result to zero to find the minimum and substituting $b$ from Eq. (2.133a) yields

$$E(\mathbf{x}\mathbf{y}_a) - E(\mathbf{y}_a)E(\mathbf{x}) - \underbrace{a[E(\mathbf{x}^2) - [E(\mathbf{x})]^2]}_{a \text{ var } \mathbf{x}} = 0$$

Solving for $a$ yields

$$a = \frac{E(\mathbf{x}\mathbf{y}_a) - E(\mathbf{y}_a)E(\mathbf{x})}{\text{var } \mathbf{x}} \tag{2.133b}$$

It is left as an exercise for the reader to show that Eqs. (2.133b) and (2.132) agree.

The following observations are stated without proof:

1   The estimators for $a$ and $b$ given in Eq. (2.132) are unbiased estimates.
2   The variances of $\tilde{a}$ and $\tilde{b}$ are given by

$$\text{var } \tilde{a} = \frac{\sigma^2}{\sum\limits_{i}^{n} (x_i - \bar{x})^2} \qquad \text{var } \tilde{b} = \left[ \frac{1}{n} + \frac{\bar{x}^2}{\sum\limits_{i=1}^{n} (x_i - \bar{x})^2} \right] \sigma^2 \tag{2.134}$$

where $\sigma^2 = \text{var } \epsilon$ and $\tilde{\sigma}^2$ is given by

$$\tilde{\sigma}^2 = \frac{1}{n-2} \sum_{i=1}^{n} [y_i - (\tilde{a}x_i + \tilde{b})]^2 \tag{2.135}$$

3   If we had assumed that the random variable $\epsilon$ in Eq. (2.130) was normally distributed with $\mu = 0$ and computed an MLE, we would have obtained the same results as given in Eqs. (2.132).

### 2.10.8   INTERVAL ESTIMATES

Rather than giving a point estimate of our unknown parameter $\theta$ it is often sensible to give an interval estimate for $\theta$. Let us suppose we have an MLE for $\theta$ computed from physical data and its variance, which are given by $\hat{\theta}$ and $(\hat{\sigma}^2)_\theta$. If many data are available, $n$ is large, and the distribution of $\theta$ is approximately normal. We can thus discuss the probability that an interval about $\hat{\theta}$ really does contain the true value of $\theta$. It is sensible to construct a symmetric interval $\hat{\theta} - k\hat{\sigma}_\theta \le \theta \le \hat{\theta} + k\hat{\sigma}_\theta$. This interval brackets the true value $\theta$ (some number) by an upper and lower limit. The limits are random variables, which are in turn functions of the random variables $\theta$ and $\delta_\theta$. If $k = 1$, the normality assumption means we can write $P(\hat{\theta} - \sigma_\theta \leq \theta \leq \hat{\theta} + \sigma_\theta) = 0.683$. Thus, we are 68 percent sure that the interval constructed from the estimates brackets the true value $\theta$. If we let $k = 2$ or 3, the interval grows, and the probability increases; i.e., our confidence that we have bracketed our parameter becomes greater. If we had used something other than the MLE, the estimate distribution might have been other than normal, and although the same procedure could be used, the numerical answer would have differed.

In fact suppose we had used an MLE for a small sample size and were very wary about assuming a normal distribution for such a small sample. In this case we would want to know whether we could construct an interval estimate knowing $\mu$ and $\sigma$ but not knowing the distribution of $\hat{\theta}$. The inequality given below, which was first developed by the Russian mathematician Chebyshev, gives us bounds on a probability interval which are independent of the distribution.

Given that $x$ is a random variable with $E(x) = \mu$ and var $x = \sigma^2$, then for any positive number $k$ the following inequality holds

$$P(|x - \mu| \geq k\sigma) \leq \frac{1}{k^2} \tag{2.136}$$

For a proof of this theorem see Meyer.[1] A slightly tighter bound which improves on Chebyshev's inequality is due to Gauss.[2] If $f(x)$ is continuous and has one maximum (mode) at $x_{max}$, and if $x_{max} = E(x)$, then

$$P(|x - \mu| \geq k\sigma) \leq \frac{4}{9k^2} \tag{2.137}$$

This bound is roughly one-half of Chebyshev's bound; however, more information on $f(x)$ is needed. For comparison purposes, the bounds calculated from Eqs. (2.136) and (2.137) are compared with the actual values for a normal and rectangular distribution in Table 2.7. The

[1] P. L. Meyer, "Introductory Probability and Statistical Applications," p. 128, Addison-Wesley Publishing Company, Inc., Reading, Mass., 1965.
[2] Lloyd and Lipow, *op. cit.*, p. 94.

**Table 2.7    Comparison of Gauss and Chebyshev bounds**

| Interval | Chebyshev | Gauss | Rectangular | Normal |
|---|---|---|---|---|
| $|x - \mu| \geq \sigma$ | 1.00 | 0.44 | 0.58 | 0.32 |
| $|x - \mu| \geq 2\sigma$ | 0.25 | 0.11 | 0.00 | 0.05 |
| $|x - \mu| \geq 3\sigma$ | 0.11 | 0.05 | 0.00 | 0.003 |

Chebyshev bound of course holds for both the normal and rectangular case. The Gauss bound does not apply in the rectangular case because a rectangular distribution does not have a unique mode. The bounds are somewhat crude, but they are still good for first estimates in many problems.

## 2.11  DIFFERENTIAL EQUATIONS

### 2.11.1  DEFINITIONS

A differential equation is an equation relating two or more variables in terms of derivatives or differentials. We shall begin our discussion with the case where one dependent variable $y$ is related to one independent variable $x$. Differential equations contain one or more partial derivatives $\partial^n y / \partial x^n$ and are called *partial differential equations*, or they contain only ordinary derivatives $d^n y / dx^n$ and are called *ordinary differential equations*. We shall discuss only ordinary differential equations. The general form for an ordinary differential equation with one dependent variable $y$ and one independent variable $t$ is[1]

$$a_0(t) \frac{d^n y}{dt^n} + a_1(t) \frac{d^{n-1}y}{dt^{n-1}} + \cdots + a_{n-1}(t) \frac{dy}{dt} + a_n y = f(t)$$

The functional form of the coefficients $a_0, a_1, \ldots, a_n$ is crucial in defining the class of differential equation in question and the associated techniques of solution. If any of the coefficients $a_0, a_1, \ldots, a_n$ are functions of $y$ or its derivatives, the equation is nonlinear. If the coefficients $a_0, a_1, \ldots, a_n$ are either constants or functions of $t$, the equation is called a *linear ordinary differential equation*. We shall discuss only linear equations.

There are two basic types of linear equations. If all the coefficients are constants, we have the simplest case of a *constant-coefficient equation*. If the coefficients vary with time, we have the more difficult case of *time-variable coefficients*. Thus, the two cases are given by:

*Ordinary linear time-varying-coefficient differential equation:*

$$a_0(t) \frac{d^n y}{dt^n} + a_1(t) \frac{d^{n-1}y}{dt^n} + \cdots + a_{n-1}(t) \frac{dy}{dt} + a_n(t)y = f(t) \tag{2.138}$$

*Ordinary linear constant-coefficient differential equation:*

$$a_0 \frac{d^n y}{dt^n} + a_1 \frac{d^{n-1}y}{dt^n} + \cdots + a_{n-1} \frac{dy}{dt} + a_n y = f(t) \tag{2.139}$$

[1] Since we are interested in the time variation of reliability functions, our independent variable will always be time.

### 2.11.2  NATURE OF THE SOLUTION

A careful mathematical approach to the solution of Eq. (2.138) [which includes Eq. (2.139)] begins with the proof of an existence and uniqueness theorem. One can prove that a unique solution $y(t)$ to Eq. (2.138) exists[1] over an interval $t_1 \leq t \leq t_2$ if the coefficients $a_0(t)$, $a_1(t)$, . . . , $a_n(t)$ are continuous over that interval and at some point $t_0$ on that interval a set of initial conditions[2] exist such that $y(t_0) = y_0$, $y^1(t_0) = y_0{}^1$, . . . , $y^{n-1}(t_0) = y_0{}^{n-1}$. The initial conditions are generally specified at the beginning of the interval, which is generally the time origin $t_0$. In other words, if one finds a solution $y(t)$ by guesswork (or more refined methods) which satisfies Eq. (2.138) plus the $n$ initial conditions, the solution is unique. Thus, knowing this theorem, we need not be too careful about proving solution techniques since we always have a definitive check on the validity of a solution.

### 2.11.3  CONSTANT–COEFFICIENT EQUATIONS

We first discuss the constant-coefficient case which encompasses most of the equations which occur in this book. In solving a constant-coefficient equation (2.139), it is convenient to divide coefficients by a constant so that $a_0 = 1$. The right-hand side, $f(t)$, is generally called the *forcing function* or *driving function*. If we set $f(t) = 0$, the resulting equation is called the *associated homogeneous equation*. The general-solution technique is to first solve the homogeneous equation for $n$ different solutions and write the homogeneous solution $y_h(t)$ as a linear combination of these $n$ solutions involving $n$ constants. Then we find a particular solution which satisfies Eq. (2.139) with $f(t) \neq 0$ and which involves no constants; it is called $y_p(t)$. The complete solution is $y(t) = y_h(t) + y_p(t)$. The $n$ initial conditions are then substituted in $y(t)$ to yield $n$ simultaneous equations which are in turn solved for the constants of the homogeneous solution. Substitution of the numerical values for these constants completes the solution for $y(t)$.

### 2.11.4  HOMOGENEOUS SOLUTION

The $n$ functions in the homogeneous solution for a constant-coefficient equation are always of the form $e^{rt}$ or $t^n e^{rt}$. Thus, the problem is reduced to solving an algebraic equation for $n$ values of $r$ which satisfy the differential equation. This is done by substituting $e^{rt}$ in the homogeneous equation and solving the resulting polynomial, called the *characteristic*

---

[1] H. S. Bean, "Differential Equations," p. 58, Addison-Wesley Publishing Company, Inc., Reading, Mass., 1962.

[2] The notation $y^n(t_0)$ is a short form for $d^n y/dt^n$ evaluated at $t = t_0$.

*polynomial* or *characteristic equation,* for the $n$ values of $r$.   For example,

$$6\frac{d^2y}{dt^2} + 5\frac{dy}{dt} + y = 0$$

$$y_h = e^{rt} \qquad \dot{y}_h = re^{rt} \qquad \ddot{y}_h = r^2e^{rt}$$
$$6r^2e^{rt} + 5re^{rt} + e^{rt} = 0$$
$$(6r^2 + 5r + 1)e^{rt} = 0$$
$$e^{rt} \neq 0 \qquad \therefore \ (6r^2 + 5r + 1) = (3r + 1)(2r + 1) = 0$$
$$r = -\tfrac{1}{2}, \ -\tfrac{1}{3}$$
$$y_h(t) = c_1e^{-t/2} + c_2e^{-t/3}$$

If any roots are repeated, the homogeneous solution is slightly modified by multiplying some exponential terms by powers of $t$.   Specifically if $r_1$ is a triple root of the characteristic equation, the solution becomes

$$c_1{}^{r_1t} + c_2te^{r_1t} + c_3t^2e^{r_1t} + \sum_{\substack{\text{other} \\ \text{roots}}} c_ie^{r_it}$$

For example,

$$\frac{d^3y}{dt^3} - 5\frac{d^2y}{dt^2} + 8\frac{dy}{dt} - 4y = 0$$
$$[(r - 1)(r - 2)^2]e^{rt} = 0$$
$$r = 1, 2, 2$$
$$y(t) = c_1e^t + c_2e^{2t} + c_3te^{2t}$$

If any roots are imaginary they must occur in complex-conjugate pairs, which later can be combined to form sines or cosines by Euler's identity

$$e^a \cos \theta = e^a\tfrac{1}{2}(e^{i\theta} + e^{-i\theta}) = \tfrac{1}{2}(e^{a+i\theta} + e^{a-i\theta})$$

$$e^a \sin \theta = e^a \frac{1}{2i}(e^{i\theta} - e^{-i\theta}) = \frac{1}{2i}(e^{a+i\theta} - e^{a-i\theta})$$

(2.140)

For example,

$$\frac{d^2y}{dt^2} + 2\frac{dy}{dt} + 5y = 0$$
$$r^2 + 2r + 5 = 0$$
$$r = -1 \pm 2i$$
$$y(t) = e^{-t}(c_1e^{2i} + c_2e^{-2i})$$

Let

$$c_1 = \frac{c_3}{2} + \frac{c_4}{2i} \qquad \text{and} \qquad c_2 = \frac{c_3}{2} - \frac{c_4}{2i}$$

$$y(t) = e^{-t}\left(\frac{c_3e^{2i} + c_3e^{-2i}}{2} + \frac{c_4e^{2i} - c_4e^{-2i}}{2i}\right)$$

$$= e^{-t}(c_3 \cos 2t + c_4 \sin 2t)$$

**Table 2.8   Derivative families**

| Term | Family |
|------|--------|
| $t^m$ | $t^m, t^{m-1}, \ldots t, 1$ |
| $\sin qt$ | $\sin qt, \cos qt$ |
| $\cos qt$ | $\sin qt, \cos qt$ |
| $e^{pt}$ | $e^{pt}$ |
| $t^2 \sin 3t$ | $t^2 \sin 3t, t \sin 3t, \sin 3t$<br>$t^2 \cos 3t, t \cos 3t, \cos 3t$ |

There are several general methods of obtaining the particular solution such as the method of variation of parameters.[1]   The simpler technique, called *undetermined coefficients*, will be discussed since it applies to almost all cases which occur in reliability work.

### 2.11.5   UNDETERMINED COEFFICIENTS

If the driving function $f(t)$ in a constant-coefficient equation is of the form $t^m$, where $m$ is an integer, $\sin qt$, $\cos qt$, $e^{pt}$, or products of two or more such functions, then the method of undetermined coefficients holds.   The key property of these functions which makes the method work is the fact that the family composed of the function and its derivatives is finite (see Table 2.8).   The last entry in Table 2.8 is a product of terms $t^2$ and $\sin 3t$. The family of terms is constructed as shown in Table 2.9.

[1] H. B. Thomas, "Calculus and Analytic Geometry," 3d ed., p. 892, Addison-Wesley Publishing Company, Inc., Reading, Mass., 1965.

**Table 2.9   Evolution of $t^2 \sin 3t$ family**

| Function | Contribution to family |
|----------|------------------------|
| $f(t) = t^2 \sin 3t$ | $t^2 \sin 3t$ |
| $\dot{f}(t) = 2t \sin 3t + 3t^2 \cos 3t$ | $t \sin 3t, t^2 \cos 3t$ |
| $\ddot{f}(t) = 2 \sin 3t + 6t \cos 3t - 9t^2 \sin 3t$ | $\sin 3t, t \cos 3t$ |
| $\dddot{f}(t) = 6 \cos 3t + 6 \cos 3t - 18t \sin 3t - 18t \sin 3t - 27t^2 \cos 3t$ | $\cos 3t$ |

. . . . . . . . . . . . . . . . . . . . . . . . . . . . . . . . . . . . . . . . . .

*Terms repeat for higher-order derivatives*

The particular solution is simply a linear combination of terms from the family of $f(t)$. Substituting in the differential equation and equating coefficients of like functions yields the constants and thereby the particular solution. If any member of the family is of the same form as a member of the homogeneous solution, it must be modified by multiplying by $t$ just as was done in the case of repeated roots in the homogeneous solution. For example,

$$\frac{d^2y}{dt^2} + 5\frac{dy}{dt} + 6y = e^{-t}$$

From a previous example $y_h(t) = c_1 e^{-2t} + c_2 e^{-3t}$. For $y_p(t)$ we choose $Ae^{-t}$

$$y_p(t) = Ae^{-t} \qquad \dot{y}_p(t) = -Ae^{-t} \qquad \ddot{y}_p(t) = Ae^{-t}$$
$$Ae^{-t} - 5Ae^{-t} + 6Ae^{-t} = e^{-t}$$
$$2Ae^{-t} = e^{-t} \qquad A = \tfrac{1}{2}$$
$$y(t) = y_h(t) + y_p(t) = c_1 e^{-2t} + c_2 e^{-3t} + \tfrac{1}{2}e^{-t}$$

If the initial conditions are $y(0) = +\tfrac{1}{2}$ $\qquad \dot{y}(0) = +\tfrac{1}{2}$,

$$y(0) = \tfrac{1}{2} = c_1 + c_2 + \tfrac{1}{2}$$
$$\dot{y}(t) = -2c_1 e^{-2t} - 3c_2 e^{-3t} - \tfrac{1}{2}e^{-t}$$
$$\dot{y}(0) = +\tfrac{1}{2} = -2c_1 - 3c_2 - \tfrac{1}{2}$$
$$\therefore c_1 + c_2 = 0$$
$$2c_1 + 3c_2 = -1$$

and

$$c_2 = 1 \qquad c_1 = -1$$

The complete solution is

$$y(t) = -e^{-2t} + e^{-3t} + \tfrac{1}{2}e^{-t}$$

To illustrate the procedure when a family member coincides with the homogeneous solution we consider the following example

$$\frac{d^2y}{dt^2} + 5\frac{dy}{dt} + 6y = e^{-2t}$$

As before,

$$y_h(t) = c_1 e^{-2t} + c_2 e^{-3t}$$

Since the family of $f(t)$ and $y_h(t)$ both contain the term $e^{-2t}$, the particular solution is taken as $y_p(t) = Ae^{-2t} + Bte^{-2t}$. Since $e^{-2t}$ is already included in the homogeneous solution, it need not be repeated here; thus

$$y_p(t) = Bte^{-2t}$$
$$\dot{y}_p(t) = +Be^{-2t} - 2Bte^{-2t}$$
$$\ddot{y}_p(t) = -2Be^{-2t} - 2Be^{-2t} + 4Bte^{-2t}$$

Substituting in the differential equation,

$$(-2Be^{-2t} - 2Be^{-2t} + 4Bte^{-2t}) + 5(+Be^{-2t} - 2Bte^{-2t})$$
$$+ 6(+Bte^{-2t}) = e^{-2t}$$

Equating coefficients of the $e^{-2t}$ and the $te^{-2t}$ terms,

$$(-2B - 2B + 5B)e^{-2t} = 1e^{-2t}$$
$$(4B - 10B + 6B)te^{-2t} = 0te^{-2t}$$

Thus, $B = 1$ and $y(t) = c_1e^{-2t} + c_2e^{-3t} + te^{-2t}$.

Substitution of two initial conditions and solution of the two simultaneous equations for $c_1$ and $c_2$ completes the solution.

### 2.11.6 TIME–VARYING COEFFICIENTS

The case of time-varying-coefficient equations is more difficult, and except in simple cases we must use certain reducing substitutions[1] to obtain homogeneous solutions and then use variation of parameters for the particular solution.   Another approach is to use a series solution.[2]

Fortunately we shall deal primarily with the simplest of all cases, the first-order equation.   The general solution for a first-order equation can be found using the following technique, which is known as the *integrating-factor method*.   A first-order equation

$$\frac{dy}{dt} + a_1(t)y = f(t) \tag{2.141}$$

can be rewritten in the form

$$\frac{dy}{dt} + \left(\frac{1}{p}\frac{dp}{dt}\right)y = f(t) \tag{2.142}$$

where $p$ is a new variable which will be related to $a_1(t)$ shortly.   Equation (2.142) may be put in the form

$$\frac{1}{p}\frac{d}{dt}(py) = f(t) \tag{2.143}$$

We can solve Eq. (2.143) simply by separating the variables and integrating

$$\int d(py) = \int pf(t)\,dt$$
$$y = \frac{1}{p}\int pf(t)\,dt + \frac{c}{p} \tag{2.144}$$

[1] Hildebrand, *op. cit.*, sec. 1.6.
[2] *Ibid.*, chap. 4.

where $c$ is the constant of integration. Now from Eqs. (2.141) and (2.142) we must find a relation for $p$

$$\frac{1}{p}\frac{dp}{dt} = a_1(t)$$

$$\int \frac{dp}{p} = \int a_1(t)\, dt$$

$$\ln p = \int a_1(t)\, dt$$

$$p = e^{\int a_1(t)\, dt} \tag{2.145}$$

where $p$ is called the integrating factor.

Equations (2.144) and (2.145) reduce the solution of any first-order equation to two successive integrations.

### 2.11.7  INTEGRATING–FACTOR SOLUTION OF MARKOV EQUATIONS

We shall also have to deal with systems of first-order equations whenever we try to solve a Markov model. It is fortunate that the system of equations often occurs in a very special form.[1] First, the equations are all first-order, as a result of the Markov assumptions. Second, the equations are coupled in a very special way such that the solution of the first serves as the forcing function for the second, the second solution forces the third, etc. The first equation is decoupled from the succeeding ones and can be solved separately. These properties will become clear when reference is made to the analog-computer solution in Chap. 5, which portrays things graphically. The following example illustrates the technique for a time-varying-coefficient problem.

A general Markov transition matrix is given in Table 2.5. As an example we shall solve a three-state Markov problem where the failure probabilities are similar to the Poisson process except that $\lambda$ increases linearly with time, $\lambda = Kt$. The transition matrix is given in Table 2.10.

[1] In Chap. 6 we shall discuss some repair models which do not have such a simple form of coupling.

Table 2.10   Transition matrix for a state problem with time-varying transition probabilities

| Initial states | Final states | | |
|---|---|---|---|
| | $s_0(t + \Delta t)$ | $s_1(t + \Delta t)$ | $s_2(t + \Delta t)$ |
| $s_0(t)$ | $1 - K_{01}t\,\Delta t$ | $K_{01}t\,\Delta t$ | 0 |
| $s_1(t)$ | 0 | $1 - K_{12}t\,\Delta t$ | $K_{12}t\,\Delta t$ |
| $s_2(t)$ | 0 | 0 | 1 |

The Markov differential equations are

$$\dot{P}_{s_0}(t) + K_{01}tP_{s_0}(t) = 0$$
$$\dot{P}_{s_1}(t) + K_{12}tP_{s_1}(t) = K_{01}tP_{s_0}(t)$$
$$\dot{P}_{s_2}(t) = K_{12}tP_{s_1}(t)$$

The solution for the first equation is given by

$$p = e^{\int K_{01}t \, dt} = e^{K_{01}t^2/2}$$
$$P_{s_0}(t) = e^{-K_{01}t^2/2}\int e^{K_{01}t^2/2}0 \, dt + c_1 e^{-K_{01}t^2/2} = c_1 e^{-K_{01}t^2/2}$$

Assuming initial conditions $P_{s_0}(0) = 1$ and $P_{s_1}(0) = P_{s_2}(0) = 0$,

$$P_{s_0}(t) = e^{-K_{01}t^2/2}$$

For the second equation by analogy $p = e^{K_{12}t^2/2}$ and

$$
\begin{aligned}
P_{s_1}(t) &= e^{-K_{12}t^2/2}\int e^{K_{12}t^2/2}K_{12}te^{-K_{01}t^2/2} \, dt + c_2 e^{-K_{12}t^2/2} \\
&= e^{-K_1 t^2/2}K_{01}\int te^{(K_{12}-K_{01})t^2/2} \, dt + c_2 e^{-K_{12}t^2/2} \\
&= -\frac{K_{01}}{K_{12} - K_{01}} e^{-K_{01}t^2/2} + c_2 e^{-K_{12}t^2/2}
\end{aligned}
$$

when $t = 0$, $P_{s_1}(t) = 0$, and $-K_{01}/(K_{12} - K_{01}) + c_2 = 0$; therefore

$$P_{s_1}(t) = \frac{K_{01}}{K_{12} - K_{01}}(-e^{-K_{01}t^2/2} + e^{-K_{12}t^2/2})$$

For the third equation $a_1(t) = 0$ and $p = 1$

$$
\begin{aligned}
P_{s_2}(t) &= \int 1K_{12} + \frac{K_{01}}{K_{12} - K_{01}}(-e^{-K_{01}t^2/2} + e^{-K_{12}t^2/2}) + c_3 \\
&= \frac{K_{12}K_{01}}{K_{12} - K_{01}}\left(\frac{1}{K_{01}}e^{-K_{01}t^2/2} - \frac{1}{K_{12}}e^{-K_{12}t^2/2}\right) + c_3
\end{aligned}
$$

when $t = 0$, $P_{s_2}(t) = 0$, and

$$\frac{K_{12}K_{01}}{K_{12} - K_{01}}\left(\frac{1}{K_{01}} - \frac{1}{K_{12}}\right) + c_3 = 0$$

$$P_{s_2}(t) = \frac{K_{12}}{K_{12} - K_{01}}e^{-K_{01}t^2/2} - \frac{K_{01}}{K_{12} - K_{01}}e^{-K_{12}t^2/2} + 1$$

As a check on our solution we simply add $P_{s_0}(t) + P_{s_1}(t) + P_{s_2}(t)$ and verify that the sum is unity.

### 2.11.8   LAPLACE TRANSFORMS

The moment-generating function has already been introduced as a technique which has many uses in probability theory. The Laplace transform, a very close relative, will now be introduced as an aid in the solution of differential equations.   The Laplace transform of a time function $f(t)$ is defined by the integral[1]

$$\mathcal{L}\{f(t)\} = F(s) = \{f(t)\}^* = f^*(s) = \int_0^\infty f(t)e^{-st}\, dt \qquad (2.146)$$

Four equivalent sets of notation for the Laplace transform are given in Eq. (2.146).  The first two are the most common, but they will not always be used since the symbol $F(s)$ causes confusion when we take the Laplace transform of both a density and a distribution function in the same equation.  The third and fourth notation will be used whenever confusion might arise.  The asterisk or the change in argument from $t$ to $s$ (or both) symbolizes the change from the time domain to the transform domain.  The utility of the Laplace transform is that it reduces ordinary constant-coefficient linear differential equations to algebraic equations in $s$ which are easily solved.  The solution in terms of $s$ is then converted back to a time function by an inverse-transform procedure.  The process works much in the same way as logarithms are used to solve complicated algebraic computations.  A pictorial representation of the Laplace transform solution of a differential equation is given in Fig. 2.21.

Since only a few basic transform techniques will be needed in this book, this discussion will be brief and will not touch on the broad aspects of the method.  The Laplace transforms of three important functions follow.

*Example 1*   For the exponential functions $f(t) = e^{-at}$

$$\mathcal{L}\{f(t)\} = f^*(s) = \int_0^\infty e^{-at}e^{-st}\, dt = \int_0^\infty e^{-(a+s)t}\, dt = \frac{-e^{-(a+s)t}}{s+a}\bigg|_0^\infty$$

$$= \frac{1}{s+a} \qquad \text{for } s > -a \quad (2.147)$$

The restriction $s > -a$ is necessary in order that the integral not diverge.

*Example 2*   Similarly, for the cosine function

$$f(t) = \cos at = \frac{e^{ia} - e^{-ia}}{2}$$

$$f^*(s) = \left\{\frac{e^{ia}}{2}\right\}^* + \left\{\frac{e^{-ia}}{2}\right\}^* = \frac{\frac{1}{2}}{s+ia} + \frac{\frac{1}{2}}{s-ia} = \frac{s}{s^2+a^2} \qquad \text{for } s > 0$$

$$(2.148)$$

Note that in the above computation two properties were used.  The Laplace transform is an integral, and the integral of a sum of two time functions is the sum of the integrals; thus, the transform of the sum is the sum of transforms.  This is referred to as the *superposition property*. Also the result of Eq. (2.147) was used for each term in Eq. (2.148).

[1] The Laplace transform is defined only over the range of $s$ for which this integral exists.

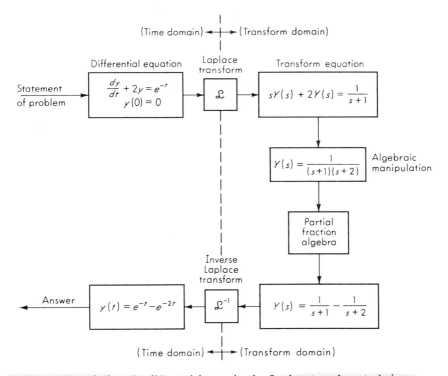

(Time domain) ◄─┼─► (Transform domain)

Differential equation | Laplace transform | Transform equation

Statement of problem → $\dfrac{dy}{dt} + 2y = e^{-t}$    $y(0) = 0$ → $\mathcal{L}$ → $sY(s) + 2Y(s) = \dfrac{1}{s+1}$

$Y(s) = \dfrac{1}{(s+1)(s+2)}$    Algebraic manipulation

Partial fraction algebra

Inverse Laplace transform

Answer ◄─    $y(t) = e^{-t} - e^{-2t}$ ◄ $\mathcal{L}^{-1}$ ◄ $Y(s) = \dfrac{1}{s+1} - \dfrac{1}{s+2}$

(Time domain) ◄─┼─► (Transform domain)

**Fig. 2.21**   The solution of a differential equation by Laplace transform techniques.

*Example 3*  As a third example we consider the step function and the constant.  When $f(t) = 1$ or $f(t) = u_{-1}(t)$

$$f^*(s) = \int_0^\infty 1 e^{-st}\, dt = \frac{e^{-st}}{-s}\Big|_0^\infty = \frac{1}{s} \qquad \text{for } s > 0 \tag{2.149}$$

Note that although a step function and a constant are different functions, their Laplace transforms are the same, since over the region from $0 < t < +\infty$ they have the same value.  Thus, the Laplace transform holds only for positive $t$.  We can view a step as the limit of an exponential as we increase the time constant, $1/a \to \infty$.  Equation (2.149) could therefore be obtained from (2.147) by letting $a \to 0$.  The transforms for several time functions of interest are given in Table 2.11.

In order to solve differential equations with Laplace transform techniques we must compute the transform of a derivative.  This can be done directly from Eq. (2.146) using integration by parts

$$\mathcal{L}\left\{\frac{df(t)}{dt}\right\} = \left\{\frac{df(t)}{dt}\right\}^* = \int_0^\infty \frac{df(t)}{dt}\, e^{-st}\, dt = \int_0^\infty e^{-st}\, df(t)$$

**Table 2.11   A short table of Laplace transforms**

| No. | $f(t)$ | $\{f(t)\}^* = f^*(s) = \mathcal{L}\{f(t)\} = F(s)$ |
|---|---|---|
| 1 | $u_0(t)$ | $1$ |
| 2 | $u_{-1}(t)$ | $\dfrac{1}{s}$ |
| 3 | $u_{-2}(t)$ | $\dfrac{1}{s^2}$ |
| 4 | $e^{-at}$ | $\dfrac{1}{s + a}$ |
| 5 | $\dfrac{1}{(n - 1)!} t^{n-1}e^{-at}$ | $\dfrac{1}{(s + a)^n}$ |
| 6 | $\sin at$ | $\dfrac{a}{s^2 + a^2}$ |
| 7 | $\cos at$ | $\dfrac{s}{s^2 + a^2}$ |
| 8 | $e^{-bt}\sin at$ | $\dfrac{a}{(s + b)^2 + a^2}$ |
| 9 | $e^{-bt}\cos at$ | $\dfrac{s + b}{(s + b)^2 + a^2}$ |
| 10 | $Ae^{-at} + Be^{-bt}$ | $\dfrac{(A + B)s + Ab + Ba}{(s + a)(s + b)}$ |

Letting $dv = df(t)$ and $u = e^{-st}$ and integrating by parts,

$$\mathcal{L}\left\{\frac{df(t)}{dt}\right\} = e^{-st}f(t)\,\bigg|_0^\infty + s \int_0^\infty f(t)e^{-st}\,dt$$

We first discuss the evaluation of the $e^{-st}f(t)$ term at its upper and lower limits.   Since the Laplace transform is defined only for functions $f(t)$ which build up more slowly then $e^{-st}$ decay [see footnote to Eq. (2.146)], $\lim_{t \to \infty} e^{-st}f(t) = 0$.   At the lower limit we obtain the initial value of the function $f(0)$.†   The integral is of course the Laplace transform itself

$$\left\{\frac{df(t)}{dt}\right\}^* = sf^*(s) - f(0) \qquad (2.150)$$

† The notation $f(0)$ means the value of the function at $t = 0$. If singularity functions occur at $t = 0$, we must use care and write $f(0^-)$, which is the limit as 0 is approached from the left.

By letting $g(t) = d^n f(t)/dt^n$ it is easy to generate a recursion relationship

$$\left\{\frac{dg(t)}{dt}\right\}^* = \left\{\frac{d^{n+1}f(t)}{dt^{n+1}}\right\}^* = s\left\{\frac{d^n f(t)}{dt^n}\right\}^* - f^n(0) \tag{2.151}$$

for the second derivative

$$\left\{\frac{d^2 f(t)}{dt^2}\right\}^* = s^2 f^*(s) - sf(0) - \dot{f}(0) \tag{2.152}$$

Using the information discussed, we can solve the homogeneous differential equation

$$\frac{d^2 y}{dt^2} + 5\frac{dy}{dt} + 6y = 0 \qquad \begin{aligned} y(0) &= 0 \\ \dot{y}(0) &= 1 \end{aligned}$$

Taking the transform of each term, we have

$$[s^2 y^*(s) - sy(0) - \dot{y}(0)] + 5[sy^*(s) - y(0)] + 6y^*(s) = 0$$
$$[s^2 y^*(s) - 1] + 5[sy^*(s)] + 6y^*(s) = 0$$
$$(s^2 + 5s + 6)y^*(s) = 1$$

$$y^*(s) = \frac{1}{(s+2)(s+3)}$$

Using transform 10 in Table 2.11,

$$A + B = 0 \qquad 2A + 3B = 0$$
$$A = +1 \qquad B = -1$$
$$y(t) = e^{-2t} - e^{-3t}$$

Suppose we add the driving function $e^{-4t}$ to the above example, that is,

$$\left\{\frac{d^2 y}{dt^2} + 5\frac{dy}{dt} + 6y\right\}^* = \{e^{-4t}\}^*$$

$$(s+2)(s+3)y^*(s) - 1 = \frac{1}{s+4}$$

$$y^*(s) = \frac{s+5}{(s+4)(s+2)(s+3)}$$

No transform for this function exists in the table, but we can use partial-fraction algebra to reduce this to known results

$$\frac{s+5}{(s+4)(s+2)(s+3)} = \frac{\frac{1}{2}}{s+4} + \frac{\frac{3}{2}}{s+2} + \frac{-2}{s+3}$$

Thus, each term represents an exponential, and

$$y(t) = \tfrac{1}{2}e^{-4t} + \tfrac{3}{2}e^{-2t} - 2e^{-3t}$$

The $e^{-4t}$ term represents the *particular solution* (driving function), and the $e^{-2t}$ and $e^{-3t}$ terms represent the *homogeneous solution* (natural response).

The partial-fraction-expansion coefficients can be found by conventional means or by the following shortcut formula

$$f(s) = \frac{N(s)}{D(s)} = \frac{N(s)}{\displaystyle\prod_{i=1}^{n}(s + r_i)} = \frac{A_1}{s + r_1} + \frac{A_2}{s + r_2} + \cdots + \frac{A_n}{s + r_n}$$

where

$$A_i = \left[\frac{N(s)}{D(s)}(s + r_i)\right]_{s = -r_i} \tag{2.153}$$

**Table 2.12   A short table of Laplace transform theorems**

| No. | Operation | $f(t)$ | $\mathcal{L}\{f(t)\} = F(s)$ |
|---|---|---|---|
| 1 | Linearity (superposition) property | $a_1 f_1(t) + a_2 f_2(t)$ | $a_1 F_1(s) + a_2 F_2(s)$ |
| 2 | Differentiation theorems | $\dfrac{df(t)}{dt}$ | $sF(s) - f(0)$ |
| | | $\dfrac{d^2 f(t)}{dt^2}$ | $s^2 F(s) - sf(0) - \dot{f}(0)$ |
| | | $\dfrac{d^n f(t)}{dt^n}$ | $s\mathcal{L}\left\{\dfrac{d^{n-1}f(t)}{dt^{n-1}}\right\} - f^{n-1}(0)$ |
| 3 | Integral theorems | $\displaystyle\int_0^t f(t)\,dt$ | $\dfrac{F(s)}{s}$ |
| | | $\displaystyle\int_{-\infty}^t f(t)\,dt$ | $\dfrac{F(s)}{s} + \dfrac{\displaystyle\int_{-\infty}^0 f(t)\,dt}{s}$ |
| 4 | Convolution theorem | $\displaystyle\int_0^t f_1(\tau) f_2(t - \tau)\,d\tau$ | $F_1(s)F_2(s)$ |
| 5 | Multiplication-by-$t$ property | $tf(t)$ | $-\dfrac{dF(s)}{ds}$ |
| 6 | Initial-value theorem | $\displaystyle\lim_{t\to 0} f(t)$ | $\displaystyle\lim_{s\to\infty} sF(s)$† |
| 7 | Final-value theorem | $\displaystyle\lim_{t\to\infty} f(t)$ | $\displaystyle\lim_{s\to 0} sF(s)$† |

† The function $sF(s)$ is a ratio of polynomials in problems we shall consider. The roots of the denominator polynomial are called *poles*. We cannot apply the initial- and final-value theorems if *any* pole of $sF(s)$ has *a zero or positive real part*. The statement is conventionally worded: the initial- and final-value theorems hold only provided that all poles of $sF(s)$ lie in the left half of the $s$ plane.

For the above example

$$A_1 = \left[ \frac{s + 5}{(s + 4)(s + 2)(s + 3)} (s + 4) \right]_{s = -4} = \frac{1}{2}$$

$$A_2 = \left[ \frac{s + 5}{(s + 4)(s + 2)(s + 3)} (s + 2) \right]_{s = -2} = \frac{3}{2}$$

$$A_3 = \left[ \frac{s + 5}{(s + 4)(s + 2)(s + 3)} (s + 3) \right]_{s = -3} = -2$$

The derivation of Eq. (2.153) as well as a similar one for the case of repeated roots is discussed in the problems at the end of the chapter.

We have already discussed two Laplace transform theorems, super-position and derivative property. Some additional ones useful in later chapters appear in Table 2.12.

The first and second theorems have already been discussed. The third theorem is simply the integral equivalent of the differentiation theorems. The convolution theorem is important since it describes the time-domain equivalent of a product of two Laplace transforms. Property 5 will be used in Chap. 5 to derive a simple expression for the MTTF. Theorems 6 and 7 are useful in computing the initial and final behavior of reliability functions.

### 2.11.9  MATRIX ALGEBRA

Markov processes give rise to systems of differential equations which are simple to solve, but the amount of labor involved becomes large as the number of system states increases. As an aid in systematizing the computations matrix algebra will be employed. The following basic matrix operations will be necessary in the computational procedure.

1  A rectangular matrix of dimension $m \times n$ is defined by the array of numbers

$$\text{Matrix } A \equiv [A] \equiv \begin{bmatrix} a_{11} & a_{12} & \cdots & a_{1n} \\ a_{21} & a_{22} & \cdots & a_{2n} \\ \cdots & \cdots & \cdots & \cdots \\ a_{m1} & a_{m2} & \cdots & a_{mn} \end{bmatrix} \begin{matrix} \uparrow \\ m \\ \text{rows} \\ \downarrow \end{matrix}$$
$$\longleftarrow n \text{ columns} \longrightarrow$$

(a)  If $m = n$, the matrix is square.

(b)  If $n = 1$, the matrix is composed of a single column and is called a *column matrix*

$$\begin{bmatrix} a_1 \\ a_2 \\ \cdot \\ \cdot \\ \cdot \\ a_n \end{bmatrix}$$

(c)   If $m = 1$, the matrix is composed of a single row and is called a *row matrix* $[a_1 \quad a_2 \quad \cdots \quad a_n]$.

(d)   The determinant associated with a square matrix of dimension $n \times n$ is

$$|A| = \begin{vmatrix} a_{11} & a_{12} & \cdots & a_{1n} \\ a_{21} & a_{22} & \cdots & a_{2n} \\ \cdots & \cdots & \cdots & \cdots \\ a_{n1} & a_{n2} & \cdots & a_{nn} \end{vmatrix}$$

The determinant is to be expanded in terms of cofactors in the conventional way

$$\begin{vmatrix} a_{11} & a_{12} \\ a_{21} & a_{22} \end{vmatrix} = a_{11}a_{22} - a_{21}a_{12}$$

$$\begin{vmatrix} a_{11} & a_{12} & a_{13} \\ a_{21} & a_{22} & a_{23} \\ a_{31} & a_{32} & a_{33} \end{vmatrix} = a_{11} \begin{vmatrix} a_{22} & a_{23} \\ a_{32} & a_{33} \end{vmatrix} - a_{12} \begin{vmatrix} a_{21} & a_{23} \\ a_{31} & a_{33} \end{vmatrix} + a_{13} \begin{vmatrix} a_{21} & a_{22} \\ a_{31} & a_{32} \end{vmatrix}$$

(f)   The $(cofactor)_{ij}$ is given by $(-1)^{i+j}$ times the determinant remaining when the $i$th row and $j$th column are deleted.

(g)   A square matrix with zeros for all elements except the main diagonal is called a *diagonal matrix*

$$\begin{bmatrix} d_1 & 0 & \cdots & 0 \\ 0 & d_2 & \cdots & 0 \\ \cdots & \cdots & \cdots & \cdots \\ 0 & 0 & \cdots & d_n \end{bmatrix}$$

(h)   The *identity matrix* $[I]$ is a diagonal matrix with

$$d_1 = d_2 = \cdots = d_n = 1$$

2   The sum of two matrices $[A]$ and $[B]$ both of dimension $m \times n$ is defined as a third matrix $[C]$ of dimension $m \times n$, where $c_{ij} = a_{ij} + b_{ij}$

$$\begin{bmatrix} a_{11} & a_{12} & a_{13} \\ a_{21} & a_{22} & a_{23} \end{bmatrix} + \begin{bmatrix} b_{11} & b_{12} & b_{13} \\ b_{21} & b_{22} & b_{23} \end{bmatrix} = \begin{bmatrix} a_{11} + b_{11} & a_{12} + b_{12} & a_{13} + b_{13} \\ a_{21} + b_{21} & a_{22} + b_{22} & a_{23} + b_{23} \end{bmatrix}$$

3   Multiplying matrix $[A]$ by a number $\alpha$ simply multiplies each element by $\alpha$, that is, $\alpha a_{ij}$

$$\alpha \begin{bmatrix} a_{11} & a_{12} & a_{13} \\ a_{21} & a_{22} & a_{23} \end{bmatrix} = \begin{bmatrix} \alpha a_{11} & \alpha a_{12} & \alpha a_{13} \\ \alpha a_{21} & \alpha a_{22} & \alpha a_{23} \end{bmatrix}$$

The difference of two matrices of equal dimension is defined by

$$[A] - [B] = [A] + (-1)[B]$$

4  The product of two matrices $[A][B]$ is a third matrix $[C]$ defined as shown below

$$\begin{bmatrix} a_{11} & a_{12} & a_{13} \\ a_{21} & a_{22} & a_{23} \end{bmatrix} \begin{bmatrix} b_{11} & b_{12} \\ b_{21} & b_{22} \\ b_{31} & b_{32} \end{bmatrix}$$
$$= \begin{bmatrix} a_{11}b_{11} + a_{12}b_{21} + a_{13}b_{31} & a_{11}b_{12} + a_{12}b_{22} + a_{13}b_{32} \\ a_{21}b_{11} + a_{22}b_{21} + a_{23}b_{31} & a_{21}b_{12} + a_{22}b_{22} + a_{23}b_{32} \end{bmatrix}$$

(a)  The number of columns of the first factor must equal the number of rows of the second factor

$$[A][B] = [C]$$
$$(m \times n)(p \times q) = (m \times q)$$

Multiplication is defined only when $n = p$.

(b)  Multiplications are not generally commutative

$$[A][B] \neq [B][A]$$

(c)  Premultiplication or postmultiplication of matrix $[A]$ by the identity matrix $[I]$ yields $[A]$

$$\begin{bmatrix} 1 & 0 & 0 \\ 0 & 1 & 0 \\ 0 & 0 & 1 \end{bmatrix} \begin{bmatrix} a_{11} & a_{12} \\ a_{21} & a_{22} \\ a_{31} & a_{33} \end{bmatrix} = \begin{bmatrix} a_{11} & a_{12} \\ a_{21} & a_{22} \\ a_{31} & a_{33} \end{bmatrix}$$

$$\begin{bmatrix} a_{11} & a_{12} \\ a_{21} & a_{22} \\ a_{31} & a_{33} \end{bmatrix} \begin{bmatrix} 1 & 0 \\ 0 & 1 \end{bmatrix} = \begin{bmatrix} a_{11} & a_{12} \\ a_{21} & a_{22} \\ a_{31} & a_{33} \end{bmatrix}$$

5  The inverse of a square matrix $[A]$, written as $[A]^{-1}$, is defined by the identities

$$[A]^{-1}[A] = [A][A^{-1}] = [I]$$

(a)  The elements $b_{ij}$ of $[A]^{-1}$ are obtained from the elements $a_{ij}$ of $[A]$ by the formula

$$b_{ij} = \frac{(\text{cofactor})_{ji}}{|A|} \qquad \begin{array}{l} \text{note the inversion of} \\ \text{subscripts: } ij \rightarrow ji \end{array}$$

$$\begin{bmatrix} a_{11} & a_{12} & a_{13} \\ a_{21} & a_{22} & a_{23} \\ a_{31} & a_{32} & a_{33} \end{bmatrix} = \cfrac{1}{\begin{vmatrix} a_{11} & a_{12} & a_{13} \\ a_{21} & a_{22} & a_{23} \\ a_{31} & a_{32} & a_{33} \end{vmatrix}}$$

$$\begin{bmatrix} a_{22}a_{33} - a_{32}a_{23} & -a_{12}a_{33} + a_{32}a_{13} & a_{12}a_{23} - a_{22}a_{13} \\ -a_{21}a_{33} + a_{31}a_{23} & a_{11}a_{33} - a_{31}a_{13} & -a_{11}a_{23} + a_{21}a_{13} \\ a_{21}a_{32} - a_{31}a_{22} & -a_{11}a_{32} + a_{31}a_{12} & a_{11}a_{22} - a_{21}a_{12} \end{bmatrix}$$

(b)   The inverse exists only when $|A| \neq 0$, in which case $[A]$ is termed *nonsingular.*

(c)   The following identities are true[1]

$$AB = C \qquad \text{or} \qquad AB = C$$
$$A^{-1}AB = A^{-1}C \qquad ABB^{-1} = CB^{-1}$$
$$IB = A^{-1}C \qquad AI = CB^{-1}$$
$$B = A^{-1}C \qquad A = CB^{-1}$$

6   A set of simultaneous linear algebraic equations can be written simply in matrix form

$$y_1 = a_{11}x_1 + a_{12}x_2 + \cdots + a_{1n}x_n$$
$$y_2 = a_{21}x_1 + a_{22}x_2 + \cdots + a_{2n}x_n$$
$$\cdots \cdots \cdots \cdots \cdots \cdots \cdots$$
$$y_m = a_{m1}x_1 + a_{m2}x_2 + \cdots a_{mn}x_n$$

$$\begin{bmatrix} y_1 \\ y_2 \\ \cdot \\ y_m \end{bmatrix} = \begin{bmatrix} a_{11} & a_{12} & \cdots & a_{1n} \\ a_{21} & a_{22} & \cdots & a_{2n} \\ \cdots & \cdots & \cdots & \cdots \\ a_{m1} & a_{m2} & \cdots & a_{mn} \end{bmatrix} \begin{bmatrix} x_1 \\ x_2 \\ \cdot \\ x_n \end{bmatrix}$$

$$Y = AX$$

(a)   An alternate form is

$$[y_1 \quad y_2 \quad \cdots \quad y_n] = [x_1 \quad x_2 \quad \cdots \quad x_n] \begin{bmatrix} a_{11} & a_{21} & \cdots & a_{m1} \\ a_{12} & a_{22} & \cdots & a_{m2} \\ \cdots & \cdots & \cdots & \cdots \\ a_{1n} & a_{2n} & \cdots & a_{mn} \end{bmatrix}$$

$$Y = XB$$

Note that the rows and columns of $A$ and $B$ are interchanged. $B$ is defined as the transpose of $A$

$$B = A^t$$

[1] Since it is clear that we are discussing matrices the brackets are omitted to simplify the notation.

(b) If the number of equations is equal to the number of unknowns, $m = n$, and $A$ and $B$ are square.

(c) If $m = n$, we can solve for

$$Y = AX \qquad \text{or} \qquad Y = XB$$
$$A^{-1}Y = A^{-1}AX \qquad\qquad YB^{-1} = XBB^{-1}$$
$$A^{-1}Y = IX = X \qquad\qquad YB^{-1} = XI = X$$
$$X = A^{-1}Y \qquad\qquad X = YB^{-1}$$

(d) As an example,

$$\begin{bmatrix} y_1 \\ y_2 \end{bmatrix} = \begin{bmatrix} a_{11} & a_{12} \\ a_{21} & a_{22} \end{bmatrix} \begin{bmatrix} x_1 \\ x_2 \end{bmatrix} \qquad A^{-1} = \cfrac{1}{\begin{vmatrix} a_{11} & a_{12} \\ a_{21} & a_{22} \end{vmatrix}} \begin{bmatrix} a_{22} & -a_{12} \\ -a_{21} & a_{11} \end{bmatrix}$$

$$\begin{bmatrix} x_1 \\ x_2 \end{bmatrix} = \begin{bmatrix} a_{22} & -a_{12} \\ -a_{21} & a_{11} \end{bmatrix} \cfrac{1}{\begin{vmatrix} a_{11} & a_{12} \\ a_{21} & a_{22} \end{vmatrix}} \begin{bmatrix} y_1 \\ y_2 \end{bmatrix}$$

$$x_1 = \cfrac{a_{22}y_1 - a_{12}y_2}{\begin{vmatrix} a_{11} & a_{12} \\ a_{21} & a_{22} \end{vmatrix}} \qquad x_2 = \cfrac{-a_{21}y_1 + a_{11}y_2}{\begin{vmatrix} a_{11} & a_{12} \\ a_{21} & a_{22} \end{vmatrix}}$$

These solutions are the same as one would have obtained using Cramer's rule and determinants.

### 2.11.10  MATRIX–TRANSFORM SOLUTION OF MARKOV EQUATIONS

Using the above techniques of matrix algebra in conjunction with Laplace transforms allows us to derive a simple technique for solving a Markov system of differential equations. The Markov transition matrix for a three-state system is given in Table 2.13. The set of differential equations associated with this transition matrix is

$$\dot{P}_{s_0} + \lambda_{01}P_{s_0} = 0$$
$$\dot{P}_{s_1} + \lambda_{12}P_{s_1} - \lambda_{01}P_{s_0} = 0 \qquad\qquad (2.154)$$
$$\dot{P}_{s_2} - \lambda_{12}P_{s_1} = 0$$

**Table 2.13  A three-state transition matrix**

|  | $s_0$ | $s_1$ | $s_2$ |
|---|---|---|---|
| $s_0$ | $1 - \lambda_{01}\,\Delta t$ | $\lambda_{01}\,\Delta t$ | $0$ |
| $s_1$ | $0$ | $1 - \lambda_{12}\,\Delta t$ | $\lambda_{12}\,\Delta t$ |
| $s_2$ | $0$ | $0$ | $1$ |

If we take the Laplace transform of this set of equations and substitute the initial conditions $P_{s_0}(0)$, $P_{s_1}(0)$, $P_{s_2}(0)$, the result is

$$
\begin{aligned}
(s + \lambda_{01})P_{s_0}(s) + 0P_{s_1}(s) + 0P_{s_2}(s) &= P_{s_0}(0) \\
-\lambda_{01}P_{s_0}(s) + (s + \lambda_{12})P_{s_1}(s) + 0P_{s_2}(s) &= P_{s_1}(0) \\
0P_{s_0}(s) - \lambda_{12}P_{s_1}(s) + sP_{s_2}(s) &= P_{s_2}(0)
\end{aligned}
\tag{2.155}
$$

In matrix form these equations become

$$
\begin{bmatrix}
s + \lambda_{01} & 0 & 0 \\
-\lambda_{01} & s + \lambda_{12} & 0 \\
0 & -\lambda_{12} & s
\end{bmatrix}
\begin{bmatrix}
P_{s_1}(s) \\
P_{s_2}(s) \\
P_{s_3}(s)
\end{bmatrix}
=
\begin{bmatrix}
P_{s_0}(0) \\
P_{s_1}(0) \\
P_{s_2}(0)
\end{bmatrix}
\tag{2.156}
$$

or alternately

$$
[P_{s_0}(s) \quad P_{s_1}(s) \quad P_{s_2}(s)]
\begin{bmatrix}
s + \lambda_{01} & -\lambda_{01} & 0 \\
0 & s + \lambda_{12} & -\lambda_{12} \\
0 & 0 & s
\end{bmatrix}
$$
$$
= [P_{s_0}(0) \quad P_{s_1}(0) \quad P_{s_2}(0)] \tag{2.157}
$$

The $3 \times 3$ matrix, in Eq. (2.157), can be decomposed as shown below

$$
[A] =
\begin{bmatrix}
s + \lambda_{01} & -\lambda_{01} & 0 \\
0 & s + \lambda_{12} & -\lambda_{12} \\
0 & 0 & s
\end{bmatrix}
=
\begin{bmatrix}
s & 0 & 0 \\
0 & s & 0 \\
0 & 0 & s
\end{bmatrix}
+
\begin{bmatrix}
\lambda_{01} & -\lambda_{01} & 0 \\
0 & \lambda_{12} & \lambda_{12} \\
0 & 0 & 0
\end{bmatrix}
$$

$$
[A] =
\begin{bmatrix}
s & 0 & 0 \\
0 & s & 0 \\
0 & 0 & s
\end{bmatrix}
-
\left(
\begin{bmatrix}
1 - \lambda_{01} & \lambda_{01} & 0 \\
0 & 1 - \lambda_{12} & \lambda_{12} \\
0 & 0 & 1
\end{bmatrix}
-
\begin{bmatrix}
1 & 0 & 0 \\
0 & 1 & 0 \\
0 & 0 & 1
\end{bmatrix}
\right)
$$

and the $A$ matrix can be written as

$$
[A] = s[I] - [T - I] \tag{2.158}
$$

This matrix identity expresses the $A$ matrix in terms of the identity matrix, the operator $s$, and the $T$ matrix, which is the transition matrix with the $\Delta t$ terms deleted. Thus to solve for the probability matrix we write

$$
\begin{aligned}
[P_s(s)][A][A^{-1}] &= [P_s(0)][A^{-1}] \\
[P_s(s)] &= [P_s(0)](s[I] - [T - I])^{-1}
\end{aligned}
\tag{2.159}
$$

Although Eq. (2.159) was derived for the problem being discussed, it holds in general.  Computing $A^{-1}$ from the $A$ matrix

$$A^{-1} = \cfrac{1}{\begin{vmatrix} s + \lambda_{01} & -\lambda_{01} & 0 \\ 0 & s + \lambda_{12} & -\lambda_{12} \\ 0 & 0 & s \end{vmatrix}}$$

$$\times \begin{bmatrix} s(s + \lambda_{12}) & \lambda_{01}s & \lambda_{01}\lambda_{12} \\ 0 & s(s + \lambda_{01}) & \lambda_{12}(s + \lambda_{01}) \\ 0 & 0 & (s + \lambda_{01})(s + \lambda_{12}) \end{bmatrix}$$

$$= \begin{bmatrix} \cfrac{1}{s + \lambda_{01}} & \cfrac{\lambda_{01}}{(s + \lambda_{01})(s + \lambda_{12})} & \cfrac{\lambda_{01}\lambda_{12}}{s(s + \lambda_{01})(s + \lambda_{12})} \\ 0 & \cfrac{1}{s + \lambda_{12}} & \cfrac{\lambda_{12}}{s(s + \lambda_{12})} \\ 0 & 0 & \cfrac{1}{s} \end{bmatrix}$$

$$[P_{s_0}(s) \quad P_{s_1}(s) \quad P_{s_2}(s)] = [P_{s_0}(0) \quad P_{s_1}(0) \quad P_{s_2}(0)]A^{-1}$$

In the special case where $P_{s_0}(0) = 1$ and $P_{s_1}(0) = P_{s_2}(0) = 0$ the result becomes

$$P_{s_0}(s) = \frac{1}{s + \lambda_{01}}$$

$$P_{s_1}(s) = \frac{\lambda_{01}}{(s + \lambda_{01})(s + \lambda_{12})} \tag{2.160}$$

$$P_{s_2}(s) = \frac{\lambda_{01}\lambda_{12}}{s(s + \lambda_{01})(s + \lambda_{12})}$$

Note that only the coefficients in the first row of $A^{-1}$ need be computed to obtain Eq. (2.160) because of the special form of the $[P_s(0)]$ matrix. The time functions are found from Eqs. (2.160) by partial-fraction expansion and inversion of the transforms.  This method is discussed in further detail in Chap. 5.

## PROBLEMS

2.1  We wish to compute the probability of winning on the first roll of a pair of dice by throwing a seven or an eleven.
   (a)  Define a sample space for the sum of the two dice.
   (b)  Delineate the favorable and unfavorable outcomes.
   (c)  Compute the probability of winning and losing.
   (d)  List any assumptions you made in this problem.
2.2  Repeat Prob. 2.1 by considering a separate sample space for each die and assuming that the two form a set of joint probabilities.
2.3  Compute the probability of drawing four of a kind or four of the same suit in four draws with replacement from a bridge deck.
2.4  Compute the probability of being dealt four of a kind in a five-card poker hand.

**2.5** The following two theorems are known as De Morgan's theorems:

$$\overline{A + B + C} = \bar{A}\bar{B}\bar{C}$$
$$\overline{ABC} \qquad = \bar{A} + \bar{B} + \bar{C}$$

Prove these two theorems using a Venn diagram. Do these theorems hold for more than three events? Explain.

**2.6** Prove Eq. (2.12) by induction. *Hint:* Let $A_2 = B_1 + B_2$ in Eq. (2.11), expand, and generalize the result.

**2.7** Compute the probability of drawing a club, a spade, or a five in one draw from a deck of cards.

**2.8** Compute and sketch the density function for the number of heads thrown in five successive flips of a fair coin.

**2.9** Compute the distribution function for Prob. 2.8.

**2.10** Assume that 1 percent of all of a certain type of resistor are bad when purchased. What is the probability that a circuit with ten resistors has exactly one bad resistor?

**2.11** A transistor amplifier contains three transistors, nine resistors, and six capacitors. The percentage of initially defective transistors, resistors and capacitors are 5, 1, and 3 percent. What is the probability of exactly one defective component? At least one defective component?

**2.12** Sketch the density function for defective resistors for Prob. 2.10.

**2.13** Assume that current surges in an electric circuit trip the circuit breaker on the average once per 1,000 hr of operation. What are the probabilities of having 0, 1, 2, 3, 4, 5 trips in 3,000 hr of operation?

**2.14** Referring to Prob. 2.13, suppose that at $t_0$ the breaker opens and is reset. What is the probability that the waiting time till the next trip will be 500, 1,000, 2,000 hr?

**2.15** Can the function shown be a probability density function? Explain. If so, compute the corresponding distribution function. What is the probability that $a - b/2 < \mathbf{x} \le a + b/2$?

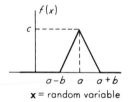

**x** = random variable

**Fig. P 2.15**

**2.16** Suppose a resistor has a resistance $R$ with mean of 100 ohms and a tolerance of 5 ohms.

(a) If the resistance values are normally distributed with $\mu = 100$ ohms and $\sigma = 5$ ohms, sketch $f(R)$.

(b) Assume that the resistance values have a Rayleigh distribution. If the peak is to occur at 100 ohms, what is the value of $K$? Plot the Rayleigh distribution on the same graph as the normal distribution of part $a$.

2.17 A certain resistor has a nominal value (mean) of 100 ohms.
  (a) Assume a normal distribution and compute the value of $\sigma$ if we wish $P(95 < \mathbf{R} < 105) = 0.95$.
  (b) Repeat part $a$ assuming a Weibull distribution and specify the values of $K$ and $m$.
  (c) Plot the density function for parts $a$ and $b$ on the same graph paper.
2.18 Derive the moment computations given in Table 2.4.
2.19 Derive the moment-generating functions given in Table 2.4.
2.20 Let a component have a good, a fair, and a bad state. Assume the transition probabilities of failure are: from good to fair, $\lambda_{gf}\,\Delta t$, from good to bad, $\lambda_{gb}\,\Delta t$, and from fair to bad, $\lambda_{fb}\,\Delta t$.
  (a) Formulate a Markov model.
  (b) Compute the probabilities of being in any state.
2.21 Can the volume shown in the figure be a joint density function? Explain.

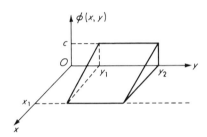

**Fig. P 2.21**

2.22 For the density given in Prob. 2.21, where $y_1 = 2$, $y_2 = 6$, $x_1 = 4$, compute:

  (a) $P_r(2 < \mathbf{x} \le 3, 2 < \mathbf{y} \le 3)$     (b) $P_r(\mathbf{x} > 2)$
  (c) $P_r(\mathbf{y} < 5)$     (d) $P_r(\mathbf{y} < 5 | \mathbf{x} > 2)$
  (e) $E(\mathbf{x})$     (f) $E(\mathbf{y})$
  (g) var $\mathbf{x}$     (h) var $\mathbf{y}$
  (i) cov $(\mathbf{x},\mathbf{y})$     (j) $\rho$

2.23 The radius of a ball bearing has a normal distribution such that $r_{\min} < \mathbf{r} < r_{\max}$. Compute the probability density function for its volume.
2.24 A rectangular distribution is defined in Sec. 2.6.4. Compute moment estimates for the parameters $a$ and $b$.
2.25 Derive MLE's for Prob. 2.24
2.26 Solve the following differential equations:

  (a) $\dfrac{dy}{dt} + 2y = 0$     (b) $\dfrac{d^2y}{dt^2} + \dfrac{4dy}{dt} + 3y = 0$
  $\qquad y(0) = -1$     $\qquad y(0) = 0,\ \dot{y}(0) = 10$
  (c) $\dfrac{d^2y}{dt^2} + 4y = 0$     (d) $\dfrac{dy}{dt} + 2y = 5e^{-t}$
  $\qquad y(0) = -5$     $\qquad y(0) = 0$

(e) $\dfrac{dy}{dt} + 2y = 5e^{-2t}$

$y(0) = 0$

(f) $\dfrac{dy}{dt} + 2y = 5\sin\omega t$

$y(0) = 0$

(g) $\dfrac{d^2y}{dt^2} + \dfrac{2dy}{dt} + 2 = 0$

$y(0) = 1,\ \dot{y}(0) = 2$

(h) $\dfrac{d^2y}{dt^2} + \dfrac{2dy}{dt} + y = e^{-t}$

$y(0) = 0,\ \dot{y}(0) = 0$

2.27  Solve the differential equations given in Prob. 2.26 using Laplace transform techniques.

2.28  Prove the Laplace transform theorems given in Table 2.12.

2.29  Solve a set of three simultaneous equations using matrix methods.

2.30  Set up and solve a four-state Markov problem using the techniques of Sec. 2.11.10.

# combinatorial reliability

## 3.1  INTRODUCTION

In performing the reliability analysis of a complex system, it is almost impossible to treat the system in its entirety.  The logical approach is to decompose the system into functional entities composed of units, subsystems, or components.  Each entity is assumed to have two states, one good and one bad.[1]  (Sometimes three or more states are necessary, e.g., an electric component may be good or may fail as an open or short circuit.  See Sec. 3.8.)  The subdivision generates a block-diagram description of system operation.  Models are then formulated to fit this logical structure, and the calculus of probability is used to compute the system reliability in terms of the subdivision reliabilities.  Series and parallel structures often occur, and their reliability can be described very simply.  In many cases the structure is of a more complicated nature, and more general techniques are needed.  It is assumed that each functional entity is independent of the others in the aforementioned models, but in many cases this is untrue.  Dependent failures occur in standby systems, interactive systems, and systems which respond to a common

---

[1] It is not essential that the system experience a catastrophic failure to be called bad.  For example, it may be convenient to define the gain of a particular amplifier as good if it exceeds 50 and bad if it is below 50.

environmental change.   The models which govern these cases contain time-dependent conditional probabilities.   When dependent failures are present, it is generally more convenient to use the Markov model approach discussed in Chap. 5.

The formulation of a structural-reliability model can be difficult in a large, sophisticated system and requires much approximation and judgment.   This is best done by a system engineer or someone closely associated with him who knows the system operation thoroughly.

The mathematical background for this chapter is covered in Secs. 2.1 to 2.4 and parts of 2.5.

## 3.2  SERIES CONFIGURATION

The simplest and perhaps most common structure in reliability analysis is the *series configuration*.   In the series case the *functional* operation of the system depends on the proper operation of all system components. A series string of Christmas tree lights is an obvious example.   The word "functional" must be stressed, since the electric or mechanical configuration of the circuit may differ from the logical structure.   For example, an alarm light, battery, and three electric switches may be connected in series to protect personnel in the neighborhood of a piece of high-voltage equipment.   When all three switches are closed, the alarm light goes on to warn others to stay clear.   In a similar case, three thermal fuse elements could be substituted for the switches to detect the overheating of a large electric motor.   In the former case *all* switches must close for the alarm light to go on, which represents successful operation.   In the latter case, failure of one fuse to melt when an excessive temperature is reached does not necessarily lead to unsuccessful operation since *any one* of the fuses will break the circuit and turn off the safe-operation lamp. Although both are series electric circuits, only the former is described by a series reliability model.

A series reliability configuration will be portrayed by the block-diagram representation shown in Fig. 3.1a, or the reliability graph shown in Fig. 3.1b.   In either case, a single path from cause to effect is created.   Failure of any component is represented by removal of the component, which interrupts the path and thereby causes the system to fail.

The system shown in Fig. 3.1 is divided into $n$ series-connected units. This system can represent $n$ parts in an electronic amplifier, the $n$ subsystems in an aircraft autopilot, or the $n$ operations necessary to place a satellite in orbit.   The event signifying the success of the $n$th unit will be $x_n$, and $\bar{x}_n$ will represent the failure of the $n$th unit.   The probability that unit $n$ is successful will be $P(x_n)$, and the probability that unit $n$ fails will

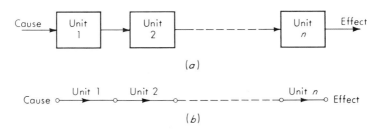

**Fig. 3.1** Series reliability configuration. (*a*) Reliability block diagram; (*b*) reliability graph.

be $P(\bar{x}_n)$. The probability of system success is denoted by $P_s$. In keeping with the definition of reliability in Chap. 1, $P_s \equiv R$, where $R$ stands for the system reliability. The probability of system failure is

$$P_f = 1 - P_s$$

Since the series configuration requires that all units operate successfully for system success, the event representing system success is the intersection of $x_1, x_2, \ldots, x_n$. The probability of this event is given by

$$R = P_s = P(x_1 x_2 x_3 \cdots x_n) \tag{3.1}$$

Expansion of Eq. (3.1) yields

$$P_s = P(x_1)P(x_2|x_1)P(x_3|x_1 x_2) \cdots P(x_n|x_1 x_2 \cdots x_{n-1}) \tag{3.2}$$

The expression appearing in Eq. (3.2) contains conditional probabilities, which must be evaluated with care. For example, $P(x_3|x_1 x_2)$ is the probability of success of unit 3 evaluated under the condition that units 1 and 2 are operating. In the case where the power dissipation from units 1 and 2 affects the temperature of unit 3 and thereby its failure rate, a conditional probability is involved. If the units do not interact, the failures are independent, and Eq. (3.2) simplifies to

$$P_s = P(x_1)P(x_2)P(x_3) \cdots P(x_n) \tag{3.3}$$

An alternative approach is to compute the probability of failure. The system fails if *any* of the units fail, and therefore we have a union of events

$$P_f = P(\bar{x}_1 + \bar{x}_2 + \bar{x}_3 + \cdots + \bar{x}_n) \tag{3.4}$$

Expansion of Eq. (3.4) yields

$$P_f = [P(\bar{x}_1) + P(\bar{x}_2) + P(\bar{x}_3) + \cdots + P(\bar{x}_n)] - [P(\bar{x}_1 \bar{x}_2) + P(\bar{x}_1 \bar{x}_3)$$
$$+ \cdots + \underset{i \neq j}{P(\bar{x}_i \bar{x}_j)}] + \cdots + (-1)^{n-1}[P(\bar{x}_1 \bar{x}_2 \cdots \bar{x}_n)] \tag{3.5}$$

Since

$$P_s = 1 - P_f \tag{3.6}$$

the probability of system success becomes

$$\begin{aligned}
P_s = 1 &- P(\bar{x}_1) - P(\bar{x}_2) - P(\bar{x}_3) - \cdots - P(\bar{x}_n) \\
&+ P(\bar{x}_1)P(\bar{x}_2|\bar{x}_1) + P(\bar{x}_1)P(\bar{x}_3|\bar{x}_1) + \cdots + P(\bar{x}_i)P(\bar{x}_i|\bar{x}_j) \\
&\qquad\qquad\qquad\qquad\qquad\qquad\qquad\qquad\qquad\quad {}_{i \neq j} \\
&- \cdots + (-1)^n P(\bar{x}_1)P(\bar{x}_2|\bar{x}_1) \cdots P(\bar{x}_n|\bar{x}_1 \cdots \bar{x}_{n-1}) \tag{3.7}
\end{aligned}$$

The reliability expression in Eq. (3.7) is equivalent to that in Eq. (3.2) but is much more difficult to evaluate because of the many terms involved. Equation (3.7) also involves conditional probabilities; for example, $P(\bar{x}_3|\bar{x}_1\bar{x}_2)$ is the probability that unit 3 will fail given the fact that units 1 and 2 have failed. In the case of independence $P(\bar{x}_3|\bar{x}_1\bar{x}_2)$ becomes $P(\bar{x}_3)$, and the other conditional probability terms in Eq. (3.7) simplify, yielding

$$\begin{aligned}
P_s = 1 &- P(\bar{x}_1) - P(\bar{x}_2) - P(\bar{x}_3) - \cdots - P(\bar{x}_n) \\
&+ P(\bar{x}_1)P(\bar{x}_2) + P(\bar{x}_1)P(\bar{x}_3) + \cdots + P(\bar{x}_i)P(\bar{x}_j) \\
&\qquad\qquad\qquad\qquad\qquad\qquad\qquad\qquad\quad {}_{i \neq j} \\
&- \cdots + (-1)^n P(\bar{x}_1)P(\bar{x}_2) \cdots P(\bar{x}_n) \tag{3.8}
\end{aligned}$$

Equation (3.8) is still more complex than Eq. (3.3). It is interesting to note that the reliability of any particular configuration may be computed by considering either the probability of success or the probability of failure. In a very complex structure both approaches may be used at different stages of the computation.

The reliability of a series system is always worse than the poorest component and is generally a disappointment from a reliability standpoint. As an example let us consider a magnetic-core computer memory. The size of the memory is $100 \times 100$, or a total of $10^4$ cores. The reliability of each memory cell is $p$. Assuming that all cells are used in a particular computation and that any cell error is a computational error, the computation reliability is given by $p^{10^4}$. If we wish an error rate of 1 in $10^3$ computations, we can solve for the required value of $p$. Letting $q = 1 - p$,

$$p^{10^4} = (1 - q)^{10^4} = 0.999$$

Since $q \ll 1$,

$$(1 - q)^{10^4} \approx 1 - 10^4 q = 0.999$$
$$q = 10^{-7}$$

Thus, the failure reliability must be four orders of magnitude smaller than the computational error probability.

## 3.3 PARALLEL CONFIGURATION

In many systems several signal paths perform the same operation. If the system configuration is such that failure of one or more paths still allows the remaining path or paths to perform properly, the system can be represented by a parallel model.

A block diagram and reliability graph for a parallel system are shown in Fig. 3.2. There are $n$ paths connecting input to output, and all units must fail in order to interrupt all the paths. This is sometimes called a redundant configuration, but in this book the term "redundant" is used only when the system configuration is deliberately changed to produce additional parallel paths, in order to improve the reliability of the original system. Thus, a parallel model may occur as a result of the basic system structure or may be produced by using redundancy in a reliability design or redesign of the system.

In a parallel configuration the system is successful if any one of the parallel channels is successful. The probability of success is given by the probability of the union of the $n$ successful events

$$P_s = P(x_1 + x_2 + x_3 + \cdots + x_n) \tag{3.9}$$

Expansion of Eq. (3.9) yields

$$\begin{aligned} P_s = &[P(x_1) + P(x_2) + P(x_3) + \cdots + P(x_n)] \\ &- [P(x_1x_2) + P(x_1x_3) + \cdots + \underset{i \neq j}{P(x_ix_j)}] \\ &+ \cdots + (-1)^{n-1}P(x_1x_2 \cdots x_n) \end{aligned} \tag{3.10}$$

The conditional probabilities which occur in Eq. (3.10) when the *intersection terms* are expanded must be interpreted properly, as in the previous section [see Eq. (3.7)]. A simpler formula can be developed in the parallel case if one deals with the probability of system failure. System

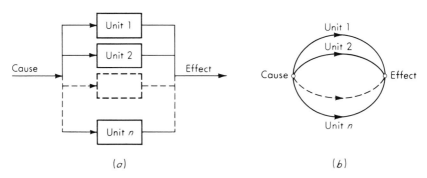

(a)  (b)

**Fig. 3.2**  Parallel reliability configuration.  (a) Block diagram; (b) reliability graph.

failure occurs if *all* the system units fail, yielding the probability of their intersection

$$P_f = P(\bar{x}_1\bar{x}_2\bar{x}_3 \cdot \cdot \cdot \bar{x}_n) \tag{3.11}$$

where

$$P_s = 1 - P_f \tag{3.12}$$

Substitution of Eq. (3.11) into Eq. (3.12) and expansion yields

$$P_s = 1 - P(\bar{x}_1)P(\bar{x}_2|\bar{x}_1)P(\bar{x}_3|\bar{x}_1\bar{x}_2) \cdot \cdot \cdot P(\bar{x}_n|\bar{x}_1\bar{x}_2 \cdot \cdot \cdot \bar{x}_{n-1}) \tag{3.13}$$

If the unit failures are independent, Eq. (3.13) simplifies to

$$P_s = 1 - P(\bar{x}_1)P(\bar{x}_2) \cdot \cdot \cdot P(\bar{x}_n) \tag{3.14}$$

A summary of the results obtained for series and parallel configurations is given in Table 3.1. In both cases the simpler computational formula is given.

As an example of how the parallel structure improves reliability we shall consider the reliability of a stable-platform inertial navigation system. In general, a stable platform includes gyros, accelerometers, and a three-axis position-control system. We shall focus our attention on the gyro reliability, assuming that the other parts of the system do not fail. A high-quality military system would use three single-degree-of-freedom

**Table 3.1  Reliability computations for series and parallel configurations**

| Configuration | Failures | Reliability expression $P_s$ |
|---|---|---|
| Series <br> $P(x_1)=p_1$  $P(x_2)=p_2$  $P(x_n)=p_n$ | Dependent | $P(x_1)P(x_2|x_1)P(x_3|x_1x_2)$ <br> $\cdot \cdot \cdot P(x_n|x_1x_2 \cdot \cdot \cdot x_{n-1})$ |
| | Independent | $\prod\limits_{i=1}^{n} P(x_i)$ |
| | Identical units | $p^n$ |
| Parallel <br> $P(x_1)=p_1$ <br> $P(x_2)=p_2$ <br> $P(x_3)=p_3$ <br> $P(x_n)=p_n$ | Dependent | $1 - P(\bar{x}_1)P(\bar{x}_2|\bar{x}_1)P(\bar{x}_3|\bar{x}_1\bar{x}_2)$ <br> $\cdot \cdot \cdot P(\bar{x}_n|\bar{x}_1\bar{x}_2 \cdot \cdot \cdot \bar{x}_{n-1})$ |
| | Independent | $1 - \prod\limits_{i=1}^{n} P(\bar{x}_i)$ |
| | Identical units | $1 - (1 - p)^n$ |

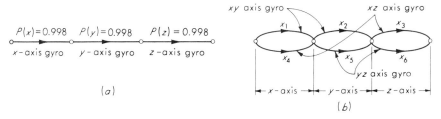

**Fig. 3.3**  Comparison of stable-platform reliability for two different systems.    (a) Three single-degree-of-freedom gyros; (b) three two-degree-of-freedom gyros.

gyros, each gyro establishing one of the three inertial reference axes $x$, $y$, and $z$.   Assuming that each gyro costs \$15,000 and has an MTTF of 5,000 hr, the gyros cost a total of \$45,000 and have a reliability of 0.998 for a 10-hr mission.[1]   Since each gyro must operate for system success, the series structure shown in Fig. 3.3a holds.   The system reliability is given by

$$P(x)P(y)P(z) = 0.998^3 = (1 - 0.002)^3 \approx 1 - 3 \times 0.002 = 0.994$$

In a commercial system the \$45,000 cost for gyros is prohibitive and we want to use three cheaper two-degree-of-freedom gyros costing \$2,000 each and having an MTTF of 1,000 hr.   The total gyro cost would be \$6,000, and the reliability of each gyro would be 0.990.   Since each gyro establishes two reference directions, proper orientation of the three gyros results in two measurements for each reference axis.   If we assume that the two reference axes in each gyro fail independently with a reliability given by 0.990, appropriate utilization of the signals can lead to the reliability graph of Fig. 3.3b.   The

$$P(x \text{ axis good}) = P(x_1 + x_4) = 1 - P(\bar{x}_1\bar{x}_4) = 1 - 0.01^2 = 0.9999$$

The reliability of the overall system is given by

$$P(x \text{ axis good}) \, P(y \text{ axis good}) \, P(z \text{ axis good}) = 0.9999^3$$
$$= (1 - 0.0001)^3 \approx 1 - 0.0003 = 0.9997$$

Thus, the cheaper system is more reliable because of the redundancy afforded by the two degrees of freedom.   (The assumption of independence of failures is open to challenge and will be discussed in the problems at the end of the chapter.)   It is important to note that some of the price advantage of the cheaper gyros will be offset by more frequent replace-

---

[1] If the failure distribution of gyros is exponential, $f(t) = \lambda e^{-\lambda t}$ and $E(t) = 1/\lambda$. Thus, $1/\lambda = 5,000$ hr.   The reliability function is $R(t) = 1 - \int_0^t f(\xi) \, d\xi = e^{-\lambda t} = e^{-t/(5 \times 10^3)}$.   For 10 hr $e^{-t/(5 \times 10^3)} \approx 1 - t/(5 \times 10^3) = 1 - \frac{10}{5} \times 10^{-3} = 0.998$.

ment and higher maintenance costs when the system is operated over a long period of time.

## 3.4   AN $r$–OUT–OF–$n$ CONFIGURATION

In many problems the system operates if $r$ out of $n$ units function, e.g., a bridge supported by $n$ cables, $r$ of which are necessary to support the maximum load.   If each of the $n$ units is identical, the probability of exactly $r$ successes out of $n$ units is given by Eq. (2.27)

$$B(r;n,p) = \binom{n}{r} p^r(1 - p)^{n-r} \qquad \text{for } r = 0, 1, 2, \ldots, n \qquad (3.15)$$

where $p$ is the probability of success of any unit.   The system will succeed if $r, r + 1, \ldots, n - 1$, or $n$ units succeed.   The probability of system success is given in Eq. (2.28)

$$P_s = \sum_{k=r}^{n} \binom{n}{k} p^k(1 - p)^{n-k} \qquad (3.16)$$

If the units all differ, Eqs. (3.15) and (3.16) no longer hold, and one is faced with the explicit enumeration of all possible successful combinations.   One can draw a reliability graph as an aid.   The graph will have $\binom{n}{r}$ parallel paths.   Each parallel path will contain $r$ different elements, corresponding to one of the combinations of $n$ things $r$ at a time.   Such a graph for a four-out-of-five system is given in Fig. 3.4.   The system succeeds if *any* path succeeds.   Each path success depends on the success of four elements

$$P_s = P(x_1x_2x_3x_4 + x_1x_2x_3x_5 + x_1x_2x_4x_5 + x_1x_3x_4x_5 + x_2x_3x_4x_5) \qquad (3.17)$$

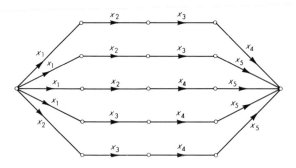

**Fig. 3.4**   Reliability graph for a four-out-of-five system.

Expanding Eq. (3.17) in terms of an intermediate set of variables gives

$$A_1 = x_1 x_2 x_3 x_4 \qquad A_2 = x_1 x_2 x_3 x_5 \qquad A_3 = x_1 x_2 x_4 x_5 \qquad A_4 = x_1 x_3 x_4 x_5$$
$$A_5 = x_2 x_3 x_4 x_5$$
$$P_s = P(A_1 + A_2 + A_3 + A_4 + A_5) = +[P(A_1) + P(A_2) + P(A_3)$$
$$+ P(A_4) + P(A_5)] - \sum_i \sum_{\substack{j \\ i \neq j}} P(A_i A_j) + \sum_i \sum_j \sum_k P(A_i A_j A_k)$$
$$- \sum_i \sum_j \sum_k \sum_l P(A_i A_j A_k A_l) + P(A_1 A_2 A_3 A_4 A_5)$$

In all terms except the $A_i$'s taken singly each $x_i$ term occurs. For example, $P(A_1 A_2) = P[(x_1 x_2 x_3 x_4)(x_1 x_2 x_3 x_5)]$ which by definition reduces to $P(x_1 x_2 x_3 x_4 x_5)$. Thus, the equation simplifies to

$$P_s = P(A_1) + P(A_2) + P(A_3) + P(A_4) + P(A_5) - \binom{5}{2} P(B)$$
$$+ \binom{5}{3} P(B) - \binom{5}{4} P(B) + \binom{5}{5} P(B)$$

where

$$B = x_1 x_2 x_3 x_4 x_5$$

Thus,

$$P_s = P(x_1 x_2 x_3 x_4) + P(x_1 x_2 x_3 x_5) + P(x_1 x_2 x_4 x_5) + P(x_1 x_3 x_4 x_5)$$
$$+ P(x_2 x_3 x_4 x_5) - 4P(x_1 x_2 x_3 x_4 x_5) \quad (3.18)$$

It is easy to check Eq. (3.18). For independent, identical elements Eq. (3.18) gives $P_s = 5p^4 - 4p^5$. From Eq. (3.16) we obtain

$$P_s = \sum_{k=4}^{5} \binom{5}{k} p^k (1 - p)^{5-k} = \binom{5}{4} p^4 (1 - p)^1 + \binom{5}{5} p^5 (1 - p)^0$$
$$= 5p^4 - 4p^5$$

### 3.5 AN AIRCRAFT ELECTRIC SYSTEM

As an example, we assume that it is necessary to build a highly reliable power source for an aircraft electric system. The maximum electric load to be supplied is assumed to be 10 kw, the average load 7 kw, and the vital functions alone may be run with only 5 kw. Three different generating means are being considered, use of a single 10-kw generator, use of two 5-kw generators with parallel outputs, and use of three 3.5-kw generators with parallel outputs. Actually three modes of system operation exist, full rated power, average power, and emergency power. The expressions for the probability of successful operation (reliability) in each mode are

**Table 3.2  Comparison of the reliability of three aircraft electric systems†**

| System | 10 $kw$ maximum-load mode | 7 $kw$ average-load mode | 5 $kw$ emergency mode |
|---|---|---|---|
| One 10-kw generator | $x_1$  $P_s = p$ | $x_1$  $P_s = p$ | $x_1$  $P_s = p$ |
| Two 5-kw generators | $x_1$  $x_2$  $P_s = p^2$ | $x_1$  $x_2$  $P_s = p^2$ | $x_1$, $x_2$  $P_s = 2p - p^2$ |
| Three 3.5-kw generators | $x_1$  $x_2$  $x_3$  $P_s = p^3$ | $x_1$, $x_2$, $x_3$, $x_1$  $P_s = 3p^2 - 2p^3$ | $x_1$, $x_2$, $x_3$, $x_1$  $P_s = 3p^2 - 2p^3$ |

† It is assumed that each generator has a $P_s$ of $p$.

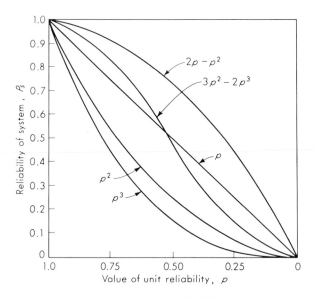

**Fig. 3.5** Comparison of several reliability functions for an aircraft electric system.

given in Table 3.2. Each of the three systems has advantages and disadvantages with regard to size, weight, cost, and performance, and to arrive at a wise decision, the reliability must also be considered. The five different reliability expressions developed in Table 3.2 are compared in Fig. 3.5. Note that the series configurations are always poorer than a single element. The system with a two-parallel-element model is the best. The two-out-of-three system is better than a single element as long as $0.5 < p \leq 1.0$ and becomes worse than a single element for $0 \leq p < 0.5$.

## 3.6 GENERAL TECHNIQUES

It is obvious that the structural nature of practical systems will generally be such that neither a pure series nor a pure parallel reliability model is appropriate. In these cases, a more general technique must be used.

### 3.6.1 INSPECTION METHODS

If the system under study involves a small number of units, it is easy to write down the combinatorial reliability expression for the system by inspection. Two units function either in a series or parallel manner. When three or more units are considered, the situation becomes more interesting. All units may be in series, all in parallel, two in series forming one path and the third unit forming a parallel path, or two in parallel connected in series with the third unit. All possible one-, two-, and three-element configurations along with their respective reliability expressions are given in Table 3.3 and all four-element cases in Table 3.4. The reliability expressions given in these tables may be written by inspection. For example, case $e$ of Table 3.3 can be viewed as a parallel combination of two units, where the probability of failure for one path is $P(\bar{x}_3)$ and for the other path is $P(\bar{x}_1 + \bar{x}_2)$. Thus, the probability of success of the combination is

$$P_s = 1 - P[(\bar{x}_1 + \bar{x}_2)(\bar{x}_3)] = 1 - [P(\bar{x}_1) + P(\bar{x}_2) \\ - P(\bar{x}_1\bar{x}_2)]\{P[x_3|(\bar{x}_1 + \bar{x}_2)]\} \quad (3.19)$$

If the units are independent, the expression simplifies, yielding

$$P_s = 1 - [P(\bar{x}_1) + P(\bar{x}_2) - P(\bar{x}_1)P(\bar{x}_2)]P(\bar{x}_3) \quad (3.20)$$

If in addition the units are independent and have identical reliabilities $p$,

$$P_s = 1 - [2P(\bar{x}) - P(\bar{x})^2]P(\bar{x}) \quad (3.21)$$

**Table 3.3   Reliability configurations for one, two, and three elements**

| *Configuration* | *Type of failure* | *Reliability expression* $P_s$ |
|---|---|---|
| (a) | | $P(x_1) = p$ |
| (b) | Dependent different units (DDU) | $P(x_1 x_2)$ |
| | Independent identical units (IIU) | $p^2$ |
| (c) | DDU | $1 - P(\bar{x}_1 \bar{x}_2)$ |
| | IIU | $2p - p^2$ |
| (d) | DDU | $P(x_1 x_2 x_3)$ |
| | IIU | $p^3$ |
| (e) | DDU | $1 - P[(\bar{x}_1 + \bar{x}_2)(\bar{x}_3)]$ |
| | IIU | $p + p^2 - p^3$ |
| (f) | DDU | $P[(x_3)(x_1 + x_2)]$ |
| | IIU | $2p^2 - p^3$ |
| (g) | DDU | $1 - P(\bar{x}_1 \bar{x}_2 \bar{x}_3)$ |
| | IIU | $3p - 3p^2 + p^3$ |

Substituting $P(x) = p$ and $P(\bar{x}) = 1 - p$ into Eq. (3.17) yields

$$P_s = p + p^2 - p^3 \qquad (3.22)$$

The computation could also have been made by considering that the system is successful if path $x_3$ or path $x_1 \, x_2$ is successful; thus

$$P_s = P(x_3 + x_1 x_2) \qquad (3.23)$$

**Table 3.4    Reliability configurations for four elements**

| *Configuration* | *Type of failure* | *Reliability expression $P_s$* |
|---|---|---|
| (h) | DDU | $P(x_1 x_2 x_3 x_4)$ |
| | IIU | $p^4$ |
| (i) | DDU | $P[x_3 x_4 (x_1 + x_2)]$ |
| | IIU | $2p^3 - p^4$ |
| (j) | DDU | $P[x_4 (x_1 + x_2 + x_3)]$ |
| | IIU | $3p^2 - 3p^3 + p^4$ |
| (k) | DDU | $P(x_1 + x_2 + x_3 x_4)$ |
| | IIU | $2p - 2p^3 + p^4$ |
| (l) | DDU | $P(x_1 + x_2 x_3 x_4)$ |
| | IIU | $p + p^3 - p^4$ |
| (m) | DDU | $P(x_1 x_3 + x_2 x_4)$ |
| | IIU | $2p^2 - p^4$ |
| (n) | DDU | $P[(x_1 + x_2)(x_3 + x_4)]$ |
| | IIU | $(2p - p^2)^2$ |
| (o) | DDU | $P[x_1 (x_2 + x_3 x_4)]$ |
| | IIU | $p^2 + p^3 - p^4$ |
| (p) | DDU | $P[x_1 + x_2 (x_3 + x_4)]$ |
| | IIU | $p + 2p^2 - 3p^3 + p^4$ |
| (q) | DDU | $1 - P(\bar{x}_1 \bar{x}_2 \bar{x}_3 \bar{x}_4)$ |
| | IIU | $4p - 6p^2 + 4p^3 - p^4$ |

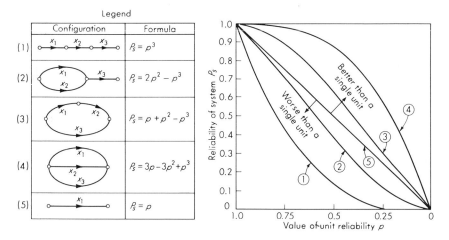

**Fig. 3.6**   Reliability comparison of various three-element configurations.

If it is assumed that the units are independent and identical, Eq. (3.23) immediately reduces to Eq. (3.22).   The other reliability expressions in Tables 3.3 and 3.4 are derived in a similar manner.   Comparisons between the reliability expressions developed in Tables 3.3 and 3.4 may be made if all the units are identical and $p$ is taken as a parameter.   For example, the reliability of the three-element configuration is compared with a single element in Fig. 3.6.   The parallel-type configurations are of course superior to the single unit, and the series-type configurations are inferior.   Curves 1 and 4 have a reversed symmetry about curve 5. For curve 4 the initial slope is zero and the final slope is 3, and the converse is true for curve 1.   These curves imply that there may be a choice among several configurations but such a choice may not be available, since at times it is operationally difficult or economically not feasible to consider more than one configuration.

### 3.6.2  EVENT–SPACE METHODS

In order to apply the event-space method, a list of all possible logical occurrences in the system must be made.   The list is then separated into favorable events and unfavorable ones.   If the list is properly prepared, all the events are mutually exclusive.   The probability of success is then merely the sum of the occurrence probabilities of each successful event. The reliability could also be computed by first finding the probability of failure, which is given by the sum of the occurrence probabilities of each of the unsuccessful events.   This technique is illustrated in the following example.

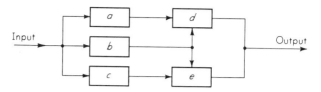

**Fig. 3.7**   Complex reliability structure.

The reliability block diagram of a system with a complex structure is given by Fig. 3.7. The tabulation of the event space for this problem requires a fair amount of care and bookkeeping skill to ensure that all events listed are mutually exclusive and that no events are omitted. A systematic tabulating and checking procedure was used to set up the event space given in Table 3.5. Group 0 of the table represents no failures, and the number of terms in this group is given by $\binom{5}{0}$. Group 1 represents one failure and contains $\binom{5}{1}$ elements. (Note that the events within each group are also ordered in a systematic manner.) In general the total number of points in the event space will be given by $2^n$, where $n$ is the number of units in the system. The favorability of an event may be determined by inspecting the reliability block diagram or reliability graph. The failed units in the event in question are deleted from the diagram, and if the remaining structure has at least one continuous path connecting the input and output, the event is successful. All events which are not successful are of course unsuccessful. All the circled events in Table 3.5 are unsuccessful ones, and the uncircled ones are all successful. Thus the probability of success is given by

$$P_s = P(E_1 + E_2 + E_3 + E_4 + E_5 + E_6 + E_7 + E_8 + E_9 + E_{10}$$
$$+ E_{11} + E_{12} + E_{13} + E_{14} + E_{15} + E_{19} + E_{22} + E_{23} + E_{25}) \quad (3.24)$$

Since all these events are *mutually exclusive*, the probability of the union of these events is the sum of the probabilities of each event taken separately. If we assume that all units are identical, and that the units have a probability of success $p$ and a probability of failure $1 - p$, Eq. (3.24) reduces to

$$P_s = p^5 + 5p^4(1 - p) + 9p^3(1 - p)^2 + 4p^2(1 - p)^3$$

Simplification yields

$$P_s = p^5 - p^4 - 3p^3 + 4p^2 \quad (3.25)$$

Table 3.5    Event space for the system of Fig. 3.7

| Group 0 | Group 2 | Group 3 | Group 4 |
|---|---|---|---|
| $E_1 = abcde$ | $E_7 = \bar{a}bcde$ | $\boxed{E_{17} = ab\bar{c}\bar{d}\bar{e}}$ | $\boxed{E_{27} = a\bar{b}\bar{c}d\bar{e}}$ |
| **Group 1** | $E_8 = \bar{a}b\bar{c}de$ | $\boxed{E_{18} = a\bar{b}c\bar{d}\bar{e}}$ | $E_{28} = \bar{a}b\bar{c}d\bar{e}$ |
| $E_2 = \bar{a}bcde$ | $E_9 = \bar{a}bc\bar{d}e$ | $E_{19} = a\bar{b}\bar{c}d\bar{e}$ | $E_{29} = \bar{a}bc\bar{d}\bar{e}$ |
| $E_3 = a\bar{b}cde$ | $E_{10} = \bar{a}bcd\bar{e}$ | $\boxed{E_{20} = a\bar{b}\bar{c}\bar{d}e}$ | $E_{30} = \bar{a}b\bar{c}\bar{d}\bar{e}$ |
| $E_4 = ab\bar{c}de$ | $E_{11} = a\bar{b}\bar{c}de$ | $\boxed{E_{21} = \bar{a}bc\bar{d}\bar{e}}$ | $E_{31} = \bar{a}\bar{b}c\bar{d}e$ |
| $E_5 = abc\bar{d}e$ | $E_{12} = a\bar{b}c\bar{d}e$ | $E_{22} = \bar{a}b\bar{c}d\bar{e}$ | **Group 5** |
| $E_6 = abcd\bar{e}$ | $E_{13} = a\bar{b}cd\bar{e}$ | $E_{23} = \bar{a}b\bar{c}\bar{d}e$ | $\boxed{E_{32} = \bar{a}\bar{b}\bar{c}\bar{d}\bar{e}}$ |
|  | $E_{14} = ab\bar{c}\bar{d}e$ | $\boxed{E_{24} = \bar{a}\bar{b}c\bar{d}\bar{e}}$ |  |
|  | $E_{15} = ab\bar{c}d\bar{e}$ | $E_{25} = \bar{a}\bar{b}cd\bar{e}$ |  |
|  | $\boxed{E_{16} = abc\bar{d}\bar{e}}$ | $\boxed{E_{26} = \bar{a}\bar{b}\bar{c}de}$ |  |

Similarly, working with the unsuccessful events, we obtain

$$P_s = 1 - Q_f = 1 - P(E_{16} + E_{17} + E_{18} + E_{20} + E_{21} + E_{24}$$
$$+ E_{26} + E_{27} + E_{28} + E_{29} + E_{30} + E_{31} + E_{32}) \qquad (3.26)$$
$$P_s = 1 - [p^3(1-p)^2 + 6p^2(1-p)^3 + 5p(1-p)^4 + (1-p)^5] \qquad (3.27)$$

Simplification of Eq. (3.27) gives the same result as Eq. (3.25).

The event-space method can be used on all systems with independent failures, the number of events involved being equal to the total number of combinations of $n$ units, $2^n$. When $n$ becomes greater than 5 or 6, this technique becomes unwieldy. A much simpler technique involving path tracing is suggested by one of the substeps in the event-space technique.

### 3.6.3 PATH-TRACING METHODS

In the application of the event-space method, it was necessary to identify the successful paths. Once this was done, the union of all events containing the successful paths was written as the reliability expression. Much of the detail in the event-space method can be bypassed if the successful paths are located at the outset. Then each successful path forms a favorable event.    The union of these favorable events (they are generally not mutually exclusive) forms the reliability expression.    The system of Fig. 3.7 will be used again for illustration purposes.

The successful paths were found previously by checking through all the tabulated events.    Now a simpler procedure can be used.    All blocks in the reliability block diagram are initially considered missing, and the units are replaced singly, in pairs, in triplets, etc.    Examination of Fig. 3.7 shows that no single element forms a successful path but that the pairs $ad$, $bd$, $be$, and $ce$ are all successful paths.    Thus, the reliability expression is given by

$$P_s = P(ad + bd + be + ce) \qquad (3.28)$$

After *expansion* and *cancellation* of terms, Eq. (3.28) becomes

$$P_s = P(ad) + P(bd) + P(be) + P(ce) - P(abd) - P(bde)$$
$$- P(bce) - P(acde) + P(abcde) \quad (3.29)$$

If all units are independent and have an individual reliability equal to $p$, Eq. (3.29) reduces to the same result given in Eq. (3.25).

The path-tracing technique is simpler than the event-space method in that it eliminates the lengthy tabulation of the event space.    The path-tracing method does involve more algebra in the simplification of the reliability expression since the events are not mutually exclusive, as they are in the event-space method.    On the whole, the path-tracing method should be the simpler to apply in complex problems.

### 3.6.4  DECOMPOSITION METHOD

A method of decomposing the reliability structure of a complex system into simpler substructures can be developed through successive application of a conditional probability theorem.    The technique begins by selection of a *keystone component* which appears to bind together the reliability structure of the problem.    The reliability may then be expressed in terms of the keystone component $X$ as[1]

$$P_s = P(X)P(\text{system good}|X) + P(\bar{X})P(\text{system good}|\bar{X}) \qquad (3.30)$$

and the unreliability expressed as

$$P_f = P(X)P(\text{system fails}|X) + P(\bar{X})P(\text{system fails}|\bar{X}) \qquad (3.31)$$

It will be shown in the following example that the conditional probabilities given in Eqs. (3.30) and (3.31) are simpler to evaluate than the original problem; thus, one difficult problem is decomposed into two easier

[1] For a proof of this expression see Eq. (2.16).

ones.   In a complex problem, the decomposition process can be repeated on the substructures formed after the first decomposition.

If a poor choice is made for the keystone component, the method still works well, but the decomposition of the reliability structure is not so dramatic.   If one applies Eq. (3.30) to the problem of Fig. 3.7, choosing $b$ as the critical component $X$,

$$P_s = P(b)P(\text{system good}|b) + P(\bar{b})P(\text{system good}|\bar{b}) \qquad (3.32)$$

The first term in Eq. (3.32) involves the probability that the system is good if $b$ is good, and this occurs if $d$ or $e$ is good; thus, one of the substructures is a parallel combination of the two elements $d$ and $e$, given by case $c$ of Table 3.3.   Evaluation of the second term in Eq. (3.32) involves the probability that the system is good if $b$ is bad, which reduces to the same substructure as configuration $m$ of Table 3.4.   Therefore, using the reliability expressions given in the tables,

$$\begin{aligned} P_s &= P(b)[1 - P(\bar{d}\bar{e})] + P(\bar{b})[P(ad + ce)] \\ &= p(2p - p^2) + (1 - p)(2p^2 - p^4) \end{aligned} \qquad (3.33)$$

Simplification of Eq. (3.33) checks with the previous result.   This approach could also have been applied by starting with Eq. (3.31) and proceeding in a similar manner.   Of course the problem could also have been solved by choosing another element of the system as the keystone element and evaluating the resulting substructures.

This method is very quick and simple when the reliability expressions for the resulting substructures can be written down by inspection or taken from a table.   In more complex problems, the method can be applied again to evaluate the substructures.   In such a case the labor involved increases rapidly, but it still should be simpler than applying the event-space technique.   The usefulness of this method depends on the location by inspection of an appropriate keystone element which yields a significant decomposition.

### 3.6.5  CUT–SET AND TIE–SET METHODS

A very efficient method for computing the reliability of any system not containing dependent failures can be developed from the properties of the reliability graph.   The reliability graph consists of a set of branches which represent the $n$ elements.   There must be at least $n$ branches in the graph, but there can be more if the same branch must be repeated in more than one path (see Fig. 3.4).   The probability of element success is written above each branch.   The nodes of the graph tie the branches together and form the structure.   A path has already been defined, but a better definition can be given in terms of graph theory.   The term *tie set*, rather than path, is common in graph nomenclature. A tie set is a group of branches which forms a connection between input and output when traversed in the arrow direction. We shall primarily be concerned with *minimal* tie sets, which are those containing a minimum number of elements. If no node is traversed more than once in tracing out a tie set, the tie set is minimal. If a system has $i$ minimal tie sets denoted by $T_1, T_2, \ldots, T_i$, then the system has a connection between input and output if at least one tie set is intact. The system reliability is thus given by

$$R = P(T_1 + T_2 + \cdots + T_i) \tag{3.34}$$

Equation (3.34) is nothing more than a more precise statement of the path-tracing method.

One can define a *cut set* of a graph as a set of branches which interrupts all connections between input and output when removed from the graph. The minimal cut sets are a group of distinct cut sets containing a minimum number of terms. All system failures can be represented by the removal of at least one minimal cut set from the graph. The probability of system failure is, therefore, given by the probability that at least one minimal cut set fails. If we let $C_1, C_2, \ldots, C_j$ represent the $j$ minimal cut sets and $\bar{C}_j$ the failure of the $j$th cut set, the system reliability is given by

$$P_f = P(\bar{C}_1 + \bar{C}_2 + \cdots + \bar{C}_j)$$
$$R = 1 - P_f = 1 - P(\bar{C}_1 + \bar{C}_2 + \cdots + \bar{C}_j) \tag{3.35}$$

As an example of the application of cut-set and tie-set analysis we consider the graph given in Fig. 3.8. The following combinations of branches are all tie sets of the system:

$$T_1 = x_1 x_2 \qquad T_2 = x_3 x_4 \qquad T_3 = x_1 x_6 x_4 \qquad T_4 = x_3 x_5 x_2 \qquad T_5 = x_1 x_6 x_5 x_2$$

Tie sets $T_1$, $T_2$, $T_3$, and $T_4$ are minimal tie sets. Tie set $T_5$ is nonminimal since the top node is encountered twice in traversing the graph. From Eq. (3.34)

$$R = P(T_1 + T_2 + T_3 + T_4) = P(x_1 x_2 + x_3 x_4 + x_1 x_6 x_4 + x_3 x_5 x_2) \tag{3.36}$$

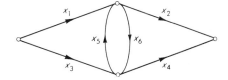

**Fig. 3.8** Reliability graph for a six-element system.

Similarly we may list *some* cut sets of the structure

$$C_1 = x_1 x_3 \qquad C_2 = x_2 x_4 \qquad C_3 = x_1 x_5 x_3 \qquad C_4 = x_1 x_5 x_4$$
$$C_5 = x_3 x_6 x_1 \qquad C_6 = x_3 x_6 x_2$$

Cut sets $C_1$, $C_2$, $C_4$, and $C_6$ are minimal. Cut sets $C_3$ and $C_5$ are nonminimal since they are both contained in cut set $C_1$. Using Eq. (3.35),

$$R = 1 - P(\bar{C}_1 + \bar{C}_2 + \bar{C}_4 + \bar{C}_6) = 1 - P(\bar{x}_1 \bar{x}_3 + \bar{x}_2 \bar{x}_4 + \bar{x}_1 \bar{x}_5 \bar{x}_4 \\ + \bar{x}_3 \bar{x}_6 \bar{x}_2) \quad (3.37)$$

The reader may verify by direct expansion the fact that if $T_5$ were included in Eq. (3.36) or if $C_3$ and $C_5$ were included in Eq. (3.37), the algebra would become more difficult but the correct result would still be obtained.

In a large problem there will be many cut sets and tie sets, and although Eqs. (3.35) and (3.36) are easily formulated, the expansion of either equation is a formidable task. (If there are $n$ events in a union, the expansion of the probability of the union involves $2^n - 1$ terms.) Several approximations[1] which are useful in simplifying the computations are discussed below.

We consider the following expression and its expansion

$$P(A + B + C) = P(A) + P(B) + P(C) - P(AB) - P(AC) \\ - P(BC) + P(ABC) \quad (3.38)$$

where events $A$, $B$, and $C$ are made up of products of other subevents. If events $A$, $B$, and $C$ are disjoint, Eq. (3.38) greatly simplifies, yielding

$$P(A + B + C) = P(A) + P(B) + P(C) \quad (3.39)$$

Thus, if the unions of tie sets or cut sets such as those given in Eqs. (3.34) and (3.35) possess the disjoint property, considerable algebraic simplification ensues. As an approximation we assume the disjoint property. We can show that[1]

$$P(A + B + C) \leq P(A) + P(B) + P(C) \quad (3.40)$$

Thus, for any set of events $A$, $B$, $C$ the disjoint approximation yields an upper bound. We can motivate the proof of Eq. (3.40) by the following example. Let $A = x_1 x_2$, $B = x_3 x_4$, and $C = x_5 x_6$, where all the $x$'s are independent and $P(x_1) = P(x_2) = \cdots P(x_6) = p$. Then Eq. (3.40) yields

$$P(A + B + C) = 3p^2 - 3p^4 + p^6 \leq 3p^2$$

---

[1] R. E. Barlow and F. Proschan, "Mathematical Theory of Reliability," John Wiley & Sons, Inc., New York, 1965; M. Messinger and M. Shooman, Reliability Approximations for Complex Structures, *Proc. 1967 Ann. Symp. Reliability IEEE,* New York.

Thus, the disjoint approximation simply drops the terms involving higher powers of $p$. If $p$ is small, clearly $p^6 < p^4$ and $3p^2 - 3p^4 < 3p^2$. The inequality in Eq. (3.40) is good for any set of events and is a close bound for small $p$. Combining the above results with Eq. (3.34), we conclude that

$$R \leq P(T_1) + P(T_2) + \cdots + P(T_i) \tag{3.41}$$

This upper bound becomes a good approximation in the low-reliability region. Similarly we can proceed with Eq. (3.35)

$$P_f \leq P(\bar{C}_1) + P(\bar{C}_2) + \cdots + P(\bar{C}_j)$$

This upper bound should be good where $1 - p$ is small, i.e., the high-reliability region. Manipulating this inequality, we obtain

$$R \geq 1 - [P(\bar{C}_1) + P(\bar{C}_2) + \cdots + P(\bar{C}_j)] \tag{3.42}$$

This lower bound is good in the high-reliability region.

For the example of Fig. 3.8, Eq. (3.36) yields

$$
\begin{aligned}
R = {} & P(x_1x_2) + P(x_3x_4) + P(x_1x_6x_4) + P(x_3x_5x_2) - P(x_1x_2x_3x_4) \\
& - P(x_1x_2x_4x_6) - P(x_1x_2x_3x_5) - P(x_1x_3x_4x_6) - P(x_2x_3x_4x_5) \\
& - P(x_1x_2x_3x_4x_5x_6) + P(x_1x_2x_3x_4x_6) + P(x_1x_2x_3x_4x_5) \\
& + P(x_1x_2x_3x_4x_5x_6) + P(x_1x_2x_3x_4x_5x_6) - P(x_1x_2x_3x_4x_5x_6)
\end{aligned}
$$

If all the $x$'s are identical and independent with $P(x) = p$, then

$$R = 2p^2 + 2p^3 - 5p^4 + 2p^5$$

The upper bound is given by Eq. (3.41) as

$$
\begin{aligned}
R_u &= P(x_1x_2) + P(x_3x_4) + P(x_1x_6x_4) + P(x_3x_5x_2) \\
&= 2p^2 + 2p^3 \geq R
\end{aligned}
$$

The lower bound is given by Eqs. (3.42) and (3.37) as

$$
\begin{aligned}
R_l &= 1 - [P(\bar{x}_1\bar{x}_3) + P(\bar{x}_2\bar{x}_4) + P(\bar{x}_1\bar{x}_5\bar{x}_4) + P(\bar{x}_3\bar{x}_6\bar{x}_2)] \\
&= 1 - [2(1 - p)^2 + 2(1 - p)^3] \leq R
\end{aligned}
$$

The expressions $R_l$ and $R_u$ are compared with $R$ in Fig. 3.9. The bounds are good approximations in the high- and low-reliability regions and greatly simplify the algebraic complexity of the problem.

Instead of working with Eqs. (3.34) and (3.35) we can write a complementary pair of expressions

$$R = 1 - P(\bar{T}_1\bar{T}_2 \cdots \bar{T}_i) \tag{3.43a}$$
$$R = P(C_1C_2 \cdots C_j) \tag{3.43b}$$

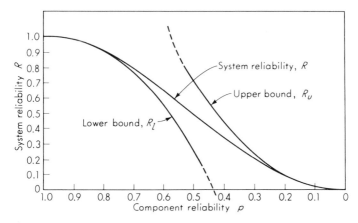

**Fig. 3.9** Comparison of the reliability function, upper bound, and lower bound for the example of Fig. 3.8.

Starting with Eqs. (3.43a) and (3.43b) and certain independence assumptions, we can derive another set of upper- and lower-bound expressions for the system reliability. These independence bounds are discussed in the problems at the end of the chapter. Another topological procedure for computing system reliability is given in Sec. 6.9. The technique given in Eq. (6.49) is discussed in terms of a switching circuit but is applicable in general.

### 3.7 CRITICAL–FAILURE MODEL

Many large-scale military, industrial, and commercial systems can easily be described in terms of a system and subsystem structure. In fact most of them have probably been designed on this basis. When such a structure exists, it is relatively easy to formulate a reliability model using the techniques of Sec. 3.6. In systems where there is much interaction and loading between the various parts it is often difficult to formulate a reliability block diagram. This is also frequently true in small electric or mechanical components where the parts interact strongly. (In some cases the difficulty is merely a lack of detailed knowledge of the system.) In such cases it is best for the equipment designer or someone equally familiar with the function of the equipment to tabulate its various parts or functional pieces and decide which component failures are critical to system operation. *Critical components* are those for which a single failure renders the system inoperative. In the case of certain components a single failure only degrades system performance, and these components must be considered critical only when they fail in pairs, triplets, or

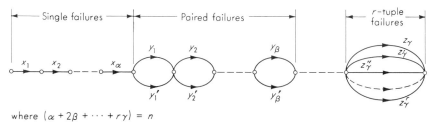

where $(\alpha + 2\beta + \cdots + r\gamma) = n$

**Fig. 3.10**   The structure of a critical-failure model for an $n$-element system.

$n$-tuples.   The general structure which corresponds to such a model is given in Fig. 3.10.   In cases where it is difficult to ascertain analytically the effect of a component failure, the failure may be simulated in the laboratory and its effect on system performance observed.   Some failures may simply be neglected on the basis of an a priori judgment that their probability of occurrence will be too small to matter.   Probabilities of success are then assigned to the various single- and multiple-component failures.   If the definition of the component failures is intelligently chosen, interaction of component failures is small, and the system reliability may be written as the product of mutually exclusive component success probabilities.

The example which follows illustrates the application of the critical-failure approach to a problem in which the structure is unclear at the outset.   The reliability of a desk typewriter is calculated as an illustration of the techniques involved in the critical-failure approach.   The first step in the analysis is to tabulate the major functions which must be performed in the successful operation of the system.   These functional operations are given in Table 3.6.   The concept of successful typewriter operation must be defined, and the criticality of the various typewritten functions must be discussed.   The reliability of a typewriter is to be evaluated on the basis of two modes of operation, business-office use and home use.   For business use all controls and keys on the typewriter must operate well, otherwise a typed letter is not perfect or certain convenience features are inoperative, thus lowering the typing efficiency.   In either case whenever the typewriter is removed from operation for repairs, it is considered to have failed.   When used at home, some minor failures may be tolerated before repair is considered; in fact some nonvital key failures may even be permitted.

In Table 3.6, items 1 and 11 may be considered to be of such a sturdy and well-studied design that the probability of failure is nil.   (This is a matter of judgment, which is of course open to discussion and interpretation.)   For business use items 2 to 10 must all operate properly.   If no

**Table 3.6  Typewriter functions**

| No. | Function |
|-----|----------|
| 1 | Roller operation |
| 2 | Paper guides and centering |
| 3 | Ribbon |
| 4 | Key operation |
| 5 | Space bar |
| 6 | Carriage return |
| 7 | Margin set |
| 8 | Shift mechanism |
| 9 | Backspace |
| 10 | Tabulator |
| 11 | Frame |

detailed failure data are available on parts failures, then as a very rough approach it may be assumed that items 2, 3, and 5 to 10 have equal probabilities of success $p$. Item 4, the key operation, is a different matter. The keys may be grouped into functional categories, as shown in Table 3.7. The five operations in category 5 may be considered to be like the operations listed in Table 3.6 and may therefore be assigned a reliability $p_1$. The remaining items, the letters, punctuation, numbers, and symbols may be lumped in another category and assigned a probability of success $p_2$. Assuming that all the operations and keys operate independently, the structure becomes a chain of 95 elements, 13 with probability $p_1$ and 82 with probability $p_2$. Thus, the probability of success of a typewriter for business use would be

$$P_s = p_1^{13} p_2^{82} \tag{3.44}$$

**Table 3.7  Categories of key operations**

| No. | Group | Total |
|-----|-------|-------|
| 1 | Uppercase letters: A–Z | 26 |
| 2 | Lowercase letters: a–z | 26 |
| 3 | Punctuation marks: ” ’ ( ) : ; ? . , | 9 |
| 4 | Numbers: 2–0 | 9 |
| 5 | Operations: tab, set, clear, backspace, margin release | 5 |
| 6 | Symbols: # $ % - & * — $\frac{1}{4}$ $\frac{1}{2}$ @ ¢ / | 12 |

For home use, functions 9 and 10 of Table 3.6 are not critical. In Table 3.7, all the symbols may be regarded as noncritical, and similarly the numbers are noncritical. As far as categories 3 and 5 are concerned, the punctuation marks may be added by hand, and the operations are convenience features. A single failure is not critical, but if three or more items from category 3 and/or 5 have failed, the typewriter will probably be returned for repairs. As to the letters, they are not all equally important. The frequency of letter use in English is given in Table 3.8. It is clear that the six letters v to z are used so infrequently that loss of a single character could be tolerated among these letters. Thus, the probability of success for home use would be given by

$$P_s = p_1{}^6 \left[ \sum_{i=11}^{i=14} \binom{14}{i} p_2{}^i (1 - p_2)^{14-i} \right] p_2{}^{40} \left[ \sum_{j=11}^{j=12} \binom{12}{j} p_2{}^j (1 - p_2)^{12-j} \right]$$

$$(3.45)\dagger$$

† The equivalent chain structure is 6 $p_1$ branches followed by 40 $p_2$ branches, an 11-out-of-14 graph structure and an 11-out-of-12 graph structure.

**Table 3.8 Frequency of occurrence of letters in English in 1,000 letters***

| Letter | frequency | Letter | frequency | Letter | frequency |
|--------|-----------|--------|-----------|--------|-----------|
| E | 131 | D | 38 | W | 15 |
| T | 105 | L | 34 | B | 14 |
| A | 86 | F | 29 | V | 9.2 |
| O | 80 | C | 28 | K | 4.2 |
| N | 71 | M | 25 | X | 1.7 |
| R | 68 | U | 25 | J | 1.3 |
| I | 63 | G | 20 | Q | 1.2 |
| S | 61 | Y | 20 | Z | 0.8 |
| H | 53 | P | 20 | | |

* These data differ somewhat from the order given by Edgar Allan Poe in "The Goldbug," namely, eaoidhnrstuycfglmwbkpqxz. (The letters j and v are omitted without explanation.) Conan Doyle also makes reference to letter frequency in the Sherlock Holmes story, The Adventure of the Dancing Men. "The order of the English letters after E is by no means well marked, and any preponderance which may be shown in an average of a printed sheet may be reversed in a single short sentence. Speaking roughly, T, A, O, I, N, S, H, R, D, and L are the numerical order in which letters occur; but T, A, O, and I are very nearly abreast of each other . . . ."
SOURCE: S. Goldman, "Information Theory," p. 16, Prentice-Hall, Inc., Englewood Cliffs, N.J., 1953.

The term $p_1^6$ represents six critical operations in Table 3.6.    The first bracket represents the success of 11, 12, 13, or 14 of the 14 operations and punctuation marks in Table 3.7.    The term $p_2^{40}$ is the successful operation of the 40 capital and small letters listed in Table 3.8 between the letters E and B.    The last bracket in the expression represents the success of 11 or 12 out of the 12 capital and small letters represented by V, K, X, J, Q, and Z.

Obviously this is only a rough approximation to the problem, since probabilities $p_1$ and $p_2$ are unknown and there is no reason to assume that all the operations have a like reliability.    It is perhaps a better approximation to assume that all the keys have a similar reliability.    In any event, this preliminary analysis at least reveals what kinds of information are necessary to solve the problem accurately.    As this information is obtained, the factors in Tables 3.6 and 3.7, the probabilities $p_1$ and $p_2$, and the combinatorial rules used to derive Eqs. (3.44) and (3.45) would change.    After a few such cycles the reliability formulas would become reasonably accurate and quite useful.    The critical-failure approach is thus nothing more than a logical search through the problem to delineate the critical-failure modes.    The critical-failure approach is most useful when the system structure is too hazy or confused to use the techniques of Sec. 3.6.

## 3.8    MULTISTATE MODELS

In all the cases previously discussed the unit in question could assume only one of two mutually exclusive states, success or failure, good or bad. Many components may assume three or more states, and a slightly different model must be formulated.    For example, a resistor may open-circuit, short-circuit, or function properly.    A transistor may exhibit even more than three states if all possible means of failure are included.    Not all the failed-component states need represent system failure, and the success or failure of each state must be evaluated in conjunction with the particular circuit and use in question.    A semiconductor diode is a device which passes current in the forward direction and blocks current in the reverse direction, controlling electric current in much the same way as a check valve controls fluid flow.    When operating properly, the resistance in the forward direction is essentially zero, and the resistance in the reverse direction essentially infinite.    A diode may fail in two ways:[1] it may open-circuit, in which case its resistance is infinite in both directions, or it may short-circuit, in which case its resistance is zero in both direc-

[1] This simplified model does not take into account the physics of diode failures, which is important for a detailed treatment.

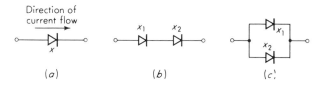

**Fig. 3.11**  Diode networks.  (a) One diode; (b) two diodes in series; (c) two diodes in parallel.

tions.    Thus, this device has three states, good, shorted, and opened.    If event $x$ represents good, event $\bar{x}_s$ shorted, and event $\bar{x}_o$ opened, the three events are mutually exclusive, and

$$P(x + \bar{x}_s + \bar{x}_o) = P(x) + P(\bar{x}_s) + P(\bar{x}_o) = 1 \tag{3.46}$$

The reliability of a single diode shown in Fig. 3.11a is given by

$$P_s = P(x) = 1 - P(\bar{x}_s + \bar{x}_o) = 1 - P(\bar{x}_s) - P(\bar{x}_o) \tag{3.47}$$

In Fig. 3.11b two diodes are shown in series, and the system fails if either diode opens or if both short.    Thus, the tie sets (the good combinations) are $x_1 x_2$, $x_1 \bar{x}_{2s}$, $x_2 \bar{x}_{1s}$ and the cut sets (the failed combinations) are $x_1 \bar{x}_{2o}$, $\bar{x}_{1s} \bar{x}_{2s}$, $\bar{x}_{1s} \bar{x}_{2o}$, $\bar{x}_{1o} x_2$, $\bar{x}_{1o} \bar{x}_{2s}$, $\bar{x}_{1o} \bar{x}_{2o}$.    Therefore in terms of the tie sets

$$P_s = P(x_1 x_2 + x_1 \bar{x}_{2s} + x_2 \bar{x}_{1s}) \tag{3.48}$$

Alternately we could have used the cut-set approach

$$P_s = 1 - P(x_1 \bar{x}_{2o} + \bar{x}_{1s} \bar{x}_{2s} + \bar{x}_{1s} \bar{x}_{2o} + \bar{x}_{1o} x_2 + \bar{x}_{1o} \bar{x}_{2s} + \bar{x}_{1o} \bar{x}_{2o}) \tag{3.49}$$

If all the failures are independent and $P(x) = p$, $P(\bar{x}_s) = q_s$, and $P(\bar{x}_o) = q_o$, then Eqs. (3.48) and (3.49) become

$$P_s = p^2 + 2pq_s \tag{3.50}$$

Equation (3.50) may be written in other forms by simultaneous solution with Eq. (3.47) which states that $p + q_s + q_o = 1$.

In the case of the two parallel diodes shown in Fig. 3.11c, the system tie sets are $x_1 x_2$, $x_1 \bar{x}_{2o}$, $x_2 \bar{x}_{1o}$.    The reliability is given by

$$P_s = P(x_1 x_2 + x_1 \bar{x}_{2o} + x_2 \bar{x}_{1o}) \tag{3.51}$$

If all failures are independent and the previous notation is used,

$$P_s = p^2 + 2pq_o \tag{3.52}$$

These expressions can also be derived using the multinomial distribution; [see Eqs. (2.30) and (2.31)].    Direct comparison of Eqs. (3.50) and (3.52) requires a bit of algebraic manipulation, and the reader is referred to the problems at the end of the chapter.

This example has illustrated how one constructs a model when there are three states, one of success and two of failure. The generalization of this procedure to the case where there are several states of success and failure is clear. Although one can draw reliability graphs for the diode circuits given in Fig. 3.11, a reliability graph is difficult to construct for complex multistate problems. It is easier to list the cut sets or tie sets of the problem and use Eq. (3.34) or (3.35) directly.

### 3.9 STANDBY–SYSTEM MODELS

All the systems discussed so far in this chapter have been analyzed by drawing a reliability graph or at least enumerating cut sets and tie sets. These techniques fail in the case of standby systems. A two-element parallel system is shown in Fig. 3.12a, and a two-element standby system in Fig. 3.12b. In the parallel system all the channels are turned on at the beginning of the problem and operate until failure occurs. Even after failure occurs, they remain connected in the circuit in their failed state. When a standby system is used, the parallel channels are not all active in the circuit at the same time. The standby system in Fig. 3.12b works as follows. At the start of operation the ideal switch $s$ connects the input to channel $a'$ and turns on $a'$. Meanwhile, channel $b'$ is left in reserve (standby) in a turned-off condition. The perfect switch $s$ can sense proper and improper operation of channel $a'$, to which it is connected, switch to the other channel $b'$, and then turn on channel $b'$. It is assumed that the switching time from $a'$ to $b'$ and the warm-up of $b'$ is short enough so that proper system operation is not interrupted.

The two-channel parallel system can fail only if both channels $a$ and $b$ have failed. The probability of success is

$$P_s = 1 - P(\bar{a}\bar{b}) = 1 - P(\bar{a})P(\bar{b}|\bar{a}) \tag{3.53}$$

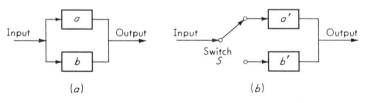

$$(a) \qquad\qquad\qquad (b)$$

**Fig. 3.12** Parallel and standby systems. (a) A two-channel parallel system; (b) a two-channel standby system.

If the units are identical and independent with unit reliability $p$,

$$P_s = 2p - p^2 \tag{3.54}$$

In the standby system, failure will occur if channel $a'$ fails, the ideal switch switches to $b'$, and subsequently $b'$ fails.   Since the switch is assumed to be perfect,

$$P_s = 1 - P(\bar{a}'\bar{b}') = 1 - P(\bar{a}')P(\bar{b}'|\bar{a}') \tag{3.55}$$

This would *seem* to say that if units $a$ and $a'$ were identical and units $b$ and $b'$ were identical the two systems would have the same reliability. This is *not* true, since the interpretation of the conditional probabilities $P(\bar{b}|\bar{a})$ and $P(\bar{b}'|\bar{a}')$ are distinctly different.   In the parallel case $P(\bar{b}|\bar{a})$ may simply be $P(\bar{b})$ if the events are independent, or it may be slightly different if the two components interact.   In the parallel case $b$ is assumed to have operated since $t = 0$.   In the standby case $P(\bar{b}'|\bar{a}')$ is always a dependent probability, since $b'$ does not start operation until $a'$ has failed. This conditional probability is obviously a function of time.   Since the system structure changes when the switch operates and the time of switching is a random variable, we cannot draw a reliability graph for a standby system.

As shown in Chap. 2 for a standby system where both components are identical and the standby component does not age at all during standby, the probability of $r$ failures is governed by the Poisson distribution

$$f(r;\mu) = \frac{\mu^r e^{-\mu}}{r!} \tag{2.32}$$

The system in Fig. 3.12$b$ is successful if there are 0 or 1 failure; thus

$$P_s = e^{-\mu} + \mu e^{-\mu} = e^{-\mu}(1 + \mu) \tag{3.56}$$

The reliabilities of a single element, two parallel elements, and a two-element standby system are compared in Fig. 3.13.   In order to compare Eq. (3.56) with the other expressions, we must relate $\mu$ to $p$.   From Eq. (2.32), the probability of zero failures equals $e^{-\mu}$, which by definition is $p$.   Therefore, $\mu = -\ln p$, and Eq. (3.56) becomes

$$P_s = p(1 - \ln p) \tag{3.57}$$

As predicted, the standby system with its ideal switch is better than the parallel system.   The situation of course changes when the standby component ages and the switch is imperfect.   A detailed discussion of standby systems appears in Chap. 5, where the Markov model is used since it eliminates any difficulty due to the switching.

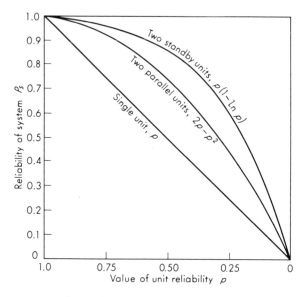

**Fig. 3.13**   Comparison of a single element, two parallel elements, and a two-element standby system.

## 3.10   DEPENDENT FAILURES

The reliability approaches discussed have all been general in that they hold for dependent as well as independent failures.   All the examples (except the standby system of Sec. 3.9) have illustrated systems with independent components.   The example of this section will treat a dependent-failure situation and show how the dependency greatly affects the system reliability.

As an example of the role of dependence we shall compare the problem of starting a single-cylinder four-cycle gasoline engine used in a power lawn mower with a multicylinder automobile engine.   We assume in both cases that the electric and fuel systems are perfect and that failure to start is due solely to a misgapped or fouled spark plug.   For a grass-cutting season of 4 months with eight grass cuttings per month and three mower starts per cutting there is a total of 96 starts per season.   If we assume two failures to start per season, the starting reliability of a power mower is approximately 0.98.   Thus if we choose a lawn mower at random without any knowledge of the engine condition, we shall be unable to start it about 2 percent of the time.

For the automobile engine we assume that combustion in any one cylinder is sufficient to start the motor.   In order to compare the two situations, we use the same reliability for each automobile cylinder as for the power mower.   (The ignition systems are similar, and the spark plugs the same.)   Thus, if the cylinder failures *are independent* for an $n$-cylinder automobile engine, the starting probability is $1 - 0.02^n$.   For a four-cylinder engine the reliability is 0.99999984.

Intuition tells us that we should expect higher reliability for automobiles engine starting but not such a tremendous improvement.   A more careful formulation of the problem reveals the error.   Denoting success of cylinder $i$ by $x_i$, we have

$$R = 1 - (\bar{x}_1\bar{x}_2 \cdots \bar{x}_i) = 1 - P(\bar{x}_1)P(\bar{x}_2|\bar{x}_1) \cdots P(\bar{x}_i|\bar{x}_1\bar{x}_2 \cdots \bar{x}_{i-1})$$

$$(3.58)$$

There is no reason to assume independence, as was done.   In fact it seems quite certain that there is dependence.   Suppose we know that two out of four spark plugs removed from an engine are fouled.   It is reasonable to assume that the probability of the third plug being fouled is greater than if we had no information about the first and second plug.   To a first approximation, the plugs do age together as engine mileage increases. As a simple model for dependence we assume

$$P(\bar{x}_1) = 1 - p$$

$$P(\bar{x}_2|\bar{x}_1) = 1 - \frac{p}{2}$$

$$P(\bar{x}_3|\bar{x}_1\bar{x}_2) = 1 - \frac{p}{3} \qquad\qquad (3.59)$$

$$\cdots \cdots \cdots \cdots \cdots \cdots$$

$$P(\bar{x}_i|\bar{x}_1\bar{x}_2 \cdots \bar{x}_{i-1}) = 1 - \frac{p}{i}$$

For $i = 4$ and $p = 0.98$, Eqs. (3.58) and (3.59) yield

$$R = 1 - (1 - 0.98)\left(1 - \frac{0.98}{2}\right)\left(1 - \frac{0.98}{3}\right)\left(1 - \frac{0.98}{4}\right)$$

$$= 1 - 0.02 \times 0.51 \times 0.673 \times 0.755$$

$$= 1 - 0.00519 = 0.99481$$

The great difference in the numerical results is clearly evident.   For the single-cylinder power lawn mower on the average about 20 per 1,000 would fail to start; for the four-cylinder engine, including the dependence, about 5.2 per 1,000 would fail.   This is about a 4:1 reduction in the failure rate.   Even if there were six cylinders, about 3.5 per 1,000 would fail.   This is very different from the 0.16 per 1,000,000 failures predicted by the incorrect assumption of independence.

The example indicates that the assumption of independence should be made with care, to avoid an invalid result.   When the dependence relation is a function of time, it is generally easier to use the Markov models discussed in Chap. 5.

## PROBLEMS

3.1 A series system is composed of $n$ identical independent components. The component probability of success is $p_c$, and $q_c = 1 - p_c$.

    (a) Show that if $q_c \ll 1$, the system reliability $R$ is approximately given by $R \approx 1 - nq_c$.

    (b) If the system has 10 components and $R$ must be 0.99, how good must the components be?

3.2 A parallel system is composed of 10 identical independent components. If the system reliability $R$ must be 0.99, how poor can the components be?

3.3 A 10-element system is constructed of independent identical components so that 5 out of the 10 elements are necessary for system success. If the system reliability $R$ must be 0.99, how good must the components be?

3.4 Check the reliability expressions in Table 3.3.

3.5 Check the reliability expressions in Table 3.4.

3.6 Find and sketch 10 different reliability graphs that can be constructed from five different system elements. Can you give a systematic method for finding all the different five-element graphs?

3.7 Draw reliability graphs for the following three reliability block diagrams. *Note:* The probabilities of system success for independent identical units are given below each figure.

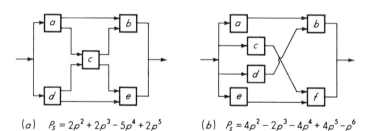

    $(a)$    $P_s = 2p^2 + 2p^3 - 5p^4 + 2p^5$      $(b)$    $P_s = 4p^2 - 2p^3 - 4p^4 + 4p^5 - p^6$

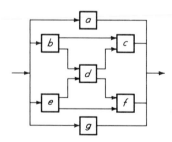

    $(c)$    $P_s = 2p + p^2 - 2p^3 - 7p^4 + 14p^5 - 9p^6 + 2p^7$

**Fig. P 3.7**

3.8 Solve for the system probability of success for system $a$ in Prob. 3.7 using the state-space technique.

3.9 Use the path-tracing method to solve for the probability of system success for parts $a$ to $c$ of Prob. 3.7.

3.10 Repeat Prob. 3.9 using the keystone-component method.

3.11 Find all the minimal tie sets and cut sets for the three systems in Prob. 3.7.

3.12 Compute the reliability of the three systems in Prob. 3.7 using:
  (a)  The tie-set approach and Eq. (3.34).
  (b)  The cut-set approach and Eq. (3.35).

3.13 Repeat Prob. 3.12 using the reliability bounds given in Eqs. (3.41) and (3.42). Draw three sketches similar to Fig. 3.9 which compare the approximate and exact expressions.

3.14 The graph shown represents a four-station communications network. The four nodes $a$, $b$, $c$, and $d$ represent the four stations. The six branches represent two-way communications links between each pair of stations.
  (a)  Find all minimal cut sets and tie sets for transmission between $a$ and $b$.
  (b)  If the elements are identical, explain why this holds for any pair of nodes.
  (c)  Approximate the system reliability in the high-reliability region. Assume all links are independent and identical with probability of success $p$.

Fig. P 3.14

3.15 The diagram shown represents a five-node communications network. Repeat Prob. 3.14 for the edge reliability $ab$ and the diagonal reliability $ac$.

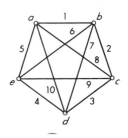

Fig. P 3.15

3.16 A traffic blinker light is mounted at a north-south–east-west intersection. It has a single bulb and a thermal flasher connected in series with a voltage source. The east-west lenses are red, and the north-south lenses are amber. Assume that the probability that the bulb burns out is $1 - p_b = 0.01$. The flasher has a probability of failing closed $1 - p_c = 0.01$ and a probability of failing open $1 - p_o = 0.01$.

(a)    Compute the probability of no failures, i.e., the system reliability.

(b)    Assume that a constant unblinking light is an undesirable but still safe condition. Compute the probability of safe operation, which is equal to unity minus the probability that the light is out.

3.17    We wish to improve the system described in Prob. 3.16. Evaluate the improvement in reliability and safety for each of the following schemes.

(a)    Replace the single bulb and flasher by two separate bulb-flasher circuits. (The flashers are assumed to be synchronized.)

(b)    Use two bulbs in parallel with two flashers in parallel in a single circuit.

(c)    Use two bulbs in parallel with two flashers in series in a single circuit.

(d)    Use three parallel flashers and one bulb.

(e)    Use three parallel bulbs and one flasher.

Assume that one bulb is ample to provide adequate intensity, and that any combination of on bulbs with blinking bulbs is a system failure but is still safe operation. Since all the reliabilities will be close to unity, it is better to compare values of $1 - R$.

3.18    Consider a red and green (no amber) traffic light mounted at a north-south–east-west intersection. Assume there is an accurate, well-built time clock running the system which does not fail. Thus, bulb burnouts are the only system failures. If the light has a separate bulb for each direction for red and for green, there is a total of eight bulbs. The probability of bulb burnout is equal to 0.01. Compute the system reliability.

3.19    We wish to improve the traffic-light system of Prob. 3.18. Compare the effectiveness of the following two techniques:

(a)    Replacement of each single bulb by two in parallel for a total of 16 bulbs.

(b)    Redesign of the optical system so that the north bulbs also cast light to the south and vice versa. With such an arrangement we could have two parallel red north-south bulbs, two parallel green north-south bulbs, two parallel red east-west bulbs, and two parallel green east-west bulbs. This system would have a total of eight bulbs.

3.20    The reliability graph shown below represents the logical operation of a particular system. Letting $a$ represent the success of element $a$ and $\bar{a}$ the failure of element $a$, etc., compute the following:

(a)    The probability of system success in terms of the component successes. Assume the elements are dependent and distinct.

(b)    The probability of system success if all the elements are identical and have a $P_s = p$.

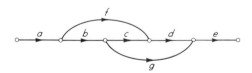

**Fig. P 3.20**

3.21    It is desired to compute the reliability of a steam shovel. The equipment is powered by a gasoline engine, which drives a set of gears through a coupling clutch. The gears rotate a cable drum, which winds up the steel cable. The cable passes over a pulley and supports the weight of the bucket, which hangs from the boom. A separate clutch-gear-drum-and-cable system opens and closes the bucket. A third clutch-gear-drum-and-cable system changes the boom angle. A clutch-and-gear mechanism rotates the boom to the left or the right. Assume that the rotating members may fail in two modes, a jammed mode and a free-rotation mode. Compute the probability of successful operation. Compute the probability of safe operation, i.e., the probability that neither the bucket, load, nor boom falls on the workers below as a result of a system failure.

3.22  It is very important in the operation of a nuclear-research reactor to know whether the reactor is operating or is shut down. Three sensors are to be used to provide a reliable warning system. Each sensor output is connected to an indicator light. When it is working properly, the sensor output turns on the indicator light as soon as the reactor starts up, and the output drops to zero, extinguishing the light, at the moment the reactor is shut down. The indicator lights are considered perfect, and the sensors yield zero output when they fail. The operator judges the reactor to be on when one, two, or three indicator lights are lighted; it is off if all lights are out. The probability of sensor success is $p$ and that of failure is $q$.

(a)  Compute the probability that the reactor operator obtains correct information that the reactor is on, $P(\text{on})$, and that he obtains correct information that the reactor is off, $P(\text{off})$.

(b)  Suppose that the sensor may fail in two modes: (1) it may fail "on," so that its output lights the indicator lamp regardless of whether the reactor is on or off, the probability of this failure being $q_{\text{on}}$; or (2) it may fail "off," so that the indicator lamp is out whether the reactor is on or off, the probability of this failure being $q_{\text{off}} = 1 - p - q_{\text{on}}$. If the operator uses the same judgment basis as above, compute $P(\text{on})$ and $P(\text{off})$.

(c)  The sensors fail in two modes as in part b, but the operator judges the reactor to be on if two or three indicator lamps are on and judges the reactor to be off if two or three of the indicator lamps are out (a "go-along-with-the-majority" decision rule). Compute $P(\text{on})$ and $P(\text{off})$ in this case.

(d)  Numerically evaluate parts a to c if $p = 0.80$, $q_{\text{on}} = 0.10$, and $q_{\text{off}} = 0.10$. Is the system of part b or c better? Explain.

3.23  Consider the operational sequence of a Tyros satellite. It is injected into orbit by the last stage of a booster rocket and is spinning at, say, 100 rpm. A Yo-Yo de-spin device reduces the spin rate to 10 rpm. A beacon transmitter is turned on for tracking purposes. A precession damper takes out any wobble present, two TV cameras take pictures of the cloud cover below, and the pictures are stored on two tape recorders. When over a ground station, a command signal from the ground received by the satellite command receiver performs switching in the satellite. The switching function reads out the stored data from either tape recorder or directly from the cameras. The picture information is sent via a TV transmitter to the ground station. The battery power supply is recharged by solar cells during orbital day. If the spin rate decays because of air friction and eddy-current damping, small spin-up rockets are fired to raise the spin rate. The spin direction can be corrected from time to time by a coil of wire wrapped around the satellite, which, when pulsed with current, torques against the earth's magnetic field, adjusting the spin direction. Assume that we wish to compute reliabilities for successful operation during the first day, first month, and first year of operation if the two different levels of success are (a) all pictures taken are received at the ground station and pictures are clear and well aimed and (b) some pictures received may be blurred or ill aimed.   For each of the six probabilities indicated above, delineate the part and subsystem reliabilities involved by drawing a reliability graph and set up an overall reliability expression.

3.24   If the following approach is used, Eqs. (3.47), (3.50), and (3.52) can be compared graphically.   The total probability of failure is assumed constant, that is, $q_s + q_o = K$, and therefore $p = 1 - K$.

(a)   Plot $P_s$ for each of the equations vs. the ratio $q_o/q_s$.   Note that when $q_o/q_s = 0$, all failures are shorts and when $q_o/q_s \to \infty$, all failures are opens. When $q_o/q_s = 1$, half the failures are shorts and half are opens.

(b)   Under what conditions is it best to place two diodes in series to improve reliability?

(c)   When does the parallel combination improve the reliability?

3.25   An amplifier must be built with a gain of 100.   The minimum circuit is shown in a of the figure.   Two other redundant configurations are shown in b and c. If all amplifiers are identical and independent with a $P_s = p$, compute the reliability of all three configurations and graph them as a function of $p$.

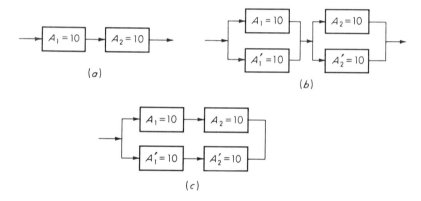

Fig. P 3.25

3.26   Suppose that in Prob. 3.25 the amplifiers are energized by a common power supply with a $P_s = P_{ps}$.   Devise a structural model including the power supply and compute the reliability of each configuration.   Repeat the computation for the case where two or four independent power sources are used to independently power each amplifier.

3.27*  The minimal tie sets and cut sets of a graph are related, and one set can be computed from the other.   Show how De Morgan's theorems (Prob. 2.5) can be used to compute the tie sets from the cut sets and vice versa.   Illustrate using the graph given in Fig. 3.8.

3.28   Assume that component reliability is 0.5 and we want a system reliability >0.99.   What is the minimum number of parallel components needed?   What is the minimum number of standby components needed?

3.29   A system is composed of four parallel elements.   We wish to evaluate several models for component dependency.

(a)   Assume that the four elements are independent and identical, with success probabilities $p_1 = p_2 = p_3 = p_4 = p$.   Compute the system reliability $R$ and sketch $R$ vs. $p_1$.

(b)   Repeat part $a$ using the same dependence assumption as in Eq. (3.59), that is,

$$q_1 = 1 - p \qquad q_2 = 1 - \frac{p}{2} \qquad q_3 = 1 - \frac{p}{3} \qquad q_4 = 1 - \frac{p}{4}$$

(c)   Repeat part $a$ using the dependence assumption

$$q_1 = 1 - p \qquad q_2 = 2(1 - p) \qquad q_3 = 3(1 - p) \qquad q_4 = 4(1 - p)$$

(d)   Repeat part $a$ using the dependence assumption

$$p_1 = p \qquad p_2 = p^2 \qquad p_3 = p^3 \qquad p_4 = p^4$$

(e)   Repeat part $a$ using the dependence assumption

$$q_1 = 1 - p \qquad q_2 = \frac{1 - p}{2} \qquad q_3 = \frac{1 - p}{3} \qquad q_4 = \frac{1 - p}{4}$$

(f)   Approximate the expressions given in parts $a$ to $e$ for the high-reliability region and discuss the results.

3.30* (a)   Using a Venn diagram, prove the inequalities
$$P(A + B + C) \le P(A) + P(B) + P(C)$$
$$P(A + B + C) \ge P(A) + P(B) + P(C) - P(AB) - P(AC) - P(BC)$$

(b)   Can you use the second inequality to obtain a closer set of bounds analogous to Eqs. (3.41) and (3.42)?   Call the upper bound $R'_u$ and the lower bound $R'_l$.

(c)   Add the new set of bounds $R'_u$ and $R'_l$ to Fig. 3.9 for the example of Fig. 3.8.

(d)   We wish to evaluate the accuracy of the approximations in the high-reliability region by comparing the errors in the system failure probabilities

$$\epsilon = \left| \frac{[(1 - R_{\text{actual}}) - (1 - R_{\text{approx}})] \times 100 \ \%}{1 - R_{\text{actual}}} \right|$$

Using the results of part $c$, find the range of $p$ for which $R_l$ approximates the true reliability to within an error $\epsilon \le 10$ percent.   Repeat this calculation for $R'_u$.   Repeat again for an improved approximation given by

$$R'' = \frac{R'_l + R'_u}{2}$$

3.31* We can formulate a different set of approximations.[1]   We start with Eqs. (3.43) and (3.44).   If we assume that all the system elements $x_i$ are *independent*, these equations become

$$R \approx 1 - P(\bar{T}_1)P(\bar{T}_2) \cdots P(\bar{T}_j)$$

and

$$R \approx P(c_1)P(c_2) \cdots P(c_j)$$

---

* A problem number followed by an asterisk indicates an extension of the theory presented in the text.

[1] Barlow and Proschan, *op. cit.*

(a)   Show that as long as the *elements* $x_i$ are *independent* $P(\bar{T}_1)P(\bar{T}_2|\bar{T}_1)$
$P(\bar{T}_3|\bar{T}_1\bar{T}_2) \cdots P(\bar{T}_j|\bar{T}_{j-1}\bar{T}_{j-2} \cdots \bar{T}_1) \leq P(\bar{T}_1)P(\bar{T}_2)P(\bar{T}_3) \cdots P(\bar{T}_j)$.
*Hint:* Use the specific example of Fig. 3.8.   Note that $T_1 = x_1 x_2$ whereas
$\bar{T}_1 = \bar{x}_1 + \bar{x}_2$.   These results lead to an independence lower bound which
is good in the high-reliability region.   Show that it is given by

$$R \geq R_{il} = 1 - P(\bar{T}_1)P(\bar{T}_2) \cdots P(\bar{T}_j)$$

(b)   Repeat the reasoning in part *a* for the cut-set equation and show that an
independence upper bound good in the high-reliability region is given by

$$R \leq R_{iu} = P(c_1)P(c_2) \cdots P(c_j)$$

(c)   Plot the $R_{il}$ and $R_{iu}$ bounds on Fig. 3.9 for the example of Fig. 3.8.   Note
that these bounds are sharper than the $R_l$ and $R_u$ bounds.   This can be
proved in general.

(d)   Is there a computational disadvantage in a complex system for the $R_{il}$
and the $R_{iu}$ bounds as compared with the $R_l$ and $R_u$ bounds?   In order
to evaluate the effect of the independence assumption apply the four
bounds to Prob. 3.29 and interpret your results.

3.32*  Another cut-set approximation can be made by considering the order of the
terms in the expansion of Eq. (3.35).   Specifically for the example in Eq. (3.37)

$$R = 1 - \overbrace{P(\bar{x}_1\bar{x}_3)}^{q^2} - \overbrace{P(\bar{x}_2\bar{x}_3)}^{q^2} - \overbrace{P(\bar{x}_1\bar{x}_4\bar{x}_5)}^{q^3} - \overbrace{P(\bar{x}_2\bar{x}_3\bar{x}_6)}^{q^3}$$
$$+ \overbrace{P(\bar{x}_1\bar{x}_2\bar{x}_3)}^{q^3} + \overbrace{P(\bar{x}_1\bar{x}_3\bar{x}_4\bar{x}_5)}^{q^4} + \overbrace{P(\bar{x}_1\bar{x}_2\bar{x}_3\bar{x}_6)}^{q^4} + \overbrace{P(\bar{x}_1\bar{x}_2\bar{x}_3\bar{x}_6)}^{q^4} + \overbrace{P(\bar{x}_1\bar{x}_2\bar{x}_3\bar{x}_4\bar{x}_5)}^{q^5}$$
$$+ \overbrace{P(\bar{x}_2\bar{x}_3\bar{x}_6)}^{q^3} + \overbrace{P(\bar{x}_1\bar{x}_2\bar{x}_3\bar{x}_4\bar{x}_5\bar{x}_6)}^{q^6} + \text{other terms}$$

The order of the term is defined as the power of $q$ which would be obtained if
each term were identical and independent with $P(\bar{x}) = q$.   The *lower-order
approximation* in this particular problem would be given by

$$R \approx R_{\text{approx}} = 1 - P(\bar{x}_1\bar{x}_3) - P(\bar{x}_2\bar{x}_3)$$

(a)   Compare this approximation with those of Fig. 3.9 and Prob. 3.31.

(b)   If we define an error as in Prob. 3.30 part *d*, show that for independent,
identical components and $q$ small

$$\epsilon \approx \frac{3q^4}{1 - 2q^2}$$

For what range of $p$ is $\epsilon < 10$ percent?

(c)   Using the thinking in part *b*, estimate the error which would occur if
one missed seeing cut set $\bar{x}_2\bar{x}_3\bar{x}_6$ in the analysis of the problem in Fig. 3.8.

3.33†  When information is to be transmitted digitally, we assign a certain sequence
of digits, which can be either ones or zeros, to each character to be transmitted.

† A problem number followed by a dagger indicates a problem based on related
material or allied applications.

Such assignment rules are called digital codes.   Consider the following three-digit (bit) code for the eight decimal digits 0 to 7:

| Decimal digit | Three-bit code |
|---------------|----------------|
| 0 | 0 0 0 |
| 1 | 0 0 1 |
| 2 | 0 1 0 |
| 3 | 0 1 1 |
| 4 | 1 0 0 |
| 5 | 1 0 1 |
| 6 | 1 1 0 |
| 7 | 1 1 1 |

Errors in digital transmission occur in such a manner that a one appears instead of a zero or vice versa.

(a)   Errors in one, two, or three bits of the message would not be discernable since we would merely interpret them as a different number.   Thus, the probability of no transmission errors is the probability of no bit errors. If $q$ is the probability of making an error in a single bit, compute the probability that the message is correct.

(b)   Suppose we wish to improve the code scheme by adding an extra check bit (generally called a *parity bit*) to detect one-bit errors.   The check bit will be coded so that there is always an even number of ones in each four-bit combination (called a *word*):

| Decimal digit | Coded four-bit word Information bits | Check bit | Number of 1s in word |
|---------------|-------------------|-----------|----------------------|
| 0 | 0 0 0 | 0 | 0 |
| 1 | 0 0 1 | 1 | 2 |
| 2 | 0 1 0 | 1 | 2 |
| 3 | 0 1 1 | 0 | 2 |
| 4 | 1 0 0 | 1 | 2 |
| 5 | 1 0 1 | 0 | 2 |
| 6 | 1 1 0 | 0 | 2 |
| 7 | 1 1 1 | 1 | 4 |

Note that the check-bit technique will detect errors in one or three bits but not errors in two or four bits.   Define the probability of good operation as the probability of no errors plus the probability of detecting an error. Compute the probability of good operation as the probability of zero errors plus the probability of one error plus the probability of three errors.   What is the probability that the message is correct but we get a false detection of error as the result of an error in the check bit?

(c)  Another way to improve the coding is to repeat each of the three digits three times and compare the three transmissions for each digit. (This method is based on the assumption that errors in adjacent digits are independent.) Such a code would be given by

| | Three transmissions for each bit of three-bit code | | |
|---|---|---|---|
| Decimal digit | First bit | Second bit | Third bit |
| 0 | 0 0 0 | 0 0 0 | 0 0 0 |
| 1 | 0 0 0 | 0 0 0 | 1 1 1 |
| 2 | 0 0 0 | 1 1 1 | 0 0 0 |
| 3 | 0 0 0 | 1 1 1 | 1 1 1 |
| 4 | 1 1 1 | 0 0 0 | 0 0 0 |
| 5 | 1 1 1 | 0 0 0 | 1 1 1 |
| 6 | 1 1 1 | 1 1 1 | 0 0 0 |
| 7 | 1 1 1 | 1 1 1 | 1 1 1 |

The three transmissions are compared and the majority rules; e.g., if we had a transmission of 111, 101, 110, 011, we would call the bit a one, and if we had a transmission of 000, 010, 001, 100, we would call the bit a zero. The probability of a bit error $q'$ can be calculated from the probability of a transmission error $q$ as the probability of 0 transmission errors plus the probability of one transmission error. Compute $q'$ and repeat the calculations in part $a$ using $q'$.

(d)  If $q = 0.01$, compare the probabilities calculated in parts $a$ to $c$.

# catastrophic-
# failure models

## 4.1 INTRODUCTION

The previous chapter has shown how one constructs various combinatorial reliability models which express system reliability in terms of element reliability. This chapter introduces several different failure models for the system elements.[1] These element failure models are related to life-test results and failure-rate data via probability theory. The reader may wonder why the reliability of an individual part is not computed from the basic physics of failure. For example, given a certain capacitor which is constructed in a known manner with a given dielectric material operating under known conditions of temperature, pressure, humidity, and voltage, one should be able to predict the component failure rate in terms of the above parameters and a "basic" capacitor failure rate. Some information exists on these subjects, and it will be discussed; however, at present such information is insufficient to formulate a general theory. An even more fundamental approach is to formulate a hypothesis that capacitor failures occur as a result of dielectric breakdown,

---

[1] The elements may be subsystems, units, or parts. It is desirable to model the reliability structure of the system in fine detail so that the elements are parts, since most available data are on parts. If the structural model contains units or subsystems, life testing of these elements will in most cases be required.

then formulate a theory which relates breakdown to dielectric defects, impurities, voltage, time, etc. Some physics-of-failure models are developed in Chap. 8, but more study is needed before such models are ready for general use. Thus, at the present stage of development of reliability theory, reliabilities must be linked to experimental or field-failure data. The first step in constructing a failure model is to locate test data or plan a test on parts substantially the same as those to be used. From these data the part failure rate is computed and graphed. On the basis of the graph, any physical failure information, engineering judgment, and sometimes statistical tests (see Chap. 8) a failure-rate model is chosen. The parameters of the model are estimated from the graph or computed using the statistical principles of point estimation, which are developed in Chap. 8. This chapter discusses the treatment of the data and the choice of a model.

The emphasis is on simple models, which are easy to work with and contain one or two parameters. This simplifies the problems of interpretation and parameter determination. Also in most cases the data are not abundant enough and the test conditions are not sufficiently descriptive of the proposed usage to warrant more complex models. The mathematical background for this chapter is given in Secs. 2.5 to 2.7.

## 4.2   TREATMENT OF FAILURE DATA

Part failure data are generally obtained from two sources, the failure times of various items in a population placed on a life test, or repair reports listing operating hours of replaced parts in equipment already in field use. Experience has shown that a very good way to present these data is to compute and plot either the failure density function or the hazard rate as a function of time.

The data we are dealing with are a sequence of times to failure, but the failure density function and the hazard rate introduced in Chap. 2 are continuous variables. We first compute a piecewise-continuous failure density function and hazard rate from the data.[1] Study of these piecewise-continuous functions is followed by the choice of a continuous model which fits the data satisfactorily. This is, of course, a specific approach to the very general engineering problem of how to model a problem from certain qualitative knowledge about the system supported by quantative data.

We begin by *defining* piecewise-continuous failure density and hazard-

---

[1] Often it is also useful to calculate a data failure distribution function and a data success distribution function (reliability function).

rate functions in terms of the data.   In Sec. 4.4 it will be shown that these discrete functions approach the continuous functions in the limit as the number of data becomes large and the interval between failure times approaches zero.   Assume that our data describe a set of $N$ items placed in operation at time $t = 0$.   As time progresses, items fail, and at any time $t$ the number of survivors is $n(t)$.   The data density function (also called empirical density function) defined over the time interval $t_i < t \leq t_i + \Delta t_i$ is given by the ratio of the number of failures occurring in the interval $t_0$ the size of the original population, divided by the length of the time interval[1]

$$f_d(t) = \frac{[n(t_i) - n(t_i + \Delta t_i)]/N}{\Delta t_i} \qquad \text{for } t_i < t \leq t_i + \Delta t_i \qquad (4.1)$$

Similarly, the data hazard rate[2] over the interval $t_i < t \leq t_i + \Delta t_i$ is defined as the ratio of the number of failures occurring in the time interval to the number of survivors at the beginning of the time interval, divided by the length of the time interval

$$z_d(t) = \frac{[n(t_i) - n(t_i + \Delta t_i)]/n(t_i)}{\Delta t_i} \qquad \text{for } t_i < t \leq t_i + \Delta t_i \qquad (4.2)$$

The failure density function $f_d(t)$ is a measure of the overall speed at which failures are occurring, whereas the hazard rate $z_d(t)$ is a measure of the instantaneous speed of failure.   Since the numerators of both Eqs. (4.1) and (4.2) are dimensionless, both $f_d(t)$ and $z_d(t)$ have the dimensions of inverse time (generally the time unit is hours).   The choice of $t_i$ and $\Delta t_i$ in Eqs. (4.1) and (4.2) is unspecified and is best discussed in terms of the examples which follow.

The failure data for a life test run on a group of 10 hypothetical electronic components are given in Table 4.1.   The computation of $f_d(t)$ and $z_d(t)$ from the data appear in Table 4.2.

The time intervals $\Delta t_i$ were chosen as the times between failure, and the first time interval $t_0$ started at the origin; that is, $t_0 = 0$.   The remaining time intervals $t_i$ coincided with the failure times.   In each case the failure was assumed to have occurred just before the end of the interval. Two alternate procedures are possible.   The failure could have been assumed to occur just after the time interval closed, or the beginning of each interval $t_i$ could have been defined as the midpoint between failures. In this book we shall consistently use the first method, which is illustrated

---

[1] In general a sequence of time intervals $t_0 < t \leq t_0 + \Delta t_0$, $t_1 < t \leq t_1 + \Delta t_1$, etc., is defined, where $t_1 = t_0 + \Delta t_0$, $t_2 = t_1 + \Delta t_1$, etc.

[2] Hazard rate is sometimes called hazard or failure rate.

Table 4.1 Failure data for ten hypothetical electronic components

| Failure number | Operating time, hr |
|---|---|
| 1 | 8 |
| 2 | 20 |
| 3 | 34 |
| 4 | 46 |
| 5 | 63 |
| 6 | 86 |
| 7 | 111 |
| 8 | 141 |
| 9 | 186 |
| 10 | 266 |

in Table 4.2. It would be an unusual example where a different choice of $t_i$ and $\Delta t_i$ led to a different model. Furthermore, the determination of model parameters using estimation theory generally results in computations which are made directly from the failure times themselves, rather than from $f_d(t)$ or $z_d(t)$. Thus the results are independent of the choice of $t_i$. For a further discussion see Hoel[1] and Chap. 8.

Since $f_d(t)$ is a density function, we can *define* a data failure distribution function and a data success distribution function by

$$F_d(t) = \int_0^t f_d(\xi)\, d\xi \qquad (4.3)\dagger$$

$$R_d(t) = 1 - F_d(t) = 1 - \int_0^t f_d(\xi)\, d\xi \qquad (4.4)\dagger$$

Since the $f_d(t)$ curve is a piecewise-continuous function consisting of a sum of step functions, its integral is a piecewise-continuous function made up of a sum of ramp functions.

The functions $F_d(t)$ and $R_d(t)$ are computed for the preceding example by appropriate integration of Fig. 4.1a and are given in Fig. 4.1c and d. The initial behavior of the $R_d(t)$ curve justifies the choice of the initial interval from $t_0 = 0$ to $t_1 = $ first failure time and our inclusion of the first failure in the first interval. If the first failure had been placed in the second interval, the $R_d(t)$ curve would have been unity from $t = 0$ to $t = t_1$. Similarly if $t_0$ had not been chosen at the origin, $R_d(t)$ would be unity from $t = 0$ to $t = t_0$. In either case the predicted system reliability would have been unity over some initial time period which does not agree

[1] Paul G. Hoel, "Introduction to Mathematical Statistics," sec. 4.2, John Wiley & Sons, Inc., New York, 1955.
† Where $\xi$ is just a dummy variable of integration.

**Table 4.2  Computation of data failure density and data hazard rate**

| Time interval, hr | Failure density per hr $f_d(t)(\times 10^{-2})$ | Hazard rate per hr $z_d(t)(\times 10^{-2})$ |
|---|---|---|
| 0–8 | $\dfrac{1}{10 \times 8} = 1.25$ | $\dfrac{1}{10 \times 8} = 1.25$ |
| 8–20 | $\dfrac{1}{10 \times 12} = 0.84$ | $\dfrac{1}{9 \times 12} = 0.93$ |
| 20–34 | $\dfrac{1}{10 \times 14} = 0.72$ | $\dfrac{1}{8 \times 14} = 0.96$ |
| 34–46 | $\dfrac{1}{10 \times 12} = 0.84$ | $\dfrac{1}{7 \times 12} = 1.19$ |
| 46–63 | $\dfrac{1}{10 \times 17} = 0.59$ | $\dfrac{1}{6 \times 17} = 0.98$ |
| 63–86 | $\dfrac{1}{10 \times 23} = 0.44$ | $\dfrac{1}{5 \times 23} = 0.87$ |
| 86–111 | $\dfrac{1}{10 \times 25} = 0.40$ | $\dfrac{1}{4 \times 25} = 1.00$ |
| 111–141 | $\dfrac{1}{10 \times 30} = 0.33$ | $\dfrac{1}{3 \times 30} = 1.11$ |
| 141–186 | $\dfrac{1}{10 \times 45} = 0.22$ | $\dfrac{1}{2 \times 45} = 1.11$ |
| 186–266 | $\dfrac{1}{10 \times 80} = 0.13$ | $\dfrac{1}{1 \times 80} = 1.25$ |

with physical reasoning. Because of the choice of $t_0 = 0$ and $t_i = i$th failure time, the $R_d(t)$ curve is simply computed at the failure times. By inspection of Eqs. (4.1) and (4.3) or Fig. 4.1a and b we see that

$$R_d(t_i) = \frac{n(t_i)}{N} \tag{4.5}$$

The simplest way to compute the $R_d(t)$ curve is to use Eq. (4.5) at each value of $t_i$ and to connect these points by a set of straight lines.[1] The $R_d(t)$ function provides a graphical picture of one reliability function which can be deduced from the data. In general it is better to fit a theoretical model to the data and use the resulting reliability function instead. As we shall shortly see, in fitting a model to the data it is most convenient to work with the $z_d(t)$ curve; therefore, the $f_d(t)$, $F_d(t)$, and $R_d(t)$ curves are less frequently displayed.

In the example given in Table 4.1, only 10 items were on test, and the computations were easily made. If many items are tested, the computation intervals $\Delta t_i$ cannot be chosen as the times between failures since

---

[1] Sometimes Eq. (4.5) is used, and the points are connected by horizontal and vertical lines to form a staircase curve. The procedure given in the text is preferred, since a step approximation to $f_d(t)$ implies a ramp approximation to $R_d(t)$.

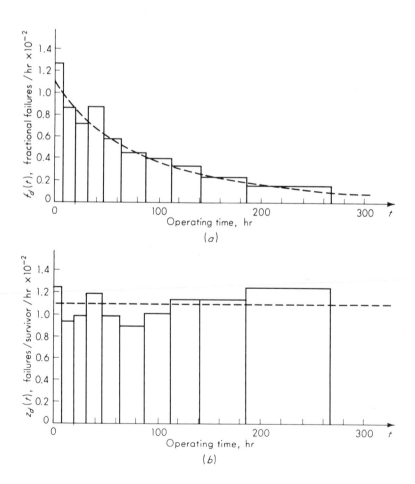

(a)

(b)

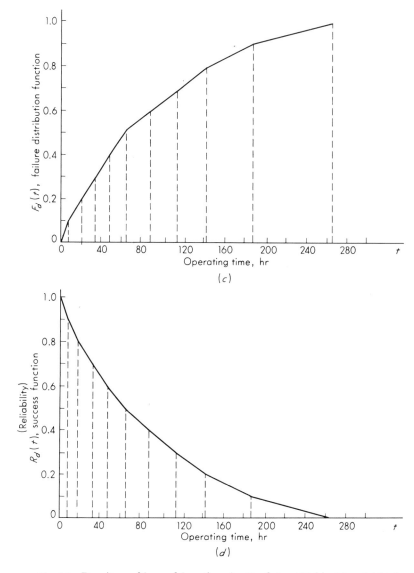

**Fig. 4.1**   Density and hazard functions for the data of Table 4.1.   (*a*) Data failure density function; (*b*) data hazard rate; (*c*) data failure distribution function; and (*d*) data success function.

**Table 4.3    Failure data for 172 hypothetical components**

| Time interval, hr | Failures in the interval |
|---|---|
| 0–1,000 | 59 |
| 1,001–2,000 | 24 |
| 2,001–3,000 | 29 |
| 3,001–4,000 | 30 |
| 4,001–5,000 | 17 |
| 5,001–6,000 | 13 |
| | Total $\overline{172}$ |

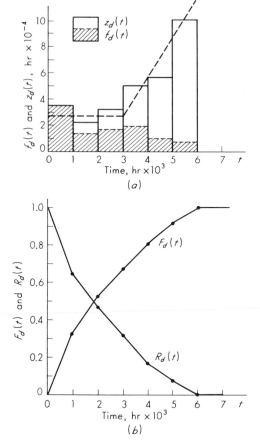

**Fig. 4.2** Reliability functions for the example given in Table 4.3.  (a) $f_d(t)$ and $z_d(t)$; (b) $F_d(t)$ and $R_d(t)$.

the computations become too lengthy.  The solution is to divide the time scale into several equally spaced intervals.  Statisticians call these *class intervals*, and the midpoint of the interval is called a *class mark*.  For example, the data in Table 4.3 represents data failure tabulated in class intervals of 1,000 hr.  The $f_d(t)$ and $z_d(t)$ functions given in Table 4.4 and graphed in Fig. 4.2a are computed from these data.  The $t_i$'s are chosen as the beginning of the class interval, and the $\Delta t_i$'s are the length of the class interval.  The $f_d(t)$ curve appears to fluctuate somewhat, but the overall trend seems to be a decreasing one.  The $z_d(t)$ curve appears to decrease initially and then increase rapidly with time.

The $F_d(t)$ and $R_d(t)$ functions are given in Fig. 4.2b and are obtained from Eqs. (4.3) and (4.4).  Note that Eq. (4.5) also holds in the case of grouped data.  Although the shape of the $f_d(t)$ and the $z_d(t)$ change, the $F(t)$ curve increases monotonically and the $R_d(t)$ curve decreases monotonically.

The reader may wonder why a class interval of 1,000 hr was chosen for this problem.  In this case it was done for the convenience of a round number.  In general, too many class intervals involve too much labor, whereas too few may average or smooth the data to such an extent that the time variations in $f_d(t)$ or $z_d(t)$ are concealed.  It has been shown that

**Table 4.4  Failure rates of hypothetical component**

| Time interval, hr | Failure density $f_d(t)(\times 10^{-4})$ | Hazard rate $z_d(t)(\times 10^{-4})$ |
|---|---|---|
| 0–1,000 | $\dfrac{59}{172 \times 10^3} = 3.43$ | $\dfrac{59}{172 \times 10^3} = 3.43$ |
| 1,001–2,000 | $\dfrac{24}{172 \times 10^3} = 1.40$ | $\dfrac{24}{113 \times 10^3} = 2.12$ |
| 2,001–3,000 | $\dfrac{29}{172 \times 10^3} = 1.69$ | $\dfrac{29}{89 \times 10^3} = 3.26$ |
| 3,001–4,000 | $\dfrac{30}{172 \times 10^3} = 1.74$ | $\dfrac{30}{60 \times 10^3} = 5.00$ |
| 4,001–5,000 | $\dfrac{17}{172 \times 10^3} = 0.99$ | $\dfrac{17}{30 \times 10^3} = 5.69$ |
| 5,001–6,000 | $\dfrac{13}{172 \times 10^3} = 0.76$ | $\dfrac{13}{13 \times 10^3} = 10.00$ |

**Table 4.5  Failure data for 1,000 B-52 aircraft**

| Time till failure, hr | Number of failures in interval | Failure density $f_d(t)$ | Hazard rate $z_d(t)$ |
|---|---|---|---|
| 0–2 | 222 | $\dfrac{222}{1{,}000 \times 2} = 0.1110$ | $\dfrac{222}{1{,}000 \times 2} = 0.1110$ |
| 2–4 | 45 | $\dfrac{45}{1{,}000 \times 2} = 0.0225$ | $\dfrac{45}{778 \times 2} = 0.0289$ |
| 4–6 | 32 | $\dfrac{32}{1{,}000 \times 2} = 0.0160$ | $\dfrac{32}{733 \times 2} = 0.0218$ |
| 6–8 | 27 | $\dfrac{27}{1{,}000 \times 2} = 0.0135$ | $\dfrac{27}{701 \times 2} = 0.0192$ |
| 8–10 | 21 | $\dfrac{21}{1{,}000 \times 2} = 0.0105$ | $\dfrac{21}{674 \times 2} = 0.0156$ |
| 10–12 | 15 | $\dfrac{15}{1{,}000 \times 2} = 0.0075$ | $\dfrac{15}{653 \times 2} = 0.0113$ |
| 12–14 | 17 | $\dfrac{17}{1{,}000 \times 2} = 0.0085$ | $\dfrac{17}{638 \times 2} = 0.0133$ |
| 14–16 | 7 | $\dfrac{7}{1{,}000 \times 2} = 0.0035$ | $\dfrac{7}{621 \times 2} = 0.0056$ |
| 16–18 | 14 | $\dfrac{14}{1{,}000 \times 2} = 0.0070$ | $\dfrac{14}{614 \times 2} = 0.0114$ |
| 18–20 | 9 | $\dfrac{9}{1{,}000 \times 2} = 0.0045$ | $\dfrac{9}{600 \times 2} = 0.0075$ |
| 20–22 | 8 | $\dfrac{8}{1{,}000 \times 2} = 0.0040$ | $\dfrac{8}{591 \times 2} = 0.0068$ |
| 22–24 | Total $\dfrac{3}{420}$ | $\dfrac{3}{1{,}000 \times 2} = 0.0015$ | $\dfrac{3}{583 \times 2} = 0.0026$ |

SOURCE: R. Horn and G. Shoup, Determination and Use of Failure Patterns, *IEEE Proc. Eighth Natl. Symp. Reliability Quality Control*, January, 1962.

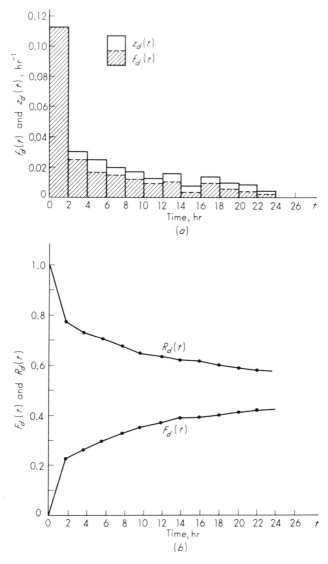

**Fig. 4.3**  Reliability functions for the example given in Table 4.5.  (a) $f_d(t)$ and $z_d(t)$; (b) $F_d(t)$ and $R_d(t)$.

the optimum number of class intervals in many cases is given by the formula[1]

$$K = 1 + 3.3 \log N \qquad (4.6)$$

where $K \equiv$ optimum number of class intervals
$\qquad N \equiv$ number of failures

Generally the number of data ranges between 10 and 1,000, which corresponds to $K$ between 4.3 and 10.9, thus the choice of $K$ is not at all critical, and convenient values such as 5, 10, or 15 will suffice.[2]

A third example of failure data is shown in Table 4.5 and Fig. 4.3. These hypothetical data depict failures in B-52 bombers performing various 24-hr missions. As can be seen in Fig. 4.3a, both $z_d(t)$ and $f_d(t)$ decrease in time. The associated $F_d(t)$ and $R_d(t)$ curves are given in Fig. 4.3b. Since the data are available for a length of time during which only 42 percent of the population failed, $R_d(t)$ never reaches zero and $F_d(t)$ never reaches unity. In such a situation, fitting the data with a model will allow us to extrapolate the reliability beyond 24 hr of operation.

The three examples illustrate the fact that many different kinds of $f_d(t)$ and $z_d(t)$ curves can occur when different types of data are analyzed. The next section discusses general trends in failure data and handbook failure data.

## 4.3  FAILURE MODES AND HANDBOOK FAILURE DATA

After plotting and examining failure data for several years, people began to recognize several modes of failure. Early in the lifetime of equipment or a part, there are a large number of failures due to initial weakness or defects: poor insulation, weak parts, bad assembly, poor fits, etc. During the middle period of equipment operation fewer failures take place, but it is difficult to determine their cause. In general they seem to occur when the environmental stresses exceed the design strengths of the part or equipment. It is difficult to predict the environmental-stress amplitudes or the part strengths as deterministic functions of time; thus the middle-life failures are often called *random failures*. As the item reaches old age, things begin to deteriorate, and many failures occur. This failure region is quite naturally called the *wearout region*. Typical $f(t)$ and $z(t)$ curves[3] illustrating these three modes of behavior are shown

---

[1] H. A. Sturges, The Choice of a Class Interval, *J. Am. Statist. Assoc.*, vol. 21, pp. 65–66, 1926.

[2] Hoel, *op. cit.*, sec. 4.5 states: "In classifying data for a continuous variable, experience indicates that for most data it is desirable to use from 10 to 20 classes."

[3] We are now referring to continuous hazard and failure density functions, which represent the limiting forms of $f_d(t)$ and $z_d(t)$ as discussed in Sec. 4.4.

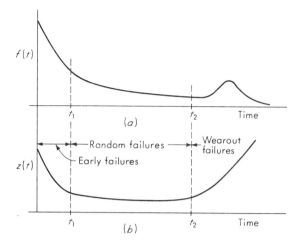

**Fig. 4.4**  General form of failure curves.  (a)  Failure density; (b)  hazard rate.

in Fig. 4.4.  The early failures, also called *initial failures* or *infant mortality*,[1] appear as decreasing $z(t)$ and $f(t)$ functions.  The random failure, or constant-hazard-rate mode, is characterized by an approximately constant $z(t)$ and a companion $f(t)$ which is approximately exponential.  In the wearout, or rising-failure-rate region, the $z(t)$ function increases whereas $f(t)$ has a humped appearance.  Physical failure models which explain in part these failure modes are discussed in Chap. 8.  It is clear that it is easier to distinguish the various failure modes by inspection of the $z(t)$ curve than it is from the appearance of the $f(t)$ function.  This is one of the major reasons why hazard rate is introduced.  Because of the monotonic nature of $F(t)$ and $R(t)$ these functions are even less useful in distinguishing failure modes.

The curve of Fig. 4.4 has been discussed by many of the early writers on the subject of reliability[2] and is often called the *bathtub curve* because of its shape.  The fact that such a hazard curve occurs for many types of equipment has been verified by experience.  Also when failed components have been dismantled to determine the reasons for failure, the conclusions have again justified the hypothesis of three failure modes.  In fact most manufacturers of high-reliability components now subject their products to an initial burn-in period of $t_1$ hr to eliminate the initial failure region shown in Fig. 4.4.  At the onset of wearout at time $t_2$, the

[1] Some of the terms, as well as the concept of hazard, have been borrowed from those used by actuaries, who deal with life insurance statistics.

[2] R. R. Carhart, A Survey of the Current Status of the Reliability Problem, *Rand Corp. Res. Mem.* RM-1131, Aug. 14, 1953.

hazard rate begins to increase rapidly, and it is wise to replace the item after $t_2$ hr of operation.  Thus, if the bathtub curve were really a universal model, one would pretest components for $t_1$ hr, place the survivors in use for an additional $t_2 - t_1$ hr, and then replace them with fresh pretested components.  This would reduce the effective hazard rate and improve the probability of survival.  Unfortunately, many types of equipment have a continuously decreasing or continuously increasing hazard and therefore behave differently.  It often happens that electronic components have a constant hazard and mechanical components a wearout characteristic.  Unfortunately, not enough comparative analysis has been performed on different types of components.  In the future, when more complete data analyses have been performed and experience gained, such hypotheses about classes of components will be useful as general statements.

As discussed in Chap. 1, many failure data on parts and components have been recorded since the beginning of formal interest in reliability in the early 1950s.  Large industrial organizations such as Radio Corporation of America, General Electric Company, Motorola, etc., publish handbooks of part failure-rate data compiled from life-test and field-failure data.  These data and other information were compiled into a

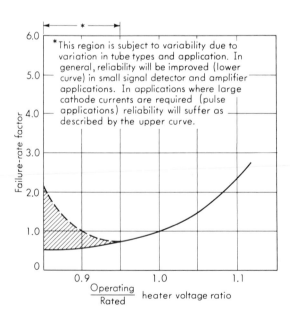

**Fig. 4.5** Vacuum-tube failure-rate adjustment factor for heater voltage.

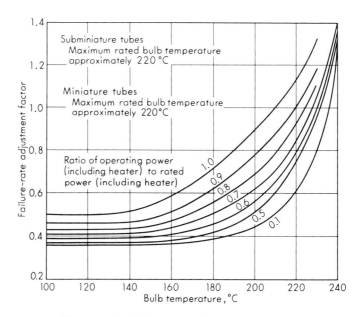

**Fig. 4.6** Vacuum-tube failure-rate adjustment factor for temperature-dissipation effects.

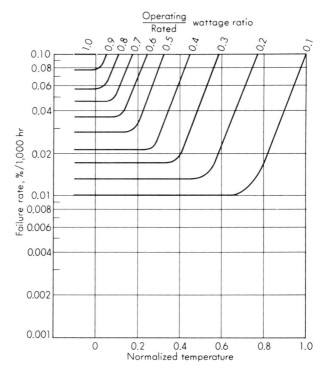

**Fig. 4.7** Diode failure rates.

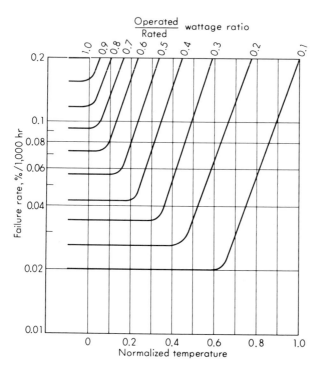

**Fig. 4.8**  Transistor failure rates.

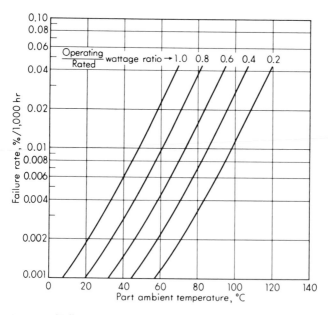

**Fig. 4.9**  Failure rates for MIL-R-11C composition resistors, temperature range GF (relative humidity less than 60 percent).

military handbook in 1962.[1]   At the outset of reliability testing it was recognized that the reliability of a part would vary greatly as the environment varied.   Thus, the reliability of a resistor is a function of the power it dissipates; capacitor reliability depends on applied working voltage; gear reliability is a function of the load transmitted.   In most cases secondary variables such as temperature, pressure, humidity, etc., are also important.   To run life tests as a function of the several environmental parameters involves huge numbers of components, lengthy tests,

[1] Figures 4.5 to 4.14 are adapted from "Reliability Stress and Failure Rate Data," MIL-HDBK-217, Government Printing Office, Washington, D.C., 1962.   The second edition bears the number MIL-HDBK-217A, and was published in 1965.   It is disquieting that in many cases 217A (based on different but supposedly equivalent data) tabulates failure rates a decade higher than 217.   Not only is the magnitude of the difference significant, but the direction is counter to the trend which one would expect during a time of component-reliability improvement.   For more details see reference to A. Golant in Bibliography for Chap. 4, page 512.   Another voluminous failure data handbook is "Failure Rate Data Handbook" (FARADA), also listed on page 512. The FARADA handbook includes such vital information as the *number on test*, the *number of failures*, and some details on the *source* of the data and the *environment*. This information allows one to use engineering judgment in selecting failure rates from this reference.

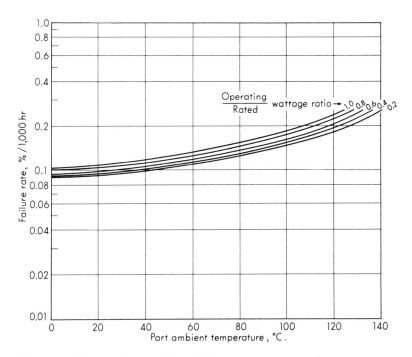

**Fig. 4.10**   Failure rates for MIL-R-93B accurate wire-wound resistors, temperature range C (relative humidity less than 60 percent).

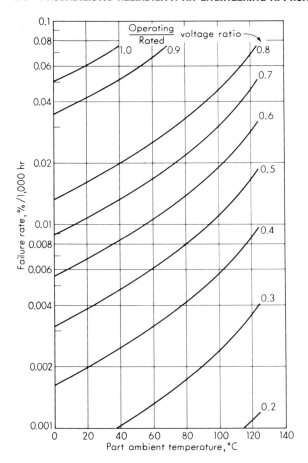

**Fig. 4.11** Failure rates for MIL-C-1415 7B high-reliability paper capacitors (relative humidity less than 60 percent).

extensive environmental laboratory facilities, and large costs. In most cases tests are run as a function of the one or two most obvious and important parameters, with all others held fixed at some nominal value or allowed to vary over some intended operating range. The failure rates (hazard values) computed from the data are plotted as a function of the environmental parameter or parameters. Typical curves[1,2] are

[1] These curves are adapted from MIL-HDBK-217, *op. cit.*

[2] These failure-rate figures for these curves are the best engineering approximation of the reliability characteristics (random failures) for the parts designated when employed repeatedly, within their specification ratings, in complex electronic equipments. Failures are considered to be opens, shorts, or radical departures from initial characteristics occurring in an unpredictable manner, and in too short a period of time to permit detection through normal preventive-maintenance practices.

given in Figs. 4.5 to 4.14, for vacuum tubes, diodes, transistors, carbon resistors, wire-wound resistors, paper capacitors, tantalum capacitors, transformers, and motor bearings.   Figures 4.5 and 4.6 give the adjustment factor in the basic failure rate of vacuum tubes due to other than rated heater voltage, operating power, and glass (or metal) bulb temperature.   The remaining eight curves present failure rates as functions of various environmental parameters.

The failure rates (hazard rates) are quoted as percent per 1,000 hr, which is equivalent to $10^{-5}$ per hr.   (Sometimes failure rates are quoted in terms of percent per million hours, which is equivalent to $10^{-8}$ per hr.) Although it is not explicitly stated, we can assume that all these data were computed on the basis that the hazard for the components was constant in time.   In such a case, the statistical principles discussed in Chap. 8 show that if the data consist of $n$ failure times $t_1, t_2, \ldots, t_n$,

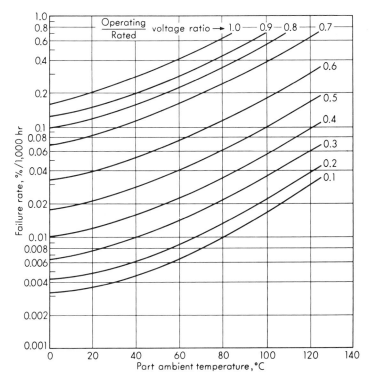

**Fig. 4.12**   Failure rates for MIL-C-26655A solid-tantalum capacitors (relative humidity less than 60 percent).

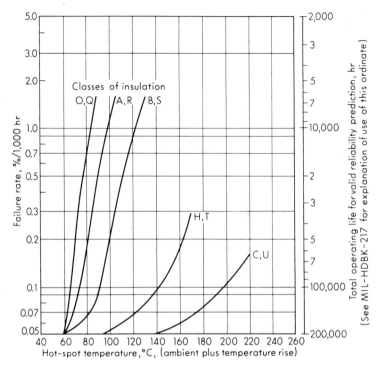

**Fig. 4.13** Failure rates for transformers, magnetic amplifiers, inductors and coils. (Class C and U characteristics will vary significantly as a function of the insulation design temperature specified. The curve given represents an estimate of the average.)

the constant hazard associated with this model is given by $n/(t_1 + t_2 + \cdots + t_n)$.† We can assume that the values given in MIL-HDBK-217 were computed in this manner. Unfortunately we cannot verify how valid a constant-hazard model is unless the actual failure times are available. If the original failure data were obtained, we could use the graphical techniques of Sec. 4.2 or the statistical methods given in Chap. 8

† This formula assumes that $n$ items were tested and all $n$ failed. If $n$ were tested for $T$ hr and only $r$ failed, the test is called a *truncated* one, and the appropriate formula for calculating a constant hazard is

$$\lambda = \frac{r}{\sum_{i=1}^{r} t_i + (n - r)T}$$

(see Chap. 8).

to check the validity of the constant-hazard assumption.   It is necessary to use good judgment in applying failure-rate information from handbooks, reports, and papers, and to uncover as much information as possible about the assumptions and limitations inherent in the reduction of the data before proceeding.

One can develop failure-rate data from life tests on circuits, units, subsystems, and systems as well as components.   A test on a larger piece of equipment involves more expensive test specimens, shorter times, and more specific information than a component test.   In general, wherever feasible it is probably better to use component failure-rate information and the techniques of combinatorial analysis presented in Chap. 3 to compute the reliability of a unit, rather than a life test of the unit itself. Because of many factors, a combination of both techniques is probably the wisest policy.   The reliabilities of a wide spectrum of different devices and systems are compared in Fig. 4.15.   The MTBF in hours, given in

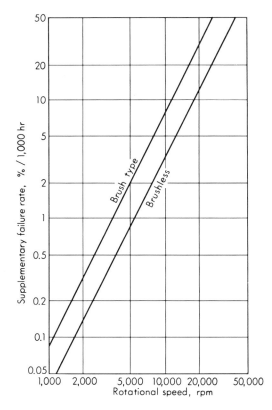

**Fig. 4.14** Supplementary failure rates for motor speeds (motor bearings).

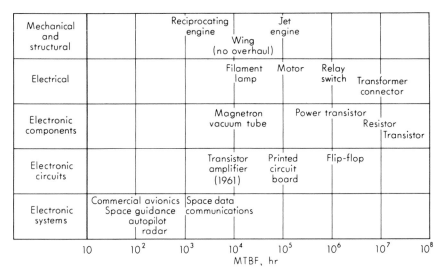

| | | Reciprocating engine | Jet engine | | |
|---|---|---|---|---|---|

**Fig. 4.15** Reliabilities of selected components. (*E. J. Nolos and R. B. Schultz, Reliability and Cost of Avionics, IEEE Trans. Reliability, October,* 1965.)

the abscissa of the graph, is simply the reciprocal of the constant failure rate.   A complete discussion of MTBF appears in Sec. 4.6.

## 4.4   RELIABILITY IN TERMS OF HAZARD RATE AND FAILURE DENSITY

In Sec. 4.2 various functions associated with failure data were defined and computed for the data given in the examples.   These functions were $z_d(t)$, $f_d(t)$, $F_d(t)$, and $R_d(t)$.   In this section we begin by defining two random variables and deriving in a careful manner the basic definitions and relations between the theoretical hazard, failure density function, failure distribution function, and reliability function.

The random variable $t$ is defined as the failure time of the item in question.   Thus, the probability of failure as a function of time is given as

$$P(\mathbf{t} \leq t) = F(t) \tag{4.7}$$

which is simply the definition of the failure distribution function.   We can define the reliability, which is a probability of success in terms of $F(t)$, as

$$R(t) = P_s(t) = 1 - F(t) = P(\mathbf{t} > t) \tag{4.8}$$

The failure density function is of course given by

$$\frac{dF(t)}{dt} = f(t) \tag{4.9}$$

We now consider a population of $N$ items with the same failure-time distribution. The items fail independently with probability of failure given by $F(t) = 1 - R(t)$ and probability of success given by $R(t)$. If the random variable $\mathbf{N}(t)$ represents the number of units surviving at time $t$, then $\mathbf{N}(t)$ has a binomial distribution with $p = R(t)$. Therefore,

$$P[\mathbf{N}(t) = n] = B[n;\mathbf{N},R(t)] = \frac{N!}{n!(N-n)!} [R(t)]^n[1 - R(t)]^{N-n}$$

$$n = 0, 1, \ldots, N \tag{4.10}$$

The number of units operating at any time $t$ is a random variable and is not fixed; however, we can compute the expected value of $\mathbf{N}(t)$. From Table 2.4 we see that the expected value of a random variable with a binomial distribution is given by $NR(t)$ and leads to

$$n(t) \equiv E[\mathbf{N}(t)] = NR(t) \quad = \text{the } \# \text{ that survive through time } t \tag{4.11}$$

Solving for the reliability yields

$$R(t) = \frac{n(t)}{N} \tag{4.12}$$

Thus, the reliability at time $t$ is the average fraction of surviving units at time $t$. This verifies Eq. (4.5), which was obtained as a consequence of the definition of $f_d(t)$. From Eq. (4.8) we obtain

$$F(t) = 1 - \frac{n(t)}{N} = \frac{N - n(t)}{N}. \tag{4.13}$$

and from Eq. (4.9)

$$f(t) = \frac{dF(t)}{dt} = -\frac{1}{N}\frac{dn(t)}{dt}$$

$$f(t) \equiv \lim_{\Delta t \to 0} \frac{n(t) - n(t + \Delta t)}{N \, \Delta t} \tag{4.14}$$

Thus, we see that Eq. (4.1) is valid, and as $N$ becomes large and $\Delta t_i$ becomes small, Eq. (4.1) approaches Eq. (4.14) in the limit. From Eq. (4.13) we see that $F(t)$ is the average fraction of units having failed between 0 and time $t$, and Eq. (4.14) states that $f(t)$ is the rate of change of $F(t)$, or its slope. From Eq. (4.14) we see that the failure density function $f(t)$ is *normalized* in terms of the size of the original population $N$. In many cases it is more informative to normalize with respect to $n(t)$, the number of survivors.  Thus, we define the hazard rate as

$$z(t) \equiv - \lim_{\Delta t \to 0} \frac{n(t) - n(t + \Delta t)}{n(t) \, \Delta t} \tag{4.15}$$

The definition of $z(t)$ in Eq. (4.15) of course agrees with the definition of $z_d(t)$ in Eq. (4.2).   We can relate $z(t)$ and $f(t)$ using Eqs. (4.14) and (4.15)

$$z(t) = - \lim_{\Delta t \to 0} \frac{n(t) - n(t + \Delta t)}{\Delta t} \frac{1}{n(t)} = N f(t) \frac{1}{n(t)}$$

Substitution of Eq. (4.12) yields

$$z(t) = \frac{f(t)}{R(t)} \tag{4.16}$$

We now wish to relate $R(t)$ to $f(t)$ and to $z(t)$.   From Eqs. (4.12) and (4.13) we see that

$$R(t) = 1 - F(t)$$
$$= 1 - \int_0^t f(\xi) \, d\xi \tag{4.17}$$

where $\xi$ is merely a dummy variable.   Substituting into Eq. (4.16) from Eqs. (4.14) and (4.12), we obtain

$$z(t) = - \frac{1}{N} \frac{dn(t)}{dt} \frac{N}{n(t)} = - \frac{d}{dt} \ln n(t)$$
$$\ln n(t) = - \int_0^t z(\xi) \, d\xi + c$$

where $\xi$ is a dummy variable and $c$ is the constant of integration,

$$n(t) = e^c \exp \left[ - \int_0^t z(\xi) \, d\xi \right]$$

Inserting initial conditions

$$n(0) = N = e^c$$

gives

$$n(t) = N \exp \left[ - \int_0^t z(\xi) \, d\xi \right]$$

Substitution of Eq. (4.12) completes the derivation

$$R(t) = \exp \left[ - \int_0^t z(\xi) \, d\xi \right] \tag{4.18}$$

Equations (4.14) and (4.15) serve to define the failure density function and the hazard rate, and Eqs. (4.16) to (4.18) relate $R(t)$ to $f(t)$ and $z(t)$.
   The concept of a hazard rate $z(t)$ is so fundamental to the material which follows that the alternative derivation of $z(t)$ given in Sec. 2.9.3 is repeated here.   In a manner analogous to Eq. (4.7) we define the prob-

ability of failure in a time interval $\Delta t$ as

$$P(t < \mathbf{t} \leq t + \Delta t) = F(t + \Delta t) - F(t) \tag{4.19}$$

Equation (4.19) can be written in terms of the probability of survival up to time $t$, $R(t)$, and the conditional probability of failure in the interval $t < \mathbf{t} \leq t + \Delta t$ given survival up to time $t$

$$P(t < \mathbf{t} \leq t + \Delta t) = R(t)P(t < \mathbf{t} \leq t + \Delta t | \mathbf{t} > t) \tag{4.20}$$

Combining Eqs. (4.19) and (4.20), we obtain

$$P(t < \mathbf{t} \leq t + \Delta t | \mathbf{t} > t) = \frac{F(t + \Delta t) - F(t)}{R(t)} \tag{4.21}$$

Dividing both sides of Eq. (4.21) by $\Delta t$ and taking the limit as $\Delta t \to 0$ yields

$$\frac{dP(t < \mathbf{t} < t + \Delta t | \mathbf{t} > t)}{dt} = \frac{dF(t)/dt}{R(t)} = \frac{f(t)}{R(t)} \tag{4.22}$$

Comparison of Eqs. (4.22) and (4.16) shows that $z(t)$ is the time rate of change of the conditional probability of failure.   Inspection of Eqs. (4.7) and (4.9) shows that $f(t)$ is the time rate of change of the ordinary failure probability.

As discussed in Sec. 4.2, it is easier to formulate models based on $z(t)$ than on $f(t)$; therefore, it is often necessary to convert from $z(t)$ to $f(t)$ and vice versa.   Using Eqs. (4.16) and (4.17), we obtain

$$z(t) = \frac{f(t)}{1 - \int_0^t f(\xi)\, d\xi} \tag{4.23}$$

and from Eqs. (4.16) and (4.18)

$$f(t) = z(t) \exp\left[ - \int_0^t z(\xi)\, d\xi \right] \tag{4.24}$$

The example discussed in Sec. 2.9.3 showed that a constant hazard $\lambda$ corresponds to an exponential density $\lambda e^{-\lambda t}$.   This can be verified in both directions, using Eqs. (4.23) and (4.24).

Now that $R(t)$ is determined in terms of $f(t)$ and $z(t)$, we can begin to discuss various density-function and hazard-rate models.   Before we start, however, we should investigate how the properties of density and distribution functions will influence $f(t)$ and $z(t)$.   This is to ensure that a model for $f(t)$ or $z(t)$ fitted to fragmentary data does not yield an invalid probability distribution.[1]   The properties of density and distribution functions are reviewed in Table 4.6.   These imply a set of constraints

---

[1] It is assumed that with sufficient data and a detailed histogram any reasonable choice of a model would yield a valid probabilistic model.

**Table 4.6    Properties of density and distribution functions**

| No. | Distribution function | Density function |
|---|---|---|
| 1 | $F(x)$     for $x_1 < \mathbf{x} \leq x_2$ <br> Distribution function defined over range $x_1 < \mathbf{x} \leq x_2$ | $f(x)$     for $x_1 < \mathbf{x} \leq x_2$ <br> Density function defined over range $x_1 < \mathbf{x} \leq x_2$ |
| 2 | $P(a < \mathbf{x} \leq b) = F(b) - F(a)$ <br> Probability that $\mathbf{x}$ lies between $a$ and $b$ | $P(a < \mathbf{x} \leq b) = \int_a^b f(x)\, dx$ <br> Probability that $\mathbf{x}$ lies between $a$ and $b$ |
| 3 | $F(x)$ cannot decrease as $\mathbf{x}$ increases | $f(x) \geq 0$ <br> $f(x)$ is never negative |
| 4 | $F(x_1) = 0$ and $F(x_2) = 1$ <br> Probability ranges from 0 to 1 | $\int_{x_1}^{x_2} f(x)\, dx = 1$ <br> Probability of the sample space is unity |

on $f(t)$ and $z(t)$, which are given in Table 4.7.   The fact that $f(t)$ and $z(t)$ are always positive is clear by inspection of Eqs. (4.14) and (4.15), since $n(t + \Delta t)$ is always equal to, or smaller than, $n(t)$.†   Logically $R(\infty)$ must be zero, and Eq. (4.17) shows that this requires a unity area under the failure density curve.   Similarly the same requirement necessitates the area under the hazard-rate curve to become infinite [see Eq. (4.18)].

An example of a valid model for $f(t)$ is $c_1 e^{-at}$, since the function is

† This assumes that once a test is started, no new items are introduced and no items are repaired.   If additional items are added, the data must be treated as the superposition of two tests.

**Table 4.7    Constraints on $f(t)$ and $z(t)$**

| No. | Density function | Hazard rate |
|---|---|---|
| 1 | $f(t)$     for $0 < \mathbf{t} \leq \infty$ <br> Density function is defined for all positive time | $z(t)$     for $0 < \mathbf{t} \leq \infty$ <br> Hazard rate is defined for all positive time |
| 2 | $f(t) \geq 0$ <br> $f(t)$ is never negative | $z(t) \geq 0$ <br> $z(t)$ is never negative |
| 3 | $\int_0^\infty f(t)\, dt = 1$ <br> Probability of sample space is unity | $\int_0^\infty z(t)\, dt \to \infty$ <br> Equivalent to condition on $f(t)$ [see Eq. (4.23)] |

always nonnegative, and if $c_1 = a$, the area constraint is satisfied.  The function $c_2 t$ is not a valid density-function model, since the area under the curve diverges as $t \to \infty$.  Conversely, $c_2 t$ is perfectly acceptable as a hazard model, since for any finite $c_2$ the area will diverge as it should.  The exponential function $c_1 e^{-at}$ is unsuitable as a hazard model, since the area is finite for any finite value of $c_1$.

## 4.5  HAZARD MODELS

On first consideration it might appear that if failure data and graphs such as Fig. 4.1a to d are available, there is no need for a mathematical model.  However, in drawing conclusions from test data on the behavior of other similar components it is necessary to fit the failure data with a mathematical model.  The discussion will start with several simple models and gradually progress to the more involved problem of how to choose a general model which fits all cases through adjustment of constants.

### 4.5.1  CONSTANT HAZARD

For a good many years, reliability analysis was almost wholly concerned with constant hazard rates.  Indeed many data have been accumulated, like those in Fig. 4.1b, which indicate that a constant-hazard model is appropriate in many cases.

If a constant hazard rate $z(t) = \lambda$ is assumed, the time integral is given by $\int_0^t \lambda \, d\xi = \lambda t$.  Substitution in Eqs. (4.18) and (4.24) yields

$$z(t) = \lambda \qquad (4.25)$$
$$f(t) = \lambda e^{-\lambda t} \qquad (4.26)$$
$$R(t) = e^{-\lambda t} = 1 - F(t) \qquad (4.27)$$

These four functions are sketched in Fig. 4.16.  A constant hazard rate implies an exponential density function and an exponential reliability function.  The reader will recall that an exponential density function is just a special case of a gamma density function or a Weibull density function [see Eqs. (2.47) and (2.50)].

The constant-hazard model forbids any deterioration in time of strength or soundness of the items in the population.  Thus if $\lambda = 0.1$ per hr, we can expect 10 failures in a population of 100 items during the first hour of operation and the same number of failures between the thousandth and thousand and first hours of operation in a population of 100 items that have already survived 1,000 hr.  A simple hazard model that admits deterioration in time, i.e., wear, is one in which the failure rate increases with time.

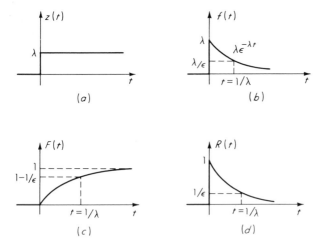

**Fig. 4.16** Constant-hazard model. (a) Constant hazard; (b) decaying exponential density function; (c) rising exponential distribution function; (d) decaying exponential reliability function.

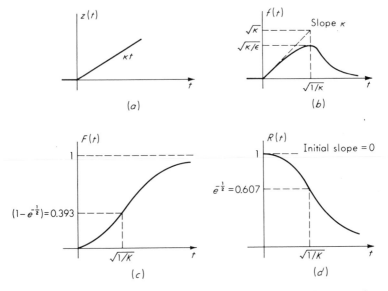

**Fig. 4.17** Linearly increasing hazard. (a) Linearly increasing hazard; (b) Rayleigh density function; (c) Rayleigh distribution function; (d) Rayleigh reliability function.

### 4.5.2  LINEARLY INCREASING HAZARD

When wear or deterioration is present, the hazard will increase as time passes.  The simplest increasing-hazard model that can be postulated is one in which the hazard increases linearly with time.  Assuming that $z(t) = Kt$ for $t \geq 0$† yields

$$z(t) = Kt \tag{4.28}$$
$$f(t) = Kte^{-Kt^2/2} \tag{4.29}$$
$$R(t) = e^{-Kt^2/2} \tag{4.30}$$

These functions are sketched in Fig. 4.17.  The density function of Eq. (4.29) is a Rayleigh density function.

A decreasing-hazard model may also be useful, especially in the case of initial failures.  Such a model is discussed in the next section.

### 4.5.3  LINEARLY DECREASING HAZARD

When a batch of new items just produced or assembled is placed in operation, the initial failure rate is generally somewhat higher than that encountered a short time later.  This is due to the initial failures of components with important weakness of structure or manufacturing faults that were not found during inspection.  A model that fits this situation is a linearly decreasing failure-rate model.

If one assumes that the failure rate starts at an initial value $K_0$ at $t = 0$ and decreases linearly to zero, the failure rate is given by $z(t) = K_0 - K_1t$. Since the failure rate cannot become negative, the domain of definition of $z(t)$ for this model must be $0 < t \leq K_0/K_1$.  This model does not satisfy the requirement that the area under the $z(t)$ curve becomes infinite; therefore, one must add an additional segment to the $z(t)$ curve at some large time $t_0$.  The quantity $t_0$ is of course chosen well beyond the range of interest.  In the model given below, a ramp function was added to the linearly decreasing hazard[1]

$$z(t) = \begin{cases} K_0 - K_1t & 0 < t \leq \dfrac{K_0}{K_1} \\ 0 & \dfrac{K_0}{K_1} < t \leq t_0 \\ K(t - t_0) & t_0 < t \leq +\infty \end{cases} \tag{4.31}$$

† Unless stated to the contrary, all reliability functions are assumed zero for $t < 0$.

[1] This would correspond physically to wearout behavior which began at time $t_0$. One could equally well add a step or impulse function at $t_0$ to fix up the model or just treat it as a portion of the $z(t)$ function defined over the restricted range $0 < t \leq K_0/K_1$.

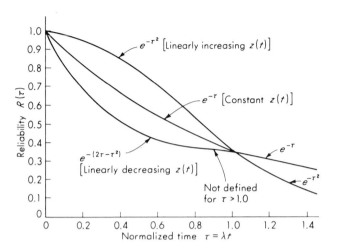

**Fig. 4.18**   Comparison of normalized reliability functions.

The resulting density and reliability functions are

$$
f(t) = \begin{cases}
(K_0 - K_1 t)e^{-(K_0 t - K_1 t^2/2)} & 0 < t \leq \dfrac{K_0}{K_1} \\[2mm]
0 & \dfrac{K_0}{K_1} < t \leq t_0 \\[2mm]
K(t - t_0)e^{-K_0{}^2/2K_1}e^{-K(t-t_0)^2/2} & t_0 < t \leq +\infty
\end{cases} \tag{4.32}
$$

$$
R(t) = \begin{cases}
e^{-(K_0 t - K_1 t^2/2)} & 0 < t \leq \dfrac{K_0}{K_1} \\[2mm]
e^{-K_0{}^2/2K_1} & \dfrac{K_0}{K_1} < t \leq t_0 \\[2mm]
e^{-K_0{}^2/2K_1}e^{-K(t-t_0)^2/2} & t_0 < t \leq +\infty
\end{cases} \tag{4.33}
$$

These functions are derived in the conventional manner, but the integral of the hazard must be evaluated with care to avoid error, because of its piecewise-linear nature.

$$
\int_0^t z(\xi)\,d\xi = \begin{cases}
\displaystyle\int_0^t (K_0 - K_1\xi)\,d\xi = K_0 t - \dfrac{K_1 t^2}{2} & 0 < t \leq \dfrac{K_0}{K_1} \\[3mm]
\displaystyle\int_0^{K_0/K_1} (K_0 - K_1\xi)\,d\xi + \int_{K_0/K_1}^t 0\,d\xi = \dfrac{K_0{}^2}{2K_1} & \dfrac{K_0}{K_1} < t \leq t_0 \\[3mm]
\displaystyle\int_0^{K_0/K_1} (K_0 - K_1\xi)\,d\xi + \int_{K_0/K_1}^{t_0} 0\,d\xi & \\[3mm]
\displaystyle\quad + \int_{t_0}^t K(\xi - t_0)\,d\xi = \dfrac{K_0{}^2}{2K_1} + \dfrac{K(t - t_0)^2}{2} & t_0 < t \leq \infty
\end{cases}
$$

Essentially, one must carefully account for the constants of integration.

It is easy to check the $R(t)$ function by using a different approach. One can assume that the three different hazard intervals correspond to three different events. The probability of surviving during event 1 is clearly given by $e^{-(K_0 t - K_1 t^2/2)}$. The probability of surviving during event 2 is $e^{-0(t_0 - K_0/K_1)}$ times the probability of having survived event 1, or $e^{-K_0^2/2K_1}$. Similarly the probability of survival in region 3 is given by the triple product

$$e^{-K_0^2/2K_1} e^{0(t_0 - K_0/K_1)} e^{-K(t-t_0)^2/2}$$

This failure model depends on two parameters $K_0$ and $K_1$. The reliability function is sketched in Fig. 4.18 and compared with the constant-hazard and linearly-increasing-hazard models in the next section.

### 4.5.4 COMPARISON OF CONSTANT-HAZARD, LINEARLY-INCREASING-HAZARD, AND LINEARLY-DECREASING-HAZARD MODELS

The constant-hazard, linearly-increasing-hazard, and linearly-decreasing hazard models are the simplest failure-rate models which can be discussed. The first two are single-parameter distributions, and the latter a two-parameter distribution of a particularly simple type.

In order to compare the reliability functions generated by these hazard models, they must be normalized in some manner. All the reliability functions start at unity when $t = 0$ and become zero at $t = \infty$. Also since the linearly decreasing hazard is "basically" defined up to $t = k_0/k_1$, the time range should be similarly restricted. The natural parameter of the exponential reliability function is $t = 1/\lambda$, the time when the reliability has dropped to $1/e = 0.368$. The other two curves will be normalized so that they also pass through this point. This is equivalent to requiring that the areas under the hazard curves between $t = 0$ and $1/\lambda$ be equal. Imposing this restriction on the linearly-increasing-hazard model leads to the constraint $K = 2\lambda^2$. In the case of the two-parameter linearly-decreasing-hazard model, we require that at $t = 1/\lambda$ the quantity $K_0 - K_1 t = 0$ and that the area criterion be satisfied. This yields $K_0 = 2\lambda$ and $K_1 = 2\lambda^2$. The resulting normalized reliability functions are:

Constant hazard: $\qquad\qquad R(t) = e^{-\lambda t}$ (4.34)

Linearly increasing hazard: $R(t) = e^{-\lambda^2 t^2}$ (4.35)

Linearly decreasing hazard: $R(t) = e^{-(2\lambda t - \lambda^2 t^2)}$ (4.36)

These three functions are compared in Fig. 4.18. In cases where the hazard function changes its curvature, none of these models is adequate in itself, and more elaborate models involving two or three adjustable parameters must be used to model the changing slope.

### 4.5.5 THE WEIBULL MODEL

In many cases, the $z(t)$ curve cannot be approximated by a straight line, and the previously discussed models fail. In order to fit various $z(t)$ curvatures, it is useful to investigate a hazard model of the form

$$z(t) = Kt^m \quad \text{for } m > -1 \qquad (4.37)$$

This form of model was discussed in detail in a paper by Weibull[1] and is generally called a *Weibull model*. The associated density and reliability functions are

$$f(t) = Kt^m e^{-Kt^{m+1}/(m+1)} \qquad (4.38)$$
$$R(t) = e^{-Kt^{m+1}/(m+1)} \qquad (4.39)$$

By appropriate choice of the two parameters $K$ and $m$, a wide range of hazard curves can be approximated. The various functions obtained for typical values of $m$ are shown in Fig. 4.19. For fixed values of $m$, a change in the parameter $K$ merely changes the vertical amplitude of the $z(t)$ curve, thus, $z(t)/K$ is plotted vs. time. Changing $K$ produces a time-scale effect on the $R(t)$ function; therefore, time is normalized so that $\tau^{m+1} = [K/(m + 1)]t^{m+1}$. The amplitude of the hazard curve affects the time scale of the reliability function; consequently, the parameter $K$ is often called the *scale parameter*. The parameter $m$ obviously affects the shape of all the reliability functions shown and is consequently called the *shape parameter*. The curves $m = 0$ and $m = 1$ are constant-hazard and linearly-increasing-hazard models, respectively. It is clear from inspection of Fig. 4.19 that a wide variety of models is possible by appropriate selection of $K$ and $m$. The drawback is, of course, that this is a two-parameter model, which means a greater difficulty in sketching the results and increased difficulty in estimating the parameters.

The Weibull model includes all the previously discussed models as special cases, except the linearly-decreasing-hazard model, which is useful in describing early failures. A decreasing-hazard function with adjustable curvature can be obtained from the Weibull family by choosing $-1 < m \leq 0$. The hazard functions for this class of Weibull models become infinite as $t \to 0$, which might seem to rule them out as appropriate models for initial failures. However, with an appropriate choice of $K$ and $m$ one should be able to minimize this effect. For example, if one wishes a model for an initial-failure region of 100 hr and the model chosen fits well between 1 and 100 hr, little harm will result from large discrepancies between the data and the model between 0 and 1 hr.

---

[1] W. Weibull, A Statistical Distribution Function of Wide Application, *J. Appl. Mech.*, vol. 18, pp. 293–297, 1951.

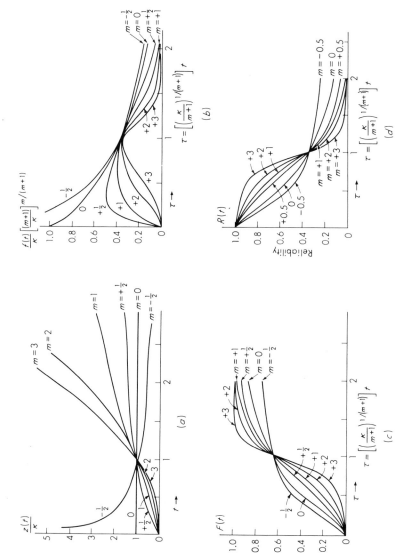

**Fig. 4.19** Reliability functions for the Weibull model. (a) Hazard function; (b) density function; (c) distribution function; (d) reliability function.

### 4.5.6 EXPONENTIAL HAZARD

As stated previously, the hazard curve provides a better characterization of the failure behavior than the density function. This effect is readily supported by the Weibull curves. Inspection of Fig. 4.19a and b shows that the curvature of the hazard function for $0 < t < 1$ determines the curvature and initial slope of the reliability function for $0 < \tau < 1$. Inspection of the density-function curve reveals no such simple correspondence.

In some cases the hazard function is initially constant and then begins to increase rapidly. This could be represented by a combination of a constant and a linearly increasing hazard or an exponentially growing hazard.[1] The hazard density and reliability functions for such a model, often called the *extreme value distribution*, are given by

$$z(t) = Ke^{\alpha t} \tag{4.40}$$
$$f(t) = Ke^{\alpha t}e^{-(K/\alpha)(e^{\alpha t}-1)} \tag{4.41}$$
$$R(t) = e^{-(K/\alpha)(e^{\alpha t}-1)} \tag{4.42}$$

The exact shape of $f(t)$ is difficult to sketch since it depends on $K$ and $\alpha$

---

[1] D. K. Lloyd and M. Lipow, "Reliability: Management, Methods and Mathematics," p. 139, Prentice-Hall, Inc., Englewood Cliffs, N.J., 1962.

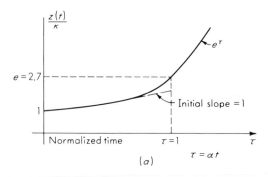

(a)

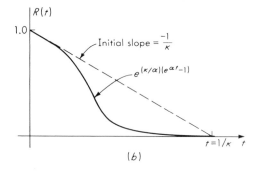

(b)

**Fig. 4.20** Exponential-hazard model. (a) Hazard function; (b) reliability function.

in a complicated fashion; however, $z(t)$ and $R(t)$ are sketched in Fig. 4.20a and b.    Initially when $\alpha t \ll 1$, $z(t) \sim K$, and $R(t) \sim e^{-Kt}$.    For slightly larger $t$, $\alpha t < 1$, $z(t) \sim K + K\alpha t$, and $R(t) \sim e^{-Kt}e^{-K\alpha t^2/2}$.    This model will be discussed further in Chap. 8.

### 4.5.7 SHIFTED MODELS

In certain cases, the hazard for an initial time period may be very small, nearly zero.    In such a case one could choose a function with a very slowly increasing hazard to model the initial behavior, but this may not match the curve later in time.    A convenient technique for such situations is to use a model of the form $z(t - t_0)$, where $t_0$ is the time at which the hazard appears to begin rising from zero.    The parameter $t_0$ is a time shift, and it is assumed that $z = 0$ for $t$ less than $t_0$.    Such an addition to any of the previously discussed models is actually very simple, but it does increase the number of model parameters by one.    Often the Weibull distribution is written as a three-parameter distribution $z(t) = K(t - t_0)^m$.    Such a model is generally called a *three-parameter Weibull* to distinguish it from the two-parameter case given by Eq. (4.37).

### 4.5.8 PIECEWISE-LINEAR MODELS

A three-parameter model such as the shifted Weibull model with parameters $K$ and $m$ can be made to fit a great variety of failure data. The approach is to fit the curve by appropriate manipulation of the several parameters.    Another approach is to subdivide the curve into a number of regions and fit each region with a simple model.    This is essentially the time-honored technique of replacing one large problem with several smaller ones.

A well-known method of approximating a function is to divide the graph of the function into a number of regions and to fit a straight line to the function in each region.    This method is known as piecewise-linear analysis, and the accuracy of the method increases as the number of fitted segments increases.    For example, consider the model shown in Fig. 4.21.    The three regions chosen are $0 < t \leq t_1$, $t_1 < t \leq t_2$, and $t_2 < t \leq +\infty$.†    In region 1, the hazard is given by

$$z(t) = a_1 - b_1 t \qquad 0 < t \leq t_1 \tag{4.43}$$

In region 2

$$z(t) = a_2 - b_2(t - t_1) \qquad t_1 < t \leq t_2 \tag{4.44}$$

† Although region 3 extends to $+\infty$, the model is required to fit well only over the range $t \leq t_3$.

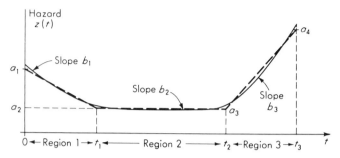

**Fig. 4.21**    Piecewise-linear failure-rate model.

and in region 3

$$z(t) = a_3 + b_3(t - t_2) \qquad t_2 < t < +\infty \tag{4.45}$$

The slopes are of course given by

$$b_1 = \frac{a_1 - a_2}{t_1 - 0} \qquad b_2 = \frac{a_2 - a_3}{t_2 - t_1} \qquad b_3 = \frac{a_4 - a_3}{t_3 - t_2}$$

If $a_3 \approx a_2$, as would appear reasonable from Fig. 4.21, $b_2 = 0$. Derivation of the reliability functions follows the same technique used in Sec. 4.5.3. The results are

$$R(t) = \begin{cases} e^{-(a_1 t - b t^2/2)} & 0 < t \le t_1 \\ e^{-(a_1 t_1 - b t_1^2/2)} e^{-a_2(t-t_1)} & t_1 < t \le t_2 \\ e^{-(a_1 t_1 - b t_1^2/2)} e^{-a_2(t_2-t_1)} e^{-[a_3(t-t_2)+b_3(t-t_2)^2/2]} & t_2 < t \le +\infty \end{cases} \tag{4.46}$$

The above expression can be obtained by direct evaluation of the hazard integral in terms of its constituent parts or by dividing the problem into three equivalent events.

It is interesting to note that a time-shifted linearly increasing hazard function may be thought of as a shifted Weibull function with $m = 1$ and $K =$ slope or equally well as a piecewise-linear model which has a hazard of zero in region 1 and a hazard given by $K(t - t_0)$ for all other positive time.

The accuracy of the piecewise-linear approximation can be improved by taking more segments. In the limit, as an infinite number of segments are taken, the approximation becomes exact. Of course, engineering judgment must be used to strike a balance between goodness of fit and computational complexity.

**4.5.9    OTHER MODELS**

The previous discussion really developed just three types of failure models, the Weibull model, the exponential model, and the piecewise-linear model, all the other forms being only special cases of these three models.  In an attempt to better fit any general failure curve various authors have suggested a wide range of different distributions.[1]  Some of these involve normal, log normal, gamma, beta, etc., distributions. The author feels that in most situations these complex models are unnecessary.  The models discussed in this chapter were devised to approximate the $z(t)$ curve.  If one were to fit the $f(t)$ curve, a different set of models might result.  For example, if one were shown the bell-shaped $f(t)$ curve which corresponds to a linearly increasing hazard without reference to the corresponding $z(t)$ curve, one might model $f(t)$ with a normal distribution.  The resulting $z(t)$ curve would not be linear but might be approximately so over the region of interest.  The piecewise-linear, exponential, and Weibull models are useful in that they are somewhat simpler than some discussed in the literature and result in mathematical functions more familiar and comfortable to the engineer and scientist.

Another general failure model that can be used to approximate $z(t)$ is a power series, that is, $z(t) = K_0 + K_1 t + K_2 t^2 + \cdots + K_n t^n$.  The power series is extensively used in all branches of engineering to fit experimental data.  The resulting reliability function is given by

$$R(t) = \exp\left[-\left(K_0 t + \frac{K_1 t^2}{2} + \frac{K_2 t^3}{3} + \frac{K_3 t^4}{4} + \cdots + \frac{K_n t^{n+1}}{n+1}\right)\right] \quad (4.47)$$

Since the various $K$'s can be positive or negative constants, a very wide variety of curves can be modeled.

The standard technique of curve fitting used to determine the parameters in this model is to select $n + 1$ points on the hazard-rate curve and pass the model through these points.  For example, in Fig. 4.21 if $z(0) = a_1$, $z(t_1) = a_2$, $z(t_2) = a_3$, and $z(t_3) = a_4$ are chosen, a four-parameter model ($n = 3$) can be chosen

$$z(t) = K_0 + K_1 t + K_2 t^2 + K_3 t^3 \quad (4.48)$$

Fitting the model to the four chosen points yields

$$
\begin{aligned}
z(0) &= a_1 = K_0 \\
z(t_1) &= a_2 = K_0 + K_1 t_1 + K_2 t_1^2 + K_3 t_1^3 \\
z(t_2) &= a_3 = a_2 = K_0 + K_1 t_2 + K_2 t_2^2 + K_3 t_2^3 \\
z(t_3) &= a_4 = K_0 + K_1 t_3 + K_2 t_3^2 + K_3 t_3^3
\end{aligned}
\quad (4.49)
$$

This set of four equations determines the unknown parameters $K_0$, $K_1$,

[1] Lloyd and Lipow, op. cit., and Marvin Zelen (ed.), "Statistical Theory of Reliability," The University of Wisconsin Press, Madison, Wis., 1963.

$K_2$, and $K_3$ in terms of the four known points $z(0)$, $z(t_1)$, $z(t_2)$, and $z(t_3)$. Using determinants, the solution for the $K$'s from these equations can be written as

$$K_0 = a_1$$

$$K_1 = \begin{vmatrix} a_2 - a_1 & t_1{}^2 & t_1{}^3 \\ a_3 - a_1 & t_2{}^2 & t_2{}^3 \\ a_4 - a_1 & t_3{}^2 & t_3{}^3 \end{vmatrix} \frac{1}{\Delta}$$

$$K_2 = \begin{vmatrix} t_1 & a_2 - a_1 & t_1{}^3 \\ t_2 & a_2 - a_1 & t_2{}^3 \\ t_3 & a_4 - a_1 & t_3{}^3 \end{vmatrix} \frac{1}{\Delta}$$

$$K_3 = \begin{vmatrix} t_1 & t_1{}^2 & a_2 - a_1 \\ t_2 & t_2{}^2 & a_2 - a_1 \\ t_3 & t_3{}^2 & a_4 - a_1 \end{vmatrix} \frac{1}{\Delta} \qquad (4.50)$$

where

$$\Delta = \begin{vmatrix} t_1 & t_1{}^2 & t_1{}^3 \\ t_2 & t_2{}^2 & t_2{}^3 \\ t_3 & t_3{}^2 & t_3{}^3 \end{vmatrix}$$

### 4.5.10 SUMMARY

The choice of reliability models must encompass more than just the problem of fitting a curve with a formula. One should not forget that in practice no $z(t)$ or $f(t)$ curve exists, only a limited set of times to failure from which one is able to construct a histographic representation of either curve. If possible, one should choose a model which is compatible with these raw data.

Sometimes the model is to be used in studying the reliability of the particular item in question, and then the model should be accurate enough to reveal the detailed reliability behavior of the part and should suggest various underlying causes and modes of failure. These latter clues can be used to further investigate the physics of failure and subsequently improve the item.

In many other cases, the study of component reliability is only a prelude, an intermediate step, in the discussion of system reliability. In such cases the model chosen must have compatible combinatorial properties so that when used with the formulas in Chap. 3, the overall result is easy to interpret and use.

Another judgment that must be made is how well the model chosen fits the data. How to determine the model parameters from the data is another question of extreme importance. These two questions will be treated in Chap. 8.

**4.6   MEAN TIME TO FAILURE**

It is often convenient to characterize a failure model or set of failure data by a single parameter. One generally uses the mean time *to* failure or the mean time *between* failures for this purpose. If we have life-test information on a population of $n$ items with failure times $t_1, t_2, \ldots, t_n$, then the MTTF is defined by [see Eq. (2.115)]

$$\text{MTTF} = \frac{1}{n} \sum_{i=1}^{n} t_i \qquad (4.51)$$

If one is discussing a hazard model, the MTTF for the probability distribution defined by the model is given by Eq. (2.51) as

$$\text{MTTF} = E(t) = \int_0^\infty t f(t) \, dt \qquad (4.52)$$

The MTBF has meaning only when one is discussing a renewal situation, where there is repair or replacement. The MTBF is discussed in Sec. 6.11. Unfortunately these two quantities are sometimes wrongly thought of as equivalent, probably because for certain simple constant-hazard cases they are equal. In a single-parameter distribution, specification of the MTTF fixes the parameter. In a multiple-parameter distribution, fixing the MTTF only places one constraint on the model parameters.

One can express Eq. (4.52) by a simpler computational expression involving the reliability function. From Eqs. (4.8) and (4.9)

$$f(t) = \frac{dF(t)}{dt} = -\frac{dR(t)}{dt} \qquad (4.53)$$

Substitution of Eq. (4.53) into (4.52) yields

$$E(t) = -\int_0^\infty t \frac{dR(t)}{dt} = -\int_0^\infty t \, dR(t)$$

Integration by parts gives

$$E(t) = -\int_0^\infty t \, dR(t) = -t R(t) \Big|_0^\infty + \int_0^\infty R(t) \, dt \qquad (4.54)$$

One must examine the function $t R(t)$ at the upper and lower limits. Since $R(0) \equiv 1$, the function disappears at the lower limit. The reliability function is $R(t) = \exp\left[-\int_0^t z(\xi) \, d\xi\right]$ and from Table 4.7, case 3, we know that $\int_0^t z(\xi) \, d\xi$ must $\to \infty$ as $t \to \infty$. Also the function $x e^{-x} \to 0$ as $x \to \infty$; therefore $t R(t)$ is zero at the upper limit, and Eq. (4.54) becomes

$$\text{MTTF} = \int_0^\infty R(t) \, dt \qquad (4.55)$$

As an example of the use of Eq. (4.55) the MTTF for several different hazards will be computed. For a single component with a constant hazard

$$\text{MTTF} = \int_0^\infty e^{-\lambda t} dt = \frac{e^{-\lambda t}}{-\lambda}\bigg|_0^\infty = \frac{1}{\lambda} \tag{4.56}$$

For a linearly increasing hazard (using the integral table in Appendix C)

$$\text{MTTF} = \int_0^\infty e^{-Kt^2/2}\, dt = \frac{\Gamma(\frac{1}{2})}{2\sqrt{K/2}} = \sqrt{\frac{\pi}{2K}} \tag{4.57}$$

For a Weibull distribution

$$\text{MTTF} = \int_0^\infty e^{-Kt^{-(m+1)}/(m+1)}\, dt = \frac{\Gamma[1/(m+1)]}{(m+1)[K/(m+1)]^{1/(m+1)}} \tag{4.58}$$

In Eq. (4.56) the MTTF is simply the reciprocal of the hazard, whereas in Eq. (4.57) it varies as the reciprocal of the square root of the hazard slope. In Eq. (4.58) the relationship between MTTF, $K$, and $m$ is more complex. The MTTF for a system and its relationship to the MTTF of the constituant components are discussed in Chap. 5.

The MTTF can also be computed from the Laplace transforms of $f(t)$ and $R(t)$. Using Eqs. (2.61), (2.64), and (2.146), we see that

$$\text{MTTF} = \left[\frac{dM(\theta)}{d\theta}\right]_{\theta=0} = -\left[\frac{df^*(s)}{ds}\right]_{s=0} \tag{4.59}$$

Another form in terms of $R^*(s)$ is obtained by considering $\int_0^t R(\tau)\, d\tau$. Using Theorem 3 of Table 2.12, we obtain

$$\mathcal{L}\left\{\int_0^t R(\tau)\, d\tau\right\} = \frac{R^*(s)}{s}$$

However,

$$\text{MTTF} = \lim_{t\to\infty} \int_0^t R(\tau)\, d\tau$$

Using Theorem 7 of Table 2.12,

$$\text{MTTF} = \lim_{t\to\infty} \int_0^t R(\tau)\, d\tau = \lim_{s\to 0} s\mathcal{L}\left\{\int_0^t R(\tau)\, d\tau\right\} = \lim_{s\to 0} s\,\frac{R^*(s)}{s}$$

Thus,

$$\text{MTTF} = \lim_{s\to 0} R(s) \tag{4.60}$$

The choice between using Eq. (4.55) or (4.60) to compute MTTF is really a matter of personal preference.

## PROBLEMS

4.1    Ten units are placed on life test, and the failure times are 9, 19, 27, 35, 40, 46, 50, 55, 56, 60 hr.

    (a)    Plot $f_d(t)$ and $z_d(t)$ for the above data.

    (b)    What kind of a model should be used for $z_d(t)$?

    (c)    Estimate the parameters of the model for $z_d(t)$ and plot the corresponding reliability function.

    (d)    Compare graphically the reliability function obtained in part $c$ with $R_d(t)$.

4.2    A 10,000-hr life test on a sample group of 15 electric motors produced the following data:

| Motor number | Hours of operation |
|:---:|:---:|
| 1–6 | 10,000 |
| 7–10 | 8,000 |
| 11 | 10,000 |
| 12–14 | 6,000 |
| 15 | 2,000 |

    (a)    Interpret the above data and plot $f_d(t)$ and $z_d(t)$. First assume that all motors have failed by the end of the test.

    (b)    Second assume that any motor with 10,000 hr of operation is still running at the close of the test.   Do the two assumptions change the result?

    (c)    Plot $F_d(t)$ and $R_d(t)$.

4.3    Life insurance companies base their computations on mortality data like those in Tables I and II.

    (a)    Plot histograms for $f_d(t)$ from the data of Tables I and II, using time intervals of 5 and 20 years.

    (b)    Repeat part $a$ for $z_d(t)$.

    (c)    Comment on the above results.   How do the data in Table I and II compare?   What is the effect of changing time intervals?

### Table I    American experience mortality table

| $x$ | $lx$ | $x$ | $lx$ | $x$ | $lx$ |
|:---:|:---:|:---:|:---:|:---:|:---:|
| 10 | 100,000 | 40 | 78,106 | 70 | 38,569 |
| 15 | 96,285 | 45 | 74,173 | 75 | 26,237 |
| 20 | 92,637 | 50 | 69,804 | 80 | 14,474 |
| 25 | 89,032 | 55 | 64,563 | 85 | 5,485 |
| 30 | 85,441 | 60 | 57,917 | 90 | 847 |
| 35 | 81,822 | 65 | 49,341 | 95 | 3 |

$x$ = age in years; $lx$ = number living at age $x$.

Table II    Commissioners 1941 standard ordinary mortality table

| $x$ | $lx$ | $x$ | $lx$ | $x$ | $lx$ | $x$ | $lx$ |
|---|---|---|---|---|---|---|---|
| 0 | 1,023,102 | 15 | 962,270 | 50 | 810,900 | 85 | 78,221 |
| 1 | 1,000,000 | 20 | 951,483 | 55 | 754,191 | 90 | 21,577 |
| 2 | 994,230 | 25 | 939,197 | 60 | 677,771 | 95 | 3,011 |
| 3 | 990,114 | 30 | 924,609 | 65 | 577,882 | 99 | 125 |
| 4 | 986,767 | 35 | 906,554 | 70 | 454,548 | | |
| 5 | 983,817 | 40 | 883,342 | 75 | 315,982 | | |
| 10 | 971,804 | 45 | 852,554 | 80 | 181,765 | | |

$x$ = age in years; $lx$ = number living at age $x$.

4.4    The data shown below represent a compilation of gyro life-test data.  It is assumed that all 61 gyros are similar and that the data can be lumped.  All

| Gyro number | Hours of operation | Gyro number | Hours of operation |
|---|---|---|---|
| 101F | 5,700 | 206F* | 600 |
| 102F | 22,500 | 206aF | 5,100 |
| 103F | 5,800 | 207R | 15,000 |
| 104F | 6,300 | 208R | 15,000 |
| 107F | 10,000 | 209F | 13,000 |
| 108F | 10,900 | 210F | 9,200 |
| 110F | 8,500 | 211F | 6,900 |
| 111F | 11,900 | 212F | 12,600 |
| 112R | 23,800 | 213R | 13,000 |
| 113F | 12,200 | 214R | 12,800 |
| 114F | 16,500 | 215R | 12,800 |
| 115F | 1,900 | 301F | 3,600 |
| 116F | 8,300 | 302R | 11,000 |
| 117F | 8,300 | 303R | 11,000 |
| 118F | 8,200 | 304R | 9,600 |
| 119F* | 7,200 | 305F | 8,300 |
| 120F | 6,000 | 306R | 7,900 |
| 121R | 21,500 | 307R | 5,900 |
| 122R | 21,000 | 308F | 5,500 |
| 123R | 21,000 | 309R | 4,800 |
| 124F | 13,500 | 310R | 4,700 |
| 125D | 3,000 | 311R | 3,900 |
| 126F | 15,700 | 312R | 3,000 |
| 127D | 2,300 | 1R | 11,500 |
| 201F | 9,200 | 2R | 11,500 |
| 202R | 16,900 | 3F | 8,200 |
| 203F | 11,000 | 4F | 4,900 |
| 204R | 16,800 | Vega 1R | 15,500 |
| 205R | 16,500 | Vega 2R | 15,500 |

SOURCE: *Minneapolis Honeywell Sales Bull.*, May, 1962.

gyros except 119* and 206* experienced mechanical failures. Gyros 119 and 206 had electrical failures. Gyros which have failed are indicated by $F$, gyros still running by $R$, and gyros discontinued from test by $D$. Note that the number of operating hours of gyros still running varies widely since they were placed on test at different times.

(a) Plot a histogram for $z_d(t)$. Explain and discuss any assumptions that you make.

(b) What kind of a model fits these data? Make an engineering estimate of the model parameters.

4.5 The following five functions are to be studied:

$$e^{-at} \qquad e^{+at} \qquad At^3 \qquad Bt^{-2} \qquad \frac{e^{+at}}{t^2}$$

(a) Which of these functions can serve as valid hazard models?

(b) Derive the corresponding $f(t)$ function and sketch both $f(t)$ and $z(t)$ for the suitable models.

4.6 Consider the following hazard models: $\lambda$, $kt$, $kt^m$, $k_1 e^{k_2 t}$, $k_1 e^{k_2 t} - k_1$.

(a) Compute the reliability function $R(t)$.

(b) Compute the first and second derivatives $\dot{R}(t)$ and $\ddot{R}(t)$.

(c) Sketch $R(t)$ for the range $0.5 < R(t) < 1.0$, using the two slopes calculated in part $b$.

(d) Compute the accuracy of the sketches at a few points.

4.7 Assume that 100 components are placed on test for 1,000 hr. From previous testing we believe that the hazard is constant and the MTTF = 500 hr. Estimate the number which would fail in the 10 time intervals 0 to 100, 100 to 200, . . . , 900 to 1,000 hr.

4.8 Assume $f(t)$ is normally distributed:

(a) Sketch $F(t)$, $R(t)$, and $z(t)$.

(b) Choose a similar Weibull curve by equating the first and second moments.

(c) Compare the $f(t)$, $F(t)$, $R(t)$, and $z(t)$ curves.

4.9 Compute $E(t)$ and var $t$ for:

(a) $z(t) = \lambda + kt$  (b) $z(t) = ke^{at}$  (c) $z(t) = ke^{at} - k$

4.10 Give the expected number of failures after 1,000 hr if 100 items are placed on test with a hazard given by:

(a) $z(t) = 10^{-4}$

(b) $z(t) = 10^{-4}t$

(c) $z(t) = 10^{-3} \exp 10^{-4}t$

# 5

# *system reliability*

## 5.1  INTRODUCTION

The previous two chapters have divided reliability into two distinct phases, a formulation of the reliability structure of the problem using combinatorial reliability, and a computation of the element probabilities in terms of hazard models. This chapter unites these two approaches to obtain the reliability function for the system.

When the element probabilities are independent, computations are straightforward. The only real difficulties encountered here are the complexity of the calculations in large problems. We shall discuss several approximate techniques and limit theorems useful in the high-reliability region which simplify reliability computations.

The situation changes when the system elements are dependent, as a result of some environmental or design effect, the standby nature of the structure, repair, or replacement. It is no longer possible in most cases to separate the structural aspects and the element-reliability portions of the problem. The techniques which apply in such a case involve joint density and distribution functions or Markov and other state-transition models.

The concluding section of this chapter discusses various analog- and digital-computer simulation and solution techniques. The very powerful Monte Carlo technique is also discussed in this section.

The mathematical background for this chapter is given in Secs. 2.8, 2.9, and 2.11.

## 5.2  THE SERIES CONFIGURATION

The *series configuration,* also called a *chain structure,* is the most common reliability model and the simplest.   Any system in which the system success depends on the success of all its components is a series reliability configuration.   Unfortunately for the reliability analyst (but fortunately for the user of the product or device), not all systems have this simple structure.

A series configuration of $n$ items is shown in Fig. 5.1.   The reliability of this structure is given by

$$R(t) = P(x_1, x_2, \ldots, x_n) = P(x_1)P(x_2|x_1)P(x_3|x_1 x_2)$$
$$\cdots P(x_n|x_1 x_2 \cdots x_{n-1}) \quad (5.1)$$

If the $n$ items $x_1, x_2, \ldots, x_n$ are independent, then

$$R(t) = P(x_1)P(x_2) \cdots P(x_n) = \prod_{i=1}^{n} P(x_i) \quad (5.2)$$

If each component exhibits a constant hazard, then the appropriate component model is $e^{-\lambda_i t}$, and Eq. (5.2) becomes

$$R(t) = \prod_{i=1}^{n} e^{-\lambda_i t} = \exp\left(- \sum_{i=1}^{n} \lambda_i t\right) \quad (5.3)$$

Equation (5.3) is the most commonly used and the most elementary system reliability formula.   In practice this formula is often misused (probably because it is so simple and does work well in many situations, people have become overconfident).   The following assumptions must be true if Eq. (5.3) is to hold for a system:

1   The system reliability configuration must truly be a series one.
2   The components must be independent.
3   The components must be governed by a constant-hazard model.

If assumptions 1 and 2 hold but the components have linearly increas-

**Fig. 5.1**  Series reliability configuration.

ing hazards $z_i(t) = K_i t$, Eq. (5.2) then becomes

$$R(t) = \prod_{i=1}^{n} e^{-K_i t^2/2} = \exp\left(-\sum_{i=1}^{n} \frac{K_i t^2}{2}\right) \tag{5.4}$$

If $p$ components have a constant hazard and $n - p$ components a linearly increasing hazard, the reliability becomes

$$R(t) = \left(\prod_{i=1}^{p} e^{-\lambda_i t}\right)\left(\prod_{i=p+1}^{n} e^{-k_i t^2/2}\right) = \exp\left(-\sum_{i=1}^{p} \lambda_i t\right)\exp\left(-\sum_{i=p+1}^{n} \frac{K_i t^2}{2}\right) \tag{5.5}$$

In some cases no simple composite formula exists, and the reliability must be expressed as a product of $n$ terms. For example, suppose each component is governed by the Weibull distribution, $z(t) = K_i t^{m_i}$. If $m$ and $K$ are different for each component,[1]

$$R(t) = \prod_{i=1}^{n} \exp\left(\frac{-K_i t^{m_i+1}}{m_i + 1}\right) = \exp\left(-\sum_{i=1}^{n} \frac{K_i t^{m_i+1}}{m_i + 1}\right) \tag{5.6}$$

Also if a piecewise-linear model is appropriate for each element but the length of the various regions differs for each of the components, no simplifications are feasible, and the reliability expression must be expressed as a product of $n$ terms. A third case in which little simplification is possible occurs when each component has a different hazard model. This is the general situation, and the only simplification possible is to group the elements into classes with the same hazard pattern.

To avoid successive computation of the exponential function in evaluation of system reliability, we may define the area under the hazard curve as $Z_i(t) = \int_0^t z_i(\xi)\, d\xi$. If all the system hazard models are polynomials, then $z_i(t)$ is a polynomial, as are $Z_i(t)$ and $\sum_{i=1}^{n} Z_i(t)$. Thus for each time value of interest $t_j$, we compute the polynomial value $\sum_{i=1}^{n} Z_i(t_j)$ and then perform the exponential computation

$$R(t) = \prod_{i=1}^{n} e^{-Z_i(t)} = \exp\left[-\sum_{i=1}^{n} z_i(t)\right] \tag{5.7}$$

In many ways the series configuration is only slightly affected by component dependence. For example, if the components of the chain structure are $n$ power resistors connected in series and they are mounted close

[1] In most large-scale systems it is probably more realistic to talk of two or three categories of failure models rather then $n$ different models.

to each other, temperature makes them dependent elements.  If the configuration assumes the temperature $T_n$ when they are all operating, in a chain containing one element less the temperature would be $T_{n-1}$. Thus the resistor hazards will be a function of temperature, $z_i(t,T_n)$. If any resistor open-circuits, the current goes to zero, and the circuit experiences a catastrophic failure.  In such a case we are not interested in the conditional probabilities of other resistor failures given one resistor failure since the problem is over.  If the resistor fails as a short circuit, the remaining components will have a different hazard, governed by temperature $T_{n-1}$, that is, $z_i(t,T_{n-1})$.  However, in a true series reliability structure any component failure is a system failure.  This means that the change in current due to one resistor's failing is excessive and is considered a failure; again we are not interested in the other dependent probabilities.

We cannot talk about a series reliability structure with standby components because standby components are a special type of parallel configuration.  Such a system must be modeled by a more complex configuration than the simple chain model.  Nor is repair of help in a series system, since the system fails as soon as any component fails.  Common sense tells us that a series system with repair is more valuable than one without, since a quick repair might restore the system with very little downtime, but the reliability function of a series system is not affected by repair, since it is in no way changed by what happens after a system failure.  A new measure of system goodness, called the availability function, is introduced in Sec. 6.11 to represent such properties of repairable systems.

The series reliability structure serves as a lower-bound configuration. To illustrate this principle we pose a hypothetical problem.  Given a collection of $n$ elements; from the reliability standpoint what is the worst possible reliability structure they can assume?  The intuitive answer, of course, is a series structure; however, a proof is in order.

To prove our hypothesis, we look at the probability of failure in terms of the system cut sets, given by

$$P_f = P(\bar{C}_1 + \bar{C}_2 + \cdots + \bar{C}_j) \tag{3.35}$$

For an $n$-element chain composed of elements $x_1, x_2, \ldots, x_n$ we have $\bar{C}_1 = \bar{x}_1, \bar{C}_2 = \bar{x}_2, \ldots, \bar{C}_n = \bar{x}_n$.  Thus, the failure probability is given by the union of $\bar{x}_1, \bar{x}_2, \ldots, \bar{x}_n$, which on a Venn diagram represents the total area enclosed by the events.  If we assume any other structure, the cut sets will change and in general will be expressed as products of the various events $\bar{x}_i$.  Thus the new failure probability expression will involve the union of other events, which will be represented by a smaller area on the Venn diagram.  Thus the probability of system failure for a series system is larger than any other configuration of the same elements. This of course implies that the reliability of a series system is lowest and a series-structure assumption is a conservative estimate. Note that we have said nothing about element independence or dependence, which becomes relevant only when we wish to assign numbers to the probability of intersection terms. A simpler proof of this result is given in Sec. 5.8.2 in terms of Markov chain models.

### 5.3  THE PARALLEL CONFIGURATION

If a system of $n$ elements can function properly when only one of the elements is good, a parallel configuration is indicated. A parallel configuration of $n$ items is shown in Fig. 5.2. The reliability expression for a parallel system may be expressed in terms of the probability of success of each component or, more conveniently, in terms of the probability of failure

$$R(t) = P(x_1 + x_2 + \cdots + x_n) = 1 - P(\bar{x}_1 \bar{x}_2 \cdots \bar{x}_n) \tag{5.8}$$

In the case of constant-hazard components, $P_f = P(\bar{x}_i) = 1 - e^{-\lambda_i t}$, and Eq. (5.8) becomes

$$R(t) = 1 - \left[ \prod_{i=1}^{n} (1 - e^{-\lambda_i t}) \right] \tag{5.9}$$

In the case of linearly increasing hazard, the expression becomes

$$R(t) = 1 - \left[ \prod_{i=1}^{n} (1 - e^{-K_i t^2/2}) \right] \tag{5.10}$$

In the general case, the system reliability function is

$$R(t) = 1 - \left[ \prod_{i=1}^{n} (1 - e^{-Z_i(t)}) \right] \tag{5.11}$$

In order to permit grouping of terms in Eq. (5.11) to simplify computation and/or interpretation, the equation must be expanded. The expansion

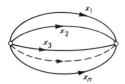

**Fig. 5.2**  Parallel reliability configuration.

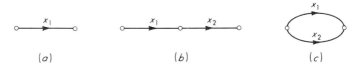

**Fig. 5.3**   Three reliability structures.   (a) Single element; (b) two series elements; (c) two parallel elements.

of $(1 + Y_1)(1 + Y_2)(1 + Y_3) \cdots (1 + Y_n)$ is given by

$$(1 + Y_1)(1 + Y_2) \cdots (1 + Y_n) = 1 + (Y_1 + Y_2 + \cdots + Y_n)$$
$$+ (Y_1Y_2 + Y_1Y_3 + \cdots + Y_iY_j) + (Y_1Y_2Y_3 + \cdots + Y_iY_jY_k)$$
$$+ \cdots + (Y_1Y_2Y_3 \cdots Y_n) \quad (5.12)$$

Using Eq. (5.12) to help simplify Eq. (5.11) results in

$$R(t) = (e^{-Z_1} + e^{-Z_2} + \cdots + e^{-Z_n}) - (e^{-(Z_1+Z_2)} + e^{-(Z_1+Z_3)} + \cdots)$$
$$+ (e^{-(Z_1+Z_2+Z_3)} + e^{-(Z_1+Z_2+Z_4)} + \cdots) - \cdots e^{-(Z_1+Z_2+Z_3+\cdots+Z_n)} \quad (5.13)$$

Note that the signs of the terms in parentheses alternate and that in the first parentheses the exponents are all the $Z$'s taken singly, in the second all the sums of $Z$'s taken two at a time, and in the last term the sum of all the $Z$'s.   The $r$th parentheses in Eq. (5.13) contain $n!/[r!(n-r)!]$ terms.

Reliability expressions for the three cases shown in Fig. 5.3 are given in Table 5.1.   Because the general shape of the reliability function is affected by both the hazard model and the system structure, generalizations are difficult.   The expressions given in Table 5.1 are plotted in Fig. 5.4.

Just as the series configuration served as a lower-bound structure, the parallel model can be thought of as an upper-bound structure.   (We exclude standby structures in this discussion; in Sec. 5.8.3 it is shown that a standby system can be better than ordinary parallel systems.)   Using

**Table 5.1   Reliability expressions**

|  | General | Constant hazard (identical) | Linearly increasing hazard (identical) |
|---|---|---|---|
| Single element | $e^{-Z}$ | $e^{-\lambda t}$ | $e^{-Kt^2/2}$ |
| Two in series | $e^{-(Z_1+Z_2)}$ | $e^{-2\lambda t}$ | $e^{-Kt^2}$ |
| Two in parallel | $e^{-Z_1} + e^{-Z_2} - e^{-(Z_1+Z_2)}$ | $2e^{-\lambda t} - e^{-2\lambda t}$ | $2e^{-Kt^2/2} - e^{-Kt^2}$ |

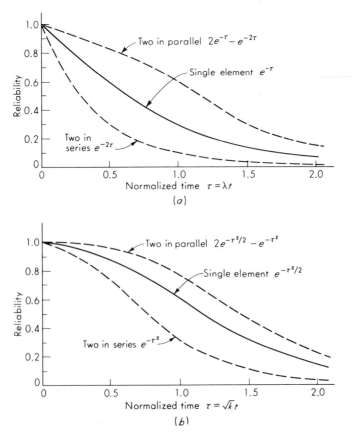

**Fig. 5.4**  Comparison of reliability functions.  (a) Constant-hazard elements; (b) linearly-increasing-hazard elements.

an argument similar to that used in the series case, we focus on

$$R = P(T_1 + T_2 + \cdots + T_i) \tag{3.34}$$

In a parallel system each element forms a tie set; therefore, $T_1 = x_1$, $T_2 = x_2, \ldots, T_i = x_i$.  The reliability of a parallel system is given by the total Venn diagram area, i.e., the union of all the $x_i$'s, which is the maximum probability obtainable.  Any other structure will involve evaluation of a lesser area with a concomitant smaller reliability.

If we have a system of $n$ elements with information on each element reliability but little or no information on their interconnection, we can bound the reliability function from below by Eq. (5.2) and from above by Eq. (5.8).  We would in general expect these bounds to be quite loose;

however, they do provide some information even when we are grossly ignorant of the system structure.

## 5.4 AN $r$–OUT–OF–$n$ STRUCTURE

Another simple structure which serves as a useful model for many reliability problems is an $r$-out-of-$n$ structure. Such a model represents a system of $n$ components in which $r$ of the $n$ items must be good for the system to succeed. Of course $r$ is less than $n$. Two simple examples of an $r$-out-of-$n$ system are (1) a piece of stranded wire with $n$ strands in which at least $r$ are necessary to pass the required current and (2) a battery composed of $n$ series cells of $E$ volts each where the minimum voltage for system operation[1] is $rE$.

We may formulate a structural model for an $r$-out-of-$n$ system, but it is simpler to use the binomial distribution if applicable. The binomial distribution can be used only when the $n$ components are independent and identical. If the components differ or are dependent, the structural-model approach must be used.[2] Success of exactly $r$ out of $n$ identical, independent items is given by

$$B(r:n) = \binom{n}{r} p^r (1 - p)^{n-r} \tag{5.14}$$

where $r:n$ stands for $r$ out of $n$, and the success of at least $r$ out of $n$ items is given by

$$P_s = \sum_{k=r}^{n} B(k:n) \tag{5.15}$$

For constant-hazard components Eq. (5.15) becomes

$$R(t) = \sum_{k=r}^{n} \binom{n}{k} e^{-k\lambda t}(1 - e^{-\lambda t})^{n-k} \tag{5.16}$$

Similarly for linearly increasing or Weibull components, the reliability functions are

$$R(t) = \left[ \sum_{k=r}^{n} \binom{n}{k} e^{-kKt^2/2} \right] (1 - e^{-Kt^2/2})^{n-k} \tag{5.17}$$

$$R(t) = \left[ \sum_{k=r}^{n} \binom{n}{k} e^{-kKt^{m+1}/(m+1)} \right] (1 - e^{-Kt^{m+1}/(m+1)})^{n-k} \tag{5.18}$$

[1] Actually when one cell of a series of $n$ cells fails, the voltage of the string does not become $(n - 1)E$ unless a special circuit arrangement is used. Such a circuit is discussed in Sec. 6.4.

[2] The reader should refer back to the example given in Sec. 3.4.

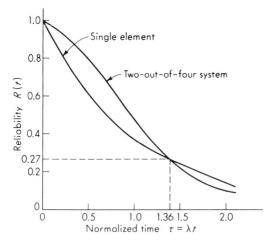

**Fig. 5.5**  Comparison of a two-out-of-four and a single-element system.

It is of interest to note that for $r = 1$, the structure becomes a parallel system and for $r = n$ the structure becomes a series system. Thus, in a sense series and parallel systems are subclasses of an $r$-out-of-$n$ structure.

As an example consider a two-out-of-four system composed of identical constant-hazard elements. The reliability function is

$$R(t) = 6e^{-2\lambda t} - 8e^{-3\lambda t} + 3e^{-4\lambda t} \tag{5.19}$$

This system is compared with a single element in Fig. 5.5. Notice that the two functions cross at $R(\tau = 1.36) = 0.27$. Although the crossover is outside the region of interest in most cases, this is not always the case (see Fig. 3.5.)

## 5.5  APPROXIMATIONS AND BOUNDS

### 5.5.1  INTRODUCTION

For years we have been relying on simple series models for large systems with complex structures. The reasons generally given for this oversimplification are ignorance of the detailed reliability structure and a dearth of component data. Both these factors are slowly changing, and engineers are beginning to use more complex system structural models. The computation involved in such cases becomes laborious, and use of a digital computer is generally required. This section deals with various approximations and bounds which can be used to achieve a simplified solution.    Such approximations are useful because they provide more insight into the problem than a column of computer data, and they can be used for quick comparison of competitive design schemes.

### 5.5.2  SERIES, PARALLEL, AND $r$-OUT-OF-$n$ STRUCTURES

In this section we shall discuss approximations for the $r$-out-of-$n$ structure and treat series and parallel systems as special cases.    For an $r$-out-of-$n$ structure of identical components the exact reliability expression is given by Eq. (5.15).    As is well known, we can approximate the binomial distribution by the Poisson or normal distributions, depending on the values of $n$ and $p$ (see Secs. 2.5.6 and 2.6.8).    It is interesting that we can also develop similar approximations for the case where the $n$ parameters are not identical.

The Poisson approximation to the binomial holds for $p \leq 0.05$ and $n \geq 20$, which represents the low-reliability region.    If we are interested in the high-reliability region, we switch to failure probabilities and require $q = 1 - p \leq 0.05$ and $n \geq 20$.    Since we are assuming different components, we define average probabilities of success and failure $\bar{p}$ and $\bar{q}$ as[1]

$$\bar{p} = \frac{1}{n} \sum_{i=1}^{n} p_i = 1 - \bar{q} = 1 - \frac{1}{n} \sum_{i=1}^{n} 1 - p_i \qquad (5.20)$$

Thus, for the high-reliability region we compute the probability of less than $n - r$ failures

$$R(t) = \sum_{k=0}^{n-r-1} \frac{(n\bar{q})^k e^{-n\bar{q}}}{k!} \qquad (5.21)$$

and for the low-reliability region we compute the probability of $r$ or more successes

$$R(t) = \sum_{k=r}^{n} \frac{(n\bar{p})^k e^{-n\bar{p}}}{k!} \qquad (5.22)$$

Equations (5.21) and (5.22) avoid a great deal of algebra in dealing with nonidentical $r$-out-of-$n$ components.    The question of accuracy is somewhat difficult to answer since it depends on $n$, $\bar{p}$ (or $\bar{q}$) and also on the system structure and the range of values of $p$ which make up $\bar{p}$.    For example, if the values of $q$ vary only over a 2:1 range, and if $\bar{q} \leq 0.05$ and $n \geq 20$, intuition tells us that we should obtain reasonably accurate results.[2]

---

[1] M. Messinger, doctoral thesis in system science, Polytechnic Institute of Brooklyn, New York, June, 1967.

[2] *Ibid.*

The conventional normal approximation to the binomial (discussed in Sec. 2.6.9) is valid for $p \leq 0.5$ and $np \geq 5$ or $p > 0.5$ and $nq > 5$. Whereas the Poisson approximations using $\bar{p}$ and $\bar{q}$ cover the ends of the reliability range, the normal approximation covers the middle. Instead of using $\mu = np$ and $\sigma^2 = np(1 - p)$, we shall substitute $\bar{p}$ for $p$, obtaining[1]

$$\mu = n\bar{p}$$
$$\sigma^2 = n\bar{p}(1 - \bar{p})$$

The normalized gaussian approximation can be used to compute the probability of $i$ or more successes

$$P(\mathbf{x} \geq i) = 1 - P(\mathbf{x} < i) = 1 - \frac{1}{\sqrt{2\pi}} \int_{-\infty}^{i'} e^{-t^2/2} \, dt$$

where

$$i' = \frac{i - \mu}{\sigma}$$

The reliability of our $r$-out-of-$n$ system is given by the probability of $r$ or more successes; thus

$$R(t) = 1 - \frac{1}{\sqrt{2\pi}} \int_{-\infty}^{i'} e^{-t^2/2} \, dt \tag{5.23}$$

where

$$i' = \frac{r - n \sum_{i=1}^{n} p_i}{\sqrt{\sum_{i=1}^{n} p_i(1 - p_i)}}$$

Again intuition and experience must be used to evaluate the errors involved.

### 5.5.3  BOUNDS FOR SERIES STRUCTURES

By this time the reader has no doubt come to the conclusion that the formulation and computation of the reliability function for a complex structure can be a mean job. In many cases the basic data on component

---

[1] Actually one can derive a more exact formula for the variance of such a group of binomially distributed variables. The more exact result is

$$\sigma^2 = \sum_{i=1}^{n} p_i(1 - p_i)$$

Of course if all the $p_i$'s are the same, the two expressions are identical. This derivation is discussed in further detail in the problems at the end of the chapter.

failures which lead to the choice of a hazard model and evaluation of its parameters are not particularly good.   These facts have led many people to abandon a detailed computation and simply assume that all $n$ elements of the system are represented by a series configuration and that each element fails independently with a constant hazard.   These assumptions of course lead to the reliability expression given by Eq. (5.3).   In a number of cases these results are sufficiently accurate for a first look at the problem, but in other cases they lead to a poor result.   Even when Eq. (5.3) "works" as a first approximation, it is useful to know how to improve the computation in a simple manner to get a more accurate and detailed solution.   Furthermore, it is desirable to study the mathematical restrictions on component reliabilities and system structures which "justify" the series approximation.   These are essentially the reasons for discussing limiting forms of reliability functions for certain cases.

In discussing limiting forms of system reliability it is useful to keep in mind that the essential nature of the problem is described by three factors: the component hazards, the system structural model, and the dependence of the components.   Since the effect of dependence on the reliability function of a complex system will be discussed in Secs. 5.8 and 5.9, this section will concentrate on independent failures.

An important failure law for complex equipment with many elements is due to Drenick.[1]   If $n$ independent elements are connected in series, the system reliability is given by

$$R(t) = \prod_{i=1}^{n} R_i(t)$$

and since $R_i(t) = e^{-Z_i(t)}$,

$$R(t) = \exp\left[ -\sum_{i=1}^{n} Z_i(t) \right]$$

and

$$\ln R(t) = -\sum_{i=1}^{n} Z_i(t) \tag{5.24}$$

We now consider a particular class of hazard functions which, as $t \to 0$, behave like $z_i(t) = \lambda_i + k_i t_m$.   Thus we are considering component hazards which for small values of $t$ behave like a constant plus a Weibull hazard function.   (Of course the hazard may behave differently for large

---

[1] R. F. Drenick, The Failure Law of Complex Equipment, *J. Soc. Ind. Appl. Math.*, vol. 8, no. 4, December, 1960.   The result presented here is a variation of Drenick's result.

values of time.)   The value of $m$ to be used is the largest $m$ found among the various components.

$$\ln R(t) = -\sum_{i=1}^{n} \int_0^t (\lambda_i + K_i \xi^m) \, d\xi$$

$$= -\sum_{i=1}^{n} \left( \lambda_i t + \frac{K_i t^{m+1}}{m+1} \right)$$

$$= -\left( \sum_{i=1}^{n} \lambda_i \right) t - \left( \sum_{i=1}^{n} \frac{K_i}{m+1} \right) t^{m+1} \qquad (5.25)$$

Defining

$$\bar{\lambda} = \sum_{i=1}^{n} \lambda_i \qquad \bar{K} = \sum_{i=1}^{n} K_i \qquad \text{and} \qquad \tau = \bar{\lambda} t$$

$$\ln R(\tau) = -\tau - \frac{\bar{K}}{m+1} \frac{\tau^{m+1}}{\bar{\lambda}^{m+1}}$$

$$= -\tau - \frac{\bar{K}}{(m+1)\bar{\lambda}} \frac{\tau^{m+1}}{\bar{\lambda}^m} \qquad (5.26)$$

Making the necessary assumptions that

1   As $n \to \infty$, $\bar{\lambda} \to \infty$ and
2   As $n \to \infty$, $\bar{K}/(m+1)\bar{\lambda}$ is bounded

ensures that as $n \to \infty$,

$$\ln R(\tau) \to -\tau$$
$$R(t) \to e^{-\bar{\lambda} t} \qquad (5.27)$$

This theorem says that the reliability function of a large series system becomes exponential for large $n$ if all the component hazards are of the form $Z_i(t) = \lambda_i + K_i t^m$ for small $t$ and satisfy assumptions 1 and 2 above.

In order to understand the result we must discuss the assumptions.[1] The theorem has been derived for a series structure.   In Sec. 5.2 it was shown that a series structure is a lower-bound configuration; thus if the actual system really contains some parallel paths, Eq. (5.27) will serve as a pessimistic estimate.   Experience has shown that the use of Eq. (5.27) leads to accurate predictions in many cases; thus there must be many practical examples in which the assumptions of a series system are adequately satisfied.   [Since there are also numerous counterexamples,

---

[1] M. Messinger and M. Shooman, Exponential and Weibull Approximations for Chain Structures, *IEEE Proc. Ann. Reliability Symp.*, New York, 1968.

in which Eq. (5.27) leads to a poor prediction, care and judgment must be used in applying this theorem.]

The component-hazard assumption $z_i(t) = \lambda_i + K_i t^m$ need hold only over some time range $0 < t < T_1$, and in practice we shall be interested in time $t \ll T_1$.

The assumption that $\bar{\lambda} \to \infty$ as $m \to \infty$ implies that a significant fraction of the components have nonzero hazards at $t = 0$. This is in general a good assumption, and the inclusion of a few components with $z_i(0) = 0$ does not invalidate the theorem but only slows down its convergence. The expression $\bar{K}/(m + 1)\bar{\lambda}$ is bounded whenever at least one $z_i(0) \neq 0$.

To appreciate the rate of convergence, we shall evaluate Eq. (5.26) for a particular example. Assume that $n$ components are connected in a chain structure and that $z_i(t) \approx \lambda_i + K_i t$ over the range $0 < t < T_1$. All components are assumed identical, the hazard doubles in a time period equal to $1/\lambda$, and $T_1 = 1/\lambda$. This implies that

$$z_i(1/\lambda) = 2\lambda = \lambda + k(1/\lambda)$$

therefore $K = \lambda^2$. Thus, Eq. (5.26) becomes

$$m = 1 \qquad \bar{\lambda} = n\lambda \qquad \bar{K} = nK = n\lambda^2$$

$$\ln R(t) = -\tau - \frac{n\lambda^2}{2n\lambda} \frac{\tau^2}{n^2\lambda^2}$$

$$= -\tau - \frac{1}{2n^2\lambda} \tau^2$$

In order to neglect the second term we take

$$\frac{1}{2n^2\lambda} \tau \ll 1$$

which implies

$$n^2 \gg \frac{\tau}{2\lambda}$$

If we are interested in the high-reliability region, $R(t) \approx 1 - \tau$. For $R(t) = 0.99$, $\tau \approx 0.01$, and

$$n^2 \gg \frac{0.005}{\lambda}$$

If $\lambda = 10^{-4}$, then $n^2 \gg 50$, and a 20- or 25-component system should lead to good convergence. Knowing that $\tau = n\lambda t$, $\lambda = 10^{-4}$, and $\tau = 0.01$, we can solve for $t$ yielding $t = 5$ hr. Since $T_1 = 1/\lambda = 10,000$ hr, the time period of interest $t$ is much less than $T_1$. Thus the assumptions on $z_i(t)$ are valid. Whenever we are in doubt as to convergence of Eq. (5.27), we can make a similar evaluation.

Equation (5.27) was developed for a reliability configuration of $n$ components with all elements in series. The result can be somewhat generalized if we assume $n$ components and a structure of $m$ series blocks. Since $n > m$, some or all of the blocks contain more than one element and thus represent a subsystem. For the theorem still to hold, the overall hazard of each subsystem must be of the form $z_i(t) = \lambda_i + K_i t^m$. For example, suppose that one subsystem consists of two series elements in parallel with a third. All elements have identical constant hazards. The reliability function is given by

$$R(t) = P(x_1 + x_2 x_3) = e^{-\lambda t} + e^{-2\lambda t} - e^{-3\lambda t}$$

From Eq. (4.16)

$$z(t) = \frac{f(t)}{R(t)} = -\frac{\dot{R}(t)}{R(t)} = \frac{\lambda t(1 + 2e^{-\lambda t} - 3e^{-2\lambda t})}{1 + e^{-\lambda t} - e^{-2\lambda t}}$$

Expanding $z(t)$ in a Taylor series,

$$z(t) = 4\lambda^2 t^2 - \lambda^3 t^3 + \cdots$$

Thus we can model the block by $z(t) \approx \lambda + Kt^m$, for $0 < t < T_1$, where $\lambda = 0$, $K = 4\lambda^2$, $m = 2$, and $T_1 = 0.63/\lambda$.† Since $z(0) = 0$, convergence will be slowed a bit, but Eq. (5.27) is still valid if only a few such blocks are present in the system. A similar discussion applies to a system with parallel subsystems or to a structural model such as that discussed in Sec. 3.2.

### 5.5.4  EXPONENTIAL EXPANSIONS

A general and very useful approximation technique commonly used in many branches of engineering is the truncated series expansion. In reliability work, terms of the form $e^{-Z}$ occur time and again, and the expressions can be simplified by series expansion of the exponential function. The Maclaurin series expansion of $e^{-Z_i}$ about $t = 0$ can be written as[1]

$$e^{-Z_i} = 1 - Z + \frac{Z^2}{2!} - \frac{Z^3}{3!} + \cdots + \frac{(-Z)^n}{n!} + \cdots \tag{5.28}$$

We can also write the series in $n$ terms and a remainder term[2] which

† We have set $T_1 = \text{MTTF}$ which is calculated by substitution in Eq. (4.57).

[1] We could of course be more general and write a Taylor series expansion about the point $t_0$, but in most cases we are interested in behavior near $t = 0$.

[2] G. B. Thomas, "Calculus and Analytic Geometry," 3d ed., p. 791, Addison-Wesley Publishing Company, Inc., Reading, Mass., 1965.

accounts for all the terms after $(-Z)^n/n!$

$$e^{-Z_i} = 1 - Z + \frac{Z^2}{2!} - \frac{Z^3}{3!} + \cdots + \frac{(-Z)^n}{n!} + R_n(Z) \tag{5.29}$$

where

$$R_n(Z) = (-1)^{n+1} \int_0^Z \frac{(Z-\xi)^n}{n!} e^{-\xi} \, d\xi \tag{5.30}$$

We can therefore approximate $e^{-Z_i}$ by $n$ terms of the series and use $R_n(Z)$ to approximate the remainder. In general we use only two or three terms of the series, since in the high-reliability region $e^{-Z} \sim 1$, $Z$ is small, and the higher-order terms $Z^n$ in the series expansion become insignificant. For example, the reliability of a single unit is given by

$$e^{-Z} = 1 - \frac{Z}{1!} + \frac{Z^2}{2!} - \frac{Z^3}{3!} + \frac{Z^4}{4!} - \frac{Z^5}{5!} + \cdots \tag{5.31}$$

and for two parallel elements the reliability expression is

$$2e^{-Z} + (-e^{-2Z}) = \left( 2 - \frac{2Z}{1!} + \frac{2Z^2}{2!} - \frac{2Z^3}{3!} + \frac{2Z^4}{4!} + \cdots \right)$$
$$+ \left[ -1 + \frac{2Z}{1!} - \frac{(2Z)^2}{2!} + \frac{(2Z)^3}{3!} - \frac{(2Z)^4}{4!} + \cdots \right]$$
$$= 1 - Z^2 + Z^3 - \tfrac{7}{12}Z^4 + \tfrac{1}{4}Z^5 + \cdots \tag{5.32}$$

Two- and three-term approximations to Eqs. (5.31) and (5.32) are compared with the complete expressions in Fig. 5.6a and b. Note that the two-term approximation is a "pessimistic" one, while the three-term expression is slightly "optimistic."

The error terms given by (5.30) can be computed and used to evaluate analytically the error obtained by truncating the series. To simplify integration we note that $e^{-\xi} < e^0 = 1$; therefore

$$|R_n(Z)| = \left| \int_0^Z \frac{(Z-\xi)^n}{n!} e^{-\xi} \, d\xi \right| \leq \left| \frac{1}{n!} \int_0^Z (Z-\xi)^n \, d\xi \right| = \frac{Z^{n+1}}{(n+1)!} \tag{5.33}$$

The result shows that the magnitude of the $n+1$ term is an upper bound on the error in an $n$-term approximation.[1] Thus the two- and three-term exponential approximations given in Fig. 5.6a are bounded by $Z^2/2$ and $-Z^3/6$. For $Z = 0.5$ we obtain error bounds of 0.125 and 0.021;

---

[1] In fact, since the terms alternate in sign, inclusion of additional terms will give a sequence of alternate upper and lower bounds. Thus, an $n$-term and an $(n+1)$-term approximation will bracket the function.

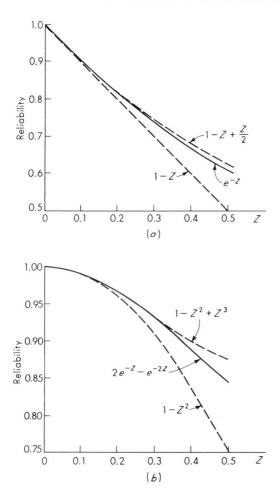

**Fig. 5.6**  Comparison of exact and approximate reliability functions.   (a) Single unit; (b) two parallel units.

these check well with the exact errors, which can be read from Fig. 5.6. For a further discussion see the problems at the end of the chapter.

As an example of exponential approximations, consider the calculation of aircraft-engine reliability discussed in Chap. 1.  The probability of failure of an aircraft due to engine loss was defined as the probability of three or four out of four engines failing.  If $q$ is the probability of any engine failing, the binomial distribution yields

$$F(t) = 4q^3(1 - q) + q^4$$

In general, $q = 1 - e^{-Z}$, and the expression becomes

$$F(t) = 4(1 - e^{-Z})^3(1 - e^{-Z}) + (1 - e^{-Z})^4 = (1 - e^{-Z})^3(5e^{-Z} - 1) \tag{5.34}$$

We could compute $Z$ and substitute into Eq. (5.34); however, for simplicity and comparison purposes we shall obtain a series approximation to $F(t)$. In the problems at the end of the chapter it is shown that a three-term approximation to $(1 - e^{-Z})^m$ is given by

$$(1 - e^{-Z})^m \approx Z^m - \frac{mZ}{2} Z^{m+1} + \frac{m(m-1)}{8} Z^{m+2} \tag{5.35}$$

Using the first two terms of Eqs. (5.35) and (5.28) and substituting into Eq. (5.34) yields

$$F(t) \approx Z^3 \left(1 - \frac{3Z}{2}\right)\left(4 - \frac{5Z}{2}\right)$$

Since we retained only two terms in approximating each of the product terms, we can retain only two terms after multiplication. [This same approach is used in the derivation of Eq. (5.35)]. Thus

$$F(t) \approx Z^3(4 - 8.5Z)$$

Assuming a constant hazard, $Z = \lambda t$, and for the problem of Chap. 1, $t = 20$ hr, $1/\lambda = 10^4$. The result is $F(20) = 3.2068 \times 10^{-8}$.

In a more complex problem than those discussed above, the form of the reliability function may be difficult to write down, and the bounds discussed in Sec. 3.6.5 can be used. One can then write out an approximate expression for the bound expression by successive application of Eqs. (5.28) and (5.35). Such approximation will hold well in the high-reliability region, where $Z \ll 1$ and the series truncation errors are small.

## 5.6  MEAN TIME TO FAILURE

In the last section it was shown that reliability calculations become very complicated in a large system when there are many components and a diverse reliability structure. Not only was the reliability expression difficult to write down in such a case, but computation was lengthy and interpretation of the individual-component contributions was not easy. One method of simplifying the situation is to ask for less detailed information about the system. A useful figure of merit for a system is the MTTF.

The MTTF in terms of the reliability function is given by

$$\text{MTTF} = \int_0^\infty R(t)\, dt \tag{4.55}$$

We can use this expression to compute the MTTF for various configurations. For a series reliability configuration of $n$ elements

$$R(t) = \exp\left[-\sum_{i=1}^{n} Z_i(t)\right]$$

and the MTTF is given by

$$\text{MTTF} = \int_0^\infty \exp\left[-\sum_{i=1}^{n} Z_i(t)\right] dt \qquad (5.36)$$

If the series system has components with more than one type of hazard model, the integral in Eq. (5.36) is difficult to evaluate. The MTTF for several series systems is given in Table 5.2.

Different relationships hold for a parallel system. For two parallel elements, $R(t) = e^{-z_1(t)} + e^{-z_2(t)} - e^{-[z_1(t)+z_2(t)]}$. If both system components have a constant hazard,

$$\text{MTTF} = \frac{1}{\lambda_1} + \frac{1}{\lambda_2} - \frac{1}{\lambda_1 + \lambda_2}$$

In the general case of $n$ parallel elements with constant hazard

$$
\begin{aligned}
\text{MTTF} = {} & \left(\frac{1}{\lambda_1} + \frac{1}{\lambda_2} + \cdots + \frac{1}{\lambda_n}\right) - \left(\frac{1}{\lambda_1 + \lambda_2} + \frac{1}{\lambda_1 + \lambda_3}\right. \\
& + \cdots + \left.\frac{1}{\lambda_i + \lambda_j}\right) + \left(\frac{1}{\lambda_1 + \lambda_2 + \lambda_3} + \frac{1}{\lambda_1 + \lambda_2 + \lambda_4}\right. \\
& + \cdots + \left.\frac{1}{\lambda_i + \lambda_j + \lambda_k}\right) - \cdots + (-1)^{n+1} \frac{1}{\displaystyle\sum_{i=1}^{n} \lambda_i}
\end{aligned}
\qquad (5.37)
$$

If the $n$ units are identical, that is, $\lambda_1 = \lambda_2 = \cdots = \lambda_n = \lambda$, then Eq. (5.37) becomes[1]

$$\text{MTTF} = \frac{1}{\lambda}\left[\frac{\binom{n}{1}}{1} - \frac{\binom{n}{2}}{2} + \frac{\binom{n}{3}}{3} - \cdots + (-1)^{n+1}\frac{\binom{n}{n}}{n}\right]$$

$$= \frac{1}{\lambda}\sum_{i=1}^{n}\frac{1}{i} \qquad (5.38)$$

---

[1] L. B. W. Jolley, "Summation of Series," p. 36, n. 200, Dover Publications, Inc., New York, 1961. Also (p. 14, n. 70)

$$\sum_{i=1}^{n}\frac{1}{i} = 0.577 + \ln n + \frac{1}{2n} - \frac{1}{12n(n+1)} \cdots$$

# Table 5.2 Table of MTTF for various series systems

| System structure | MTTF | Comment |
|---|---|---|
| $z(t)$ | $\dfrac{1}{\lambda}$ | Single constant-hazard element |
| $z(t) = Kt$ | $\sqrt{\dfrac{\pi}{2K}}$ | Single linearly-increasing-hazard element |
| $z(t) = Kt^m$ | $\Gamma\left(\dfrac{1}{m+1}\right)\left[(m+1)\left(\dfrac{K}{m+1}\right)^{1/(m+1)}\right]^{-1}$ | Single Weibull hazard element |
| $z_1=\lambda_1 \quad z_2=\lambda_2 \quad \cdots \quad z_n=\lambda_n$ | $\dfrac{1}{\displaystyle\sum_{i=1}^{n}\lambda_n}$ | $n$ series constant-hazard elements |
| $z_1=K_1 t^m \quad z_2=K_2 t^m \quad \cdots \quad z_n=K_n t^m$ | $\Gamma\left(\dfrac{1}{m+1}\right)\left[(m+1)\left(\dfrac{\displaystyle\sum_{\lambda=1}^{n}K_i}{m+1}\right)^{1/(m+1)}\right]^{-1}$ | $n$ series Weibull hazard elements all with same value of $m$ |
| $z_1=\lambda_1 \quad z_2=\lambda_2 \quad \cdots \quad z_n=\lambda_n$ <br> $z_1=K_1 t \quad z_2=K_2 t \quad \cdots \quad z_r=K_r t$ | $\sqrt{\dfrac{\pi}{K}}\,e^{\lambda^2/K}\left(\dfrac{1}{\sqrt{2\pi}}\displaystyle\int_{\lambda/\sqrt{2K}}^{\infty}e^{-x^2/2}\,dx\right)$ <br><br> where <br> $\lambda = \dfrac{1}{2}\displaystyle\sum_{i=1}^{n}\lambda_i$ <br> $K = \dfrac{1}{2}\displaystyle\sum_{i=1}^{r}K_i$ <br> $\dfrac{1}{\sqrt{2\pi}}\displaystyle\int_{\lambda/\sqrt{2K}}^{+\infty}e^{-x^2/2}\,dx =$ area under the unit normal curve between $\lambda/\sqrt{2K}$ and $\infty$ | $n + r$ series elements, $n$ with constant hazard and $r$ with linearly increasing hazard |

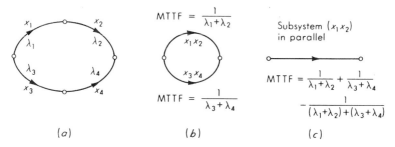

**Fig. 5.7**   MTTF calculations for a reduced grouping.   (a) Four-element structure; (b) reduced series branches; (c) equivalent MTTF.

where the numerator terms $\binom{n}{r}$ are the binomial coefficients.   If $n = 5$, Eq. (5.38) becomes

$$\text{MTTF} = \frac{1}{\lambda}\left(\frac{5}{1} - \frac{10}{2} + \frac{10}{3} - \frac{5}{4} + \frac{1}{5}\right) = \frac{1}{\lambda}\left(\frac{1}{1} + \frac{1}{2} + \frac{1}{3} + \frac{1}{4} + \frac{1}{5}\right) = \frac{2.28}{\lambda}$$

Formulas for the MTTF for various parallel structures are given in Table 5.3.

Another elementary structure is an $r$-out-of-$n$ system.   The reliability function of such a structure of $n$ identical constant-hazard elements is given in Eq. (5.16).   If this expression is expanded in a binomial expansion, the finite series can be integrated term by term.   For example, for a two-out-of-four system

$$R(t) = \binom{4}{2} e^{-2\lambda t}(1 - e^{-\lambda t})^2 + \binom{4}{3} e^{-3\lambda t}(1 - e^{-\lambda t}) + \binom{4}{4} e^{-4\lambda t}(1 - e^{-\lambda t})^0$$
$$= 6 (e^{-2\lambda t} - 2e^{-3\lambda t} + e^{-4\lambda t}) + 4 (e^{-3\lambda t} - e^{-4\lambda t}) + e^{-4\lambda t}$$
$$= 6e^{-2\lambda t} - 8e^{-3\lambda t} + 3e^{-4\lambda t}$$

The MTTF for this structure is given by

$$\text{MTTF} = \frac{13}{12\lambda}$$

The MTTF of an arbitrary structure can sometimes be computed by combining the elements in groups.   For example, consider the system of Fig. 5.7a.   The structure is composed of four elements with constant hazards.   In Fig. 5.7b branches $x_1 x_2$ and $x_3 x_4$ are combined, and the equivalent MTTF for each branch is computed.   The equivalent MTTF expression is given in Fig. 5.7c.   This can be verified by direct calculation.

In Fig. 5.8 a different structure is considered, where the reduction technique fails.   The reduction from Fig. 5.8a to b goes smoothly; how-

**Table 5.3   Table of MTTF for various parallel systems**

| System structure | MTTF | Comment |
|---|---|---|
| | $$\frac{1}{\lambda_1} + \frac{1}{\lambda_2} - \frac{1}{\lambda_1 + \lambda_2}$$ | Two parallel constant-hazard elements |
| | $$\Gamma\left(\frac{1}{m+1}\right)(m+1)^{-m/(m+1)}\left[\frac{1}{K_1^{1/(m+1)}} + \frac{1}{K_2^{1/(m+1)}} - \frac{1}{(K_1+K_2)^{1/(m+1)}}\right]$$ | Two parallel Weibull elements, same value of $m$ |
| | $$\left(\frac{1}{\lambda_1} + \frac{1}{\lambda_2} + \cdots + \frac{1}{\lambda_n}\right) - \left(\frac{1}{\lambda_1+\lambda_2} + \frac{1}{\lambda_1+\lambda_3} + \cdots + \frac{1}{\lambda_i+\lambda_j}\right)$$ $$+ \left(\frac{1}{\lambda_1+\lambda_2+\lambda_3} + \frac{1}{\lambda_1+\lambda_2+\lambda_4} + \cdots + \frac{1}{\lambda_i+\lambda_j+\lambda_k}\right) - \cdots$$ $$+ (-1)^{n+1}\frac{1}{\sum_{i=1}^{n}\lambda_i}$$ | $n$ parallel constant-hazard elements |
| | $$\Gamma\left(\frac{1}{m+1}\right)(m+1)^{-m/(m+1)}\left[\left(\frac{1}{K_1^{1/(m+1)}} + \frac{1}{K_2^{1/(m+1)}} + \cdots\right)\right.$$ $$- \left(\frac{1}{K_1+K_2\,m+1} + \frac{1}{K_1+K_3\,m+1} + \cdots + \frac{1}{K_i+K_j\,m+1}\right) + \cdots$$ $$\left.+ (-1)^{m+1}\frac{1}{\sum_{i=1}^{n}K_i}\right]$$ | $n$ parallel Weibull elements, same value of $m$ |

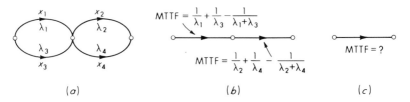

**Fig. 5.8** MTTF calculations for a nonreducible grouping. (a) Four-element structure; (b) reduced series branches; (c) no simple expression.

ever, the reliability functions in 5.7b are no longer simple exponentials but are given by $e^{-\lambda_1 t} + e^{-\lambda_3 t} - e^{-(\lambda_1+\lambda_3)t}$ and $e^{-\lambda_2 t} + e^{-\lambda_4 t} - e^{-(\lambda_2+\lambda_4)t}$. Calculation of the example in Fig. 5.8 yields

$$
\begin{aligned}
R(t) &= (e^{-\lambda_1 t} + e^{-\lambda_3 t} - e^{-(\lambda_1+\lambda_3)t})(e^{-\lambda_2 t} + e^{-\lambda_4 t} - e^{-(\lambda_2+\lambda_4)t}) \\
&= e^{-(\lambda_1+\lambda_2)t} + e^{-(\lambda_1+\lambda_4)t} + e^{-(\lambda_2+\lambda_3)t} + e^{-(\lambda_3+\lambda_4)t} \\
&\quad - e^{-(\lambda_1+\lambda_2+\lambda_4)t} - e^{-(\lambda_2+\lambda_3+\lambda_4)t} - e^{-(\lambda_1+\lambda_2+\lambda_3)t} - e^{-(\lambda_1+\lambda_3+\lambda_4)t} \\
&\quad + e^{-(\lambda_1+\lambda_2+\lambda_3+\lambda_4)t}
\end{aligned}
$$

and the MTTF becomes

$$
\begin{aligned}
\text{MTTF} &= \frac{1}{\lambda_1+\lambda_2} + \frac{1}{\lambda_1+\lambda_4} + \frac{1}{\lambda_2+\lambda_3} + \frac{1}{\lambda_3+\lambda_4} - \frac{1}{\lambda_1+\lambda_2+\lambda_4} \\
&\quad - \frac{1}{\lambda_2+\lambda_3+\lambda_4} - \frac{1}{\lambda_1+\lambda_2+\lambda_3} - \frac{1}{\lambda_1+\lambda_3+\lambda_4} \\
&\quad + \frac{1}{\lambda_1+\lambda_2+\lambda_3+\lambda_4}
\end{aligned}
$$

For identical components this reduces to

$$
\text{MTTF} = \frac{11}{12\lambda}
$$

The complexity of this computation for a nonreducible system makes it questionable whether it is not just as easy to consider the actual system reliability function in such cases.

One can compute not only the MTTF but also the variance of the time to failure

$$
\text{var } t = E(t^2) - [E(t)]^2
$$

In the case of a single constant-hazard component the variance is $1/\lambda^2$, and the standard deviation is $1/\lambda$. Thus the distribution is not well concentrated but spread out. A series system of constant-hazard components has a standard deviation of the TTF of $1 / \left( \sum_{i=1}^{n} \lambda_i \right)$. A moment's reflection explains these results. A constant-hazard distribution has an exponential reliability function and an exponential TTF distribution. Since an exponential is a monotonically decreasing function, the variance of the function does not define a band about the mean, like the normal or quasi-normal distribution. Since a series combination of exponential functions reproduces itself, the same is true of the series system. Knowing the distribution to be exponential and knowing the value of the MTTF completely defines this one-parameter distribution (the variance information is interesting but unnecessary).

To be more general, any series combination of Weibull elements with the same value of $m$ reproduces the same distribution, which is a single-parameter distribution completely defined by the new composite MTTF.

### 5.7 COMPLICATIONS DUE TO DEPENDENT FAILURES, REPAIR, AND STANDBY OPERATION

In the preceding sections of this chapter we have discussed how system reliability is determined in terms of the structural models of Chap. 3 and the failure models of Chap. 4. In Chap. 4 we always spoke of the reliability of single components and thus avoided problems associated with the interactions when a group of components is considered. To be specific we shall discuss how component dependence, repair, and standby operation affect reliability computations in a two-element series and a two-element parallel system.

For simplicity our system will be composed of two 10-watt resistors which fail only as open circuits. When connected in series, they will yield a desired circuit resistance of 200 ohms and will carry 0.1 amp. Thus, each resistor will dissipate 10 watts, its maximum rating (this is poor design practice, as discussed in Sec. 6.3). Since the two resistors dissipate a significant amount of heat, it is easy to see that the total temperature of the pair will differ from that of a single resistor. We assume that a single resistor mounted in the circuit operates at 40°C and the pair, which are mounted near each other because of space limitations, operate at 60°C.[1] If we use composition resistors for our example and consult Fig. 4.9, we find constant failure rates of $6 \times 10^{-6}$ failure per hr at 40°C and $23 \times 10^{-6}$ failure per hr at 60°C. Thus, with both resistors operating we have $\lambda_1 = 23 \times 10^{-6}$ for both resistors, and with one resistor operating we have $\lambda_2 = 6 \times 10^{-6}$ for the single resistor. In our series circuit we are interested only in the failure rate associated with both resistors operating, since we can tolerate no failures in a successful system. Thus, the reliability of the two series resistors is given by

[1] This is just an assumption. In an actual situation one would have to perform a thermal analysis or experimentally determine the two temperatures in the laboratory.

$e^{-46 \times 10^{-6}t}$.   If we consider a parallel circuit, the situation is different.    Let us assume our two 1,000-ohm resistors are connected in parallel to yield 500 ohms and that the circuit will exhibit a marginal but acceptable performance if one resistor open-circuits, leaving 1,000 ohm in the circuit. Thus, the two resistors also form a parallel *reliability* configuration. Again we assume that each resistor will carry 0.1 amp and that the pair is mounted so that with both operating the temperature of the pair rises to 60°C.    As before, the failure rate with both operating is $\lambda_1 = 23 \times 10^{-6}$. The situation changes in two respects when one resistor has open-circuited: (1) there is only one resistor present to cause heating and temperature rise, and (2) the current in the single resistor will change.    If the resistors are connected to a voltage source,[1] the single 1,000-ohm resistor will draw only one-half the previous current, or 0.05 amp.    Since the current is halved, the power will be one-fourth, or 2.5 watts.    Assuming a 30°C temperature at this reduced power dissipation and a wattage ratio of 0.25, we find these conditions below the range of Fig. 4.9.    Thus in lieu of more detailed failure data we use $\lambda_2 < 1 \times 10^{-6}$, the lowest value given.    Since we have a parallel circuit, the reliability of the circuit is given by the probability of zero failures plus the probability of one failure.    The probability of zero failures is given by $e^{-46 \times 10^{-6}t}$; however, the probability of one failure is not such a simple calculation.    From another viewpoint we can say that the two parallel resistors $x_1$ and $x_2$ have a reliability expression given by

$$R = P(x_1 + x_2) = P(x_1) + P(x_2) - P(x_1 x_2) = P(x_1) + P(x_2) \\ - P(x_1)P(x_2|x_1)$$

The interpretation of $P(x_1)$, $P(x_2)$, and $P(x_2|x_1)$ in terms of the physical problem is not at all clear.

Calculations of the dependent probabilities which arise in the parallel-system configuration are best handled using the methods of Sec. 5.8.    It should be clear to the reader that there are a great number of physical situations which lead to dependent failures.    Whenever one component contributes significantly to the environmental temperature, pressure, humidity, radiation levels, etc., and these parameters in turn significantly affect the reliability of other system components, then dependent failures are involved.    Another frequent situation occurs whenever more than one subsystem is powered by a common source of energy.    If one of the subsystems should fail, the source load is reduced and so is its failure rate.    Specific examples of power-source dependence are when several electronic subsystems are operated from the same power supply or several

---

[1] If we assumed a current source was producing the current drain, the current in the single resistor would jump to 0.2 amp.

torque loads applied to a number of different shafts emanating from the same gear train.   Certainly many other situations produce dependent failures.   It is clear that only the design engineer in charge of a circuit design or someone equally familiar with the problem can ferret out such dependent failures and judge whether the effects are significant or inconsequential.

We also encounter difficulty using the previous techniques if the system involves repair.   Continuing with our example of two resistors, we can discuss the effects of repair on a series and a parallel system.   Suppose one of our series resistors fails and we remove it to repair or replace it. The minute the failure occurs the entire system fails, and in a reliability sense we are no longer interested in the system.   Logically, though, a failed resistor is no problem.   If the lead has separated from the circuit connection, inspection and resoldering take little time and so does complete replacement of a burned-out resistor.   Certainly we should get some credit for quickly restoring the circuit to operation.   Since the definition of reliability gives no credit to such repairs on a series system, repair has no effect on the reliability of a series system.   An additional probability function, called the availability function (discussed in Sec. 6.11), is used to supplement the reliability function in repairable systems.

The effects of repair on a parallel system are significant and beneficial. If one resistor fails, the system still operates with the other resistor alone. If the bad resistor is rapidly removed, repaired or replaced, and reinserted in the circuit before the second resistor fails, the circuit is completely restored.   The system will fail only if the first resistor fails and then the second resistor fails before the first is repaired or replaced.   It is obvious that the reliability computation in such a system depends on the failure density function or failure hazard of each resistor as well as the repair density function or repair hazard.   The system reliability is still the probability that both are good plus the probability that one is good; however, both these terms are difficult to calculate directly.   For example, the probability that both resistors are good is the probability of no failures plus the probability of one failure and one completed repair plus the probability of two failures and two completed repairs, etc.   Calculations such as these are best handled by the methods of the next section.

A standby system has some of the same features which can make calculations difficult as the two systems described above.   In a standby system, of course, we are only discussing a special type of parallel system. The feature which prevents us from using the techniques of Chaps. 3 and 4 is the fact that the off-line components have a different failure rate than the on-line ones.   Thus, the system hazards change abruptly whenever a failure occurs.   We can visualize a standby system of two resistors in the following terms.   The first resistor is connected in series with a relay coil.   When the single-pole double-throw contacts of the relay are in the energized position, resistor 1 is in the circuit.   The current flowing through this resistor and the relay coil holds it in this position.   When resistor 1 open-circuits, the relay-coil current is removed, and the relay contacts switch to the deenergized position, switching resistor 2 into the circuit.   If we consider the relay perfect, we can actually view this system as simply a parallel dependent-failure system with on-line failure rate for resistor 1 equal to $\lambda_1$, off-line failure rate for resistor 2 equal to $\lambda_2$, and on-line failure rate for resistor 2 equal to $\lambda_3$.   Of course for effective operation $\bar{\lambda}_2 = 0$ or $\lambda_2 \ll \lambda_3$.   We have already shown in Sec. 2.9 that a standby system can be treated by considering its failure time as a sum of the component failure times.   We shall find the methods of the following section more convenient, however, in most cases.

## 5.8   GENERAL APPROACHES TO COMPUTATION

### 5.8.1   INTRODUCTION

In the preceding section we discussed how dependent failures, repair, or standby operation complicates the direct calculation of element reliabilities.   In this section we shall discuss three different approaches to reliability computations for systems involving such computations.   The first technique is the use of Markov models, which works well and has much appeal as long as the failure hazards $z(t)$ and repair hazards $w(t)$ are constant.   When $z(t)$ and $w(t)$ become time-dependent, the method breaks down, except in a few special cases.   The second method, using joint density functions, and the third method, using convolutionlike integrations, are more difficult to set up, but they are still valid when $z(t)$ or $w(t)$ is time-dependent.

### 5.8.2   MARKOV MODELS

The basic properties of Markov models have already been discussed in Sec. 2.8.   In this section we shall briefly review some of the assumptions necessary for formulation of a Markov model and show how it can be used to make reliability computations.

In order to formulate a Markov model (to be more precise we are talking about continuous-time and discrete-state models) we must first define all the mutually exclusive states of the system, much as was done in Chap. 3.   For example, in a system composed of a single nonreparable element $x_1$ there are two possible states: $s_0 = x_1$, the element is good, and $s_1 = \bar{x}_1$, the element is bad.   The states of the system at $t = 0$ are called the *initial states*, and those representing a final or equilibrium state are called *final states*.  The set of Markov state equations describes the probabilistic transitions from the initial to the final states.

The transition probabilities must obey the following two rules:

1   The probability of transition in time $\Delta t$ from one state to another is given by $z(t)\ \Delta t$, where $z(t)$ is the hazard associated with the two states in question.  If all the $z_i(t)$'s are constant, $z_i(t) = \lambda_i$, and the model is called *homogeneous*.  If any hazards are time functions, the model is called *nonhomogeneous*.

2   The probabilities of more than one transition in time $\Delta t$ are infinitesimals of a higher order and can be neglected.

For the example under discussion the state-transition equations can be formulated using the above rules.  The probability of being in state $s_0$ at time $t + \Delta t$ is written $P_{s_0}(t + \Delta t)$.  This is given by the probability that the system is in state $s_0$ at time $t$, $P_{s_0}(t)$, times the probability of *no* failure in time $\Delta t$, $1 - z(t)\ \Delta t$, plus the probability of being in state $s_1$ at time $t$, $P_{s_1}(t)$, times the probability of repair in time $\Delta t$, which equals zero.

The resulting equation is

$$P_{s_0}(t + \Delta t) = [1 - z(t)\ \Delta t]P_{s_0}(t) + 0P_{s_1}(t) \qquad (5.39)$$

Similarly, the probability of being in state $s_1$ at $t + \Delta t$ is given by

$$P_{s_1}(t + \Delta t) = [z(t)\ \Delta t]P_{s_0}(t) + 1P_{s_1}(t) \qquad (5.40)$$

The transition probability $z(t)\ \Delta t$ is the probability of failure (change from state $s_0$ to $s_1$), and the probability of remaining in state $s_1$ is unity.[1]  One can summarize the transition equations (5.39) and (5.40) by writing the transition matrix given in Table 5.4.

---

[1] Conventionally, state $s_1$ would be called an absorbing state since transitions out of the state are not permitted.

**Table 5.4   State transition matrix for a single element**

| | Final states | |
|---|---|---|
| *Initial states* | $s_0$ | $s_1$ |
| $s_0$ | $1 - z(t)\ \Delta t$ | $z(t)\ \Delta t$ |
| $s_1$ | $0$ | $1$ |

Note that it is a property of transition matrices that its rows must sum to unity. Rearrangement of Eqs. (5.39) and (5.40) yields

$$\frac{P_{s_0}(t + \Delta t) - P_{s_0}(t)}{\Delta t} = -z(t)P_{s_0}(t)$$

$$\frac{P_{s_1}(t + \Delta t) - P_{s_1}(t)}{\Delta t} = z(t)P_{s_0}(t)$$

Passing to a limit as $\Delta t$ becomes small, we obtain

$$\frac{dP_{s_0}(t)}{dt} + z(t)P_{s_0}(t) = 0 \tag{5.41}$$

$$\frac{dP_{s_1}(t)}{dt} = z(t)P_{s_0}(t) \tag{5.42}$$

Equations (5.41) and (5.42) can be solved in conjunction with the appropriate initial conditions for $P_{s_0}(t)$ and $P_{s_1}(t)$, the probabilities of ending up in state $s_0$ or state $s_1$, respectively. The most common initial condition is that the system is good at $t = 0$, that is, $P_{s_0}(t = 0) = 1$ and $P_{s_1}(t = 0) = 0$. Equations (5.41) and (5.42) are simple first-order linear differential equations which are easily solved by classical theory. Equation (5.41) is homogeneous (no driving function), and separation of variables yields

$$\frac{dP_{s_0}(t)}{P_{s_0}(t)} = -z(t) \, dt$$

$$\ln P_{s_0}(t) = - \int_0^t z(\xi) \, d\xi + C_1$$

$$P_{s_0}(t) = \exp\left[ - \int_0^t z(\xi) \, d\xi + C_1 \right] = C_2 \exp\left[ - \int_0^t z(\xi) \, d\xi \right] \tag{5.43}$$

Inserting the initial condition $P_{s_0}(t = 0) = 1$,

$$P_{s_0}(t = 0) = 1 = C_2 e^{-0}$$
$$\therefore C_2 = 1$$

and one obtains the familiar reliability function

$$R(t) = P_{s_0}(t) = \exp\left[ - \int_0^t z(\xi) \, d\xi \right] \tag{5.44}$$

Formal solution of Eq. (5.42) proceeds in a similar manner. The homogeneous equation is given by

$$\frac{dP_{s_1}(t)}{dt} = 0$$
$$\therefore P_{s_{1h}}(t) = C_3$$

The particular solution is

$$P_{s_{1p}}(t) = C_4 \exp\left[- \int_0^t z(\xi)\, d\xi\right]$$

Substituting the particular solution into Eq. (5.42),

$$-C_4 z(t) \exp\left[- \int_0^t z(\xi)\, d\xi\right] = z(t) \exp\left[- \int_0^t z(\xi)\, d\xi\right]$$
$$\therefore C_4 = 1$$

the total solution is

$$P_{s_1}(t) = C_3 - \exp\left[- \int_0^t z(\xi)\, d\xi\right]$$

substitution of the initial condition yields

$$P_{s_1}(t = 0) = 0 = C_3 - e^{-0}$$
$$\therefore C_3 = 1$$

and finally

$$P_{s_1}(t) = 1 - \exp\left[ \int_0^t z(\xi)\, d\xi\right] \tag{5.45}$$

Of course a formal solution of Eq. (5.42) is not necessary to obtain Eq. (5.45), since it is possible to recognize at the outset that

$$P_{s_0}(t) + P_{s_1}(t) = 1$$

The role played by the initial conditions is clearly evident from Eq. (5.43). Since $C_2 = P_{s_0}(0)$, if the system was initially bad, $P_{s_0}(t) = 0$, and $R(t) = 0$. If there is a fifty-fifty chance that the system is good at $t = 0$, then $P_{s_0}(t) = \frac{1}{2}$, and

$$R(t) = \frac{1}{2} \exp\left[- \int_0^t z(\xi)\, d\xi\right]$$

Equations (5.41) and (5.42) can also be solved using Laplace transforms. If $z(t)$ is constant (constant hazard corresponds to a homogeneous Markov model), the solution is very simple.

This method of computing the system reliability function yields the same results, of course, as the techniques of Chaps. 3 and 4. Even in a single-element problem it generates a more general model. The initial condition allows one to include the probability of initial failure before the system in question is energized.

It is often easier to characterize Markov models by a graph composed of nodes representing system states and branches labeled with transition probabilities. Such a Markov graph for the problem described by Eqs. (5.39) and (5.40) or Table 5.4 is given in Fig. 5.9. Note that the sum

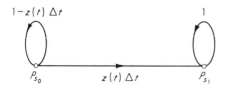

$1 - z(t) \, \Delta t$                    $1$

$P_{s_0}$            $z(t) \, \Delta t$            $P_{s_1}$

**Fig. 5.9**  Markov graph for a single non-repairable element.

of transition probabilities for the branches leaving each node must be unity. Treating the nodes as signal sources and the transition probabilities as transmission coefficients, we can write Eqs. (5.39) and (5.40) by inspection. Thus, the probability of being at any node at time $t + \Delta t$ is the sum of all signals arriving at that node. All other nodes are considered probability sources at time $t$, and all transition probabilities serve as transmission gains. A simple algorithm for writing Eqs. (5.41) and (5.42) by inspection is to equate the derivative of the probability at any node to the sum of the transmissions coming into the node. Any unity gain factors of the self-loops must first be set to zero, and the $\Delta t$ factors are dropped from the branch gains. Referring to Fig. 5.9, the self-loop on $P_{s_1}$ disappears, and the equation becomes $\dot{P}_{s_1} = z P_{s_0}$. At node $P_{s_0}$ the self-loop gain becomes $-z$, and the equation is $\dot{P}_{s_0} = -z P_{s_0}$. The same algorithm holds at each node for more complex graphs.

One can illustrate dependent failures, standby operation, and repair by discussing a two-element system. For simplicity repair is ignored at first. If a two-element system consisting of elements $x_1$ and $x_2$ is considered, there are four system states: $s_0 = x_1 x_2$, $s_1 = \bar{x}_1 x_2$, $s_2 = x_1 \bar{x}_2$, and $s_3 = \bar{x}_1 \bar{x}_2$. The state transition matrix is given in Table 5.5 and the Markov graph in Fig. 5.10.

The probability expression for state $s_0$ is given by

$$P_{s_0}(t + \Delta t) = \{1 - [z_{01}(t) + z_{02}(t)] \, \Delta t\} P_{s_0}(t) \tag{5.46}$$

where $[z_{01}(t) + z_{02}(t)] \, \Delta t$ is the probability of a transition in time $\Delta t$ from $s_0$ to $s_1$ or $s_2$. For state $s_1$

$$P_{s_1}(t + \Delta t) = [z_{01}(t) \, \Delta t] P_{s_0}(t) + [1 - z_{13}(t) \, \Delta t] P_{s_1}(t) \tag{5.47}$$

where $z_{13}(t) \, \Delta t$ is the probability of a transition from state $s_1$ to $s_3$. Similarly for state $s_2$

$$P_{s_2}(t + \Delta t) = [z_{02}(t) \, \Delta t] P_{s_0}(t) + [1 - z_{23}(t) \, \Delta t] P_{s_2}(t) \tag{5.48}$$

where $z_{23}(t) \, \Delta t$ is the probability of a transition from state $s_2$ to $s_3$. For state $s_3$ the transition equation is

$$P_{s_3}(t + \Delta t) = [z_{13}(t) \, \Delta t] P_{s_1}(t) + [z_{23}(t) \, \Delta t] P_{s_2}(t) + 1 \, P_{s_3}(t) \tag{5.49}$$

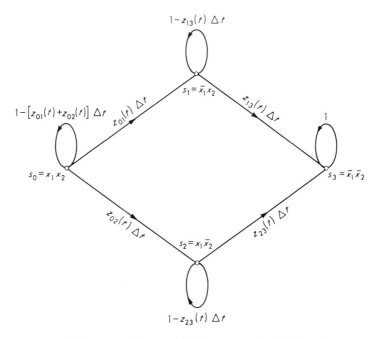

**Fig. 5.10**  Markov graph for two distinct nonrepairable elements.

Equations (5.46) to (5.49) can easily be summarized in the state transition matrix given in Table 5.5 and the matrix equation[1]

$$[P_{s_0}(t + \Delta t) \quad P_{s_1}(t + \Delta t) \quad P_{s_2}(t + \Delta t) \quad P_{s_3}(t + \Delta t)]$$
$$= [P_{s_0}(t) \quad P_{s_1}(t) \quad P_{s_2}(t) \quad P_{s_3}(t)]$$

$$\begin{bmatrix} 1 - (z_{01} + z_{02}) \Delta t & z_{01} \Delta t & z_{02} \Delta t & 0 \\ 0 & 1 - z_{13} \Delta t & 0 & z_{13} \Delta t \\ 0 & 0 & 1 - z_{23} \Delta t & z_{23} \Delta t \\ 0 & 0 & 0 & 1 \end{bmatrix} \quad (5.50)$$

Rearranging Eqs. (5.46) to (5.49) and passing to a limit yields

$$\lim_{\Delta t \to 0} \frac{P_{s_0}(t + \Delta t) - P_{s_0}(t)}{\Delta t} = \frac{dP_{s_0}(t)}{dt} = -[z_{01}(t) + z_{02}(t)]P_{s_0}(t) \quad (5.51)$$

$$\lim_{\Delta t \to 0} \frac{P_{s_1}(t + \Delta t) - P_{s_1}(t)}{\Delta t} = \frac{dP_{s_1}(t)}{dt}$$
$$= -[z_{13}(t)]P_{s_1}(t) + [z_{01}(t)]P_{s_0}(t) \quad (5.52)$$

---

[1] Some authors prefer to use column matrices rather than the row matrices shown, see Sec. 2.11.9, property 6.

**Table 5.5 State transition matrix for two elements**

| Initial states | | $s_0$ | $s_1$ | $s_2$ | $s_3$ |
|---|---|---|---|---|---|
| | | | *Final states* | | |
| Zero failures | $s_0$ | $1 - [z_{01}(t) + z_{02}(t)]\,\Delta t$ | $z_{01}(t)\,\Delta t$ | $z_{02}(t)\,\Delta t$ | $0$ |
| One failure | $s_1$ | $0$ | $1 - [z_{13}(t)]\,\Delta t$ | $0$ | $z_{13}(t)\,\Delta t$ |
| | $s_2$ | $0$ | $0$ | $1 - [z_{23}(t)]\,\Delta t$ | $z_{23}(t)\,\Delta t$ |
| Two failures | $s_3$ | $0$ | $0$ | $0$ | $1$ |

$$\lim_{\Delta t \to 0} \frac{P_{s_2}(t + \Delta t) - P_{s_2}(t)}{\Delta t} = \frac{dP_{s_2}(t)}{dt}$$

$$= -[z_{23}(t)P_{s_2}(t) + [z_{02}(t)]P_{s_0}(t) \tag{5.53}$$

$$\lim_{\Delta t \to 0} \frac{P_{s_3}(t + \Delta t) - P_{s_3}(t)}{\Delta t} = \frac{dP_{s_3}(t)}{dt}$$

$$= [z_{13}(t)]P_{s_1}(t) + [z_{23}(t)]P_{s_2}(t) \tag{5.54}$$

The initial conditions associated with this set of equations are $P_{s_0}(0)$, $P_{s_1}(0)$, $P_{s_2}(0)$, $P_{s_3}(0)$. These equations, of course, could have been written by inspection using the algorithms previously stated.

It is difficult to solve these equations for a general hazard function $z(t)$, but if the hazards are specified, the solution is quite simple. If all the hazards are constant, $z_{01}(t) = \lambda_1$, $z_{02}(t) = \lambda_2$, $z_{13}(t) = \lambda_3$, and $z_{23}(t) = \lambda_4$. The solutions are

$$P_{s_0}(t) = e^{-(\lambda_1 + \lambda_2)t} \tag{5.55}$$

$$P_{s_1}(t) = \frac{\lambda_1}{\lambda_1 + \lambda_2 - \lambda_3}\,(e^{-\lambda_3 t} - e^{-(\lambda_1 + \lambda_2)t}) \tag{5.56}$$

$$P_{s_2}(t) = \frac{\lambda_2}{\lambda_1 + \lambda_2 - \lambda_4}\,(e^{-\lambda_4 t} - e^{-(\lambda_1 + \lambda_2)t}) \tag{5.57}$$

$$P_{s_3}(t) = 1 - [P_{s_0}(t) + P_{s_1}(t) + P_{s_2}(t)] \tag{5.58}$$

where

$$P_{s_0}(0) = 1 \quad \text{and} \quad P_{s_1}(0) = P_{s_2}(0) = P_{s_3}(0) = 0$$

Note that we have not as yet had to say anything about the configuration of the system, but only have had to specify the number of elements and the transition probabilities. Thus, when we solve for $P_{s_0}$, $P_{s_1}$, $P_{s_2}$, we have essentially solved for all possible two-element system configurations.[1]

---

[1] It is easy to see why a series configuration of $n$ components has the poorest reliability and why a parallel configuration has the best. The only successful state for a series system is where all components are good; thus, $R(t) = P_{s_0}(t)$. In the case of a parallel system all states except the one in which all components have failed is good, and $R(t) = P_{s_0}(t) + P_{s_1}(t) + P_{s_2}(t)$. It is clear that any other system configuration falls somewhere in between.

In a two-element system, formulation of the reliability expressions in terms of $P_{s_0}$, $P_{s_1}$, and $P_{s_2}$ is trivial, but in a more complex problem we can always formulate the expression using the tools of Chap. 3.

For a series system, the only state representing success is no failures; that is, $P_{s_0}(t)$. Therefore

$$R(t) = P_{s_0}(t) = e^{-(\lambda_1+\lambda_2)t} \qquad (5.59)$$

If the two elements are in parallel, one failure can be tolerated, and there are three successful states, $P_{s_0}(t)$, $P_{s_1}(t)$, $P_{s_2}(t)$. Since the states are mutually exclusive,

$$R(t) = P_{s_0}(t) + P_{s_1}(t) + P_{s_2}(t) = e^{-(\lambda_1+\lambda_2)t}$$
$$+ \frac{\lambda_1}{\lambda_1 + \lambda_2 - \lambda_3} (e^{-\lambda_3 t} - e^{-(\lambda_1+\lambda_2)t})$$
$$+ \frac{\lambda_2}{\lambda_1 + \lambda_2 - \lambda_4} (e^{-\lambda_4 t} - e^{-(\lambda_1+\lambda_2)t})$$
$$\qquad (5.60)$$

Equation (5.60) is very general and represents the reliability function for any two-element parallel system with constant-hazard elements. We can now solve the problem posed in the last section involving the two temperature-dependent resistors in parallel. If we let both resistors be identical and call the hazard with both operating $\lambda_b$ and with a single one operating $\lambda_s$, then $\lambda_1 = \lambda_2 = \lambda_b$ and $\lambda_3 = \lambda_4 = \lambda_s$. Substituting into Eq. (5.60) yields

$$R(t) = \frac{2\lambda_b e^{-\lambda_s t} - \lambda_s e^{-2\lambda_b t}}{2\lambda_b - \lambda_s} \qquad (5.61)$$

Similarly if Eq. (5.60) represents a two-element standby system initially in state zero, then $\lambda_1 = \lambda_A$, and $\lambda_2 = 0$, since element 2 cannot fail prior to failure of element 1 because it is in an unenergized state.[1] The hazard $\lambda_3 = \lambda_B$. [Note that hazard $\lambda_4$ need not be specified since if $P_{s_0}(0) = 1$ and $\lambda_2 = 0$, state $s_2$ has a probability which is zero; see Eq. (5.57).]

With these substitutions Eq. (5.60) becomes

$$R(t) = \frac{\lambda_A}{\lambda_A - \lambda_B} e^{-\lambda_B t} - \frac{\lambda_B}{\lambda_A - \lambda_B} e^{-\lambda_A t} \qquad (5.62)$$

If $\lambda_A = \lambda_B = \lambda$, Eq. (5.62) gives an indeterminate result; however, by use of L'Hospital's rule we differentiate both numerator and denominator with respect to $\lambda_B$ and then let $\lambda_A = \lambda_B = \lambda$. The result is

$$R(t) = e^{-\lambda t} + \lambda t e^{-\lambda t}$$

[1] One could of course assume that $\lambda_2 = \lambda_C$, that is, that the off-line component could also age and fail.

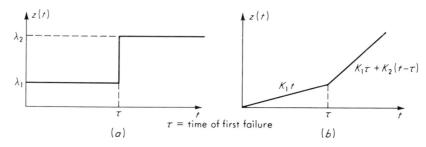

**Fig. 5.11**  Dependent-hazard models.

which of course agrees with the result given by the final two terms of Eq. (2.35).   Up to now we have discussed constant hazards and have found that in principle we can use the Markov model to handle component dependence or standby systems.   The situation changes if we consider a time-varying hazard, e.g., a linearly increasing hazard function.   In both the component-dependence case and the standby case previously discussed, the hazard function changed abruptly at the time of first failure $\tau$, as shown in Fig. 5.11a.   Although the time of switching is a function of $\tau$, the hazard for $t > \tau$ is independent of $\tau$.   Such is not the case in Fig. 5.11b, where we consider linearly increasing hazards.

With linearly increasing hazards the hazard for $t > \tau$ is $k_1\tau + k_2(t - \tau)$, obviously a function of $\tau$.   Thus, the state probabilities will be functions of $t$ and $\tau$, and the technique is no longer directly applicable; the methods of Secs. 5.8.4 and 5.8.5 should be used.   This same difficulty also occurs when any other time-varying hazard is combined with component dependence or standby operation.[1,2]

The complexity of a Markov model depends on the number of system states.   In general we obtain for an $m$-state problem a system of $m$ first-order differential equations.   The number of states is given in terms of the number of components $n$ as

$$m = \binom{n}{0} + \binom{n}{1} + \binom{n}{2} + \cdots + \binom{n}{n} = 2^n$$

Thus, our two-element model has four states, and a four-element model 16 states.   This means that an $n$-component system may require a solution of as many as $2^n$ first-order differential equations.   In many cases we are interested in fewer states.   Suppose we want to know only how many failed items are present in each state and not which items have

[1] Of course we can handle time-varying hazards if there is no component dependence, standby operation, or repair; however, the simpler techniques of Chaps. 3 and 4 are preferred in such a case.

[2] A special method involving the introduction of dummy states allows one to simulate effects of time-varying failure or repair hazards (see Fig. 6.38).

failed. This would mean a model with $n + 1$ states rather than $2^n$, which represents a tremendous saving. To illustrate how such simplifications affect the Markov graph we consider a collapsed flow graph shown in Fig. 5.12 for the example given in Fig. 5.10. Collapsing the flow graph is equivalent to the restriction $P_{s_1'}(t) = P_{s_1}(t) + P_{s_2}(t)$ applied to Eqs. (5.51) to (5.54). Note that this can collapse the flow graph only if $z_{13} = z_{23}$; however, $z_{01}$ and $z_{02}$ need not be equal. These results are obvious if Eqs. (5.52) and (5.53) are added.

Markov graphs for a system with repair are shown in Fig. 5.13$a$ and $b$. The graph in Fig. 5.13$a$ is a general model, and that of Fig. 5.13$b$ is a collapsed model.

The system equations can be written for Fig. 5.13$a$ by inspection using the algorithm previously discussed.

$$\begin{aligned}
\dot{P}_{s_0} &= -(z_{01} + z_{02})P_{s_0} + w_{10}P_{s_1} + w_{20}P_{s_2} \\
\dot{P}_{s_1} &= -(z_{13} + w_{10})P_{s_1} + z_{01}P_{s_0} \\
\dot{P}_{s_2} &= -(z_{23} + w_{20})P_{s_2} + z_{02}P_{s_0} \\
\dot{P}_{s_3} &= Z_{13}P_{s_1} + z_{23}P_{s_2}
\end{aligned} \tag{5.63}$$

Similarly for Fig. 5.13$b$

$$\begin{aligned}
\dot{P}_{s_0'} &= -z_{01}'P_{s_0'} + w_{10}'P_{s_1'} \\
\dot{P}_{s_1'} &= -(z_{12}' + w_{10}')P_{s_1'} + z_{01}'P_{s_0'} \\
\dot{P}_{s_2'} &= z_{12}'P_{s_1'}
\end{aligned} \tag{5.64}$$

The probabilities in the general and the collapsed model are related by

$$\begin{aligned}
P_{s_0'} &= P_{s_0} \\
P_{s_1'} &= P_{s_1} + P_{s_2} \\
P_{s_2'} &= P_{s_3}
\end{aligned}$$

and the hazards must satisfy

$$\begin{aligned}
z_{01}' &= z_{01} + z_{02} \\
w_{10}' &= w_{10} + w_{20} \\
z_{12}' &= z_{13} = z_{23}
\end{aligned}$$

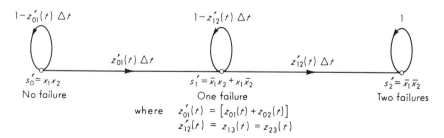

Fig. 5.12 Collapsed Markov graph corresponding to Fig. 5.10.

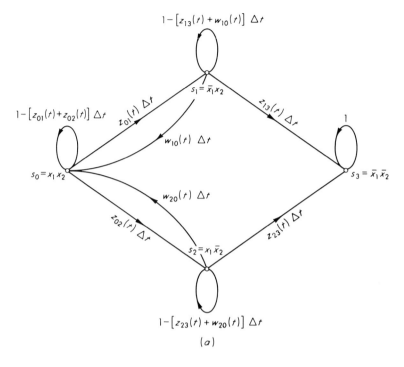

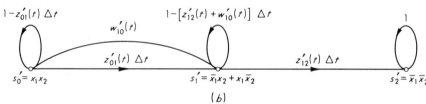

**Fig. 5.13**   Markov graphs for a system with repair.   (a) General model; (b) collapsed model.

The solution to Eqs. (5.63) and (5.64) for various values of the $z$'s and $w$'s will be deferred until Sec. 6.10.   It is also true that we cannot use this approach to formulate the equations for time-varying repair hazards, for the same reasons as when there was component dependence or standby operation.

More complex system structures can be handled in a similar manner, like the examples shown in Fig. 5.14.   Both these three-element systems can be solved at the same time because the Markov approach solves for all the state probabilities.   For a three-element system, the system states are:

$$s_0 = x_1 x_2 x_3$$
$$s_1 = \bar{x}_1 x_2 x_2$$
$$s_2 = x_1 \bar{x}_2 x_3$$
$$s_3 = x_1 x_2 \bar{x}_3$$
$$s_4 = \bar{x}_1 \bar{x}_2 x_3$$
$$s_5 = \bar{x}_1 x_2 \bar{x}_3$$
$$s_6 = x_1 \bar{x}_2 \bar{x}_3$$
$$s_7 = \bar{x}_1 \bar{x}_2 \bar{x}_3$$

The reliability functions for systems $A$ and $B$ are given by

$$R_A(t) = P_{s_0}(t) + P_{s_1}(t) + P_{s_2}(t) \qquad (5.65)$$
$$R_B(t) = P_{s_0}(t) + P_{s_1}(t) + P_{s_2}(t) + P_{s_3}(t) + P_{s_6}(t) \qquad (5.66)$$

The solutions for the probabilities $P_{s_0}(t)$, $P_{s_1}(t)$, etc., in Eqs. (5.65) and (5.66) can be obtained in the same manner as the previous problems. The main difference is the amount of labor involved. In this problem there are eight states and eight simultaneous first-order differential equations to be solved. If some of the elements are identical, the problem can be at least partially collapsed. For example, if $x_1 = x_2$, then for system $A$ we can define $P_{s_0'}(t) = P_{s_0}(t)$, $P_{s_1'}(t) = P_{s_1}(t) + P_{s_2}(t)$, and $P_{s_2'}(t) = P_{s_3}(t) + P_{s_4}(t) + P_{s_5}(t) + P_{s_6}(t) + P_{s_7}(t)$. This reduces the problem to a three-state collapsed form, where $z_{01}' = z_{01} + z_{02}$, $z_{02}' = z_{03}$, and $z_{12}' = z_{14} + z_{15} + z_{24} + z_{26}$. If no such simplification is possible, simplified solution techniques are needed for even a three-element problem.

If the transition matrix contains constant-hazard elements, the Laplace transform solution can be mechanized using matrix algebra (see Sec. 2.11.10). The procedure is as follows. The matrix $[T]$ is formed from the ordinary transition matrix (the $\Delta t$ terms deleted). One then subtracts from $[T]$ the unit matrix $[I]$ to form $[T] - [I]$. Another identity matrix is formed with each term multiplied by the Laplace operator $s[I]$. The difference between this matrix and the former matrix is computed

$$s[I] - [[T] - [I]]$$

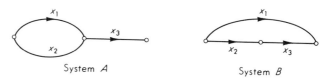

System A          System B

**Fig. 5.14** Two three-element systems.

The inverse of this matrix is obtained.

$$[s[I] - [[T] - [I]]]^{-1} = [(s + 1)[I] - [T]]^{-1}$$

The initial conditions are written as a row matrix $[P(0)]$, and the row matrix of transforms is given by

$$[P(s)] = [P(0)][s[I] - [[T] - [I]]]^{-1} \tag{5.67}$$

This technique is illustrated by solution of a two-element system with constant hazards.   The transition matrix is given by

$$[T] = \begin{bmatrix} 1 - (\lambda_1 + \lambda_2) & \lambda_1 & \lambda_2 & 0 \\ 0 & 1 - \lambda_3 & 0 & \lambda_3 \\ 0 & 0 & 1 - \lambda_4 & \lambda_4 \\ 0 & 0 & 0 & 1 \end{bmatrix}$$

$$[T] - [I] = \begin{bmatrix} -(\lambda_1 + \lambda_2) & \lambda_1 & \lambda_2 & 0 \\ 0 & -\lambda_3 & 0 & \lambda_3 \\ 0 & 0 & -\lambda_4 & \lambda_4 \\ 0 & 0 & 0 & 0 \end{bmatrix}$$

$$s[I] - [[T] - [I]] = \begin{bmatrix} s + (\lambda_1 + \lambda_2) & -\lambda_1 & -\lambda_2 & 0 \\ 0 & s + \lambda_3 & 0 & -\lambda_3 \\ 0 & 0 & s + \lambda_4 & -\lambda_4 \\ 0 & 0 & 0 & s \end{bmatrix} \tag{5.68}$$

Note that because of the diagonal nature of Eq. (5.68) the determinant is found by inspection as the product of the main diagonal terms.

Before one finds the inverse, inspection of Eq. (5.67) allows some shortcuts.   If the initial conditions are

$$P_{s_0}(0) = 1, \qquad P_{s_1}(0) = P_{s_2}(0) = P_{s_3}(0) = 0$$

then

$$[P(0)] = [1 \quad 0 \quad 0 \quad 0]$$

Because of the nature of this row matrix only the first row of the inverse matrix is needed.   [This means only the cofactors of the first column in Eq. (5.68) need be computed].   Furthermore, since $P_{s_2}(t)$ can be found in terms of the other probabilities, only the first three terms in the first row of the inverse matrix are needed.   Thus Eq. (5.68) becomes

$$[P(s)] = [1 \quad 0 \quad 0 \quad 0]$$

$$\begin{bmatrix} \dfrac{1}{(s + \lambda_1 + \lambda_2)} & \dfrac{-\lambda_{11}}{(s + \lambda_1 + \lambda_2)(s + \lambda_3)} & \dfrac{-\lambda_2}{(s + \lambda_1 + \lambda_2)(s + \lambda_4)} & \cdots \\ \cdots & \cdots & \cdots & \cdots \\ \cdots & \cdots & \cdots & \cdots \\ \cdots & \cdots & \cdots & \cdots \end{bmatrix}$$

$$\tag{5.69}$$

Performing the indicated multiplication and expanding in partial fractions,

$$[P_{s_0}(s) \quad P_{s_1}(s) \quad P_{s_2}(s) \quad P_{s_3}(s)] = \left[ \frac{1}{s + \lambda_1 + \lambda_2} \quad \frac{-\lambda_1}{(\lambda_1 + \lambda_2) - \lambda_3} \frac{}{s + \lambda_1 + \lambda_2} \right.$$

$$+ \frac{\frac{-\lambda_1}{\lambda_3 - (\lambda_1 + \lambda_2)}}{s + \lambda_3} \quad \frac{\frac{-\lambda_2}{(\lambda_1 + \lambda_2) - \lambda_4}}{s + \lambda_1 + \lambda_2} + \left. \frac{\frac{-\lambda_2}{\lambda_4 - (\lambda_1 + \lambda_2)}}{s + \lambda_4} \quad \cdots \right] \qquad (5.70)$$

The corresponding time functions are

$$P_{s_0}(t) = e^{-(\lambda_1 + \lambda_2)t}$$

$$P_{s_1}(t) = \frac{\lambda_1}{\lambda_1 + \lambda_2 - \lambda_3} \left( e^{-\lambda_3 t} - e^{-(\lambda_1 + \lambda_2)t} \right) \qquad (5.71)$$

$$P_{s_2}(t) = \frac{\lambda_2}{\lambda_1 + \lambda_2 - \lambda_4} \left( e^{-\lambda_4 t} - e^{-(\lambda_1 + \lambda_2)t} \right)$$

These results are of course identical with Eqs. (5.55) to (5.57).

Another simplification technique is to partition the original transition matrix $[T]$. If all the good states are written first along the left column and top border of the matrix, then the upper left corner forms a square submatrix of good states $[T_g]$, which can be solved in lieu of the entire matrix. This technique is further discussed in the problems at the end of the chapter. These simplifications measurably reduce the labor in solving a problem as compared with the classical solution. In the event that the equations are too complex for analytical solution, the computer methods of Sec. 5.10 can be used.

### 5.8.3 MTTF CALCULATIONS

One can calculate the system MTTF directly from the reliability function using Eq. (4.55), but it is easier to use Eqs. (4.60) and (5.67). If the Markov equations have already been put in the form shown in Eq. (5.67), one merely makes the following modifications. All states in the transition matrix corresponding to absorbing states are eliminated by crossing out the appropriate rows and columns. Since an absorbing state represents a state with only incoming branches, it does not affect the remaining states. The new reduced transition matrix is denoted by $[T']$. The mean times to reach each of the good system states, $\bar{t}_1, \bar{t}_2, \ldots,$ $\bar{t}_n$ are then given by the expression

$$[\bar{t}] = [P(0)][[I] - [T']]^{-1} \qquad (5.72)$$

The system MTTF is then given by the sum of all the $\bar{t}_n$ terms. The result seems to contradict intuition; however, the expression can be verified as follows.

The reliability function is given by

$$R(t) = \sum_{i}^{g} P_i(t)$$

where the summation of state probabilities is taken over the $g$ good states. The MTTF is given by

$$\text{MTTF} = \int_0^t R(t)\, dt = \sum_{i}^{g} \int_0^t P_i(t)\, dt$$

Defining

$$f_i(t) = \frac{dF_i(t)}{dt} = -\frac{dP_i(t)}{dt}$$

and using Eqs. (4.52) and (4.55), we obtain

$$\text{MTTF} = \sum_{i}^{g} \int_0^\infty tf_i(t)\, dt = \sum_{i}^{g} \bar{t}_i$$

Equation (5.72) is obtained by applying Eq. (4.60) to Eq. (5.67).[1]
For the example given in Eq. (5.68) we obtain

$$T' = \begin{bmatrix} 1 - (\lambda_1 + \lambda_2) & \lambda_1 & \lambda_2 \\ 0 & 1 - \lambda_3 & 0 \\ 0 & 0 & 1 - \lambda_4 \end{bmatrix}$$

$$[I] - [T'] = \begin{bmatrix} \lambda_1 + \lambda_2 & -\lambda_1 & -\lambda_2 \\ 0 & \lambda_3 & 0 \\ 0 & 0 & \lambda_4 \end{bmatrix}$$

$$[[I] - [T']]^{-1} = \begin{bmatrix} \dfrac{1}{\lambda_1 + \lambda_2} & \dfrac{\lambda_1}{(\lambda_1 + \lambda_2)\lambda_3} & \dfrac{\lambda_2}{(\lambda_1 + \lambda_2)\lambda_4} \\ \cdots\cdots\cdots\cdots\cdots\cdots\cdots \\ \cdots\cdots\cdots\cdots\cdots\cdots\cdots \end{bmatrix}$$

Thus

$$\text{MTTF} = \frac{1}{\lambda_1 + \lambda_2} + \frac{\lambda_1}{(\lambda_1 + \lambda_2)\lambda_3} + \frac{\lambda_2}{(\lambda_1 + \lambda_2)\lambda_4} \tag{5.73}$$

The reader may check the result of Eq. (5.73) by direct integration of Eqs. (5.71).

It is easy to extend this technique to the computation of the variance of the time to failure. Since

$$\text{var } t = E(t^2) - [E(t)]^2$$

[1] Note that one must use $[T']$ rather than $[T]$ in Eq. (5.72) since $[I] - [T]$ is singular because of the absorbing states.

the problem reduces to a computation of

$$E(t^2) = \int_0^\infty t^2 r(t)\, dt = - \int_0^\infty t^2 \frac{dR(t)}{dt}\, dt = - \int_0^\infty t^2\, dR(t)$$

Integration by parts and passing to a limit, we obtain[1]

$$E(t^2) = 2 \int_0^\infty tR(t)\, dt$$

From another Laplace transform theorem we obtain

$$\mathcal{L}\{tR(t)\} = - \frac{dR(s)}{ds}$$

Thus, taking the derivative of both sides of Eq. (5.67), we obtain

$$- \frac{d}{ds} P(s) = -[P(0)] \frac{d}{ds} [(s+1)[I] - [T]]^{-1}$$

and

$$E(t^2) = \lim_{s \to 0} \left\{ -2[P(0)] \frac{d}{ds} [(s+1)[I] - [T]]^{-1} \right\} \qquad (5.74)$$

Application of Eq. (5.74) is discussed in the problems at the end of the chapter. In any event, it is still relevant to question how much additional information is given by var $t$ if MTTF is already known.

#### 5.8.4 JOINT–DENSITY–FUNCTION APPROACH

The Markov model approach, given in Sec. 5.8.2, is perhaps the best and most straightforward approach to computations in systems with dependence, repair, or standby operation. If the equations become numerous, we always have recourse to a computer solution. Unfortunately, the method rapidly breaks down when either failure or repair hazards become nonconstant. The joint-density-function approach discussed below is one way of proceeding in such a case.

In order to develop the approach in practical terms, a particular example will be discussed. Consider an electronic amplifier with two transistors. The transistors are mounted close by on the same heat sink, such that the heat dissipation of the first elevates the operating temperature of the second and vice versa.[2] Since transistors fail faster at elevated temperatures, temperature causes dependence between the two

[1] The term $\lim_{t \to 0} t^2 R(t)$ is zero for the same reasons as those given for the $\lim_{t \to 0} tR(t)$ in Eq. (4.54).

[2] Of course it is desirable design procedure to use separate heat sinks or at least one large enough so that there is little thermal interaction; however, miniaturization or other design constraints often force an important compromise on this issue.

transistors. This means that two hazard models are needed for each transistor, one which holds at the temperature obtained when only one transistor is operating and another at the elevated temperature when both are operating. If for simplicity one assumes constant-hazard models, the two hazards are $\lambda_b$, the hazard with both operating, and $\lambda_s$, the hazard with only a single one operating. If both transistors are assumed to be identical, the conditional probabilities involved can easily be computed. This problem was solved before, in Sec. 5.8.2 [see Eq. (5.61)], but we repeat the calculation here from the joint-density-function viewpoint.

If $\tau$ is the failure time for the first failure, then $g_1(\tau)$ is the density function for the first failure, which holds for $0 < \tau < t$. The time of the second failure is $t$, and a dependent probability density function $g_2(t|\tau)$ holds for $\tau < t$. These density functions are given by

$$g_1(\tau) = 2\lambda_b e^{-2\lambda_b \tau} \qquad 0 < \tau < t \tag{5.75}$$

$$g_2(t|\tau) = \begin{cases} \lambda_s e^{-\lambda_s(t-\tau)} & 0 < \tau < t \\ 0 & \tau > t \end{cases} \tag{5.76}$$

It should be noted that for $g_2(\tau)$ the hazard is $2\lambda_b$, since either of the two transistors could cause the first failure. If the two transistors are connected in series, the system fails when the first transistor fails, and $f(t) = g_1(t)$. The reliability function is

$$R(t) = 1 - \int_0^t f(\xi)\, d\xi = 1 - \int_0^t 2\lambda_b e^{-2\lambda_b \tau}\, d\tau = e^{-2\lambda_b t} \tag{5.77}$$

The result given in Eq. (5.77) could have been derived directly without resort to conditional density functions, but this emphasizes the point previously made that dependence only complicates the calculations in parallel-type structures.

If the two transistors are in parallel, the computation is more complicated. A joint density function $\phi(\tau,t)$ may be defined with the two failure times as random variables

$$\phi(\tau,t) = g_1(\tau)g_2(t|\tau) \qquad 0 < \tau < t \tag{5.78}$$

System failure is governed by $f(t)$, which is a marginal density function given by

$$\begin{aligned} f(t) &= \int_0^\infty \phi(\tau,t)\, d\tau \\ &= \int_0^t (2\lambda_b e^{-2\lambda_b \tau})(\lambda_s e^{-\lambda_s(t-\tau)})\, d\tau \\ &= 2\lambda_s \lambda_b e^{-\lambda_s t} \int_0^t e^{-(2\lambda_b - \lambda_s)\tau}\, d\tau \\ &= \frac{2\lambda_b \lambda_s}{2\lambda_b - \lambda_s} (e^{-\lambda_s t} - e^{-2\lambda_b t}) \end{aligned} \tag{5.79}$$

Computing the reliability function from $f(t)$,

$$R(t) = 1 - \int_0^t f(t) \, dt$$

$$= \frac{2\lambda_b}{2\lambda_b - \lambda_s} e^{-\lambda_s t} - \frac{\lambda_s}{2\lambda_b - \lambda_s} e^{-2\lambda_b t} \tag{5.80}$$

Equation (5.80) is of course the same result as the previous computation given in Eq. (5.61).

If a particular example is chosen for the transistors and heat sink, specific numbers can be derived. Typical values are[1] one transistor, 85°C, $\lambda_s = 0.15 \times 10^{-6}$ failure per hr, and both transistors, 110°C, $\lambda_b = 0.39 \times 10^{-6}$ failure per hr. The resulting reliability expression is

$$R(t) = 1.24e^{-0.15 \times 10^{-6} t} - 0.24e^{-0.78 \times 10^{-6} t}$$

which is plotted in Fig. 5.15. It is clear that an upper bound on the reliability expression can be computed by using $\lambda_i = \lambda_s$ in Eq. (5.9). A lower bound is obtained by substituting $\lambda_i = \lambda_b$ in the same expression. The comparison of these three functions in Fig. 5.15 shows that a large error is made if dependence is ignored.

A second example, involving a standby system, is now discussed. A standby system is one in which two or more components are connected in parallel such that power is applied to only one component. When the energized component fails, it is deenergized and removed from operation, and the next component is energized and connected in the former's place.

[1] J. Kart, Effects of Thermal Proximity on Transistor Reliability, M.S. project, Department of Electrical Engineering, Polytechnic Institute of Brooklyn, New York, June, 1965.

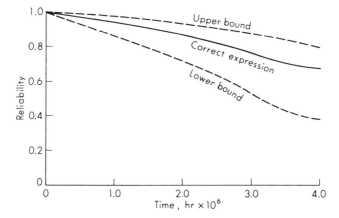

**Fig. 5.15**  Reliability functions for two parallel transistors.

The switching and warm-up are assumed to be instantaneous. To simplify the discussion it is assumed that the switch does not fail and that the components that are in standby do not fail or age unless switched into operation. Because of the special nature of a standby system, it is more probable that such a structure will occur in a system which has been designed with reliability in mind than as a naturally occurring system structure.

Using the joint-density-function approach, two conditional density functions are defined. The first, on-line, component is assumed to have a constant hazard $\lambda_1$ and the second, standby, component is assumed to have a constant hazard $\lambda_2$. The conditional density functions become

$$g_1(\tau) = \lambda_1 e^{-\lambda_1 \tau} \qquad 0 < \tau < t \tag{5.81a}$$

$$g_2(t|\tau) = \begin{cases} \lambda_2 e^{-\lambda_2(t-\tau)} & 0 < \tau < t \\ 0 & \tau > t \end{cases} \tag{5.81b}$$

System failure is a function of $t$ and $\tau$; therefore, defining a joint density function

$$\phi(t,\tau) = g_1(\tau)g_2(t|\tau) \tag{5.82}$$

and an associated marginal density function

$$
\begin{aligned}
f(t) &= \int_0^\infty \phi(t,\tau)\, d\tau \\
&= \int_0^t (\lambda_1 e^{-\lambda_1 \tau})(\lambda_2 e^{-\lambda_2(t-\tau)})\, d\tau
\end{aligned}
\tag{5.83}
$$

leads to

$$f(t) = \frac{\lambda_1 \lambda_2}{\lambda_1 - \lambda_2}\, (e^{-\lambda_2 t} - e^{-\lambda_1 t}) \tag{5.84}$$

Computation gives the reliability function

$$
\begin{aligned}
R(t) &= 1 - \int_0^t \frac{\lambda_1 \lambda_2}{\lambda_1 - \lambda_2}\, (e^{-\lambda_2 t} - e^{-\lambda_1 t})\, dt \\
&= \frac{\lambda_1 e^{-\lambda_2 t} - \lambda_2 e^{-\lambda_1 t}}{\lambda_1 - \lambda_2}
\end{aligned}
\tag{5.85}
$$

The result is very similar to the derivation of the previous example, the difference being that during the first failure interval only one element is operating and the hazard is $\lambda_1$ rather than the $2\lambda_b$ due to two operating components. If both the on-line and standby components are identical, that is, $\lambda_1 = \lambda_2$, then Eq. (5.85) is indeterminate, and L'Hospital's rule can be used. [One could also revert to Eq. (5.83) and write it as $\lambda^2 \int_0^t e^{-\lambda(t-2\tau)}\, d\tau$ and continue.]

Differentiation of the numerator and denominator of Eq. (5.85) with respect to $\lambda_2$ yields

$$\frac{-\lambda_1 t e^{-\lambda_2 t} - e^{-\lambda_1 t}}{-1}$$

Now if $\lambda_1 = \lambda$ and $\lambda_2 \to \lambda$, then

$$R(t) = e^{-\lambda t}(1 + \lambda t) \qquad (5.86)$$

Now that the joint-density-function technique has been illustrated we shall use it to compute the reliability function for a system with non-constant hazard. We assume two identical parallel components. When both are operating, the hazards are linearly increasing, that is,

$$z_1(t) = z_2(t) = k_1 t$$

After one has failed, the hazard of the remaining unit is assumed to increase abruptly, as shown in Fig. 5.11$b$. The conditional densities are given by

$$g_1(\tau) = 2k_1 \tau e^{-k_1 \tau^2/2} \qquad 0 < \tau < +\infty \qquad (5.87)$$

$$g_2(t|\tau) = \begin{cases} [k_1 \tau + k_2(t - \tau)]e^{-[k_1 \tau t + k_2(t-\tau)^2/2]} & 0 < \tau < t \\ 0 & \tau > t \end{cases} \qquad (5.88)$$

The joint density function is

$$\phi(\tau,t) = (2k_1 \tau e^{-k_1 t^2})[k_1 \tau + k_2(t - \tau)]e^{-[k_1 \tau t + k_2(t-\tau)^2/2]} \qquad (5.89)$$

The density function is given by

$$f(t) = 2k_1^2 \int_0^t \tau^2 e^{-[k_1 t^2 + k_1 \tau t + k_2(t-\tau)^2/2]} \, d\tau$$

$$+ 2k_1 k_2 \int_0^t \tau(t - \tau)e^{-[k_1 t^2 + k_1 \tau t + k_2(t-\tau)^2/2]} \, d\tau \qquad (5.90)$$

Some manipulation with the integrals in Eq. (5.90) and reference to the integral table in Appendix C show that some of the integrals can be reduced to areas under the unit normal density function. Thus, although formulation is straightforward, computation is difficult. Detailed solutions of Eq. (5.90) can be obtained using normal-probability tables, or approximate results can be derived by expanding the exponentials in truncated series. Further discussion of these approaches is deferred to the problems at the end of the chapter and to a similar example in Sec. 6.9.

### 5.8.5 COMPOUND–EVENTS APPROACH

Another approach to dependent-failure calculations is to view the state probabilities as compound events. This leads directly to multiple integral expressions for the state probabilities in terms of the system hazards.[1] As an introductory example we shall compute the state proba-

[1] M. Messinger, *op. cit.*

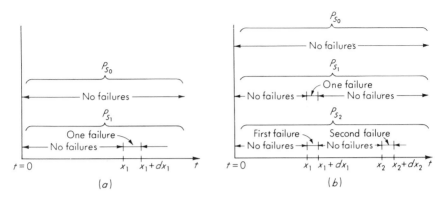

**Fig. 5.16**　Time intervals for compound-events approach.　(a) Single element; (b) two elements.

bilities of a single unit.　The basic approach is most easily visualized by reference to Fig. 5.16a.　The probability of no failures $P_{s_0}$ is by definition the element reliability and is given by

$$P_{s_0}(t) = \exp\left[-\int_0^t z_{01}(\xi)\, d\xi\right] \tag{5.91}$$

where $z_{01}(t)\, \Delta t$ is the transition probability.　The probability of one failure is a probability distribution function which is the integral (between 0 and $t$) of the associated density function.　Let us assume that the failure in question occurs at some arbitrary time $t = x_1$.　The density function is then the probability of survival up to time $x_1$ times the probability of failure in $dx_1$ sec

$$
\begin{aligned}
P_{s_1}(t) &= \int_0^t \text{(density function for one failure)}\, dt \\
&= \int_0^t \text{(probability of survival to } x_1\text{)}\ \text{(probability of failure in } dx_1\text{)} \\
&= \int_0^t \left\{\exp\left[-\int_0^{x_1} z_{01}(\xi)\, d\xi\right]\right\} [z_{01}(x_1)\, dx_1] \\
&= 1 - \exp\left[-\int_0^t z_{01}(\xi)\, d\xi\right] \tag{5.92}
\end{aligned}
$$

We may now use the same approach to compute the state probabilities for two identical elements.　The transition probability from state 0 to state 1 is given by $2z_{01}(t)$ [if the problem were a standby one, the transition probability would be $z_{01}(t)$].　The transition probability from state 1 to state 2 is $z_{12}(t)$.

The probability of no failures is, of course,

$$P_{s_0}(t) = \exp\left[-\int_0^t 2z_{01}(\xi)\, d\xi\right] \tag{5.93}$$

The other two state probabilities are

$$P_{s_1}(t) = \int_0^t \left\{ \exp\left[ -\int_0^{x_1} 2z_{01}(\xi)\, d\xi \right] \right\} \underbrace{[2z_{01}(x_1)\, dx_1]}_{}$$

$\underbrace{\phantom{\exp\left[ -\int_0^{x_1} 2z_{01}(\xi)\, d\xi \right]}}_{\substack{\text{probability of no}\\\text{failures to } x_1}}$ $\underbrace{\phantom{[2z_{01}(x_1)\, dx_1]}}_{\substack{\text{probability of one}\\\text{failure in } dx_1}}$

$$\left\{ \exp\left[ -\int_{x_1}^t z_{12}(\xi)\, d\xi \right] \right\} \quad (5.94)$$

$\underbrace{\phantom{\exp\left[ -\int_{x_1}^t z_{12}(\xi)\, d\xi \right]}}_{\substack{\text{probability of no}\\\text{failures } x_1 \text{ to } t}}$

$$P_{s_2}(t) = \int_0^t \int_0^{x_2} \left\{ \exp\left[ -\int_0^{x_1} 2z_{01}(\xi)\, d\xi \right] \right\} [2z_{01}(x_1)\, dx_1]$$

$\underbrace{\phantom{\exp\left[ -\int_0^{x_1} 2z_{01}(\xi)\, d\xi \right]}}_{\substack{\text{probability of no}\\\text{failures to } x_1}}$ $\underbrace{\phantom{[2z_{01}(x_1)\, dx_1]}}_{\substack{\text{probability of one}\\\text{failure in } dx_1}}$

$$\left\{ \exp\left[ -\int_{x_1}^{x_2} z_{12}(\xi)\, d\xi \right] \right\} [z_{12}(x_2)\, dx_2] \quad (5.95)$$

$\underbrace{\phantom{\exp\left[ -\int_{x_1}^{x_2} z_{12}(\xi)\, d\xi \right]}}_{\substack{\text{probability of no}\\\text{failures } x_1 \text{ to } x_2}}$ $\underbrace{\phantom{[z_{12}(x_2)\, dx_2]}}_{\substack{\text{probability of one}\\\text{failure in } dx_2}}$

For the case of constant hazards, $z_{01} = \lambda_1$ and $z_{12} = \lambda_2$,

$$P_{s_0}(t) = e^{-2\lambda_1 t}$$

$$P_{s_1}(t) = \int_0^t (e^{-2\lambda_1 x_1})(2\lambda_1\, dx_1)(e^{-\lambda_2(t-x_1)})$$

$$= 2\lambda_1 e^{-\lambda_2} \int_0^t e^{-(2\lambda_1 - \lambda_2)x_1}\, dx_1$$

$$= \frac{2\lambda_1}{2\lambda_1 - \lambda_2}(e^{-\lambda_2 t} - e^{-2\lambda_1 t}) \quad (5.96)$$

$$P_{s_2}(t) = \int_0^t \int_0^{x_2} [(e^{-2\lambda_1 x_1})(2\lambda_1\, dx_1)(e^{-\lambda_2(x_2-x_1)})(\lambda_2\, dx_2)]$$

$$= 2\lambda_1\lambda_2 \int_0^t (e^{-\lambda_2 x_2} \int_0^{x_2} e^{(\lambda_2 - 2\lambda_1)x_1}\, dx_1)\, dx_2$$

$$= \frac{2\lambda_1\lambda_2}{\lambda_2 - 2\lambda_1} \int_0^t (e^{-2\lambda_1 x_2} - e^{-\lambda_2 x_2})\, dx_2$$

$$= 1 + \frac{\lambda_2 e^{-2\lambda_1 t} - 2\lambda_1 e^{-\lambda_2 t}}{2\lambda_1 - \lambda_2} \quad (5.97)$$

As a check we see that $P_{s_0}(t) + P_{s_1}(t) + P_{s_2}(t) = 1$. Further exploitation of this technique and comparison with the techniques of Sec. 5.8.4 are left for the problems at the end of the chapter.

## 5.9 DEPENDENT GROUPINGS

The size and complexity of a physical problem with dependency are directly related to the number of system states. For a Markov model solution if there are $n$ distinct elements, there are $2^n$ states, and even if the $n$ elements are identical, there are still $n$ states. Thus, it is important to reduce the number of system states in every way possible. This is easily done in a practical way by grouping a problem into portions which involve dependent probabilities and other portions which are independent, as in the following example.

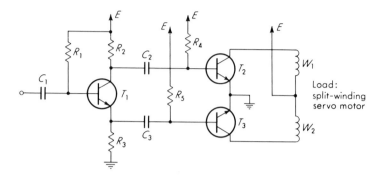

**Fig. 5.17**  Push-pull servo amplifier for split-winding servomotor.

The circuit diagram given in Fig. 5.17 is a three-transistor control amplifier which drives a split-winding servomotor. Power transistors $T_2$ and $T_3$ generate an appreciable amount of heat and as a result of packaging requirements are mounted close enough together to cause temperature dependence. Signal transistor $T_1$ is located so that the heat caused by $T_2$ and $T_3$ produces a negligible temperature rise in $T_1$. Thus, $T_2$ and $T_3$ form a dependent-element pair. We assume that every component of the signal stage is necessary for proper operation. For best performance both the upper and lower halves of the push-pull power stage are necessary, with degraded but acceptable operation occurring with only one-half of the stage operating. The reliability graphs based on these assumptions is given in Fig. 5.18.

If we let $P(C_1)$ denote the success probability of capacitor $C_1$, etc., the reliability expression becomes

$$R = P(C_1R_1R_2R_3T_1)P(C_2R_4T_2W_1 + C_3R_5T_3W_2) \qquad (5.98)$$

Since we are assuming that all the resistors, capacitors, and transistor $T_1$

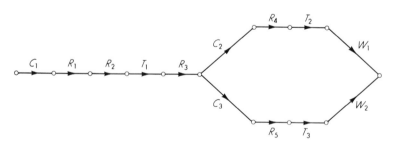

**Fig. 5.18**  Reliability graph of push-pull servo amplifier.

are independent of transistors $T_2$ and $T_3$, Eq. (5.98) becomes

$$R = [P(C_1)P(R_1)P(R_3)P(T_1)][P(C_2)P(R_4)P(W_1)P(T_2)$$
$$+ P(C_3)P(R_5)P(W_2)P(T_3)$$
$$- P(C_2)P(R_4)P(W_1)P(C_3)P(R_5)P(W_2)P(T_2T_3) \quad (5.99)$$

All but three of the terms in Eq. (5.99) can be evaluated independently, but $P(T_2)$, $P(T_3)$, and $P(T_2T_3)$ must be calculated as dependent terms. If we define a set of Markov states for the two transistors $s_0 = T_2T_3$, $s_1 = \bar{T}_2T_3$, $s_2 = T_2\bar{T}_3$, $s_3 = \bar{T}_2\bar{T}_3$, then

$$\begin{aligned} P(T_2) &= P_{s_0} + P_{s_2} \\ P(T_3) &= P_{s_0} + P_{s_1} \\ P(T_2T_3) &= P_{s_0} \end{aligned} \quad (5.100)$$

The dependency in the problem is modeled by the dependent hazards in the two-state Markov model. Thus, by splitting a large problem with dependence into several dependent groupings the complexity is kept within bounds.

## 5.10 COMPUTER METHODS OF ANALYSIS

### 5.10.1 INTRODUCTION

The analog and digital computer play a major role in the analysis of difficult reliability problems in the same way they serve other fields of engineering. It is important that the computer not be used as a substitute for paper-and-pencil analysis but as an adjunct. This is why this chapter has emphasized approximate techniques. In most cases it is desirable (and in some cases imperative) to supplement a large-scale computer study by a pencil-and-paper solution obtained by approximation or simplification of the system model. This will give insight into the mass of data which a computer can churn out.

The analog computer can be used to solve the differential equations which are obtained when a Markov model is made. These can also be simply solved using an analog-equation subroutine on a digital computer. One may also solve on a digital computer the difference equations generated by a Markov model or the integrals obtained in Secs. 5.8.4 and 5.8.5. In each of these cases the computer is merely being used as an equation or integral solver. One can also build a stochastic model of the stochastic process being studied on the computer by using Monte Carlo techniques. Random variables, represented by random numbers, are generated on the computer, and the system is allowed to operate in computer time, producing a large number of experiments in a short time.

Probabilistic conclusions are then drawn on the basis of these statistical data.

### 5.10.2 ANALOG SIMULATION

Since most readers will have some familiarity with analog computers, the emphasis in this section will be on philosophy and limitations rather than specific details. For the reader unfamiliar with the standard techniques, a simple example and a summary are given in Appendix A.

The analog-computer diagram corresponding to Eqs. (5.63) is given in Fig. 5.19. The failure and repair hazards are both assumed constant and are denoted by $\lambda$ and $\mu$, respectively. Note that we shall require one first-order differential equation for each system state and one integration for each equation. Also observe the great similarity between Figs. 5.19 and 5.13$a$. Each integrator represents a node, the self-loops represent feedback around the integrator, and the coupling branches are integrator inputs.

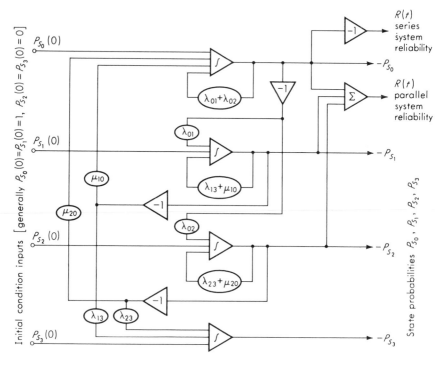

**Fig. 5.19** Analog-computer simulation of Eq. (5.63) for constant failure and repair hazards.

If dependency is present such that no simple Markov model exists, we must use the approach of Sec. 5.8.4 or 5.8.5. The integral expressions we obtain may be converted to differential equations by successive differentiation. The resulting differential equations are then solved as in the preceding example. This is discussed in further detail in the problems at the end of the chapter.

One limitation of analog computation of reliability functions is accuracy. An analog-computer solution is generally accurate to three to four places. If the system has very high reliability, or if the computation involves the difference between two numbers, this can become a significant problem.

### 5.10.3 DIGITAL SIMULATION

The purpose of this section and Appendix B is to point out by a simple example how a digital computer can be used to solve a reliability model numerically. No attempt will be made to use sophisticated techniques. The example discussed uses the Basic program language (a simple language for beginners) and was run on the GE-235 time-shared computer.

The two-element Markov model given in Fig. 5.10 is used as an example of how one can solve differential equations on a digital computer. Generally the first step in preparing differential equations for computer solution is to use numerical analysis to convert them into difference equations. In formulating a Markov model, difference equations are automatically available as an intermediate step. If we assume constant hazards, the difference equation (5.46) becomes

$$P_{s_0}(t + \Delta t) = (1 - \lambda_{01} \Delta t - \lambda_{02} \Delta t) P_{s_0}(t) \qquad (5.101)$$

Similar expressions are obtained for Eqs. (5.47) to (5.49). The computer program for solving this set of difference equations is given in Table 5.6.

The first seven lines of the program merely serve to introduce the user and identify the program, which was stored in the memory. The LIST command directs the computer to control the teletypewriter so as to type out the program. The computer symbols for $\lambda_1$, $\Delta t$, and $P_0$ are LI, T, and P0, respectively. The other problem variables are defined in a similar manner. Lines 1 and 2 print the program heading, and line 3 requests the values of the four hazards in the problem as well as the computation interval. Lines 10 to 13 define the initial conditions. Lines 25 and 120 produce a repetitive loop, which cycles from statement 25 to 120 twenty-five times as it performs the intermediate statements. Statements 30, 50, 70, and 90 define the four system difference equations; e.g., statement 30 is the computer version of Eq. (5.101). Statement 91 is merely a check, since obviously the sum must be unity. In statements

**Table 5.6  Basic program for the solution of a two-element Markov model**

---

```
HELLO
USER NUMBER—N12662
SYSTEM—BASIC
NEW OR OLD—OLD
OLD PROBLEM NAME—MARKOV
WAIT.
READY.

LIST

MARKOV    13:46    MON.    12/13/65

1 PRINT "DIFFERENCE EQUATION COMPUTATION OF MARKOV
  METHOD"
2 PRINT "INPUT DATA FOR L1,L2,L3,L4,T"
3 INPUT L1,L2,L3,L4,T
10 LET P0 = 1
11 LET P1 = 0
12 LET P2 = 0
13 LET P3 = 0
25 FOR N = 1 TO 25
30 LET X0 = (1−L1*T−L2*T)*P0
50 LET X1 = (1−L3*T)*P1+L1*T*P0
70 LET X2 = L2*T*P0+(1−L4*T)*P2
90 LET X3 = P3+L3*T*P1+L4*T*P2
91 LET S = P0+P1+P2+P3
92 LET R1 = P0
93 LET R2 = P0+P1+P2
95 LET P0 = X0
96 LET P1 = X1
97 LET P2 = X2
98 LET P3 = X3
100 LET T1 = (N−1)*T
110 PRINT "TIME =" T1, "SERIES =" R1, "PARALLEL =" R2
111 PRINT "CHECK SUM =" S
120 NEXT N
201 END
```

---

92 and 93 the reliabilities of a series and a parallel system are computed. Statements 95 to 98 update the values of the calculations so that $P_{s_0}(t + \Delta t)$ becomes $P_{s_0}(t)$ from the previous cycle. Statements 100, 110, and 111 provide a heading for the problem.

Table 5.7 presents a portion of the problem solution. (Only 10 of the 25 computations in the program are presented.) The third line, with the question mark, is the point at which the data $\lambda_1 = 1$, $\lambda_2 = 1$, $\lambda_3 = 1$, $\lambda_4 = 1$, and $\Delta t = 0.1$ are fed to the program. Because of the values of $\lambda$ which were chosen, the system time constants are on the order of 1 sec. The computation interval is only $\frac{1}{10}$ this value; therefore, the results

**Table 5.7    Computer run of the program given in Table 5.6**

RUN

MARKOV        13:38       MON.       12/13/65

DIFFERENCE EQUATION COMPUTATION OF MARKOV METHOD
INPUT DATA FOR L1, L2, L3, L4, T
? 1, 1, 1, 1, .1

| | | |
|---|---|---|
| TIME = 0 | SERIES = 1 | PARALLEL = 1 |
| CHECK SUM = 1 | | |
| TIME = .1 | SERIES = .8 | PARALLEL = 1. |
| CHECK SUM = 1. | | |
| TIME = .2 | SERIES = .64 | PARALLEL = .98 |
| CHECK SUM = 1. | | |
| TIME = .3 | SERIES = .512 | PARALLEL = .946 |
| CHECK SUM = 1. | | |
| TIME = .4 | SERIES = .4096 | PARALLEL = .9026 |
| CHECK SUM = 1. | | |
| TIME = .5 | SERIES = .32768 | PARALLEL = .8533 |
| CHECK SUM = 1. | | |
| TIME = .6 | SERIES = .262144 | PARALLEL = .800738 |
| CHECK SUM = 1. | | |
| TIME = .7 | SERIES = .209715 | PARALLEL = .746879 |
| CHECK SUM = 1. | | |
| TIME = .8 | SERIES = .167772 | PARALLEL = .693162 |
| CHECK SUM = 1. | | |
| TIME = .9 | SERIES = .134218 | PARALLEL = .640623 |
| CHECK SUM = 1. | | |
| TIME = 1. | SERIES = .107374 | PARALLEL = .589983 |
| CHECK SUM = 1. | | |
| TIME = 1.1 | | |

STOP.

are not that accurate.   In a practical computation one would probably choose $\Delta t = 0.01$ or $0.001$ and only print out the data every 10 or 100 computations.   The accuracy of such computations is limited by two factors, the smallness of $\Delta t$ chosen (essentially related to program time and cost) and the number of digits the computer carries.   In general one obtains more than sufficient accuracy in a reasonable amount of time. The accuracy of such a digital-computer solution in general far exceeds analog-computer accuracy.   One can also incorporate plotting routines into a digital-computer program so that a graph as well as a data table is obtained for the program output.

#### 5.10.4   MONTE CARLO METHODS

The previous two sections have discussed the use of the analog and digital computer as equation-solving devices to evaluate analytical models formulated to describe a reliability problem. Another approach, known as the *Monte Carlo* technique, is to set up an analogous stochastic process which behaves as much like the actual problem as possible. The model process is then observed, and the results are tabulated and treated as if they were experimental data representing the actual problem. The origin of the Monte Carlo method is difficult to trace,[1] but the term became popular about 1944, when Ulam, von Neumann, and Fermi used such techniques to perform neutron-diffusion calculations connected with atomic-bomb work during World War II. Actually the classical Buffon needle problem, in which one computes the value of $\pi$ from data on the number of intersections made by a needle dropped at random on a pattern of parallel lines, is a Monte Carlo simulation.

The key features in a Monte Carlo simulation are generation of a series of values of one or more random variables with specified probability densities, examination of the way the system behaves for paired values of these random values, and tabulation of the result as if it were the outcome of an experiment. These techniques are best illustrated by example.

Suppose we wish to evaluate the reliability of a certain reliability graph. For simplicity we shall assume that the branches of the graph are all identical and have a constant hazard. Thus we must generate a sequence of random numbers which are exponentially distributed.

One technique for obtaining such a sequence is to observe some natural phenomenon with an exponential distribution, e.g., time between disintegrations of radioactive material or lifetimes of fruitflies enclosed in a jar. These numbers can be recorded and used whenever desired. Of course, if we wish to run an experiment with $n$ random numbers, we must first observe and record the physical process long enough to obtain $n$ occurrences. The RAND corporation built an electronic roulette wheel in 1947 to generate sequences of uniformally distributed random numbers. Between April and July of that year 1 million random digits were generated and statistically tested to reveal any correlation between digits.[2]

Such techniques of tabulating random numbers are suitable only if the Monte Carlo simulation is to be done manually by looking up sequences in a table. If the simulation is to be run on a digital computer, the time involved in feeding in such a sequence recorded on tape becomes prohibitive. In such a case one tries to generate approximately random numbers by using some sort of computational algorithm on the computer.

---

[1] Monte Carlo Method, *Natl. Bur. Std. Appl. Mech. Ser.* 12, June, 1951; J. M. Hammersley and D. C. Handscomb, "Monte Carlo Methods," John Wiley & Sons, Inc., New York, 1964; R. P. Chambers, Random-number generation on digital computers, *IEEE Spectrum*, p. 48, February, 1967.

[2] "A Million Random Digits," The Free Press of Glencoe, New York, 1966.

For example, one of the first such methods proposed by von Neumann was to select a number, square it, and select the middle digits, square this new number, and repeat the process.    Such techniques generate sequences which repeat but with long periods, and these numbers are called *pseudo-random numbers*.    If the repetition period is greater than the number of digits desired and the correlations between digits are satisfactorily small, the pseudorandom numbers are quite suitable.    In addition they possess the repeatability property so that results can be rerun and checked if desired.

Von Neumann's midsquare method has been replaced by better techniques.    An important class of these techniques is known as *congruential methods*.    For example, we consider the recursion relation[1]

$$x_i \equiv a x_{i-1} + c \qquad \text{modulo } m \tag{5.102}$$

where $x_i$ = $i$th pseudorandom number
  $a, c_1, x_i$ = integers between 0 and $m - 1$
  $m$ = quantity which sets repetition period

To readers who have studied number theory or number systems the operation implied by modulo $m$ is clear.    For those who have not encountered this term we may define the operation $x_i$ (modulo $m$) as the remainder which results when $a x_{i-1} + c$ is divided by $m$.    The maximum period obtainable using Eq. (5.102) is $m$ digits, but shorter periods are also possible if $m$, $a$, and $c$ are chosen without restriction.    For example, if $m = 16$, $a = 3$, $c = 1$, and $x_0 = 2$, then for our second number Eq. (102) yields $x_1 = 3 \times 2 + 1 = 7$.    (Since the number is less than 16, we do not have to perform our modulo 16 calculation, the result being automatically modulo 16.)    The third number is $x_2 = 3 \times 7 + 1 = 22$.    Dividing by 16, we obtain $22/16 = 1 + 6/16$; thus our next number is 6. The first 10 numbers are: 2, 7, 6, 3, 10, 15, 14, 11, 2, 7, . . . , and the period is 8.    In order to realize the full period $m$ we must restrict our choice of $m$, $a$, and $c$.    In general, in a computer the largest number $m$ we can choose is the capacity, which is $m = 2^\alpha$ and $\alpha$ is 20 to 30.    With such a choice we realize a full period of $m$ if $c$ is odd and $a$ is 1 greater than a multiple of 4.[†]    Thus if $m = 2^4 = 16$, $c = 1$, $x_0 = 2$, and $a = 4 + 1 = 5$, we obtain from Eq. (5.102) the following 18 numbers: 2, 11, 8, 9, 14, 7, 4, 5, 10, 3, 0, 1, 6, 15, 12, 13, 2, 11, . . . .    The period is, of course, 16, as predicted.    Since $2^{30}$ is approximately 1 billion and we need 1,000, 10,000, or 100,000 trials in our simulation, we have an ample supply of digits available.    Most large-scale digital computers have a subroutine for random-number generation operating on this principle or similar principles.

[1] Hammersley and Handscomb, *op. cit.*
[†] *Ibid.*, p. 29.

The sequence of random numbers generated above represents a uniform distribution over the interval 0 to 1 if each number obtained is divided by $m$. In the problem posed we had units with an exponential time to failure. We can map our uniform distribution into any other distribution by using the cumulative distribution function. For an exponential set of numbers $u_0$, $u_1$, . . . , $u_m$ we use the relationship

$$x_i = 1 - e^{-\lambda u_i} \tag{5.103}$$

The inverse relation is

$$u_i = -\frac{1}{\lambda} \ln (1 - x) \tag{5.104}$$

A moment's thought shows that if $x$ is uniformly distributed, so is $1 - x$; therefore, Eq. (5.104) can be written as

$$u_i = -\frac{1}{\lambda} \ln x \tag{5.105}$$

The reason for using the inverse relation given by (5.104) is easily seen by referring to Eq. (2.91) and Fig. 2.18a. The transformation problem is a bit different in this case. In Eq. (2.91) we compute the density function for $u$ given the density function for $x$ and the monotonically increasing relationship $x(u)$. In the present case we are given that $f[x(u)]$ is uniform, and we wish to find the relationship $x(u)$ which results in a given (desired) $h(u)$. Since $f[x(u)]$ is uniform, Eq. (2.91) becomes

$$h(u) = \frac{dx}{du} 1$$
$$\int_0^u h(u)\, du = \int_0^x dx$$
$$H(u) = x \tag{5.106}$$
$$u = H^{-1}(x) \tag{5.107}$$

Thus, $x$ is given by the distribution function for $u$, Eq. (5.106), and $u$ is given by the inverse relationship, Eq. (5.107). Since we assumed that all system components have the same failure density, we need only apply (5.105) successively for each component. If several components had different distributions, there would be a set of relations similar to Eq. (5.105) which would be employed for each component. The next question to be answered is how to assess the effects of these random failures on the overall system.

The graph cut sets provide one convenient technique for relating component failure time to system failure time. We first generate an exponentially distributed time to failure for each system component. We then examine each cut set and call the cut-set time to failure the *longest* failure time for any element in the cut set.   We then compare the cut-set failure times and choose the *shortest* one as the system time to failure. This is recorded as the result of the first trial, and the experiment is repeated.   Of course other techniques can be used to relate component failure to system failure, but this is a simple method.

The final question to be discussed is how many trials we should run and how to analyze the data.   If the data are treated as the result of a statistical experiment, we can compute histograms for $f_d(t)$ or $z_d(t)$ using Eqs. (4.1) and (4.2) or a data reliability function from Eq. (4.5).   The number of trials is directly related to the accuracy we expect from our simulation.   If we assume that the random numbers are perfect and our system model is perfect, the only errors we can obtain are due to the basic laws of statistics.   We know that these errors (deviations from the true value) decrease with $1/\sqrt{n}$, where $n$ is the number of trials.   In the high-reliability region we wish to use the ratio of the expected statistical error to the probability of failure as a measure of accuracy.   Using the statistical principles discussed in Appendix D, the curves given in Fig. 5.20 were derived.

As an example of the Monte Carlo simulation technique, we shall com-

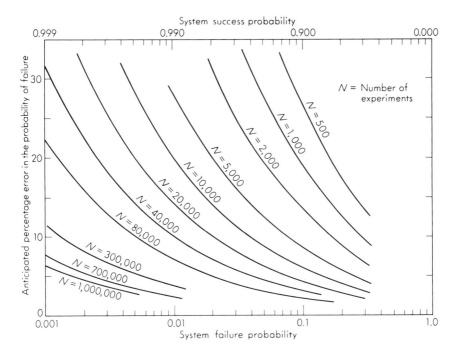

**Fig. 5.20**  Accuracy vs. number of experiments for Monte Carlo simulation.

pute the reliability for a system of three parallel elements each with constant hazard rates $\lambda = 1$ failure per hr.   The problem is of course a trivial one analytically, but it will allow us to compare the Monte Carlo solution with the true analytical result.   The analytical reliability function is given by

$$R(t) = 1 - (1 - e^{-t})^3 \tag{5.108}$$

A simple program for calculation of $R(t)$ is given in Table 5.8.

A Monte Carlo program for this problem[1] is given in Table 5.9.   It was decided that the reliability would be computed at 10 intervals of 0.1 for

[1] For details of this program and other Monte Carlo simulations see Messinger, op. cit.

**Table 5.8   Program and computation of** $R(t) = 1 - (1 - e^{-t})^3$

RELCOM      13:09      NY MON 02/27/67

```
10 PRINT "RELIABILITY COMPUTATION"
20 PRINT "FOR 3 IDENTICAL PARALLEL COMPONENTS"
25 PRINT "TIME, RELIABILITY"
30 PRINT "R = 1 - (1 - EXP( - T))↑3"
40 FOR T = 0 TO 1 STEP 0.1
50 LET R = 1 - (1 - EXP( - T))↑3
60 PRINT T,R
70 NEXT T
80 END
```

RUN

RELCOM      13:10      NY MON 02/27/67

RELIABILITY COMPUTATION
  FOR 3 IDENTICAL PARALLEL COMPONENTS
TIME, RELIABILITY
R = 1 - [1 - EXP[ - T]]↑3

| | |
|---|---|
| 0 | 1 |
| .1 | .999138 |
| .2 | .994044 |
| .3 | .982589 |
| .4 | .964167 |
| .5 | .939084 |
| .6 | .908151 |
| .7 | .872421 |
| .8 | .833015 |
| .9 | .791018 |
| 1. | .74742 |

TIME:      0 SECS.

**Table 5.9   Program for Monte Carlo reliability analysis of three parallel elements**

```
MONTEC      12:31    NY MON 02/27/67

10 PRINT "MONTE CARLO ANALYSIS"
20 PRINT "HOW MANY TRIALS DO YOU WANT" ;
30 INPUT E
40 LET D = 0.1
50 LET N = 1
60 LET T(1) = 0
70 LET X(1) = D
80 FOR K = 2 TO 10 STEP 1
90 LET T(K) = 0
100 LET X(K) = X(K−1) +D
110 NEXT K
120 FOR K = 1 TO 3 STEP 1
130 LET A(K) = − LOG(RND(Z))
140 NEXT K
150 LET B = A(1)
160 IF A(1) > A(2) THEN 180
170 LET B = A(2)
180 IF B > A(3) THEN 200
190 LET B = A(3)
200 IF N > E THEN 490
210 LET N = N+1
220 FOR K = 1 TO 10 STEP 1
230 IF B > X(K) THEN 250
240 GO TO 260
250 LET T(K) = T(K) +1
260 NEXT K
270 GO TO 120
490 FOR K = 1 TO 10
500 LET R(K) = T(K)/E
505 NEXT K
510 PRINT "RELIABILITY ANALYSIS"
520 PRINT "FOR 3 IDENTICAL PARALLEL COMPONENTS"
530 PRINT "NUMBER OF TRIALS", E
540 PRINT
550 PRINT
560 PRINT "TIME", "RELIABILITY"
564 FOR K = 1 TO 10 STEP 1
570 PRINT X(K), R(K)
580 NEXT K
590 END
```

$0 < t < 1.0$. The 10 intervals along the axis are denoted by $x(1)$, $x(2)$, . . . , $x(10)$. The number of systems surviving $x(1)$ sec is given by $T(x)$, etc. A random number for each component is generated and mapped (line 130) in accordance with Eq. (5.105). On trial 1 the times to failure of each component are $A(1)$, $A(2)$, and $A(3)$; and lines 150 to

**Table 5.10   Computer runs for the program given in Table 5.9**

RUN

MONTEC     12:34     NY MON 02/27/67

MONTE CARLO ANALYSIS
HOW MANY TRIALS DO YOU WANT?   10
RELIABILITY ANALYSIS
  FOR 3 IDENTICAL PARALLEL COMPONENTS
NUMBER OF TRIALS                 10

| TIME | RELIABILITY |
|------|-------------|
| .1   | 1           |
| .2   | .9          |
| .3   | .9          |
| .4   | .9          |
| .5   | .9          |
| .6   | .7          |
| .7   | .7          |
| .8   | .7          |
| .9   | .7          |
| 1.   | .5          |

TIME:  2 SECS.


RUN

MONTEC     12:35     NY MON 02/27/67

MONTE CARLO ANALYSIS
HOW MANY TRIALS DO YOU WANT?   100
RELIABILITY ANALYSIS
  FOR 3 IDENTICAL PARALLEL COMPONENTS
NUMBER OF TRIALS                 100

| TIME | RELIABILITY |
|------|-------------|
| .1   | 1           |
| .2   | .98         |
| .3   | .98         |
| .4   | .97         |
| .5   | .94         |
| .6   | .91         |
| .7   | .87         |
| .8   | .86         |
| .9   | .81         |
| 1.   | .76         |

TIME:  6 SECS.

**Table 5.10    Computer runs for the program given in Table 5.9** (*Continued*)

RUN

MONTEC      12:36      NY MON 02/27/67

MONTE CARLO ANALYSIS
HOW MANY TRIALS DO YOU WANT?    1000
RELIABILITY ANALYSIS
    FOR 3 IDENTICAL PARALLEL COMPONENTS
NUMBER OF TRIALS                          1000

| TIME | RELIABILITY |
|------|-------------|
| .1 | .999 |
| .2 | .989 |
| .3 | .984 |
| .4 | .969 |
| .5 | .945 |
| .6 | .918 |
| .7 | .894 |
| .8 | .846 |
| .9 | .8 |
| 1. | .746 |

TIME:    50 SECS.

190 select the largest of these three numbers $B$, which is the system time to failure.    Lines 30, 50, 200, and 210 control the number of trials $E$. Lines 220 to 505 assign each value of $B$ to a particular time interval $x(k)$ and compute the reliability as the ratio of the number of survivors $T(R)$ which have failure times greater than $x(k)$.    This program was run for 10, 100, and 1,000 experiments, and the results are given in Table 5.10.

**Table 5.11    Comparison of actual and expected errors in a Monte Carlo simulation†**

| Time | $R_{\text{actual}}$ (*from Table 5.8*) | $R_{MC}$ (*from Table 5.10*) | $\dfrac{\lvert R_{MC} - R_{\text{actual}} \rvert}{1 - R_a} \times 100$ % | Error, % (*from Fig. 5.20*) |
|------|------|------|------|------|
| 1.0 | 0.7474 | 0.746 | 0.6 | 15 |
| 0.6 | 0.9081 | 0.918 | 11 | 19 |
| 0.4 | 0.9640 | 0.969 | 14 | 32 |

† The cost of calculating 1,000 experiments on the time-shared computer was $3. (The costs are roughly 5 cents per second for computer time and 20 cents per minute for telephone tie-line time.)    The cost for 10,000 would have been $25 to $30.    A higher-speed batch-process computer would be more practical and cheaper for large numbers of experiments.

The percentage error in failure probability of the 1,000-experiment Monte Carlo simulation is compared with the expected errors as read from Fig. 5.20, in Table 5.11.

Note that the predicted error from Fig. 5.20 is conservative. Of course, in general we cannot compute $R_{\text{actual}}$ (this is why we are using a Monte Carlo solution) and must use Fig. 5.20 as a guide to how many experiments are necessary.

## PROBLEMS

5.1  Write the reliability expressions for the following systems composed of independent, identical constant-hazard components:

(a) Four series elements        (b) A three-out-of-four system
(c) A two-out-of-four system      (d) A parallel system of four elements

5.2  Sketch the reliability functions of Prob. 5.1 vs. normalized time $\tau = \lambda t$. The range of interest is $1.0 \geq R(t) \geq 0.5$.

5.3  Let $t_1$ be the time at which system reliability drops to 0.9; that is, $R(t_1) = 0.9$. Sketch $t_1$ vs. the number of good elements necessary for system success for parts $a$ to $d$ of Prob. 5.1.

5.4  Repeat Probs. 5.1 to 5.3 for systems with independent, identical linearly increasing hazards.

5.5  Write reliability expressions in terms of the integrated hazard, $Z(t) = \int_0^t z(\xi)\, d\xi$, for the structures shown in Prob. 3.7.

5.6  Assume identical constant-hazard components for the system reliability functions of Prob. 5. Expand the functions in a power series and form a three-term approximation for each function.

5.7  Sketch the approximate reliability functions developed in Prob. 5.6. Check their accuracy against the true functions by computing $R(t_1)$, where $t_1$ is defined as in Prob. 5.3. Determine $t_1$ from the graph of the approximate function, and estimate the truncation error from Eq. (5.33).

5.8  A communication system is composed of a fixed-frequency transmitter $T_1$ and a fixed-frequency receiver $R_1$. The fixed frequency is $f_1$, and both receiver and transmitter have constant hazards $\lambda$. In order to improve the reliability, a second receiver and transmitter operating on frequency $f_2$ are used to provide a redundant channel. Both channels are identical, except for frequency. Construct a reliability diagram for the system and write the reliability function. In order to improve reliability a tuning unit is added to each receiver so that it can operate at frequency $f_1$ or $f_2$. The hazard for each tuning unit is given by $\lambda'$. Draw the new reliability diagram and write the reliability function. Sketch the reliability of the improved system and the original two-channel system. Assume that $\lambda' = 0.1\lambda$ and repeat for $\lambda' = 10\lambda$. (Use series approximations, if necessary.)

5.9  Referring to Prob. 5.8, for some value of $\lambda'/\lambda$ the addition of the tuning unit will not produce any significant increase in reliability. Find this value and explain. State any assumptions.

5.10 Compute the MTTF for the two systems given in Prob. 5.8. For what value of $\lambda'/\lambda$ are the two MTTF's equal? Compare this value with that obtained in Prob. 5.9.

5.11 Compute the MTTF for the systems given in Table 3.3. Assume identical components with $z(t) = \lambda$.

5.12 Repeat Prob. 5.11 for Table 3.4.

5.13 Repeat Prob. 5.11 for the systems given in Prob. 3.7.

5.14 Repeat Probs. 5.11 to 5.13 for the case of a Weibull hazard $z(t) = Kt^m$.

5.15 Consider a series system composed of $n$ units, each with identical hazard models $z(t) = a + bt$. Sketch the system reliability functions for $n = 5$, 10, and 100. Compare the results with the predictions given by Drenick's theorem.

5.16 It would be very convenient if Drenick's theorem could be applied to the system shown above. Each component $x_n$ would first be combined with its parallel partner $x_n'$ to form a new component $y_n$. All the $y_n$'s would then form a simple series system. This does not work. Why?

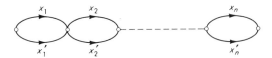

**Fig. P 5.16**

5.17 A logic circuit contains 10 relays. The specific logic circuit used is unknown. Suppose it is known that the reliability function for relays is $R(t) = e^{-\lambda k}$, where $k$ is the number of cycles. What range could $k$ have for the system reliability to be 0.95?

5.18 Two 100-ohm 1-watt resistors are connected in parallel with a 0.2-amp current source. When both resistors are operating, each carries 0.1 amp of current. (When one resistor fails as an open circuit, the remaining one must carry 0.2 amp of current.) Assume that each resistor has a constant hazard of $10^{-5}$ failures per hr when operating at rated power. Neglect any temperature dependence between the two resistors but assume that the failure rate increases as the ratio (power dissipated)/(power rated). The circuit operates satisfactorily with a resistance of either 50 or 100 ohms. Compute the system reliability function $(a)$ ignoring the dependence and $(b)$ including dependence. What is the predicted reliability for 1 year's operation? How important is the dependence?

5.19 An automobile voltage regulator lengthens battery life by protecting it from overloads or overcharging. Assume that the battery has a hazard model given by $z(t) = a + bt$. When the regulator is working, $a = 2 \times 10^{-5}$ failure per hr and $b = 30 \times 10^{-10}$. When the regulator has failed, $a$ remains the same but $b$ increases to $150 \times 10^{-10}$ failure per hr. Compute and sketch the reliability of the system. *Hint:* Use the techniques of Sec. 5.8.4 or 5.8.5 and approximate the integrand by a truncated series.

5.20 Using the approach of Sec. 5.8.2, compute the reliability of two parallel components. Both components are different, and the failures are dependent. All failure modes have an exponential density function. Repeat using the techniques of Sec. 5.8.4. Repeat using the techniques of Sec. 5.8.5.

5.21 Repeat Prob. 5.21 assuming again that the system is a standby one with all failure modes governed by identical Rayleigh density functions.

5.22 Assume that in a two-element parallel system all failure modes are constant-hazard. The components are identical, and with no failures the hazard is $\lambda$, and with one failure it is $\lambda'$. When $\lambda'/\lambda = 1$, there is no dependence. Compute $t_1$ (defined in Prob. 5.3) for the case of no dependence. Now assume dependence and find what ratio of $\lambda'/\lambda$ yields $R(t_1) = 0.91$. What ratio yields $R(t_1) = 0.89$? How important is dependence in this problem?

5.23 Repeat Prob. 5.22 for the case where the two elements are in standby redundancy.

5.24 Assume that elements $x_1$ and $x_2$ form an ordinary parallel circuit. Since all three units dissipate substantial heat and are confined in a small space, failures are dependent. The units are identical and the following constant hazards govern system behavior: with one element operating the hazard is $\lambda$, with two elements operating the hazard is $2\lambda$, and with three elements operating the hazard is $3\lambda$. Compute the reliability function for the system.

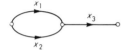

**Fig. P 5.24**

5.25 Repeat Prob. 5.24 for the case where $x_1$ and $x_2$ are connected in standby.

5.26 We wish to compare the approximations discussed in Secs. 5.5.2 and 5.5.4. Assume the following three systems of IIU with constant hazard $\lambda'$.
(a) A one-out-of-ten system (a parallel system)
(b) A five-out-of-ten system
(c) A ten-out-of-ten system (a series system)
Compare the reliabilities predicted by the Poisson, normal, and truncated series approximations with the true reliability, at the point $t = 0.1\lambda$, for the systems a to c.

5.27 Repeat Prob. 5.26 for the case of nonidentical components where five units have a hazard $10\lambda$ and five units have a hazard $0.1\lambda$.

5.28 Solve for the reliability expressions for system $A$ and system $B$ of Fig. 5.14 assuming that all units are IIU with constant hazard $\lambda$. Use the direct approach. Formulate the Markov graph and Markov differential equations. Substitute the solution obtained by the direct approach into the Markov equations to show that the Markov model yields identical results.

5.29 Solve for the reliability expression for a three-element standby system using a Markov model. All elements are IIU with constant hazard $\lambda$.

5.30 Repeat Prob. 5.29 using the joint-density-function approach.

5.31 Repeat Prob. 5.29 using the compound-events approach.

5.32 Explain how you would solve for the reliability of the amplifier shown in Fig. 5.17 if all three transistors had dependent constant hazards.

5.33 Prepare an analog-computer diagram for the solution of Prob. 5.32.

5.34 Write a digital-computer program (use any computer language) for the solution of Prob. 5.32.

5.35 Generate the following sequences of pseudorandom numbers using Eq. (5.102):
(a)  $m = 16$    $a = 2$    $c = 1$    $x_0 = 2$
(b)  $m = 16$    $a = 5$    $c = 1$    $x_0 = 9$
(c)  $m = 16$    $a = 9$    $c = 1$    $x_0 = 2$

5.36 Write a Monte Carlo program for the solution of Prob. 5.32.

5.37 Can we fit the curves given in Fig. 5.20 by the function $k/\sqrt{n}$? Any theoretical justification?

# *reliability improvement*

## 6.1 INTRODUCTION

This chapter contains a diversity of topics, but they are bound together by the fact that each presents techniques for increasing system reliability. The first few merely preach sound design principles, most of which are suggested by common sense. Many of the early reliability studies (referred to in Sec. 1.2) found that a great number (sometimes half) of component failures were attributable to improper design or nonconservative choice of component ratings. Once these simple but often effective matters have been investigated, other techniques must be used for further reliability improvement.

One approach is to try to procure or develop superior component parts with smaller failure rates. Much work along these lines has already been done in connection with the Minuteman program. Although it is often possible to trade time, money, size, and weight to buy improved reliability, obviously such an approach soon reaches limits. Some of the predictions given in Figs. 1.4 to 1.6 illustrate what can be expected.

Another approach to reliability improvement is to alter the system structure so as to obtain higher reliability while maintaining the basic system function. Except for certain cases of ingenious solutions, this is generally accomplished by creating additional paths and is usually

termed redundancy.   Certain simple redundancy techniques are discussed and evaluated, and then the more sophisticated schemes, such as
majority voting and standby systems, are discussed.   Redundancy is
easy to apply and yields very effective results when there are many
similar units in a system.   This is just the case in digital circuitry, and
therefore a separate section on digital reliability is included.

The last sections of this chapter discuss the class of repairable and
replaceable systems.   In many respects these systems allow the greatest
margin of reliability improvement in very complex systems.   It is
important to note that repairable systems are a subset of the entire class
of problems which are amenable to reliability analysis.   In fact the very
large group of missile and space systems are almost automatically
excluded.[1]   When we discuss repair and replacement, other measures of
system performance such as availability, up time, downtime, and number
of renewals must also be considered along with system reliability.


## 6.2   PROPER DESIGN AND SIMPLICITY

The title of this section implies that equipment is often poorly designed
or overly complex, and unfortunately such is too frequently the case.
In fact many of the early reliability studies which focused on dissection
of failed components revealed that misapplication was a great source of
component failure (see Sec. 1.2).   It is probable that at least one accom-
plishment of reliability engineering has been to alert designers to this
fact and to encourage them to reduce the number of misapplications
sharply by checks and design reviews.

Any experienced designer probably knows of many cases in which a
sophisticated scheme is being used to accomplish a task which could be
done much more simply and reliably.   One that is fresh in the author's
mind is an attitude-control system for a recent satellite.   In order to
rotate the satellite, three orthogonal motor-flywheel combinations were
used.   Since momentum is conserved, a rotation of a flywheel in one
direction causes an opposite rotation of the satellite.   If external disturbance torques such as solar pressure happen to act always in the same
direction, the control motor for that axis is constantly speeding up to
counteract the disturbance.   Control is maintained up to the point
where the motor saturates and the speed remains constant.   After that
no further momentum changes are possible and hence no torques.   In
order to prevent this, a set of jets and a tank of compressed gas are added.
When the motor reaches, say, 80 percent of maximum speed, the gas jets
are turned on to cause an opposite disturbance and run the wheel speed

[1] In the future, on long space missions, equipment repair may be feasible.

down to zero. This process is called *momentum dumping*. The device in question was the means of sensing wheel speed and triggering the gas jets. The actual system was composed of a notched wheel on the motor shaft with a reluctance transducer, a digital pulse-counting circuit, and additional logic to determine direction of rotation. The electronic circuit which accomplished these tasks was quite complex, and the entire circuit could simply have been replaced with an ordinary dc tachometer built into the motor-flywheel unit.

Although proper usage and simplicity seem elementary and intuitive, they play such an important role in reliability that they have been discussed briefly as a reminder of their importance.

## 6.3 CONSERVATIVE DESIGN AND DERATING

The idea of operating components below their basic ratings is fundamental to various fields of engineering design. The rated parameters can be voltages, currents, powers, force or torque loads, velocities, temperatures, humidity, etc. In the structural-engineering field the idea of a safety factor is a basic one. The electronics field has been slower to accept this as a basic tenet of design. A vivid example of the neglect of conservative design principles was brought to the author's attention several years ago when many vacuum-tube circuits were being transistorized. A standard *vacuum-tube* servo amplifier with two driving stages and a push-pull output was to be transistorized, the purpose of the change being to provide a new standard *transistor* servo amplifier which was smaller and more reliable. The new circuit was considerably reduced in volume and weight, but a preliminary reliability analysis revealed that the transistor amplifier had roughly the same reliability as the vacuum-tube version. This came as a shock, since even the very sketchy failure information on transistors revealed that they were superior to vacuum tubes. (Qualitative reasoning also predicted a great superiority of transistors over vacuum tubes.) A careful look at the problem showed that overzealousness to achieve maximum miniaturization had led to two important errors in the transistor-amplifier design. Tantalum capacitors were used at their maximum rated voltage wherever large capacitances were needed. Although reliable tantalum capacitors are now available, at that time tantalum capacitors were still new, and the early reliability data predicted sizable failure rates. In contrast, the vacuum-tube version used aluminum electrolytic capacitors, which were operated well below their maximum voltages. The transistors used were also operated near their maximum ratings, while the vacuum-tube model used tubes whose maximum plate dissipations comfortably exceeded the circuit design levels. In all fairness it should be mentioned that both tantalum capacitors and silicon transistors were very expensive at that time, and only a limited number of models were available. For example, there were two common silicon power transistors available, a medium-power one, which cost $25, and a high-power one, which cost $100.

The improvement in failure rates due to component derating varies

Table 6.1 Some typical effects of derating (all components assumed to have constant-hazard models)

| Component | Hazard-rated condition | Hazard-derated condition | Improvement | Comment |
|---|---|---|---|---|
| Vacuum tube (small-signal applications | Rated heater voltage $\lambda$ | 90% rated heater voltage $0.5\lambda$ | 2:1 | Results differ for large-signal applications |
| Miniature vacuum tubes | Rated power (bulb temp. = 200°C) $0.9\lambda$ | 50% rated power (bulb temp. = 200°C) $0.5\lambda$ | 1.8:1 | Effect smaller at low temp. |
| Semiconductor diodes | Rated wattage $10^{-6}$/hr | 50% rated wattage $0.3 \times 10^{-6}$/hr | 3.3:1 | Ambient temp. low, no derating necessary with signal off |
| Transistors | Rated wattage $2 \times 10^{-6}$/hr | 50% rated wattage $0.55 \times 10^{-6}$/hr | 3.6:1 | |
| Composition resistors | Rated wattage $6 \times 10^{-8}$/hr | 50% rated wattage $1.0 \times 10^{-8}$/hr | 6:1 | 40°C ambient, results much different for other types such as film resistors or power resistors |
| Accurate wire-wound resistors | Rated wattage $1.2 \times 10^{-6}$/hr | 50% rated wattage $1 \times 10^{-6}$/hr | 1.2:1 | |
| High-reliability paper capacitors | Rated voltage $7.5 \times 10^{-7}$ | 50% rated voltage $0.5 \times 10^{-7}$ | 15:1 | 40°C ambient, results much different for other types such as mica, glass, tantalum, foil, etc. |
| Solid-tantalum capacitors | Rated voltage $3.0 \times 10^{-6}$ | 50% rated voltage $0.28 \times 10^{-6}$ | 10.7:1 | |
| Transformers | Internal temp. = 100°C $1.1 \times 10^{-5}$ | Internal temp. = 60°C $0.05 \times 10^{-5}$ | 22:1 | Insulation rated for 105°C material |
| Motor bearings | 10,000 rpm operation $3.2 \times 10^{-5}$ | 5,000 rpm $0.8 \times 10^{-5}$ | 4:1 | Brushless motor |

greatly with the particular class of device.    In some cases a small derating yields sizable gains, while in others the change is negligible.    The basic data in Figs. 4.6 to 4.14 illustrate what sort of changes can be expected. As a means of rough comparison, some typical effects of derating are summarized in Table 6.1.    The results show that a reduction of about 50 percent in the ratings can produce hazard improvements ranging from a factor of 1.2 to a factor of 22.    In the former case, the improvement is probably not worth the effort, whereas in the latter case the results are spectacular.    Figures 4.6 to 4.14 and Table 6.1 are only a representative selection of the material available on component derating. The current literature or handbooks such as MIL-217 can provide a complete set of up-to-date failure-rate information.

## 6.4  CREATIVE DESIGN

The design principles stressed in the preceding chapter are those which one would expect to find in any competent design.    A superior job can often be done if the designer uses some thought to create a new or improved circuit with better reliability.

For example, electronic designers well know that push-pull circuits have definite advantages in terms of power output and linearity.    They also provide a measure of redundancy, however, since failure of one side of the circuit generally results in continued circuit operation at a degraded level.    Of course there are generally added parts in the push-pull driver stage, but the *redundancy gain* should far outweigh the *complexity loss*.

Another clever design is used in connection with automobile warning lights.    In many cars, four warning lights, hot, cold, generator, and oil, all light up when the car is first started in the morning, giving a check on all the warning systems.    When the key is turned to the start position, the engine is cold, and the cold light goes on.    The generator turns slowly during starting, so that little output is produced, and the generator light also comes on.    Similarly, the cranking speed is too slow for much oil circulation, and the oil light goes on.    The start circuit is wired so that the hot light also comes on.    (This checks the bulb and wiring but not, of course, the temperature sensor.)    When the key start switch is released, the hot light goes off, and if the motor starts, the generator light goes out, followed shortly by the oil-pressure light.    The cold light stays on for a few minutes, until the engine warms up, and then goes off.    If the driver glances at these lights briefly during start and the first few minutes of travel, all three systems are checked out.

Another important design principle is the *fail-safe* concept, often used in vehicle control systems and in other applications.    For example, in an automobile power steering system, the force boost provided by the hydraulic system is summed with the manually applied force. In the event of a power-steering failure the boost force is absent, and the manual force controls the wheels directly. If the power-steering system fails while the car is being parked, the car may become inoperable. If a failure occurs while the car is moving, it will still be under good control, but major steering effort would be involved.[1] A manual-control channel in parallel with an automatic one proved invaluable as a backup in the early Project Mercury flights.

A final example is a technique for improving the reliability of a cascade of low-voltage sources. This might represent many series cells of a high-

_____

[1] This assumes that the driver does not panic but recognizes the difficulty and compensates with additional manual steering effort.

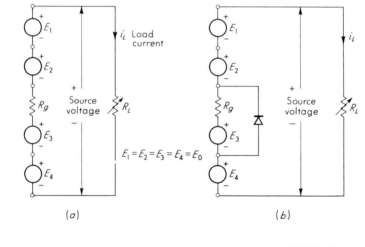

$$E_1 = E_2 = E_3 = E_4 = E_0$$

(a)          (b)

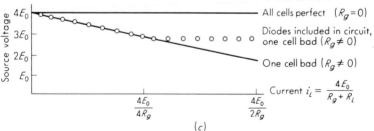

(c)

**Fig. 6.1** Improved power-supply circuit. (a) Four series sources; (b) parallel diode circuit; (c) terminal characteristics.

voltage battery or a series connection of many solar cells.  The basic circuit is shown in Fig. 6.1a with four series cells.  Resistance $R_g$ represents the internal resistance of source $E_3$, which is beginning to fail. Sources $E_1$, $E_2$, and $E_4$ are assumed to be good and to have zero resistance. In Fig. 6.1b a diode is placed across the bad cell.  When the current drain is sufficient to drop the source voltage to $3E_0$, the voltage drop across $R_g$ is $-E_0$, and there are zero volts across the diode.  At this point the diode conducts, and the bad cell $E_3$ is effectively short-circuited. The remaining three cells hold the terminal voltage at $3E_0$.  Of course, in practice, diodes are placed across each cell to provide the desired effect.

Each of the above examples illustrates a technique of design improvement which enhances the system reliability.  The next section explores how reliability can be improved through component improvement.

## 6.5  COMPONENT IMPROVEMENT

Another approach to bettering system reliability is to improve the reliability of all the constituent components.  Actually we assume that preliminary reliability studies have identified the most critical components so that effort can be focused on these components.  The first attempt in this direction was the manufacture of rugged five-star tubes in the late 1940s and early 1950s.  These tubes were supposed to be less sensitive to environmental stresses and have improved lifetimes.  The most recent and comprehensive high-reliability-parts development program was for the Minuteman missile system.  Manufacturers developed lines of high-reliability components at premium prices.  This is a costly and difficult means of achieving reliability, but is quite effective up to a point. An example of Minuteman failure rates compared with ordinary parts and space parts is given in Table 6.2.  It is interesting to note that a few ordinary parts do meet these specifications while many are far from the chosen levels.

In discussing parts improvement, the idea is often advanced that if one could find all the failure modes of a part and through part improvement eliminate them all, the part would not fail.  Even theoretically this is unacceptable, since the perfect component cannot exist.  However, given a certain lifetime, it is perfectly possible to construct a component with a negligible failure rate.  For example, if one were to examine the reliability of an automobile over a 5-year span, one would probably ignore any failures due to a broken chassis, the hypothesis being that the design involves a safety factor large enough to make this an almost nonexistent occurrence.  However, in the history of the automobile industry

**Table 6.2   Failure-rate comparisons (constant hazards, hr⁻¹)**

| Part | Minuteman parts[a] | Ordinary parts[b] | Space parts[c] |
|---|---|---|---|
| Paper capacitors | $1.5 \times 10^{-8}$ | $1.0 \times 10^{-8}$ | |
| Solid-tantalum capacitors | $3.5 \times 10^{-8}$ | $6.0 \times 10^{-8}$ | $10 \times 10^{-8}$ |
| Foil-tantalum capacitors | $4.0 \times 10^{-8}$ | $9.0 \times 10^{-8}$ | |
| Glass capacitors | $8.0 \times 10^{-10}$ | $70 \times 10^{-10}$ | $1,700 \times 10^{-10}$ [d] |
| Carbon composition resistors | $1.0 \times 10^{-9}$ | $5.0 \times 10^{-9}$ | $2.4 \times 10^{-9}$ |
| Carbon film resistors | $1.8 \times 10^{-9}$ | $28 \times 10^{-9}$ | $2.4 \times 10^{-9}$ |
| Wire-wound resistors | $7 \times 10^{-9}$ | $180 \times 10^{-9}$ | $10 \times 10^{-9}$ |
| Transistors | $1.0–3.0 \times 10^{-8}$ [b] | $100 \times 10^{-8}$ [b] | $0.97 \times 10^{-8}$ |
| Diodes | $2.5–1,000 \times 10^{-10}$ [e] | $3.5–1,410 \times 10^{-7}$ [b,e] | $52 \times 10^{-10}$ |

[a] "Reliability Stress and Failure Rate Data," MIL-HDBK-217, p. 169, Government Printing Office, Washington, D. C., 1962.   All parts at 40°C and 0.2 times stress level.

[b] *Ibid.*, same conditions as Minuteman parts except [b], which are for unknown environment.

[c] W. M. Redler, Parts Reliability Problems in Aerospace Systems, *IEEE Proc. Sixth Ann. New York Conf. Electron. Reliability*, May 1965.   Environment unspecified.

[d] Variable capacitor.

[e] Depending on type.

it is probable that this has happened at least a few times.   In fact the object of the study of the physics of failures (which is discussed in Chap. 8) is to locate cause-and-effect relationships between component failures and basic properties of the component materials and construction.   Once these are known, a part could be built to have a certain failure rate predicted by its construction and the basic properties of the materials from which it is made.   Even if one could not synthesize reliability in the way described, one could at least determine the sensitive parameters and use screening measurements to reject potential early failures.   Until sufficient theory is developed, part improvement will have to remain more an art than a science.

## 6.6  REDUNDANCY

### 6.6.1  REDUNDANCY CONCEPTS

As noted earlier, the term *redundancy* in this book is used to mean, in a broad sense, the creation of new parallel paths in a system structure to improve the system reliability.  The straightforward approach is to take the existing system and connect a duplicate one in parallel.  For example, to increase the reliability of an automobile braking system[1] one might install a duplicate set of brake shoes and cylinders on each wheel and feed these with separate hydraulic lines attached to a second master cylinder.  (One could probably assume to a good approximation that the brake pedal and linkage will not fail, and therefore these need not be duplicated.)  This results in two separate systems and just about doubles the cost, weight, and volume of the braking system.  An approach like this which involves paralleling the entire system or unit is called *system* or *unit redundancy*.  Another technique is to parallel two master cylinders and run two parallel hydraulic lines to each wheel which connect to a parallel pair of wheel cylinders.  In this case each component is individually paralleled.  Such an approach is called *component redundancy*.  In the early 1960s several American automobiles appeared with redundant braking systems.  In some a compromise system was used. A single brake pedal activates two separate master cylinders.  One master cylinder feeds a set of hydraulic lines, which connects to the front-wheel brake cylinders, and the other master cylinder operates the rear-wheel brake cylinders through its own set of lines.  Obviously this compromise system must operate on the principle that one set of brakes, either the front or rear, while not providing perfect operation, still yields safe operation.

This example will be discussed in order to illustrate how various redundancy concepts can improve system reliability.  A major task in any reliability analysis or synthesis problem is to go from a verbal statement of what the system is required to do to a functional reliability diagram. This is especially important since paralleling of components or units generally involves loading, interaction, changes in power and signal levels, etc.  Such practical considerations are discussed in Sec. 6.6.3. For simplicity in the following analysis we shall assume that such effects are insignificant and that components or units can be parallel at will without further consideration.

The three systems described above are diagrammed in Fig. 6.2. Reliability diagrams can be drawn for the various systems for the case of perfect operation and for safe operation.  A moment's thought will show, however, that it is easier to draw one basic reliability diagram for the

[1] How Effective Are Dual Brakes?  *Consumer Rept.*, August, 1965, p. 410.

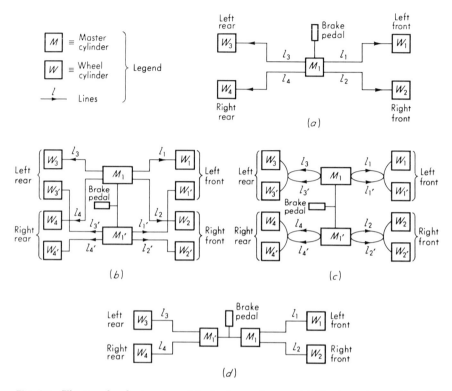

**Fig. 6.2**   Three redundant automobile brake systems.   (*a*) Single system; (*b*) unit redundancy: two identical systems are paralleled; (*c*) component redundancy: all components are individually paralleled; (*d*) compromise redundancy.

success of each wheel brake (see Fig. 6.3).   It is then simple to define the reliability of perfect braking $R_p$ and the reliability of safe braking $R_s$ in terms of various combinations of the wheels.   The definition of perfect braking will be that all four wheel brakes work.   The definition of safe braking will be that at least both rear wheel brakes work or at least both front wheel brakes work.[1]   This of course includes all four working, as well as both rear and one front or both front and one rear. The case of one front and one rear is excluded on the guess that the unbalance would be unsafe (actual experiments seem to prove the contrary[2]).

The probabilities of perfect braking for systems *a* to *d* of Fig. 6.3 are

---

[1] Standard American automobiles have 60 percent of the braking force supplied by the rear wheels and 40 percent by the front.   Thus, even front brakes alone are satisfactory except for a real panic stop.

[2] *Consumer Rept., loc. cit.*

given respectively by

$$R_{p_a} = P(B_1 B_2 B_3 B_4)$$
$$= P(M_1 l_1 W_1 l_2 W_2 l_3 W_3 l_4 W_4) \tag{6.1}$$
$$P_{p_b} = P(B_1 B_2 B_3 B_4 + B_1' B_2' B_3' B_4')$$
$$= P(M_1 l_1 W_1 l_2 W_2 l_3 W_3 l_4 W_4 + M_1' l_1' W_1' l_2' W_2' l_3' W_3' l_4' W_4') \tag{6.2}$$
$$R_{p_e} = P(B_1 B_2 B_3 B_4)$$
$$= P[(M_1 + M_1')(l_1 + l_1')(W_1 + W_1')(l_2 + l_2')(W_2 + W_2')$$
$$(l_3 + l_3')(W_3 + W_3')(l_4 + l_4')(W_4 + W_4')] \tag{6.3}$$
$$R_{p_d} = P(B_1 B_2 B_3 B_4)$$
$$= P(M_1 l_1 W_1 l_2 W_2 M_2 l_3 W_3 l_4 W_4) \tag{6.4}$$

All these reliabilities are of course the probability that all four brakes work. Inspection of these expressions shows that Eqs. (6.4) and (6.1) are almost identical except that Eq. (6.4) predicts a slightly poorer reliability then Eq. (6.1), since there is an extra component which may fail, that is, $M_2$. Inspection also shows that both Eqs. (6.2) and (6.3) predict higher

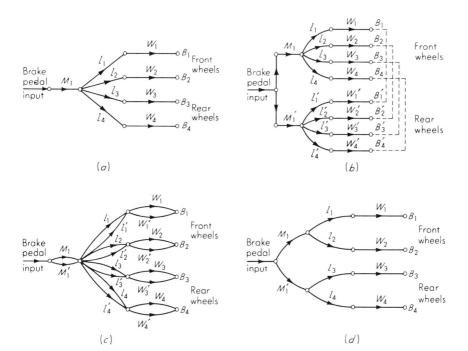

**Fig. 6.3**  Reliability diagrams for automobile-brake redundancy. (a) Single system; (b) unit redundancy; (c) component redundancy; (d) compromise redundancy.

reliabilities than Eq. (6.1); however, one must have numerical values to substitute in order to identify the configuration with the highest reliability. (The reader should not lose sight of the other factors involved such as size, weight, and cost.) A very simple, if not too realistic, comparison can be made by assuming that all elements are *independent* and have *identical* reliabilities of $p$. Thus, Eqs. (6.1) to (6.4) become

$$R_{p_a} = P(x_1 x_2 \cdots x_9) = p^9 \tag{6.5}$$
$$R_{p_b} = P[x_1 x_2 \cdots x_9 + x_1' x_2' \cdots x_9') = 2p^9 - p^{18} = p^9(2 - p^9) \tag{6.6}$$
$$R_{p_c} = P[(x_1 + x_1')(x_2 + x_2') \cdots (x_9 + x_9')]$$
$$= (2p - p^2)^9 = p^9(2 - p)^9 \tag{6.7}$$
$$R_{p_d} = P(x_1 x_2 \cdots x_{10}) = p^{10} \tag{6.8}$$

Inspection of these equations confirms the fact that system $d$ is slightly poorer than $a$ and both $b$ and $c$ are superior to $a$. In order to compare systems $b$ and $c$, that is, Eqs. (6.6) and (6.7), their ratio is formed

$$\frac{R_{p_c}}{R_{p_b}} = \frac{p^9(2 - p)^9}{p^9(2 - p^9)} = \frac{(2 - p)^9}{2 - p^9} \tag{6.9}$$

This ratio can be shown to be greater than unity. In fact, Roberts proves by induction[1] that the ratio

$$Q_n = \frac{(2 - r)^n}{2 - r^n} > 1 \qquad \begin{array}{l} 0 < r < 1 \\ \text{all } n \geq 2 \end{array} \tag{6.10}$$

A numerical comparison of the results is instructive. If one chooses a reliability of 0.9 for the single system, then $p^9 = 0.9$. In order to compute the equivalent value of $p$, one must take care. (In fact, whenever one is dealing with high reliabilities represented by a decimal point followed by a string of nines, great caution should be used to avoid truncation errors.) With a table of five-place ordinary logarithms and a slide rule[2] one obtains $p = \frac{1}{9} \log 0.900$ and $p = 0.988$. Using a series expansion, $p^9 = (1 - q)^9 = 0.900$. Since $q$ is very small,

$$(1 - q)^9 \approx 1 - 9q = 0.900$$

This approach yields $p = 0.989$. The second technique is very quick and quite accurate.

We can now compare the reliabilities of systems $b$, $c$, and $d$. For system $b$, $R_{p_b} = p^9(2 - p^9)$, which is $0.9(2 - 0.9) = 0.990$. For system $c$ one is tempted to calculate $R_{p_c} = p^9(2 - p)^9 = 0.9(2 - 0.988)^9$ and to use logarithms or a series expansion. This gives an erroneous answer

---

[1] Norman H. Roberts, "Mathematical Methods in Reliability Engineering," p. 260, McGraw-Hill Book Company, New York, 1964.

[2] A desk calculator is often necessary to avoid time-consuming errors due to truncation at the third digit.

because $p$ has not been computed to sufficient accuracy.    If one uses the $R_{p_c} = (2p - p^2)^9 = [2(0.988) - 0.988^2]^9$, one obtains

$$R_{p_c} = 0.999196^9 = 0.9928$$

For system $d$, $R_{p_d} = p^9 p = 0.9 \times 988 = 0.889$.    Thus, the single system fails 10 percent of the time, the compromise system 11 percent of the time, the unit-redundant system 1 percent of the time and the component-redundant system 0.72 percent of the time.    As was suspected, if we expect *perfect* braking, the compromise system is no improvement, but when we investigate the probabilities of safe braking, the situation changes.

For safe braking the probabilities become, for system $a$

$$R_{s_a} = P(B_1 B_2 + B_3 B_4) = P(M_1 l_1 W_1 l_2 W_2 + M_1 l_3 W_3 l_4 W_4)$$

For *identical independent* components with reliability $p$

$$R_{s_a} = P(x_1 x_2 x_3 x_4 x_5 + x_1 x_6 x_7 x_8 x_9) = 2p^5 - p^9 \tag{6.11}$$

For system $b$

$$\begin{aligned} R_{s_b} &= P(B_1 B_2 + B_3 B_4 + B_1' B_2' + B_3' B_4') \\ &= P(\underbrace{M_1 l_1 W_1 l_2 W_2 + M_1 l_3 W_3 l_4 W_4}_{\alpha} \\ &\quad + \underbrace{M_1' l_1' W_1' l_2' W_2' + M_1' l_3' W_3' l_4' W_4'}_{\beta}) = P(\alpha + \beta) \end{aligned}$$

Inspection of Eq. (6.11) reveals that $P(\alpha) = P(\beta) = R_{s_a}$.    For *identical independent* components with reliability $p$

$$R_{s_b} = 2R_{s_a} - (R_{s_a})^2 = 2(2p^5 - p^9) - (2p^5 - p^9)^2 \tag{6.12}$$

For system $c$

$$\begin{aligned} R_{s_c} &= P(B_1 B_2 + B_3 B_4) \\ &= P[\underbrace{(M_1 + M_1')}_{Y_1} \underbrace{(l_1 + l_1')}_{Y_2} \underbrace{(W_1 + W_1')}_{Y_3} \underbrace{(l_2 + l_2')}_{Y_4} \underbrace{(W_2 + W_2')}_{Y_5} \\ &\quad + \underbrace{(M_1 + M_1')}_{Y_1} \underbrace{(l_3 + l_3')}_{Y_6} \underbrace{(W_3 + W_3')}_{Y_7} \underbrace{(l_4 + l_4')}_{Y_8} \underbrace{(W_4 + W_4')}_{Y_9}] \\ &= P(Y_1 Y_2 Y_3 Y_4 Y_5 + Y_1 Y_6 Y_7 Y_8 Y_9) \end{aligned}$$

The form is the same as Eq. (6.11) but with different reliabilities.    For *identical independent* components with reliability $p$

$$\begin{aligned} P(Y) &= P(x + x') = 2p - p^2 \\ P_{s_c} &= 2(2p - p^2)^5 - (2p - p^2)^9 \end{aligned} \tag{6.13}$$

For system $d$

$$R_{s_d} = P(B_1B_2 + B_3B_4) = P(M_1l_1W_1l_2W_2 + M_1'l_3W_3l_4W_4)$$

For *identical independent* components with reliability $p$

$$R_{s_d} = P(x_1x_2x_3x_4x_5 + x_6x_7x_8x_9x_{10}) = 2p^5 - p^{10} \qquad (6.14)$$

We can now compare the probability of safe braking for the four systems. Using a component reliability of $p = 0.988$, we obtain

$$R_{s_a} = 2(0.988^5) - 0.988^9 = 0.9856$$
$$R_{s_b} = 2(0.980) - 0.980^2 = 0.9996$$
$$R_{s_c} = 2[2(0.988) - 0.988^2]^5 - [2(0.988) - 0.988^2]^9 = 0.9996$$
$$R_{s_d} = 2(0.988^5) - 0.988^{10} = 0.9956$$

Thus, the single system is unsafe 1.4 percent of the time, the compromise system is unsafe 0.44 percent of the time, the component-redundancy system 0.013 percent of the time, and the unit-redundancy system 0.04 percent of the time.

These results show that as far as safe operation goes, the compromise system offers about a $3:1$ improvement in failures over the single system. This is actually a much smaller gain then one would expect, since the unit- and component-redundancy systems offer large improvements (factor of 30 to 90). Of course the model used in this analysis is far from complete. First, the various component lines, master cylinders, and wheel cylinders surely have different reliabilities. Also, only a two-state model was used. In actuality perhaps a three-state model with one state being successful operation, one blockage, and one leakage might be more appropriate (see Sec. 3.8). Thus, the two-state model used may be thought of as a three-state model in which the probability of leakage is zero. A little thought will show that if leakage is included, the compromise system improves its relative standing.

There is of course much more to designing a redundant hydraulic-brake system than the material discussed above. We are of course assuming that such problems as force levels, flow rates, pressure drops, seals, etc., are within the realm of ordinary design practice. Also if we find that actuator housings seldom fail, it will probably be wise to use the same casing to house a redundant pair of brake cylinders. In any event it is clear that reliability studies of simple models such as given in Fig. 6.2 can be of great help at the initial design stage. They furnish comparative reliability information which must be considered along with cost, weight, size, etc., in making a wise choice of which system to pursue.

This example has illustrated various ways of utilizing redundancy in a practical system. The following sections will discuss reliability optimization with respect to various standard system configurations.

### 6.6.2 COMPONENT AND UNIT REDUNDANCY

The example of the previous section has shown that there are several ways in which to apply redundancy. The two techniques which are easily classified and studied are component and unit redundancy. In fact one can prove that component redundancy is superior to unit redundancy in a wide variety of situations.

Consider the three systems shown in Fig. 6.4. The reliability expressions for system $a$ is

$$R_a(p) = P(x_1)P(x_2) = p^2 \tag{6.15}$$

where both $x_1$ and $x_2$ are independent and identical and $P(x_1) = P(x_2) = p$. The reliability for the system of $b$ is given simply by

$$R_b(p) = P(x_1 x_2 + x_1' x_2')$$

For IIU with individual reliabilities of $p$

$$R_b(p) = 2R_a - R_a{}^2 = p^2(2 - p^2) \tag{6.16}$$

In the case of system $c$ one can combine each component pair in parallel to obtain

$$R_c(p) = P(x_1 + x_1')P(x_2 + x_2')$$

Assuming IIU, we obtain

$$R_c(p) = p^2(2 - p)^2 \tag{6.17}$$

To compare Eqs. (6.17) and (6.16) we take the ratio

$$\frac{R_c(p)}{R_b(p)} = \frac{(2 - p)^2}{2 - p^2} \tag{6.18}$$

Algebraic manipulation yields

$$\frac{R_c(p)}{R_b(p)} = \frac{(2 - p)^2}{2 - p^2} = \frac{4 - 4p + p^2}{2 - p^2} = \frac{(2 - p^2) + 2(1 - p)^2}{2 - p^2}$$

$$= 1 + \frac{2(1 - p)^2}{2 - p^2} \tag{6.19}$$

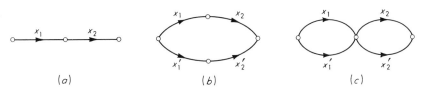

**Fig. 6.4** Comparison of three different systems. (a) Single system; (b) unit redundancy; (c) component redundancy.

Since $0 < p < 1$, the term $2 - p^2 > 0$, and $R_c(p)/R_b(p) > 1$; thus, component redundancy is superior to unit redundancy for this structure.

We can extend these chain structures into an $n$-element series structure, two parallel $n$-element unit-redundant structures, and a series of $n$ structures of two parallel elements. In this case Eq. (6.18) becomes

$$\frac{R_c(p)}{R_b(p)} = \frac{(2 - p)^n}{2 - p^n} \tag{6.20}$$

Roberts[1] proves by induction that this ratio is always greater than 1 and that component redundancy is superior regardless of the number of elements $n$.

The superiority of component redundancy over unit redundancy also holds for nonidentical elements. For example, we shall consider the three systems given in Fig. 6.4. For the case where $P(x_1) = 0.7$ and $P(x_2) = 0.9$:

For system $a$: $R_a = 0.7(0.9) = 0.630$
For system $b$: $R_b = 2(0.63) - 0.63^2 = 0.863$
For system $c$: $R_c = [2(0.7) - 0.7^2][2(0.9) - 0.9^2] = 0.901$

Again component redundancy is superior to unit redundancy.

A more general proof of the superiority of component redundancy over unit redundancy extends the principle to the case of nonidentical components.[2] If the model given in Fig. 6.4a is extended to include $n$ independent series items, the reliability of the single system is given by

$$R_s = \prod_{i=1}^{n} P(x_i) \tag{6.21}$$

If unit redundancy is used, the reliability expression becomes

$$R_u = 2 \prod_{i=1}^{n} P(x_i) - \left[ \prod_{i=1}^{n} P(x_i) \right]^2 = \prod_{i=1}^{n} P(x_i) \left[ 2 - \prod_{i=1}^{n} P(x_i) \right] \tag{6.22}$$

If component redundancy is used, we obtain

$$R_c = \prod_{i=1}^{n} [2P(x_i) - P(x_i)^2] = \prod_{i=1}^{n} P(x_i) \left[ \prod_{i=1}^{n} [2 - P(x_i)] \right] \tag{6.23}$$

Forming the difference function $\Delta R = R_c - R_u$, we get

$$\Delta R = \prod_{i=1}^{n} P(x_i) \left\{ \prod_{i=1}^{n} [2 - P(x_i)] - \left[ 2 - \prod_{i=1}^{n} P(x_i) \right] \right\} \tag{6.24}$$

---

[1] Roberts, *op. cit.*, p. 260.

[2] M. L. Shooman, Comparison of Component Redundancy with Unit Redundancy, *Sperry Gyroscope Co.*, *Tech. Mem.* 3280, April 18, 1957.

and manipulation yields

$$\Delta R = \prod_{i=1}^{n} P(x_i) \left\{ \prod_{i=1}^{n-1} [2 - P(x_i)][2 - P(x_n)] - \left[ 2 - \prod_{i=1}^{n} P(x_i) \right] \right\} \quad (6.25)$$

Now since $0 < P(x_i) < 1$, the following inequalities hold

$$2 - P(x_n) \geq 2 - \prod_{i=1}^{n} P(x_i)$$

also

$$1 \leq \prod_{i=1}^{n-1} [2 - P(x_i)] \leq 2^{n-1}$$

and

$$\prod_{i=1}^{n} P(x_i) \geq 0$$
$$\therefore \Delta R \geq 0$$

which proves that component redundancy is superior to unit redundancy.

A simpler proof of the above principle can be formulated by considering the system tie sets. Clearly in Fig. 6.4b, the tie sets are: $x_1x_2$, $x_1'x_2'$, whereas in Fig. 6.4c the tie sets are: $x_1x_2$, $x_1'x_2'$, $x_1x_2'$, $x_1'x_2$. Since the system reliability is the probability of the union of the tie sets, and since system c has the same two tie sets as system b as well as two additional ones, the component redundancy configuration has a larger reliability than the unit redundancy configuration. It is easy to see that this tie-set proof can be extended to the general case.

The specific result can be broadened to include a large number of structures. The system of Fig. 6.5a can be reduced to a simple series structure by considering the parallel combination of $x_1$ and $x_2$ to be replaced by an equivalent branch $x_5$. Then $x_5$, $x_3$, and $x_4$ form a simple chain structure and component redundancy, as shown in Fig. 6.5b, is clearly superior. Many complex configurations can be examined in a

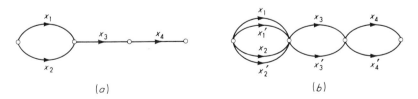

**Fig. 6.5**  Component redundancy.  (a) Original system; (b) redundant system.

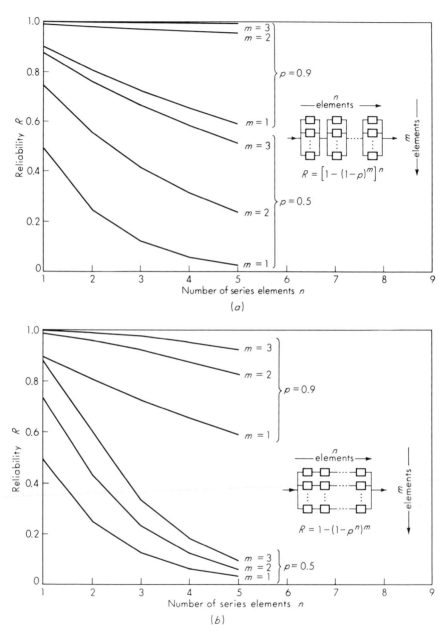

**Fig. 6.6**   Redundancy comparison.   (*a*) Component redundancy; (*b*) unit redundancy. (*Adapted from Figs. 7.10 and 7.11, "Reliability Engineering," ARINC Research Corp., Prentice-Hall, Inc., Englewood Cliffs, N.J., 1964.*)

similar manner. Unit and component redundancy are compared graphically in Fig. 6.6.

Another interesting case where one can compare component and unit redundancy is in an $r$-out-of-$n$ system. Immediately one can see that for $r = n$, the structure is a series one and the previous result applies. If $r = 1$, the structure reduces to $n$ parallel elements, and component and unit redundancy are identical. The interesting cases are then $2 \leq r < n$. The results for two-out-of-four and three-out-of-four systems are plotted in Fig. 6.7. Again component redundancy is superior.

The superiority of component over unit redundancy in an $r$-out-of-$n$ system is easily proved by considering the system tie sets. For example, the four-out-of-five system shown in Fig. 3.4 has five tie sets; if unit

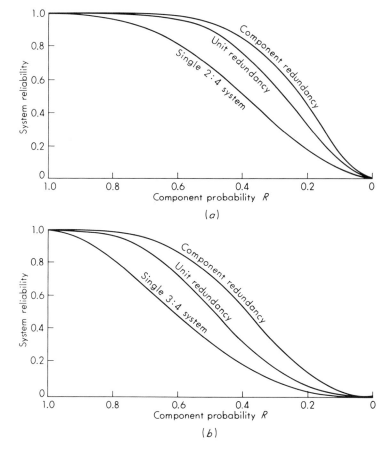

**Fig. 6.7** Comparison of component and unit redundancy for $r$-out-of-$n$ systems. (*a*) A two-out-of-four system; (*b*) a three-out-of-four system.

redundancy is used, there will be ten tie sets. If component redundancy is used a total of 80 tie sets are present including the 10 unit redundancy tie sets. This result generalizes, and component redundancy is superior to unit redundancy in $r$-out-of-$n$ systems.

All the above analysis applies to two-state systems. Different results are obtained for multistate models. The diode has already been given as an example of a device with more than two states. It is clear that electric elements often fail as short or open circuits; therefore, three-state models for electric elements should be useful. In many cases mechanical elements can also be viewed in the same manner. For example, a rotational mechanical system may jam, so that rotation is blocked, or a shaft may shear, so that an input rotation causes no output rotation. The hydraulic brake system of Sec. 6.6.1 was discussed in terms of line blockage and line leaks. Thus, three-state models are really more general than one might think. The terms *open* and *short*, which directly apply to the electric system, will be used in their more general sense.

As a simple example of redundancy applied to a multistate element, consider the following example. If a single element has two states $p = 0.8$ and $q = 0.2$, the reliability is 0.8. A system composed of two such elements in parallel has a reliability given by $1 - q^2 = 0.96$. Now assume the elements have three states with $p = 0.8$ and that the probabilities of short and open failures are $q_s = 0.1$ and $q_o = 0.1$. The system fails when both elements open-circuit $\bar{x}_{1o}\bar{x}_{2o}$ and when either element shorts $\bar{x}_{1s} + \bar{x}_{2s}$. The reliability is given by

$$R = 1 - p(\bar{x}_{1o}\bar{x}_{2o} + \bar{x}_{1s} + \bar{x}_{2s}) = 1 - q_o^2 - 2q_s + q_s^2 = 0.8$$

(Note that some of the states are mutually exclusive.) This example clearly shows that some or all of the advantages of redundancy can be lost if the units have short failures.

In formulating redundancy expressions for a three-state model, the following notation will be used:

$x_i$ = success of element $i$
$\bar{x}_{io}$ = open failure of element $i$
$\bar{x}_{is}$ = short failure of element $i$
$P(x_i) = p_i$
$P(\bar{x}_{io}) = q_{io}$
$P(\bar{x}_{is}) = q_{is}$

where

$$p_i + q_o + q_s = 1$$

The reliability of a series system is still given by Eq. (6.21) and that of a unit-redundant system by Eq. (6.22). The expression for component redundancy changes, since additional failure modes are introduced by the element short failures. A parallel combination of two elements $x_i$ and $x_i'$ may fail if both elements open or if either element shorts. Thus,

$$R = 1 - P[(\bar{x}_{io}\bar{x}_{io}') + (\bar{x}_{is} + \bar{x}_{is}')] \tag{6.26}$$

Expansion yields

$$R = 1 - [P(\bar{x}_{io}\bar{x}_{io}') + P(\bar{x}_{is} + \bar{x}_{is}')] - P[(\bar{x}_{io}\bar{x}_{io}')(\bar{x}_{is} + \bar{x}_{is}')] \tag{6.27}$$

Since events $\bar{x}_{io}$, $\bar{x}_{is}$ and $\bar{x}_{io}'$, $\bar{x}_{is}'$ form mutually exclusive events, the last term in Eq. (6.27) is identically zero. Therefore, if the units are independent,

$$\begin{aligned} R &= 1 - P(\bar{x}_{io})P(\bar{x}_{io}) - P(\bar{x}_{is}) - P(\bar{x}_{is}') + P(\bar{x}_{is})P(\bar{x}_{is}) \\ &= 1 - q_{io}q_{io}' - q_{is} - q_{is}' + q_{is}q_{is}' \end{aligned} \tag{6.28}$$

Assuming that both elements are identical yields

$$R = 1 - q_{io}^2 - 2q_{is} + q_{is}^2 \tag{6.29}$$

Thus, for a series system of $n$ elements, the expression for component redundancy becomes

$$R_c' = \prod_{i=1}^{n} (1 - q_{io}^2 - 2q_{is} + q_{is}^2) \tag{6.30}$$

Again forming a $\Delta R'$ expression by subtracting Eq. (6.22) from Eq. (6.30), we obtain

$$\Delta R' = R_c' - R_u = \prod_{i=1}^{n} (1 - q_{io}^2 - 2q_{is} + q_{is}^2)$$
$$- \left[ 2 \prod_{i=1}^{n} p_i - \left( \prod_{i=1}^{n} p_i \right)^2 \right] \tag{6.31}$$

The reader should note that $p_i$ was first substituted into Eq. (6.22) for $P(x_i)$ to obtain a uniform notation. In order to study Eq. (6.31) we can compare the two terms with Eqs. (6.23) and (6.22) respectively. If we allow $p_i$ to be the same in both cases, the term in brackets is identical. Thus, $\Delta R - \Delta R' = R_c - R_c'$. Now to compare the $R_c$ and $R_c'$ terms we write

$$P(x_i) = p_i = 1 - q_i = 1 - (q_{io} + q_{is})$$

and substitute into Eq. (6.23), yielding

$$R_c = \prod_{i=1}^{n} [2(1 - q_i) - (1 - q_i)^2]$$

which can be reduced to

$$R_c = \prod_{i=1}^{n} (1 - q_i^2) = \prod_{i=1}^{n} [1 - (q_{io} + q_{is})^2]$$

$$= \prod_{i=1}^{n} (1 - q_{io}^2 - 2q_{io}q_{is} - q_{is}^2) \quad (6.32)$$

Forming the difference $R_c - R_c'$ yields

$$R_c - R_c' = \prod_{i=1}^{n} [(-q_{is}^2 - 2q_{io}q_{is}) - (q_{is}^2 - 2q_{is})]$$

$$= \prod_{i=1}^{n} 2q_{is}(1 - q_{is} - q_{io}) = \prod_{i=1}^{n} 2q_{is}p_i \geq 0$$

Since this term is positive, $R_c > R_c'$, and $\Delta R > \Delta R'$. Thus, the three-state component-redundant system is inferior to the two-state component-redundant system. No general conclusions were reached regarding the relative superiority of component and unit redundancy when three-state models are involved, and therefore specific numerical studies must be made.

An interesting problem to study is the optimum number of three-state parallel elements for highest reliability. Because of the short failures, the reliability will not continuously improve as more components are added; it will reach a maximum and then decrease. Equation (6.29) can be generalized for $n$ identical elements

$$R = \prod_{i=1}^{n} (1 - q_{is}) - \prod_{i=1}^{n} q_{io} \qquad (6.33)$$

and for identical elements

$$R = (1 - q_s)^n - q_o^n \qquad (6.34)$$

Maximizing $R$ with respect to $n$ yields[1]

$$\frac{\partial R}{\partial n} = (1 - q_s)^n \ln (1 - q_s) - q_o^n \ln q_o = 0$$

Solution for $n$ yields

$$n = - \frac{\ln \{\ln [q_o/(1 - q_s)]\}}{\ln [q_o/(1 - q_s)]} \qquad (6.35)$$

The optimum number of elements $n$ predicted by Eq. (6.35) is plotted in Fig. 6.8. The bottom and left axes are used for $q_o > q_s$. If $q_s > q_o$,

[1] The derivative with respect to $x$ of $u^x$ is $u^x \ln u$.

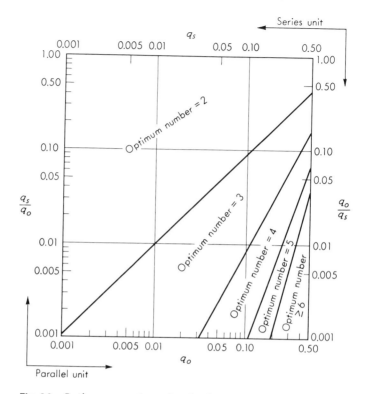

**Fig. 6.8**   Optimum number of redundant elements for elements with both open and short failures.   (*From ARINC Research Corp., "Reliability Engineering," fig. 7.14, Prentice-Hall, Inc., 1964.*)

paralleling elements makes matters worse, and it is advantageous to place additional units in series.   The solution is similar, and the same graph can be used, if one reads the top and right axes.

This section has discussed some general conclusions which can be drawn for certain particular redundancy models.   The next section treats the subject of how such models can be physically realized and discusses some of the limitations.

### 6.6.3   PRACTICAL REDUNDANCY

The previous sections on redundancy have discussed various redundancy models without regard to how such models can be realized.   The main problem is that one cannot simply parallel elements without special attention to impedance levels, power and signal gains, linearity, etc.

If we try to add redundancy to the voltage-divider network shown in

Fig. 6.9$a$, some problems will be encountered. The first idea is to parallel the 90- and 10-ohm resistors. This yields a slightly different circuit (same divider ratio but twice the current drain and half the internal impedance). Also failures in any component would result in a different transformation ratio. A slight improvement over the above situation is obtained in the circuit of Fig. 6.9$b$. The transformation ratio, current drain, and internal impedances all are identical to the circuit of Fig. 6.9$a$ as long as all components are good. The network of Fig. 6.9$b$ will give an output voltage of 10 volts if all components are working. If either $R_1$ or $R_1'$ open-circuits, the output voltage will drop to 5.25 volts, and if either $R_2$ or $R_2'$ open-circuits, the output voltage will rise to 18.2 volts. In most situations such a variation in output would be considered intolerable, and the reliability of circuit $b$ is actually poorer than that of $a$. Thus, the reliability of Fig. 6.9$a$ is given by $p^2$, where $p$ represents the reliability of any resistor and that of Fig. 6.9$b$ is $p^4$. If voltage variations between 5.25 and 18.20 volts are acceptable, the redundant circuit has a reliability of $(2p - p^2)^2$. In order to apply redundancy in voltage-divider circuits where tight tolerances on the voltage variations are required, other techniques must be used. One approach is to forget redundancy and use other means of reliability improvement. Another approach is to devise a substitute technique which could replace the voltage divider and which might be more amenable to redundancy. Finally, one could devise some sort of switching scheme with relays or diodes to switch in the redundant element only when the primary one fails. Such a system is represented by a standby model (see Sec. 6.9). It is interesting that practical application of redundancy often leads to a standby system.

To avoid giving the impression that redundancy is an impractical concept, we shall cite a few examples in which redundant circuits are

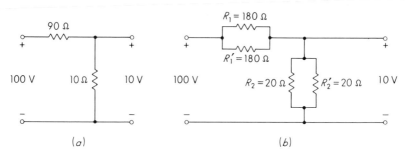

**Fig. 6.9**   Voltage divider networks.   ($a$) Normal voltage divider; ($b$) semi-redundant voltage divider.

easily constructed. As a first example let us discuss the feasibility of building a redundant transistor power amplifier used to drive a control motor. In order to connect two parallel channels we might merely parallel the inputs and outputs of the two amplifiers. Thus, the same input signal would appear at both inputs, and the same output voltage would appear across the motor. The output currents of each amplifier would add, doubling the power input to the motor. In the case of an open-circuit failure at the input, in the middle, or at the output of an amplifier, the bad amplifier would in effect be disconnected from the circuit. In this case the power gain would drop by 50 percent. An internal short-circuit failure in an amplifier would have essentially the same effect, but a short-circuit failure at the input or output would be more serious. An input or output short failure could fail the entire system. We can easily protect against output short failures by fusing each output circuit so that the extra current drawn by the short will burn out the fuse and effectively convert the short into an open circuit. Similarly, the addition of series input resistors would probably remove the possibility that one input short circuit will fail both amplifiers. We still have the problem of the 50 percent reduction in gain due to a single failure. A simple, standard feedback connection could minimize this effect. We could easily sum the amplifier output currents using a trans-former with two primary windings or a split winding on the motor. A third winding might be added (transformer or motor windings have rela-tively low failure rates) to produce a feedback voltage. The feedback voltage would be summed with the input. If we wished to obtain a system gain of 100, we could start with individual amplifier gains of 500 and use a feedback loop gain of 9. The forward gain would drop to 500 after one failure, the loop gain would become 4.5, and the system gain would be 91. This 9 percent reduction in gain would be acceptable in most circumstances.

Another simple example of practical redundancy is the paralleling of two constant-frequency power sources. We denote the first source by $e_1 = A \sin \omega t$ and the second by $e_2 = A \sin (\omega t + \theta)$. Assume $\theta$ can be adjusted by a phase-shift network. Then setting $\theta = 120°$, the sum of the voltages $e_1 + e_2 = A \sin (\omega t + 60°)$. Thus, an open-circuit failure of either voltage causes only a change in phase and no change in amplitude.

Another interesting example is the application of redundancy in an integrated circuit. It is often assumed that an integrated circuit has the same reliability as a transistor, independent of the complexity of the integrated circuit. Deeper study of the problem reveals that the failure rate does go up slowly with the number of elements on the chip. Some preliminary data on models illustrating this effect are given in Table 6.3. Let us assume that the failure rate is constant and proportional to $\sqrt{n}$.

**Table 6.3   Relative failure rates of silicon planar integrated circuit as a function of complexity**

| Model | 1 transistor | 10 equivalent parts | 30 equivalent parts | 100 equivalent parts |
|---|---|---|---|---|
| Good 1965 | 1 | 2.0 | 4.0 | 7.0 |
| Best 1965 | 1 | 1.7 | 3.0 | 5.0 |
| Best 1968 | 1 | 1.5 | 2.5 | 4.0 |
| Weighted rate | 1 | 2.1 | 3.6 | 6.0 |
| $n^{\frac{1}{2}}$ | 1 | 3.2 | 5.5 | 10.0 |
| $n^{\frac{1}{3}}$ | 1 | 2.2 | 3.1 | 4.6 |

SOURCE: "Handbook for Systems Applications of Redundancy," p. 4-130, U.S. Naval Applied Science Laboratory, August, 1966.

Thus $\lambda = \lambda_0 \sqrt{n}$, and $p = \exp(-\lambda_0 \sqrt{n}\, t)$. If $\lambda_0 \sqrt{n}\, t < 1$, $p \approx 1 - \lambda_0 \sqrt{n}\, t$, and $q = 1 - p = \lambda_0 \sqrt{n}\, t$. Suppose we wish to build a circuit of 20 components in cascade and must use integrated-circuit chips with a density of 10 components. The reliability of such a two-chip system would be given by

$$R_1 = \exp(-\lambda_0 \sqrt{10}\, t) \exp(-\lambda_0 \sqrt{10}\, t) \approx 1 - 2\lambda_0 \sqrt{10}\, t$$

If we agree to use four chips, we can employ unit redundancy and obtain

$$R_2 = 2 \exp(-2\lambda_0 \sqrt{10}\, t) - \exp(-4\lambda_0 \sqrt{10}\, t) \approx 1 - 40\lambda_0^2 t^2$$

Or we could use the four chips to obtain component redundancy, yielding

$$R_3 = [2 \exp(-\lambda_0 \sqrt{10}\, t) - \exp(-2\lambda_0 \sqrt{10}\, t)]^2 \approx 1 - 20\lambda_0^2 t^2$$

Another possibility is to use two larger chips, each capable of accommodating a circuit of 20 components. We could then build an entire circuit on each chip and place them in parallel. The reliability in this case would be

$$R_4 = 2 \exp(-\lambda_0 \sqrt{20}\, t) - \exp(-2\lambda_0 \sqrt{20}\, t) \approx 1 - 20\lambda_0^2 t^2$$

Thus, either two large chips or four smaller ones in a component redundancy configuration are superior to four chips used for unit redundancy.

Another type of circuit in which redundancy is easily applied is a digital system. If a digital system uses the binary number system, all inputs and outputs are either 0 or 1. In addition there is much repetition of similar building blocks. Such systems use specialized redundancy techniques, which are discussed in the following section.

## 6.7   REDUNDANCY IN DIGITAL SYSTEMS

### 6.7.1   INTRODUCTION

The discussion of redundancy in the previous section dealt only with analog devices and systems. This section will treat a different set of redundancy techniques which are feasible because of the special nature of digital system. Among the many reasons why redundancy is especially attractive in digital systems are the following:

1   The binary nature of signals represented by 0 or 1 greatly simplifies the normal considerations of voltage gain, impedance matching, and distortion, which are present in analog-system redundancy.
2   A digital system can be specified by a set of switching functions or state tables (for a sequential machine). Many circuits can be built which satisfy the same specifications.
3   In general only a handful of basic digital circuits are needed to construct a vast array of functions; therefore we can use redundancy on the circuit or function level.
4   Digital integrated circuits are simple and can achieve a high volume density.

Even the reader who has not studied digital logic can appreciate the rudiments of the theory by applying the same principles of set theory which have been used in the study of reliability. If we denote the universal set by 1 and the null set by 0, set-theory relations become Boolean algebra rules. The two most fundamental logic relations are the AND and OR functions, shown in Fig. 6.10$a$ and $b$. Three basic descriptions of these functions, the logic function (switching function), the logic-circuit (logic-gate) symbols, and the logic table (truth table) are given in Fig. 6.10$a$ and $b$. Two additional functions, the not-and (NAND) and the not-or (NOR) functions are defined in Fig. 6.10$c$ and $d$. Sometimes it is more expedient to use these as the primitive building blocks rather than AND and OR functions. They are shown in the figure in terms of their own logic notation as well as combined circuits of NOT gates (complement) preceding ordinary AND and OR gates. A direct approach to digital redundancy is shown in Fig. 6.11$a$. Gates 1 and 2, parallel AND gates, are combined in gate 3, which is an OR gate. If we assume that the reliability of an OR gate is about the same as an AND gate, the circuit of Fig. 6.11$a$ actually has a poorer reliability than a single AND gate.

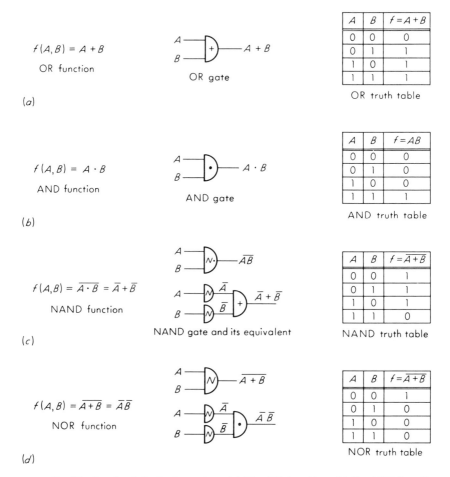

$f(A,B) = A + B$

OR function

(a)

$f(A,B) = A \cdot B$

AND function

(b)

$f(A,B) = \overline{A \cdot B} = \overline{A} + \overline{B}$

NAND function

(c)

$f(A,B) = \overline{A + B} = \overline{A}\overline{B}$

NOR function

(d)

**Fig. 6.10** The four basic logic elements. (a) The OR function; (b) the AND function; (c) the NAND function; (d) the NOR function. (In part c, the logic expression was originally called a Scheffer stroke, and the term is used extensively in the literature.)

Thus, the direct approach to logic-gate redundancy does not improve the reliability, and one must either use more sophisticated techniques to apply redundancy at the logic-gate level or use unit redundancy. In order to study other approaches to digital redundancy we shall discuss the logic circuit and number system used in a binary half-adder.

The decimal number system uses 10 symbols, 0, 1, 2, 3, 4, 5, 6, 7, 8, and 9, and represents numbers as powers of 10, that is, $10^0 = 1$, $10^1 = 10$, $10^2 = 100$, etc. Thus, 1,349.2 is given by

$$1{,}349.2 = 1 \times 10^3 + 3 \times 10^2 + 4 \times 10^1 + 9 \times 10^0 + 2 \times 10^{-1}$$

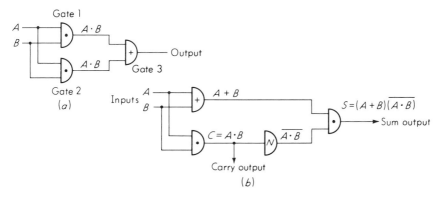

**Fig. 6.11**   Digital circuits.   (*a*) A redundant AND gate.   (*b*) One logic realization of a binary half-adder.

In a similar manner the binary number system uses two symbols 0 and 1 and represents numbers in terms of powers of 2, that is, $2^0 = 1$, $2^1 = 2$, $2^2 = 4$, etc.   The numbers 1 to 10 are given in Table 6.4 in the binary and decimal number systems.

In order to perform addition in the binary number system we must learn the binary addition table, i.e., the rules for forming the sum and carry digits, which are given in Table 6.5.   It is easy to formulate a pair of switching functions for binary addition if we examine the truth table in Table 6.6.   Inspection of the carry column and the truth table of Fig. 6.10*b* shows that the carry operation is present only when both $A$ and $B$ are present, that is,

$$C = A \cdot B$$

**Table 6.4   Decimal and binary numbers**

| Decimal number | Binary number |
|:---:|:---:|
| 0 | 0000 |
| 1 | 0001 |
| 2 | 0010 |
| 3 | 0011 |
| 4 | 0100 |
| 5 | 0101 |
| 6 | 0110 |
| 7 | 0111 |
| 8 | 1000 |
| 9 | 1001 |
| 10 | 1010 |

**Table 6.5   Addition rules in the binary number system**

| Addend   0 | Addend   0 | Addend   1 | Addend   1 |
|---|---|---|---|
| Augend +0 | Augend +1 | Augend +0 | Augend +1 |
| Sum        0 | Sum        1 | Sum        1 | Sum        0 |
| Carry 0 | Carry 0 | Carry 0 | Carry 1 |

The sum operation is not given by any single term but can be made up of two terms.   The sum function occurs whenever either the addend or augend is present (OR gate) along with (AND gate) the carry being absent (NOT gate).   The logic equation is

$$S = (A + B)\bar{C} = (A + B)(\overline{A \cdot B})$$

One of the several logic realizations of these two equations is given in Fig. 6.11$b$, which is a binary *half-adder*.[1]   Now that we have shown by example what is meant by a logic circuit and a number system, we can discuss how redundancy can be employed.

We have already illustrated in Fig. 6.11$a$ that *logic-gate* redundancy, at least in its primitive form, is not successful.   We can achieve some success if we apply redundancy at the *logic-circuit* level.   As an example let us consider the binary-half adder given in Fig. 6.11$a$.   The carry signal is merely the output of a single AND gate, and attempts to parallel this signal directly reduce to component redundancy.   If we try to parallel the sum output as shown in Fig. 6.12, we shall meet with some success.

In order to analyze the system shown in Fig. 6.12 we must assume a model for how digital gates fail.   We assume that when a logic gate fails, its output is a zero regardless of the inputs.   This means that any gate

[1] The term half-adder is used since we have not allowed for a carry in from a less significant pair of digits.   If a carry in is needed, a more complex circuit called a *full adder* is required.

**Table 6.6   Truth table for two-digit binary addition**

| Addend A | Augend B | Sum S | Carry C |
|---|---|---|---|
| 0 | 0 | 0 | 0 |
| 0 | 1 | 1 | 0 |
| 1 | 0 | 1 | 0 |
| 1 | 1 | 0 | 1 |

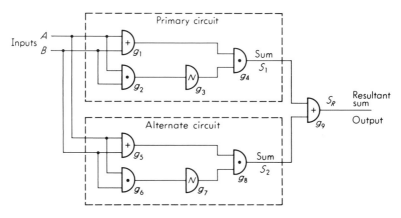

**Fig. 6.12**   A redundant binary half-adder circuit.

failure will result in an alteration of some of the terms in the circuit truth table, producing a different function, which we shall call a failure.[1] If we assume that any zero failure of a gate in the primary circuit produces a zero at $S_1$, and similarly for the alternate circuits, then the output OR gate will combine the two signals $S_1$ and $S_2$ in a redundant fashion. (Actually this is true only for three of the four gates in the half-adder.) On the basis of the assumptions we can say that proper operation of the primary circuit depends on all four gates working properly.   The reliability structure becomes that shown in Fig. 6.13.   For independent identical elements this becomes

$$R_2 = p(2p^4 - p^8) \tag{6.36}$$

[1] Anyone who has studied digital logic of course realizes that if the switching function for a circuit is not in primitive form, there is some built-in redundancy, and not all gate failures are circuit failures.   Also it may be more realistic to assume a three-state gate model where the gate is good, stuck at 0 output, or stuck at 1 output.

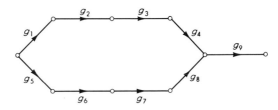

**Fig. 6.13**   Reliability graph for the circuit in Fig. 6.12.

We can compare this with the reliability expression for the single circuit of Fig. 6.11a, $R_1 = p^4$, by forming the ratio

$$\frac{R_2}{R_1} = p(2 - p^4) \tag{6.36a}$$

If $p$ is close to unity, we can write $p = (1 - q)$ and

$$p^4 = (1 - q)^4 \approx 1 - 4q$$

Substituting gives

$$\frac{R_2}{R_1} = (1 - q)[2 - (1 - 4q)] = (1 - q)(1 + 4q) = 1 + 3q - 4q^2 \tag{6.36b}$$

Whenever $q < 1$, the ratio is greater than unity, and the redundant circuit is an improvement.   Attempts to extend these redundancy techniques to three or more elements will lead to the voting techniques described below.

### 6.7.2  MAJORITY VOTING

The assumptions necessitated in the analysis of Fig. 6.12 leave several unresolved problems.   In fact, it is clear that if the assumptions are probed, the reliability improvement predicted by Eq. (6.36b) will decrease and may entirely disappear.   Another approach is clearly in order.

If we forget about the details of how a particular digital circuit operates, we can view it merely as a device which accepts several input variables which are 0 or 1 and produces an output which is 0 or 1.   Thus, if we had two parallel systems, we would compare the outputs to make a judgment on the proper answer.   If the two outputs agree, we conclude that both systems are working correctly, yielding the right answer with a probability $p^2$, or both systems have failed, giving the wrong answer with a probability $q^2$.   If one output is a 0 and the other output a 1, clearly one of the two circuits is in error.   We cannot tell from the information provided, however, which is correct.   Obviously the answer is to use an odd number of parallel circuits and side with the majority.   This in essence creates a $k$-out-of-$m$ system.   This technique is called *majority voting* or *majority logic*.

The system shown in Fig. 6.14 consists of three parallel digital circuits, $A$, $B$, and $C$, with the same input.   The outputs of all three circuits are compared by the voter.   The voter sides with the majority and gives the majority opinion as the system output.   If all three circuits are operating properly, all outputs agree, and the system output is correct.   If one element has failed, so that it produces an incorrect output, the voter will choose as the system output the output of the two good ele-

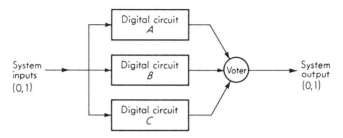

**Fig. 6.14**   Majority logic.

ments, since they agree; the system output will therefore be correct.   If two elements have failed, the voter will agree with the majority, the two which have failed, and the system output will be incorrect.   The system output will also be incorrect if all three circuits have failed.   All the above conclusions assume that a circuit fails in such a way that it always yields the complement of the correct input.   Using the above assumption, and assuming that the *voter does not fail*, the system reliability is given by

$$R = P(AB + AC + BC)$$

If all the digital circuits are independent and identical with probability of success $p$, then this equation can be rewritten in terms of the binomial theorem

$$R = B(3:3) + B(2:3)$$
$$= \binom{3}{3} p^3(1 - p)^0 + \binom{3}{2} p^2(1 - p)^1$$
$$= 3p^2 - 2p^3 = p^2(3 - 2p) \quad (6.37)$$

This is, of course, the reliability expression for a two-out-of-three system. The assumption that the digital elements fail so as to produce the complement of the correct input may not be valid.   (It is, however, a worst-case type of result and should yield a lower bound, i.e., a pessimistic answer.)

The probability model derived above enabled us to compute the system reliability, i.e., the probability of no failures.   In many problems this is the primary measure of interest; however, there are also a number of applications in which another approach is important.   For example, in a digital communications system we are interested in the probability that the system makes no errors but also in the error rate.   In other words, we assume that errors due to temporary equipment malfunction or noise are not catastrophic if they occur only rarely, and we wish to compute the probability of such occurrence.   Similarly in a ground-based digital computer we could occasionally tolerate an error without shutting down operation for repair. A third example, which is less clear-cut, is that of an inertial guidance computer for a rocket. Every computation cycle the computer generates a course change and directs the missile control system accordingly. An error in one computation will direct the missile off course. If the error is large, the time between computations moderately long, the missile control system and dynamics quick to respond, and the flight near its end, then the target may be missed, and a catastrophic failure occurs. But if these factors are reversed, a small error will temporarily steer the missile off course much as a wind gust does. As long as the error has cleared in one or two computation cycles, the missile will rapidly return to its proper course. A model for computing transmission-error probabilities is discussed below.

To construct the type of failure model discussed above we assume that there are one good and two failed states:

$A$ = element $A$ good
$\bar{A}_1$ = element $A$ gives a one output regardless of input
$\bar{A}_0$ = element $A$ gives a zero output regardless of input

In order to work with this three-state model, we shall change our definition of reliability to "the probability that the digital circuit gives the correct output to any given input." Thus, for the circuit of Fig. 6.14, if the correct output is to be a one, the probability expression is

$$P_1 = 1 - P(\bar{A}_0\bar{B}_0 + \bar{A}_0\bar{C}_0 + \bar{B}_0\bar{C}_0) \qquad (6.38)$$

Equation (6.38) states that the probability of correctly indicating a one output is given by unity minus the probability of two or more "zero failures." Similarly, the probability of correctly indicating a zero output is given by

$$P_0 = 1 - P(\bar{A}_1\bar{B}_1 + \bar{A}_1\bar{C}_1 + \bar{B}_1\bar{C}_1) \qquad (6.39)$$

If we assume that a one output and a zero output have an equal probability of occurrence, $\frac{1}{2}$, on any particular transmission, then the system reliability is the average of Eqs. (6.38) and (6.39). If we let

$P(A) = P(B) = (PC) = p,$
$P(\bar{A}_1) = P(\bar{B}_1) = P(\bar{C}_1) = q_1$, and $P(\bar{A}_0) = P(\bar{B}_0) = P(\bar{C}_0) = q_0$, then

Eq. (6.38) yields

$$P_1 = 1 - P(\bar{A}_0\bar{B}_0) - P(\bar{A}_0\bar{C}_0) - P(\bar{B}_0\bar{C}_0) + 2P(\bar{A}_0\bar{B}_0\bar{C}_0)$$
$$= 1 - 3q_0^2 + 2q_0^3$$

and similarly Eq. (6.39) becomes

$$P_0 = 1 - P(\bar{A}_1\bar{B}_1) - P(\bar{A}_1\bar{C}_1) - P(\bar{B}_1\bar{C}_1) + 2P(\bar{A}_1\bar{B}_1\bar{C}_1)$$
$$= 1 - 3q_1^2 + 2q_1^3$$

Averaging $P_1$ and $P_0$ gives

$$P = \frac{P_0 + P_1}{2}$$

$$= 1 - \tfrac{1}{2}(3q_0{}^2 + 3q_1{}^2 - 2q_0{}^3 - 2q_1{}^3) \tag{6.40}$$

In order to compare Eq. (6.40) with (6.37) we let $q_0 = q_1 = q$; therefore, $p + q + q = 1$, and $q = (1 - p)/2$. Substitution in Eq. (6.40) yields

$$P = \tfrac{1}{2} + \tfrac{3}{4}p - \tfrac{1}{4}p^3 \tag{6.41}$$

The two probabilities are compared in Fig. 6.15.

To interpret the results, it will be assumed that the digital circuit in Fig. 6.14 is turned on at $t = 0$ and initially the probability of each digital circuit's being successful is $p = 1.00$. Thus, both the reliability and the probability of successful transmission are unity. If after 1 year of continuous operation $p$ drops to 0.750, the system reliability becomes 0.844; however, the probability that any one message is successfully transmitted is 0.957. To put the result another way, if 1,000 such digital circuits were operated for 1 year, on the average 156 would not be operating properly at that time. However, the mistakes being made by these machines would amount to 43 mistakes per 1,000 on the average. Thus, for the entire group, the error rate would be 4.3 percent after 1 year.

The simple concepts of majority logic introduced in the preceding

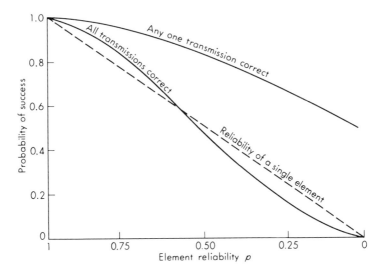

**Fig. 6.15** Comparison of probability of successful transmission and reliability.

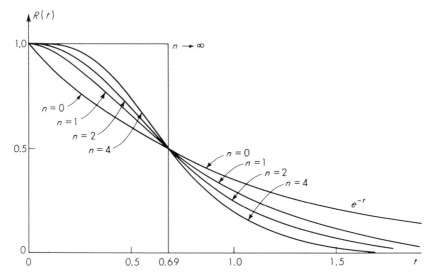

**Fig. 6.16** Reliability of a majority voter containing $2n + 1$ circuits. (*Adapted from J. K. Knox-Seith, A Redundancy Technique for Improving the Reliability of Digital Systems, Stanford Electron. Lab. Tech. Rept. 4816-1, p. 12, December, 1963.*)

example have been considerably extended.[1,2]  If one considers a system of $2n + 1$ (note this is an odd number) parallel digital elements and a single perfect voter, the reliability expression is given by

$$R = \sum_{i=n+1}^{2n+1} B(i:n) = \sum_{i=n+1}^{2n+1} \binom{2n + 1}{i} p^i (1 - p)^{2n+1-i} \tag{6.42}$$

This expression is plotted in Fig. 6.16 for the case of one, three, five, and nine elements assuming that $p = e^{-\lambda t}$. Note that as $n \to \infty$, the MTTF of the system $\to 0.69/\lambda$, and the reliability function approaches the three straight lines shown.

The limiting behavior of Eq. (6.42) for $n \to \infty$ is easily explained by referring to the normal approximation given in Eq. (5.23). Since all elements are identical, $\bar{p} = p$, and we wish $n + 1$ successes out of $2n + 1$ elements. For large values of $n$, the upper limit of integration $i'$ in Eq. (5.23) becomes

$$\lim_{n \to \infty} i' = \frac{(n + 1) - (2n + 1)p}{\sqrt{(2n + 1)p(1 - p)}} \to \lim_{n \to \infty} \frac{n(1 - 2p)}{\sqrt{2np(1 - p)}}$$

[1] W. H. Pierce, Improving the Reliability of Digital Systems by Redundancy and Adaptation, *Stanford Electron. Lab. Tech. Rept.* 1552-3, July 17, 1961.

[2] J. K. Knox-Seith, A Redundancy Technique for Improving the Reliability of Digital Systems, *Stanford Electron. Lab. Tech. Rept.* 4816-1, December, 1963.

The value of $i'$ depends on the value of $p$, and $i'$ determines the area under the integral, which in turn specifies the probability

$$\lim_{n\to\infty} i' = \begin{cases} +\infty \\ 0 \\ -\infty \end{cases} \qquad \lim_{n\to\infty} R(t) = \begin{cases} 0 & 0 < p < \frac{1}{2} \\ \frac{1}{2} & p = \frac{1}{2} \\ 1 & \frac{1}{2} < p < +\infty \end{cases}$$

This of course verifies the limiting behavior shown in Fig. 6.16. The discontinuity occurs at a point in time given by $p = 0.5 = e^{-\lambda t}$. Thus $t = 0.692/\lambda$.

Note that in the above analysis we have assumed a perfect voter, i.e., one with a reliability equal to unity. Shortly we shall discard this assumption and assign a more realistic reliability to voting elements. However, before we investigate the effect of the voter it is germane to study the benefits of partitioning the original system into subsystems and using voting techniques on the subsystem level.

Assume that a digital system is composed of $m$ series subsystems. Each subsystem has a constant failure rate $\lambda$, and voting is to be applied at the subsystem level. The majority voting circuit is shown in Fig. 6.17. Since this configuration is just $m$ independent series groups of the same configuration as previously considered, the reliability is simply given by Eq. (6.42) raised to the $m$th power.

$$R = \left[ \sum_{i=n+1}^{2n+1} \binom{2n+1}{i} p_{ss}^{i}(1 - p_{ss})^{2n+1-i} \right]^{m} \tag{6.43}$$

where $p_{ss}$ is the subsystem reliability.

The subsystem reliability $p_{ss}$ is of course not equal to $p$. In fact, if we assume all subsystems are identical, then $p_{ss} = e^{-\lambda t/m}$, where $\lambda$ is the system hazard. Making this substitution in Eq. (6.43) yields $R(t)$ for the system of Fig. 6.17. Numerical computations of the system

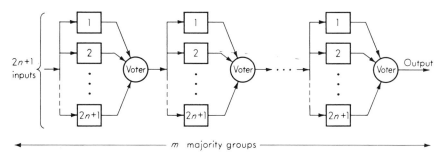

Total number of circuits $= (2n+1)\,m$

**Fig. 6.17** Component redundancy and majority voting.

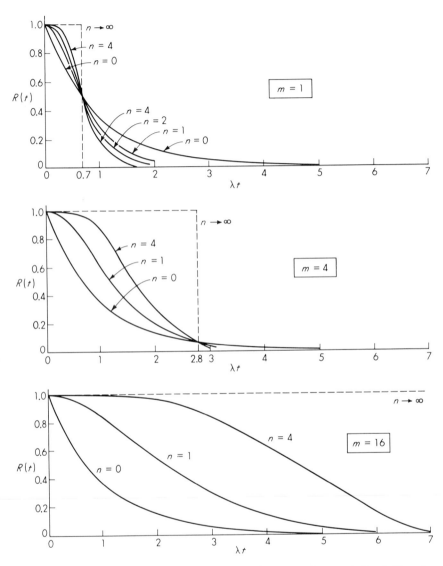

**Fig. 6.18**   Reliability for a system with $m$ majority vote takers and $(2n + 1)m$ circuits. (*Adapted from J. K. Knox-Seith, A Redundancy Technique for Improving the Reliability of Digital Systems, Stanford Electron. Lab. Tech. Rept. 4816-1, p. 19, December, 1963.*)

reliability are plotted for several values of $m$ and $n$ in Fig. 6.18.    Knox-
Seith points out that as $n \to \infty$ the MTTF $\approx 0.7m/\lambda$. This is, of
course, a direct consequence of the limiting behavior of Eq. (6.42), as
previously discussed.

In the analysis presented so far in this section we have assumed that
the voter itself cannot fail.    This is of course untrue; in fact intuition
tells us that if the voter is poor, its unreliability will wipe out the gains
of the redundancy scheme. Returning to the example of Fig. 6.14, the
digital-circuit reliability will be called $p_c$ and the voter reliability $p_v$.
The system reliability formerly given by Eq. (6.37) must be modified so
that

$$R = p_v(3p_c^2 - 2p_c^3) = p_v p_c^2(3 - 2p_c) \qquad (6.44)$$

In order to achieve an overall gain, the voting scheme must be better
than a single element, and

$$R > p_c \qquad \text{or} \qquad \frac{R}{p_c} > 1$$

Obviously this requires that

$$\frac{R}{p_c} = p_v p_c(3 - 2p_c) > 1 \qquad (6.45)$$

The minimum value of $p_v$ for reliability improvement can be computed
by setting $p_v p_c(3 - 2p_c) = 1$.    A plot of $p_c(3 - 2p_c)$ is given in Fig. 6.19.

Since $p_v$ is a probability $0 < p_v < 1$, the majority-voter system is an
improvement only if $0.5 < p_c < 1.0$.    (This result of course agrees with
the lower curve shown in Fig. 6.15.)    The minimum $p_c$ value is $\frac{8}{9}$, which
occurs in the vicinity of $p_c = 0.75$, where $p_c(3 - 2p_c) = \frac{9}{8}$.    The minimum value of $p_v$ for various numbers of redundant circuits is given in
Table 6.7, which shows that the voter element must be considerably
better than each digital channel is, and if $p_v < 0.75$, no combination will
result in improvement.

Before leaving the subject of majority voting we should speak briefly
about how one can realize a voter.    One approach is to synthesize a

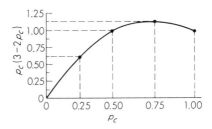

**Fig. 6.19**    Plot of function $p_c(3 - 2p_c)$
vs. $p_c$.

**Table 6.7** **Minimum voter reliability**

| Number of redundant circuits $2n + 1$ | 3 | 5 | 7 | 9 | 11 | $\infty$ |
|---|---|---|---|---|---|---|
| Minimum voter reliability $p_v$ | 0.889 | 0.837 | 0.807 | 0.789 | 0.777 | 0.75 |

SOURCE: N. T. Grisamone, Calculation of Circuit Reliability by Use of von Neumann Redundancy Logic Analysis, *IEEE Proc. Fourth Ann. N.Y. Conf. Electron. Reliability*, October, 1963.

majority-voting function from logic gates. The logic function for a three-input voter is given by

$$f = x_1x_2 + x_1x_3 + x_2x_3 \qquad (6.46)$$

This function can be verified by reference to the truth table given in Table 6.8.[1]

Two logic realizations for the switching function given in Eq. (6.46) are shown in Fig. 6.20. (In order to simplify the output logic expression in Fig. 6.20$b$ we have used De Morgan's theorem, which was discussed in Prob. 2.5.)

In order to appreciate how we can physically construct the circuit of Fig. 6.20 (or in fact those of Figs. 6.9 and 6.11) we must briefly discuss logic realization techniques. Of the many different logic schemes integrated-circuit techniques are probably superior in most cases. It is

---

[1] One must also use the following identities: $0 \cdot 0 = 0$, $0 \cdot 1 = 0$, $1 \cdot 1 = 1$, $0 + 0 = 0$, $0 + 1 = 1$, $1 + 1 = 1$.

**Table 6.8 A truth table for a three-input majority voter**

| Inputs | | | Output | |
|---|---|---|---|---|
| $x_1$ | $x_2$ | $x_3$ | $f = x_1x_2 + x_1x_3 + x_2x_3$ | |
| 0 | 0 | 0 | 0 | Two or |
| 0 | 0 | 1 | 0 | three |
| 0 | 1 | 0 | 0 | zeros |
| 1 | 0 | 0 | 0 | |
| 1 | 1 | 0 | 1 | Two or |
| 1 | 0 | 1 | 1 | three |
| 0 | 1 | 1 | 1 | ones |
| 1 | 1 | 1 | 1 | |

probably possible for many subsystems to include the redundant groups as well as the voter on the same circuit chip.  If this is possible, we probably pay a rather small reliability penalty for the addition of the voter.  (See the example in Sec. 6.6.3.)  Because of the specialized nature of integrated-circuit logic we shall focus our attention on a simpler logic scheme, resistor-transistor logic.  Detailed analysis shows that it is simpler to build NAND and NOR gates with transistors than AND and OR gates.  A simplified transistor-resistor circuit which can serve as a NAND or NOR gate, depending on the resistance values, is shown in Fig. 6.21a.

For our purposes we can view a transistor as a controlled switch.  When the base current is zero or very small, we can think of the connection between collector and emitter as an open circuit, which forces $i_c = 0$. If $i_c = 0$, the voltage drop across resistor $R$ is zero, and the output voltage equals $+E$ volts.  (This is called the *nonconducting* or *off state* of the transistor.)  The base-to-emitter connection looks like a very low impedance, and the base current is approximately given by

$$i_b = \frac{e_a}{R_1} + \frac{e_b}{R_2}$$

If the base current exceeds a certain value, which we will call $i_{b,\text{on}}$, the collector-to-emitter connection becomes a short circuit.  (This is called

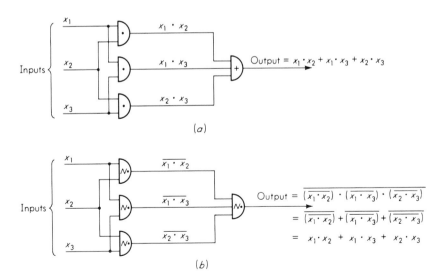

**Fig. 6.20**  Logic realization of majority voters.  (*a*) A majority voter consisting of three AND gates and one OR gate; (*b*) a majority voter consisting of four NAND gates.

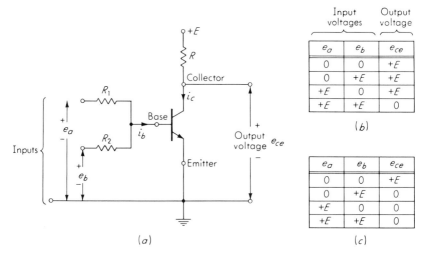

**Fig. 6.21** Resistor-transistor circuit realization of NAND and NOR gates. (*a*) Resistor-transistor logic; (*b*) NAND truth table; (*c*) NOR truth table.

the *conducting* or *on state* of the transistor.) Since the voltage output is across this short circuit, the output is zero. (Another way of showing the same result is to consider that the voltage drop across the resistor $Ri_c$ must equal $-E$.) In the case of the NAND circuit we size the input currents so that neither one can turn on the transistor alone, but both are needed.[1] If we assume that the input voltages $e_a$ and $e_b$ are either 0 or $+E$ volts, we adjust $R_1$ and $R_2$ such that $R_1 = R_2$ and

$$i_{b,\text{on}} \leq \frac{e_a}{R_1} + \frac{e_b}{R_2} = \frac{2E}{R_1}$$

but

$$i_{b,\text{on}} \geq \frac{e_a}{R_1} = \frac{e_b}{R_2} = \frac{E}{R_1}$$

In the case of the NOR circuit we size $R_1$ and $R_2$ such that either input can turn on the transistor, that is, $R_1 = R_2$, and

$$i_{b,\text{on}} \leq \frac{e_a}{R_1} = \frac{e_b}{R_2} = \frac{E}{R_1}$$

[1] Actually we have oversimplified the circuit—there is generally another voltage source and resistor which supplies a fixed negative-bias component to current $i_b$ to make certain that a single input does not supply enough positive current to partially turn the transistor on.

If we compare the truth tables given in Fig. 6.21$b$ and $c$ with Fig. 6.9$e$ and $d$, we see that as long as $+E$ represents a 1 the logic is identical. Additional inputs can be realized using additional voltages and sources at the base.

Knowing that we can build a two-input NAND gate using three resistors and a transistor, we can see that realization of the voter shown in Fig. 6.20 will take four transistors and nine resistors. In general, a $(n + 1)$-out-of-$(2n + 1)$ voter requires[1]

$$\text{Transistors} = \binom{2n + 1}{n + 1} + 1$$
$$\text{Resistors} = (n + 2) \binom{2n + 1}{n + 1}$$

We can reduce the number of components by designing a special-purpose voter, shown in Fig. 6.22. The output of this circuit is given by

$$\text{Output} = R_c\beta \left( \frac{e_1}{R_1} + \frac{e_2}{R_2} + \frac{e_3}{R_3} - \frac{e_4}{R_4} \right)$$

If $e_1 = e_2 = e_3 = e_4 = e_0$, $R_1 = R_2 = R_3 = R$, and $R_4 = R/1.5$, then the output is given by

$$\text{Output} = R_c\beta \left( \frac{e_0}{R} + \frac{e_0}{R} + \frac{e_0}{R} - 1.5 \frac{e_0}{R} \right)$$

With no inputs or one input, the output is negative (called *zero*), and with two or three inputs, the output is positive (called *one*). In some cases additional circuit would be added to change positive voltage and negative voltage into one and zero.

[1] Again we have oversimplified and neglected bias resistors.

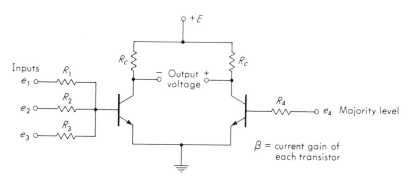

**Fig. 6.22** A two-transistor majority voter.

The circuit in Fig. 6.22 requires only two transistors and six resistors. In general, we need[1]

Transistors $= 2$
Resistors $= 2n + 4$

The details of optimum voter-circuit design are best left to an experienced integrated-circuit or lumped-circuit designer.

More sophisticated techniques of voting redundancy generally follow two approaches. In one case the system still functions as a voter but the voting law is not a simple majority function and changes with time, depending upon system operation. Such a system is called an *adaptive voter* and is discussed in Sec. 6.7.5. The other techniques center about attempts to make a universal highly reliable logic circuit (organ). Since it can be shown than any logic function can be constructed from interconnections of NAND elements, the NAND gate is used as the building block. The concept is briefly discussed below.

The original paper on majority logic to improve redundancy was written by von Neumann.[2] He developed the basic idea of majority voting into a sophisticated scheme with many NAND elements in parallel. Each input to the NAND element is supplied by a bundle of $N$ identical inputs, and the $2N$ inputs are cross-coupled so that each NAND element has one input from each bundle. These ideas were extended in an attempt to give a logical model for the human nervous system and to explain how so many interconnections function almost error-free in man. The mathematical aspects of von Neumann's work can be found in the cited reference.

### 6.7.3  REDUNDANT SWITCHES

In the preceding section we discussed various techniques for improving reliability by applying redundancy on the gate, subsystem, and system level. In this section, we shall go inside the logic gate and apply redundancy to the controlled switches from which it is made.

One can show that any logic function can be reduced to a form where it can be realized by combinations of AND plus OR gates or NAND gates alone. AND and OR gates can each be constructed from two controlled switches. In the early days of switching theory (which preceded logic theory) the most complicated networks encountered were telephone switching networks, where relays acted as the controlled switches. An AND gate and an OR gate can be made from two transistors as shown

---

[1] There are practical limits to the number of input resistors which can be used.

[2] J. von Neumann, Probabilistic Logics and the Synthesis of Reliable Organisms from Unreliable Components, in C. E. Shannon and J. McCarthy (eds.), "Automata Studies," Princeton University Press, Princeton, N.J., 1956.

in Fig. 6.23.[1]   The circuits can be used as gates, i.e., producing a voltage $+E$ representing a 1 and a voltage 0 representing a zero.   Also one can apply them as a switching circuit,[2] where a closed circuit is a 1 and an open circuit a 0.   Thus, we have shown that all logic functions can be realized by appropriate combinations of transistor switches.   We now turn our attention to the problem of how to make a transistor switch more reliable by redundancy.[3]

In a classical paper,[4] Moore and Shannon investigated in depth techniques for improving the reliability of controlled switches.   The paper in question considers relays as the switching elements, but, we can equally well apply their results to networks containing transistor switches. The symbol for a controlled switch which is normally open is shown in Fig. 6.24$a$.   The control variable is $x$, that is, the switch is open when $x_1 = 0$ and closed when $x_1 = 1$.   We assume that the controlled switch is represented by a three-state model: state 1 good, state 2 stuck opened, and state 3 stuck closed.   The two switches in series shown in Fig. 6.24$b$

[1] One might argue that the NAND and NOR gates shown in Fig. 6.21 are simpler since they only use one transistor.

[2] This assumes that we are always switching a positive direct current; i.e., the voltage from $c_1$ to ground is always positive.   A circuit which switches either positive and negative direct currents or alternating currents requires a more complex design.

[3] The transistor is actually quite a reliable element.   The data given in Fig. 4.8 predict a MTTF of 50 to 500 years.   This is not so impressive when one considers that a modern digital computer contains 50,000 transistors which reduces the computer MTTF to between 8.7 and 87 hours.   Stanford Research Institute is investigating the preliminary design of a future computer containing $10^{11}$ active components!

[4] E. F. Moore and C. E. Shannon, Reliable Circuits Using Less Reliable Relays, *J. Franklin Inst.*, pt. 2, October, 1956.

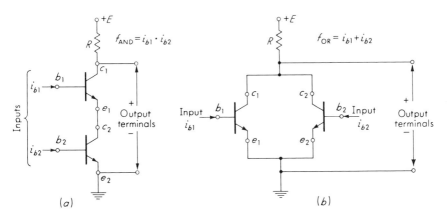

**Fig. 6.23**  Transistor switch AND and OR gates.   ($a$) A transistor AND gate; ($b$) a transistor OR gate.

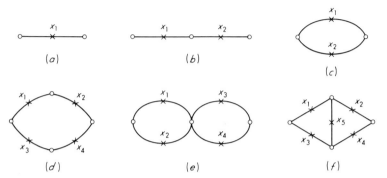

Note: The inputs of all switches are connected together, i.e., $x_1 = x_2 = x_3 = x_4 = x_5$.

**Fig. 6.24**  Some simple networks of controlled switches.  (a) A normally open controlled switch; (b) two series switches; (c) two parallel switches; (d) four switches series-parallel; (e) four switches parallel-series; (f) a five-switch bridge circuit.

are both driven by the same input variable, that is, $x_1 = x_2$.  The series arrangement reduces the probability of failure due to a short circuit but increases the probability of open failures.  If the converse is true, the parallel configuration shown in Fig. 6.24c is superior.  Circuits in Fig. 6.24d to f are more complicated arrangements which reduce the probability of system failure due to either opens or shorts.  A transistor switching circuit equivalent to the bridge circuit of Fig. 6.24f is shown in Fig. 6.25.  The transistor circuit should not be viewed as the direct equivalent of Fig. 6.24f, since in the latter all switches are independent whereas in

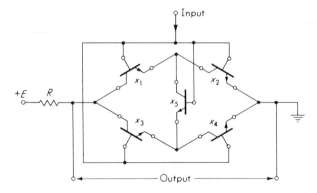

**Fig. 6.25**  A bridge network of controlled switches.

Fig. 6.25 all elements may not be independent. (This is especially true of switch $x_5$, which will behave differently when current flows down than when it flows up through the switch.)

Since we have assumed that a controlled switch has two modes of failure, stuck open and stuck closed, we must use a three-state model. Moore and Shannon developed a clever approach to avoid this complication. The reliability of a single switch can be written as

$$P_S = 1 - P(Q_c + Q_o)$$

where $Q_c \equiv$ switch (stuck) closed with no signal applied
$\quad\ \ Q_o \equiv$ switch (stuck) open with signal applied
Since the two events are disjoint,

$$P_S = 1 - P(Q_c) - P(Q_o) = 1 - q_c - q_o \qquad (6.47)$$

where

$$P(Q_c) = q_c \qquad P(Q_o) = q_o$$

Now suppose we have a network composed of several switches, as Fig. 6.24b. The probability that the circuit is stuck closed can be written in terms of the circuit probabilities of being stuck in the open or closed position

$$R = 1 - P(Q'_c) - P(Q'_o) \qquad (6.48)$$

where $Q'_c \equiv$ circuit (stuck) closed with no signal applied
$\quad\ \ Q'_o \equiv$ circuit (stuck) open with a signal applied
The probability that the circuit is failed closed $P(Q'_c)$ is given by the probability-of-closure expression with $q_c$ substituted for $c$, that is, if the switches are IIU,

$$P(Q'_c) = P(Q_{c_1})P(Q_{c_2}) = q_c{}^2$$

Similarly for IIU

$$P(Q'_o) = P(Q_{o_1} + Q_{o_2}) = P(Q_{o_1}) + P(Q_{o_2}) - P(Q_{o_1})P(Q_{o_2}) = 2q_o - q_o{}^2$$

We can now observe that the expressions $P(Q'_c)$ and $P(Q'_o)$ are symmetrical in the sense that one expression can be obtained from the other by algebraic manipulation. We see that

$$P(Q'_c) = q_c q_c$$
$$P(Q_o) = P(Q_{o_1} + Q_{o_2}) = 1 - P(\bar{Q}_{o_1}\bar{Q}_{o_2}) = 1 - P(\bar{Q}_{o_1})P(\bar{Q}_{o_2})$$
$$= 1 - (1 - q_o)(1 - q_o)$$

If we write a probability-of-closure expression for the circuit,

$$P(C) = P(C_1)P(C_2)$$

we can simply write $P(Q'_c)$ and $P(Q'_o)$ as

$$P(Q'_c) \rightarrow P(C_1)P(\bar{C}_2) \rightarrow q_c{}^2$$
$$P(Q'_o) \rightarrow 1 - P(\bar{C}_1)P(\bar{C}_2) \rightarrow 1 - (1 - q_o)(1 - q_o)$$

This same approach can be extended to more complex networks.

The quantities $P(C)$, $P(Q'_o)$, $P(Q'_c)$, and $R$ are given in Table 6.9 for all the circuits of Fig. 6.24. These expressions are numerically evaluated for the specific case where $q_o = q_c = 0.1$ in Table 6.10.

Of course the purpose of these circuits is to replace each single switch by a switching network with higher reliability: Thus, if we put circuit $a$ in a black box with a left-hand input terminal and a right-hand output terminal, it is a controlled switch with reliability = 0.8. If circuit $f$ is placed in a black box, it will be a controlled switch with a reliability equal to 0.956. Inspection of Table 6.10 shows that while circuit $b$ decreases the probability of a stuck-closed failure, it increases the probability of an open failure. The overall reliability of this network is still the same as a single switch. Circuit $c$ behaves in the same manner as circuit $b$ except that the roles of stuck open and stuck closed are interchanged. Circuits like these which have the same behavior when $q_o$ and $q_c$ are interchanged are called *duals*. A circuit like $f$, which behaves the same for stuck open and stuck closed, is called a *self-dual*.

Moore and Shannon go on to point out several other interesting properties of switching-circuit reliability. A plot of any $P(C)$ function vs. $C$ is S-shaped. Several examples of such curves were plotted in Fig. 3.5. In fact, the lower curve in Fig. 6.15 is such an S-shaped curve. They prove in their paper that the S-shaped curve will intersect the single-element straight line no more than once, and as more and more elements are used, the slope at the crossover point becomes steeper [see Fig. 6.16 and the discussion following Eq. (6.42)].

There are three general techniques for building more complex networks from elementary networks: (1) connecting the networks in series, (2) connecting the networks in parallel, and (3) substituting for each branch of the first network a copy of the second network (Fig. 6.26). The probability-of-closure expressions $P(C)$ for the networks are shown in Fig. 6.26 in terms of the component closure probabilities. In the case of a series network $P(C)$ is just the product of $P_1(C_1)$ and $P_2(C_2)$. In the parallel case it is unity minus the product. In the substituted case, the probabilities $P_2(C_2)$ are computed and substituted for $C_1$ in the $P_1(C_1)$ expression to find the overall reliability $P(C)$.

The networks in Fig. 6.24 were chosen by intuition in expectation that they would constitute interesting or important structures. There is a more general technique for formulating switching networks. The classification is an outgrowth of a general procedure for writing down the prob-

**Table 6.9 Switching-circuit failure probabilities and reliabilities**

| Circuit | $P(C)$ | $P(Q'_o)$ | $P(Q'_c)$ | $R$ |
|---|---|---|---|---|
| (a) | $C$ | $q_o$ | $q_c$ | $1 - q_o - q_c$ |
| (b) | $C^2$ | $2q_o - q_o^2$ | $q_c^2$ | $1 - 2q_o + q_o^2 - q_c^2$ |
| (c) | $2C - C^2$ | $q_o^2$ | $2q_c - q_c^2$ | $1 - q_o^2 - 2q_o + q_c^2$ |
| (d) | $2C^2 - C^4$ | $4q_o^2 - 4q_o^3 + q_o^4$ | $2q_c^2 - q_c^4$ | $1 - P(Q'_o) - P(Q'_c)$ |
| (e) | $(2C - C^2)^2$ | $2q_o^2 - q_o^4$ | $(2q_c - q_c^2)^2$ | $1 - P(Q'_o) - P(Q'_c)$ |
| (f) | $2C^2 + 2C^3 - 5C^4 + 2C^5$ | $2q_o^2 + 2q_o^3 - 5q_o^4 + 2q_o^5$ | $2q_c^2 + 2q_c^3 - 5q_c^4 + 2q_c^5$ | $1 - P(Q'_o) - P(Q'_c)$ |

**Table 6.10  Switching-circuit failure probabilities and reliabilities for circuits of Table 6.9 with $q_o = q_c = 0.1$**

| Circuit | Probability of stuck open | Probability of stuck closed | Reliability |
|---|---|---|---|
| (a) | 0.1 | 0.1 | 0.8 |
| (b) | 0.19 | 0.01 | 0.8 |
| (c) | 0.01 | 0.19 | 0.8 |
| (d) | 0.0396 | 0.0199 | 0.9405 |
| (e) | 0.0199 | 0.0396 | 0.9405 |
| (f) | 0.02152 | 0.02152 | 0.95606 |

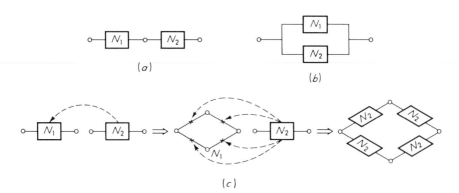

**Fig. 6.26**  Combinations of switching networks.  (a) Series networks $P(C) = P_1(C_1) P_2(C_2)$; (b) parallel networks $P(C) = 1 - P_1(C_1)P_2(C_2)$; (c) substituted networks $P(C) = P_1[P_2(C_2)]$.

ability-of-closure expression for any switching network. This latter analysis technique will be discussed first. The probability of closure for any switching network can be written as

$$P(C) = \sum_{n=0}^{m} A_n C^n (1 - C)^{m-n} \tag{6.49}$$

where $m$ = total number of switches
  $n$ = number of switches in any grouping which form a closed path from input to output
  $A_n$ = number of different groupings for each value of $n$ = probability that any one of the $n$ identical switches close

As an illustration of the use of Eq. (6.49), this calculation procedure is used to compute $P(C)$ for circuits $d$ and $f$ of Table 6.9. The details of these computations are shown in Table 6.11.

On the basis of Eq. (6.49), one can characterize a switching network in terms of the minimum path length $l$ and the number of parallel elements $w$. When all the paths are of equal length $l$ and $w$ is the same at each stage, the network has many symmetrical properties. Three networks of length 5 and width 3 are shown in Fig. 6.27$a$ to $c$. In each case the network contains $lw = 15$ contacts. Networks $b$ and $c$ may both be viewed as an evolution of $a$. To obtain network $b$ four vertical shorting bars are added, and to obtain network $c$, eight vertical shorting bars are

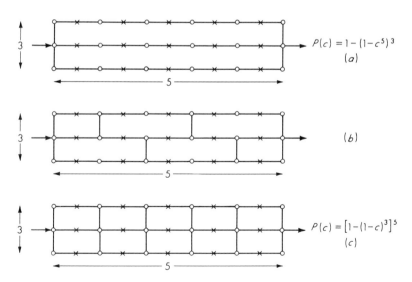

**Fig. 6.27** Evolution of hammock networks. ($a$) Three parallel chains five contacts long; ($b$) a 3 × 5 hammock network; ($c$) five series sets of three parallel contacts.

**Table 6.11   Computation of $P(C)$ using Eq. (6.49)**

| Network | $n = 2$ groups | $n = 3$ groups | $n = 4$ groups |
|---|---|---|---|
| $m = 4$ | $2c^2(1-c)^2$ | $4c^3(1-c)$ | $c^4$ |

$$P(c) = 2c^2(1 - c)^2 + 4c^3(1 - c) + c^4 = 2c^2 - c^4$$

| Network | $n = 2$ groups | $n = 3$ groups | $n = 4$ groups | $n = 5$ groups |
|---|---|---|---|---|
| $m = 5$ | $2c^2(1-c)^3$ | $8c^3(1-c)^2$ | $5c^4(1-c)$ | $c^5$ |

$$P(c) = 2c^2(1 - c)^3 + 8c^3(1 - c)^2 + 5c^4(1 - c) + c^5 = 2c^2 + 2c^3 - 5c^4 + 2c^5$$

added. The name *hammock network*, used by Moore and Shannon, was probably due to the meshlike appearance of the network when the nodes connected by the shorting bars are collapsed. These networks form an interesting class of switching networks, but they are not all-inclusive, since even the simple and useful bridge network of Fig. 6.24f is not included, one path being of length 3 and two paths of length 2.

The hammock networks are important since we can write bound relations for networks in general and even sharper ones for hammock networks in particular. For any switching network with normally open switches the following inequality holds

$$m \geq \frac{\log \delta_1}{\log q_c} \frac{\log \delta_2}{\log q_o} \qquad (6.50)[1]$$

where
$m$ = total number of switches in networks
$q_o$ = probability that a single switch is stuck open
$q_c$ = probability that a single switch is stuck closed
$P(q_c) \leq \delta_1$ = probability of network stuck open when switches are energized
$P(1 - q_o) \geq 1 - \delta_2$ = probability of network closure when switches are energized

To illustrate the application of this theorem suppose that $q_o = q_c = 0.1$ and that for the overall network we wish $\delta_1 = \delta_2 = 10^{-6}$, that is, to improve the reliability of a single relay from 0.8 to 0.999998 for the network. Thus, a lower bound on $m$ is given by Eq. (6.50)

$$m \geq \frac{\log 10^{-6}}{\log 10^{-1}} \frac{\log 10^{-6}}{\log 10^{-1}} = 36$$

For the class of hammock networks with normally open switches we can further show that[2]

$$\delta_1 \leq \left( \frac{1 - \sqrt{1 - 16q_c^2}}{4q_c} \right)^{l-1} wq_c \qquad (6.51)$$

$$\delta_2 \leq \left( \frac{1 - \sqrt{1 - 16q_o^2}}{4q_o} \right)^{w-1} lq_o \qquad (6.52)$$

In the case where $q_o$ and $q_c$ are small, Eqs. (6.51) and (6.52) become approximately

$$\delta_1 \leq (2q_c)^{l-1} wq_c$$
$$\delta_2 \leq (2q_o)^{w-1} lq_o$$

For a $9 \times 9$ hammock network, substitution in Eq. (6.51) yields $\delta_1 \leq 2.29 \times 10^{-6}$, and for a $10 \times 10$ hammock network $\delta_1 \leq 0.512 \times 10^{-6}$.

[1] *Ibid.*
[2] *Ibid.*

Since this network is a self-dual, we obtain the same values for $\delta_2$. Thus, around 80 to 100 switches would suffice for the example under discussion.

Another technique is to substitute a $3 \times 3$ hammock network into each branch of another $3 \times 3$ hammock network. Applying Eq. (6.51) for $3 \times 3$ network yields $\delta_1 = \delta_2 \leq 12 \times 10^{-3}$. For a second cycle, we substitute $\delta_1$ and $\delta_2$ for $q_o$ and $q_c$ in Eq. (6.51), obtaining $\delta'_1 = \delta'_2 \leq 20.6 \times 10^{-6}$. This technique is a little less efficient than using a $9 \times 9$ hammock network. It is probable that other relay networks with $36 \leq m \leq 81$ could be devised which would satisfy the specifications in a more efficient manner.

The reader may argue that to replace a single switch with 80 others for improved reliability sounds grossly impractical; however, this is not necessarily the case. In the first place, improvements in $q_o$ and $q_s$ from $10^{-1}$ to $10^{-6}$ are rather extreme, and second, using integrated-circuit techniques, an 80-switch network might not be at all unreasonable. In fact this might be a good way of overcoming low yields in the fabrication of integrated switching circuits. In effect, it might become unnecessary to test for certain fabrication errors in an integrated circuit if sufficient redundancy were employed.

### 6.7.4 REDUNDANT CODES

All communication systems and some control systems face the problem of transmitting a message or data without error. Whenever we use some symbolic representation for components of a message, we are using a code. We have already discussed how the binary and decimal number systems can be used to represent numerical data. Similarly, we can represent language by English letters or Chinese characters. The measures of merit for such a system are: (1) the reliability, or probability of no errors in a time interval or for a certain number of messages, and (2) the error rate, or probability that any particular message is incorrect.

Most codes which are used have three important features: code redundancy, error detection, and error correction. The term *redundancy*, when used in the coding sense, means that not all characters or combinations of the code have meaning and we can detect certain errors by knowing the facts. For example, if the word transmitted is "me" but we actually receive the word "xe," we know that a mistake has been made but cannot correct it since there are many two-letter words ending in "e." In fact, if we had received the word "be," we would have detected no error since this is a perfectly legitimate word. If we received the word "thr," we can detect an error and could probably correct the message. Discounting "tho," the only three-letter English words beginning with "th" are "the" and "thy." The rest of the message or the fact that "thy" is archaic would generally allow us to correct "thr" to "the."

As a further example, let us assume that the reader has received the following telegram from a prospective employer: "Positiop now avxilable. Can bou sta4t July 1? Annual sal23y $24,000." Because of the redundancy in the English language one could easily detect and correct the errors in the words in the message.    The date might be wrong, but we could not detect such an error unless we knew the date to be *illogical*, e.g., 10 days ago or July 37.    We certainly cannot detect or correct the salary if there is an error because there is no redundancy in the decimal number system, since every combination is a number.    (If the job in question were a teaching position, the error in salary would be apparent enough.)

We shall focus our attention on digital data transmission, which essentially amounts to transmittal of a sequence of zeros and ones.    An obvious technique for introducing redundancy is to repeat each digit. If we repeat each digit twice, then as long as the two agree, we know that either both digits are right or both are wrong.    If the two digits differ, we have detected a single error, where one digit is right and one is wrong, but we cannot tell which is which.    Clearly we want to repeat our transmission of each digit an odd number of times and represent our transmission as a zero or one depending on the majority of the received digits. Obviously this reduces to a majority-voter system, and the techniques of Sec. 6.7.2 are applicable.

Another technique of mechanizing a redundant code is to add a single check bit (often called a *parity bit*) to each number transmitted.    The check bit is chosen as a zero or a one in order that each transmission contain an even or odd number of ones.    For example, suppose we are to transmit the digits 0 to 9 using the binary number system.    This would normally require four digits; however, an added "even" check bit is shown in Table 6.12.    Thus, as we transmit information we check the number of ones in each word.    A moment's thought will show that we can use the binary half-adder circuit to accomplish this.    We feed the first two digits to the two inputs and examine the sum output.    A one at the sum output indicates an odd number of ones for the input.    The output is then "circulated" to the input and compared with the next digit.

If we obtain an even number of ones, we are fairly sure the answer is correct, since a one-, three- or five-digit error would be detected.    However, a two- or four-bit error would still produce an even number of ones. Thus, if we have no check bit, the probability of obtaining at least one error in a four-bit word is given by

$$P_E = 1 - p^4 = 1 - (1 - q)^4 \qquad (6.53)$$

where $p$ = probability a single bit is correct
$q = 1 - p$

**Table 6.12  A five-bit code with an even check bit**

| | Code word | | Number of 1s |
|---|---|---|---|
| Number | Binary code | Check bit | in code word |
| 0 | 0000 | 0 | 0 |
| 1 | 0001 | 1 | 2 |
| 2 | 0010 | 1 | 2 |
| 3 | 0011 | 0 | 2 |
| 4 | 0100 | 1 | 2 |
| 5 | 0101 | 0 | 2 |
| 6 | 0110 | 0 | 2 |
| 7 | 0111 | 1 | 4 |
| 8 | 1000 | 1 | 2 |
| 9 | 1001 | 0 | 2 |

The probability that an error occurs and is not detected $P_{E,\mathrm{nd}}$ is the same as the probability that the error occurs, since we have no redundancy. With our five-bit even check code, the probability of obtaining a two- and a four-bit error is given by

$$P_{2E} = \binom{5}{2} q^2 p^3 = 10q^2 p^3$$

$$P_{4E} = \binom{5}{4} q^4 p = 5q^4 p$$

The probability that an error occurs and is not detected for the five-bit system, $P'_{E,\mathrm{nd}}$, is given by

$$P'_{E,\mathrm{nd}} = P_{2E} + P_{4E} = 5q^2 p(2p^2 + q^2) \tag{6.54}$$

To compare Eqs. (6.53) and (6.54) we examine the ratio $P'_{E,\mathrm{nd}}/P_{E,\mathrm{nd}}$ for $q \ll 1$

$$\frac{P'_{E,\mathrm{nd}}}{P_{E,\mathrm{nd}}} = \frac{1 - (1 - q)^4}{10q^2(1 - q)^3(1 + q^2/2p^2)}$$

$$\approx \frac{4q}{10q^2(1 - 3q)(1 + q^2/2p^2)} \approx \frac{2}{5q}(1 + 3q)$$

Thus, if $q = 0.1$, there is about a 5:1 reduction in undetected errors, and if $q = 0.01$ the improvement is 41:1. Other more sophisticated schemes for error detection and correction can be found in the literature.[1]

[1] Jack Wolf, Notes on Coding for Course EE115, Department of Electrical Engineering, Polytechnic Institute of Brooklyn, New York, September, 1966; Yaohan Chu, "Digital Computer Design Fundamentals," p. 78, McGraw-Hill Book Company, New York, 1962.

### 6.7.5 ADAPTIVE SCHEMES

In recent years engineers have become increasingly interested in the remarkable ability of a human organism to act as a sensor, computer, and control system.   One of the prime features of such behavior is the ability of the organism to adapt to changes in the environment so as to restructure its behavior and operate satisfactorily under new circumstances. For example, a human being can react to the loss of certain neural pathways by retraining others to do the same task.

Reasoning along these lines, we might try to devise a complex system which would respond to failures by restructuring itself so that it could still perform its mission.   To be more specific, let us assume that we are dealing with a complex control system and that we define success as a stable system and failure as an unstable system.   We assume one can detect system stability and that each of the $m$ system variables can be changed in steps to try and obtain a stable system.   Thus, if the system is initially unstable, the parameters are randomly switched until a stable state is found, and the system settles down to operate in this state.   If a failure occurs, the process repeats itself until stability is reestablished. Assuming one could build such a system,[1] perhaps the first question to ask is how long it would take to establish stability.   If we assume that the probability of stability is $p$ and instability $q$, then the number of trials $n$ needed to reach stability has the geometric distribution

$$P(n) = q^{n-1}p$$

The average number of trials is given by the expected value:

$$E(n) = \sum_{n-1}^{\infty} nq^{n-1}p = p(1 + 2q + 3q^2 + \cdots + nq^{n-1} + \cdots)$$

$$= \frac{p}{(1-q)^2} \quad (6.55)$$

$$= \frac{p}{p^2} = \frac{1}{p}$$

Thus, the expected number of trials is the reciprocal of the probability of stability.   To evaluate $p$, we could assume that each of the parameters has two states, 0 or 1, and that only one combination would yield a stable system.   Thus, $p = 1/2^m$ and $E(n) = 2^m$.   If $m = 100$, $2^{100} \approx 10^{30}$. If we allow $10^9$ switchings per second (about as fast as a good switching transistor can go) and assume $3 \times 10^7$ sec per year, we need about $3 \times 10^{13}$ years.   Obviously any system built along these lines must have

---

[1] H. S. Tsien, "Engineering Cybernetics," chap. 17, McGraw-Hill Book Company, New York, 1954.

either a smaller number of variables or more good combinations so that $E(n)$ is within reason. This same philosophy of adaptive behavior can be mechanized in other ways.

Another technique is to make an adaptive majority voter.[1] An ordinary majority voter may be visualized as a device which takes the average of the outputs and gives a one output if the average is $>0.5$ and zero output if the average is $<0.5$. An adaptive voter may be viewed as a weighted sum where each output $X_i$ is weighted by a coefficient $a_i$. The coefficient $a_i$ could be adjusted to equal the probability that the output $X_i$ was correct. Thus, the adaptive-voter test quantity would be

$$\frac{a_1 X_1 + a_2 X_2 + \cdots + a_{2n+1} X_{2n+1}}{a_1 + a_2 + \cdots + a_{2n+1}} \tag{6.56}$$

The coefficients $a_1$ can be adjusted by taking statistics on the agreement between $X_i$ and the voter output. Another technique is to periodically transmit test inputs and compare each output $X_i$ with the known correct output. In effect, if some $X_i$ is frequently in error, it should be disconnected. The adaptive voter adjusts $a_i$ to be a very small number, which is in essence the same thing. The reliability of the adaptive-voter scheme is superior to the ordinary voter; however, there are many problems in realizing an adaptive voter in practice.

Another adaptive scheme is based upon the fact that logic functions can be made up of standard combinations of *canonical* terms. By providing more than the minimum number of such canonical terms, redundancy is introduced. The system inputs are acted upon by a canonical-term generator. The canonical terms are included or excluded from the output by a set of "statistical" switches. As in the adaptive voter, we assume that there is some means of determining correct performance, and we adjust the switch connections until the correct logic function is obtained. If a failure in one canonical term occurs, the system automatically disconnects that term and reorganizes so as to effect the same logic function by a different combination of canonical terms.[2]

## 6.8 THE HUMAN OPERATOR AS AN ADAPTIVE CONTROLLER

The previous section has established that there is great interest in exploiting adaptive behavior as a means of providing a sophisticated

---

[1] Pierce, *op. cit.*

[2] A Study of the Feasibility of Using Artificial Neurons to Develop More Reliable Flight Control Systems, *Wright-Patterson Air Force Base Tech. Rept.* ASD-TDR-63-143, April, 1963. See also reference to E. Miller in the bibliography for Chap. 6 (page 514) for a micro-programming approach to computer adaptivity.

level of system redundancy. Many of the complex systems which modern technology has developed include a human operator, and it is only natural to try to use his adaptive capabilities.

Most of the studies of how a human being functions in a control system have been aimed at trying to describe his transfer function and how it adapts to varying conditions.[1] Such information is useful in a control analysis of the performance and stability of the system but does not help in describing how a human being affects the reliability of the system.[2] As an illustration of how the human being can enhance system reliability, the role of an astronaut in controlling a spacecraft will be discussed.

Project Mercury marked the beginning of the United States manned space-flight program. A single astronaut provided a limited amount of manual control as a backup to the automatic control systems. The main control function was to provide attitude control, adjustment of the relative rotation about the vehicle's center of gravity, which is necessary for in-orbit observations and proper positioning of the retrothrust for return to earth. Because there were several control-system failures, the astronaut had to exercise his limited manual control functions on several occasions. In each case the human operator activated an alternate manual or semimanual control mode and salvaged the mission.

The Gemini Project which followed Project Mercury, decided on the basis of the former experience to emphasize astronaut control of the vehicle. The Gemini was more sophisticated. It included two pilots and both attitude control and translation control. The translational controls were necessary for orbit-changing maneuvers as well as rendezvous and docking with a target vehicle.

The spacecraft was composed of a cylindrical adapter module and a conical and cylindrical reentry module[3] (see Fig. 6.28). The adapter module housed an orbit-attitude control system, a translational control system (called the orbit attitude and maneuver system, OAMS), and other equipment. The adapter module was discarded upon reentry. The reentry module contained the crew, a separate pair of redundant attitude-control systems (called the reentry control system, RCS), and other equipment. Thus, in orbit the pilot could choose between three

[1] Duane McRuer et al., Human Pilot Dynamics in Compensatory Systems, *Wright-Patterson Air Force Base, Tech. Rept.* AFFDL-TR-65-15, July, 1965; G. Cole et al., Study of Pilot-Controller Integration for Emergency Conditions, *Wright-Patterson Air Force Base Tech. Doc. Rept.* RTD-TDR-63-4092, January, 1964; and L. Young and R. Winblade, M.I.T.–NASA Working Conference on Manual Control, *IEEE Spectrum*, November, 1966, p. 88.

[2] W. G. Ireson, "Reliability Handbook," pp. 12–21, McGraw-Hill Book Company, New York, 1966.

[3] W. H. Geissler and R. P. Gillooly, "The Gemini Attitude and Maneuvering Control Systems," McDonnell Aircraft Co., St. Louis, Mo., 1963.

Thrust chamber arrangement

Attitude control
25 lb thrust per unit

Maneuver control
100 lb thrust per unit
(except 85 lb for forward firing units)

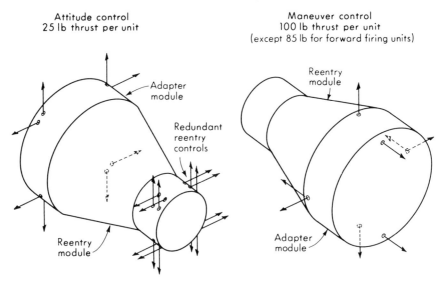

**Fig. 6.28**   Location of translational and rotational thrusters on the Gemini spacecraft.

independent attitude-control systems, and during reentry he had a choice of two identical attitude controllers.   During one of the missions, an adapter thruster "stuck on," causing an uncontrollable roll motion. As soon as the pilot diagnosed the trouble he activated the RCS system and regained control of the vehicle.   The defective thruster was then deenergized.   Fuel depletion during this disturbance caused early termination of the mission, but the adaptive role which the human being played avoided more disastrous consequences.

In addition to these redundant controls, electronics packages, rate gyros, and power sources were duplicated, and the redundances were manually initiated from switches on the astronaut's control panel. Since the spacecraft contained an inertial guidance system, a horizon sensor, rate gyros, and a rendezvous radar, the replication of sensors provided considerable redundancy.   This is illustrated in Fig. 6.29, where the key role of the pilot as an adaptive controller is indicated. Using this figure as a guide, we can formulate reliability diagrams for the system.

In analyzing the reliability of a complex system such as this we must assign a certain probability of success to the branches which represent the pilot.   This is a difficult problem which depends on several variables. Some preliminary approaches to the problem are discussed in Sec. 8.6.

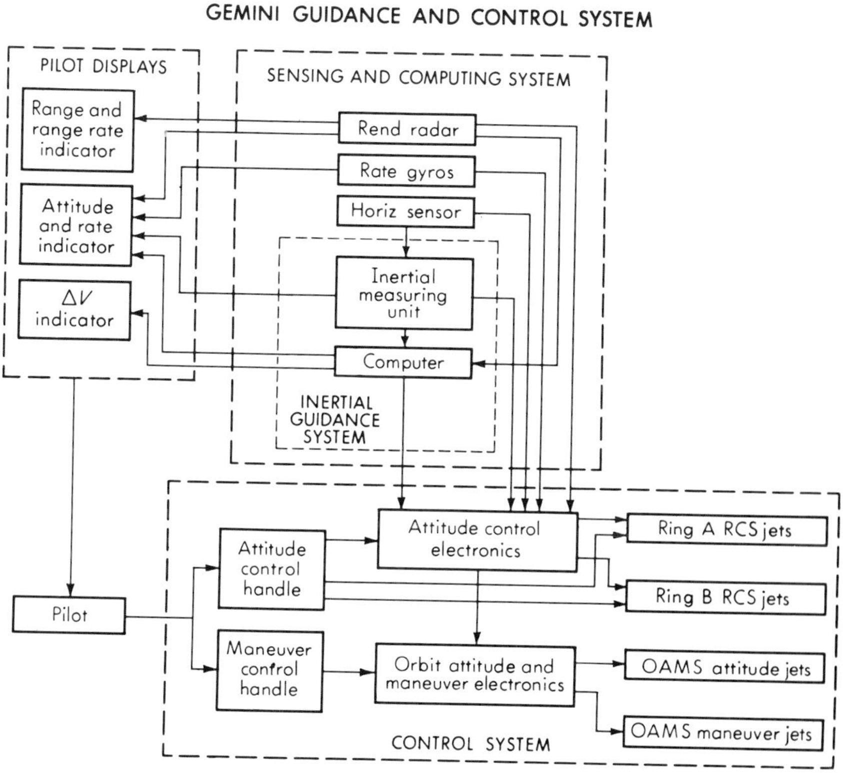

## GEMINI GUIDANCE AND CONTROL SYSTEM

**Fig. 6.29**   Block diagram of Gemini control and guidance system showing the redundant paths.

## 6.9  STANDBY REDUNDANCY

Standby systems are frequently used both on their own merits and when it is difficult to connect units in parallel in the normal fashion.   In such a system, the overall reliability is very much dependent on the reliability of the standby switch.   A poor switch can even yield a system which is worse than a single element.   The design of such a system centers on the design of a simple and reliable switching element.

The switch in a standby system must perform three functions: (1) It must have some sort of decision element which is capable of sensing improper operation; (2) the switch must then remove the signal input[1] from

---

[1] In some cases it might be better to feed both units with the same input signal and switch at the output.   One could also switch at both input and output.   In this section only input switching is considered; however, the results will also apply to output-switching systems  and both input and output switching if the same number of states of switch failure is used.

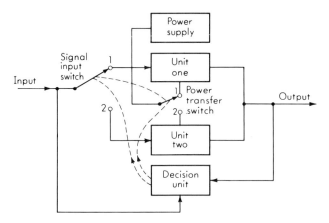

**Fig. 6.30** A standby system.

unit 1 and apply it to unit 2; (3) if the element is an active one, the power must also be transferred from element 1 to 2. These three functions are shown symbolically in Fig. 6.30. Often the decision unit, input switch, and power switch can be incorporated into one unit. For example, if two electronic amplifiers are to be connected in standby, we could use a relay to perform all the decision and switching functions. If the amplifier is to operate properly, the output voltage must be equal to some amplification constant $A$ times the input voltage. The relay could be built so as to have two opposing coils with the number of turns sized so that the force of coil 1 is equal and opposite to the force of coil 2 when $e_1$ volts is applied to coil 1 and $Ae_1$ volts to coil 2.† Whenever this balance was off by too large an amount, the relay would operate. One set of relay contacts would transfer the input signal from amplifier 1 to amplifier 2, while other contacts would transfer the power. Another contact might turn on a warning light to notify the operator that the system had switched to standby. Capacitors across the relay coils could be added to provide time delays, which would avoid any false switching introduced by transients. It might also be desirable to provide a latching circuit for the second position, and if there is a human operator, a manual-override switching mode.

In a similar manner, one could parallel two hydraulic actuators. A linkage connected to both input and output displacement could be used as the decision unit. If there was a large disparity between expected and actual output motion, the linkage output would trip a microswitch which would activate solenoid-operated hydraulic valves. These valves would transfer the hydraulic power and input motion to the second

† Because of the limited frequency response of a relay, such a technique would only check whether the amplifier low-frequency gain is satisfactory.

actuator.    Of course there might be transient problems when the second actuator switched in.    These could be severe enough to call for a straight parallel system in which both actuators were always in operation, dividing the signal between them.    Detailed engineering studies would be required to evaluate the reliability and feasibility of the two systems in order to make a proper choice between ordinary parallel and standby reliability.

The reliability expression for a two-element standby system with constant hazards and a perfect switch was stated in Sec. 3.9 and derived in Eq. (5.86) as

$$R_{sb}(t) = e^{-\lambda t}(1 + \lambda t) \tag{6.57}$$

In Fig. 3.13 it is shown that the standby system is always superior to the ordinary parallel one.    This will not be the case if the switch is imperfect. The role of the switching device in determining system reliability will depend on the failure model used.    As a first approach we shall assume that whenever the switch fails, the system fails, even if both standby units are perfect.    This is a rather simplified but conservative model.

If the switch has a constant hazard $\lambda_s$, Eq. (6.57) is modified, yielding

$$R_1(t) = e^{-\lambda_s t} e^{-\lambda t}(1 + \lambda t) \tag{6.58}$$

If we compare this last reliability expression with that of an ordinary parallel system,

$$R_p(t) = 2e^{-\lambda t} - e^{-2\lambda t} \tag{6.59}$$

We can obtain some idea of how good the switch must be in order to maintain any improvement over an ordinary parallel system.    Equating Eq. (6.58) to Eq. (6.59), we obtain

$$e^{-(\lambda_s + \lambda)t}(1 + \lambda t) = 2e^{-\lambda t} - e^{-2\lambda t}$$

The obvious solutions to this nonlinear, transcendental equation are $t = 0$ and $t = \infty$.    To study the initial behavior we expand both sides in the power series

$$\left[ 1 - \lambda_s t + \frac{(\lambda_s^2 - \lambda^2)t^2}{2} - \frac{(\lambda_s + \lambda)^2(2\lambda - \lambda_s)t^3}{6} + \cdots \right]$$
$$= 1 - \lambda^2 t^2 + \lambda^3 t^3 - \cdots$$

where the left-hand side is the standby system and the right-hand side the parallel system.    The initial slope of the reliability curve for the standby system is $-\lambda_s$, whereas the parallel-system reliability function has zero slope at $t = 0$.    One thus concludes that the parallel system is superior to the standby one for small $t$.    A detailed numerical study for several values of $\lambda_s/\lambda$ would be necessary to establish over what range this superiority persists.

Obviously, to achieve any gain with standby reliability, the switch must be built so that not all switch failures are system failures. Let us now assume that the switch never operates when the on-line component is good but may fail to switch when the on-line component fails. The system then has three elements and can be analyzed by utilizing a three-element Markov model. For example, if $x_1$ is the on-line element, $x_2$ the standby element, and $x_3$ the switch, then

$$P(x_1x_2x_3) = P_0(t) = e^{-(\lambda_1+\lambda_2+\lambda_3)t}$$

but for a standby system, $\lambda_1 = \lambda$, $\lambda_2 = 0$, and $\lambda_3 = \lambda_s$; therefore

$$P_0(t) = e^{-\lambda_s t}e^{-\lambda t} \tag{6.60}$$

The other probabilities involved can be derived in a similar manner, but since we are ignoring dependence, a simpler procedure can be used. Examining the system states, we see that there are three system failures: $s_5$, a bad on-line element and a failed switch; $s_4$, both elements bad; and $s_7$, both elements and the switch bad[1]

$$s_0 = x_1x_2x_3$$
$$s_1 = \bar{x}_1x_2x_3$$
$$s_2 = x_1\bar{x}_2x_3$$
$$s_3 = x_1x_2\bar{x}_3$$
$$s_4 = \bar{x}_1\bar{x}_2x_3 \qquad \text{failure}$$
$$s_5 = \bar{x}_1x_2\bar{x}_3 \qquad \text{failure}$$
$$s_6 = x_1\bar{x}_2\bar{x}_3$$
$$s_7 = \bar{x}_1\bar{x}_2\bar{x}_3 \qquad \text{failure}$$

The reliability expression can be written as the sum of the disjoint successful states, which can be grouped as

$$R = P(x_1x_2x_3) + P(x_1x_2\bar{x}_3) + P(\bar{x}_1x_2x_3) + P(x_1\bar{x}_2x_3) + P(x_1\bar{x}_2\bar{x}_3)$$

Since the events are independent,

$$R = P(x_1x_2)\underbrace{[P(x_3) + P(\bar{x}_3)]}_{1} + P(x_1\bar{x}_2)\underbrace{[P(x_3) + P(\bar{x}_3)]}_{1} + P(\bar{x}_1x_2)P(x_3)$$

$$= P(x_1x_2) + P(x_1\bar{x}_2) + P(\bar{x}_1x_2)P(x_3)$$

This reduction shows that one can make use of the simpler two-state model given by Eqs. (5.55) to (5.58). Thus the reliability becomes

$$R(t) = P_{s_0}(t) + P_{s_2}(t) + P_{s_1}(t)e^{-\lambda_s t} \tag{6.61}$$

For a standby system $\lambda_1 = \lambda_3 = \lambda_4 = \lambda$ and $\lambda_2 = 0$. Substitution in

[1] One might argue that $s$ is still a successful state if the switch failure occurs after the component $x_1$ has failed. This implies splitting state $s_5$ into two *ordered* states. Such a model will be discussed in the problems at the end of the chapter.

Eqs. (5.55) to (5.57) and application of L'Hospital's rule for the indeterminate terms yields

$$P_{s_0}(t) = e^{-\lambda t}$$
$$P_{s_1}(t) = \lambda t e^{-\lambda t}$$
$$P_{s_2}(t) = 0$$

Substitution in Eq. (6.61) yields

$$R(t) = e^{-\lambda t} + e^{-\lambda t}e^{-\lambda_s t}\lambda t$$
$$= e^{-\lambda t} + \lambda t e^{-\lambda t}e^{-\lambda_s t} = e^{-\lambda t}(1 + \lambda t e^{-\lambda_s t}) \qquad (6.62)$$

To compare standby reliability with ordinary parallel reliability the series expansions of Eqs. (6.62) and (6.59) are formed

$$1 - \left(\frac{\lambda^2}{2} + \lambda\lambda_s\right)t^2 + \left[\frac{\lambda}{2}(\lambda + \lambda_s)^2 - \frac{\lambda^3}{6}\right]t^3 - \cdots$$
$$= 1 - \lambda^2 t^2 + \lambda^3 t^3 - \cdots$$

where the left-hand side is the standby system and the right-hand side the parallel system. By comparing first derivatives at $t = 0$, we see that the standby system is superior if $\lambda_s < \lambda/2$.† Some typical curves are given in Fig. 6.31.

We can deal with a more flexible switching model by assuming that the switch has two failure modes: $\bar{x}_3$, the switch does not respond to a failed component and $\bar{\bar{x}}_3$, the switch actuates by mistake when the component is good. This leads to the set of states

$$s_0 = x_1x_2x_3$$
$$s_1 = \bar{x}_1x_2x_3$$
$$s_2 = x_1\bar{x}_2x_3$$
$$s_3 = x_1x_2\bar{x}_3$$
$s_4 = x_1x_2\bar{\bar{x}}_3$  switch may jitter back and forth between $x_1$ and $x_2$, both of which are good
$s_5 = \bar{x}_1\bar{x}_2x_3$  failure
$s_6 = \bar{x}_1x_2\bar{x}_3$  failure
$s_7 = \bar{x}_1x_2\bar{\bar{x}}_3$  failure; switch either sticks in position 1 or jitters back and forth between $\bar{x}_1$ and $x_2$
$s_8 = x_1\bar{x}_2\bar{x}_3$
$s_9 = x_1\bar{x}_2\bar{\bar{x}}_3$  failure; switch either sticks in position 2 or jitters back and forth between $x_1$ and $\bar{x}_2$
$s_{10} = \bar{x}_1\bar{x}_2\bar{x}_3$  failure
$s_{11} = \bar{x}_1\bar{x}_2\bar{\bar{x}}_3$  failure

† The two curves are very close for $\lambda_s = \lambda/2$. The first derivatives are equal, and the second derivatives are

$$\frac{23}{24}\frac{\lambda^3 t^2}{3} \quad \text{and} \quad \frac{\lambda^3 t^2}{3}$$

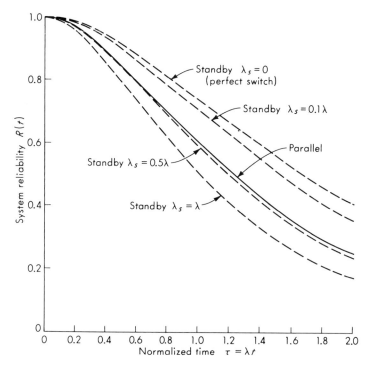

**Fig. 6.31** Ordinary redundancy vs. standby redundancy with imperfect switching.

Writing the system reliability as the sum of all the good states and grouping yields

$$R = [P(x_1x_2x_3) + P(x_1x_2\bar{x}_3) + P(x_1\bar{x}_2\bar{x}_3)] + [P(x_1\bar{x}_2x_3) + P(x_1\bar{x}_2\bar{x}_3)] + P(\bar{x}_1x_2x_3) \quad (6.63)$$

If the switch failures are independent of the component failures (the component failures may, however, depend on each other), considerable simplification of Eq. (6.63) is possible

$$R = P(x_1x_2)[P(x_3) + P(\bar{x}_3) + P(\bar{\bar{x}}_3)] + P(x_1\bar{x}_2)[P(x_3) + P(\bar{x}_3)] + P(\bar{x}_1x_2)P(x_3)$$

$$= P(x_1x_2) + P(\bar{x}_1x_2)P(x_3) + P(x_1\bar{x}_2)[P(x_3) + P(\bar{x}_3)]$$

Letting $P(x_3) = e^{-(\lambda_{s_1}+\lambda_{s_2})t}$, where $\lambda_{s_1}$ and $\lambda_{s_2}$ correspond to $\bar{x}_3$ and $\bar{\bar{x}}_3$, respectively, and again using the two-element model given in Eqs. (5.55) (5.57) to solve for $P_{s_0}$, $P_{s_1}$, and $P_{s_2}$, we obtain

$$R(t) = e^{-\lambda t}(1 + \lambda t e^{-(\lambda_{s_1}+\lambda_{s_2})t}) \quad (6.64)$$

If we consider situations in which $\lambda_{s_1} + \lambda_{s_2} = \lambda_s$, Eq. (6.64) predicts results identical with those in Eq. (6.62). If there is dependence in the problem, a 12-state model must be formulated to compute $P_{s_0}$ to $P_{s_{11}}$.

If nonidentical elements are used in standby, the reliability function becomes quite complex. For $n$ nonidentical elements in a standby configuration with a perfect switch the reliability function becomes

$$R(t) = \frac{\lambda_2\lambda_3\lambda_4 \cdots \lambda_n e^{-\lambda_1 t}}{(\lambda_2 - \lambda_1)(\lambda_3 - \lambda_1) \cdots (\lambda_n - \lambda_1)}$$
$$+ \frac{\lambda_1\lambda_3\lambda_4 \cdots \lambda_n e^{-\lambda_2 t}}{(\lambda_1 - \lambda_2)(\lambda_3 - \lambda_2) \cdots (\lambda_n - \lambda_2)}$$
$$+ \cdots + \frac{\lambda_1\lambda_2 \cdots \lambda_{i-1}\lambda_{i+1} \cdots \lambda_n e^{-\lambda_i t}}{(\lambda_1 - \lambda_i) \cdots (\lambda_{i-1} - \lambda_i)(\lambda_{i+1} - \lambda_i) \cdots (\lambda_n - \lambda_i)}$$
$$+ \cdots + \frac{\lambda_1\lambda_2\lambda_3 \cdots \lambda_{n-1} e^{-\lambda_n t}}{(\lambda_1 - \lambda_n)(\lambda_2 - \lambda_n) \cdots (\lambda_{n-1} - \lambda_n)} \qquad (6.65)\dagger$$

In the normal case all units in a standby system are identical, and the distribution becomes Poisson. Thus a standby system of $n$ components would consist of one on-line unit and $n - 1$ standby units. The reliability is given by the probability of one failure, plus the probability of two failures, plus . . . of $n - 1$ failures, which can be written as

$$R(t) = e^{-\lambda t} \sum_{i=0}^{n-1} \frac{(\lambda t)^i}{i!}$$

If one is dealing with a large number of standby components, another approach is convenient and useful. A standby system possesses the interesting and useful property that the system time to failure $t_f$ is the sum of $n$ individual component failures $t_1, t_2, \ldots, t_n$. Thus, the system failure time is a random variable which is the sum of $n$ other random variables, and its density function is $g(t_f)$. As discussed in Sec. 2.6.9, sums of random variables have very interesting, useful, and special properties. If each component has a failure time $t_n$ with an identical exponential distribution, the $g(t_f)$ is a gamma distribution

$$f(t_i) = \lambda e^{-\lambda t_i}$$
$$t_f = t_1 + t_2 + \cdots t_n$$
$$g(t_f) = \frac{1}{\lambda^n \Gamma(n)} t^{n-1} e^{-\lambda t_f}$$

The reliability function is given by

$$R(t) = 1 - F(t) = 1 - \int_0^t \frac{1}{\lambda^n \Gamma(n)} t^{n-1} e^{-\lambda t} \qquad (6.66)$$

† I. Bazovsky, "Reliability Theory and Practice," p. 117, Prentice-Hall, Inc., Englewood Cliffs, N.J., 1961.

Since the function $F(t)$ has been tabulated,[1] Eq. (6.66) is relatively easy to evaluate. Furthermore, as $n$ becomes large, the distribution $g(t_f)$ approaches a normal distribution even if the $f(t_n)$ distributions are different as long as the variables $t_1, t_2, \ldots, t_n$ are independent. Therefore,

$$\lim_{n \to \infty} g(t_f) \to \frac{1}{\sigma \sqrt{2\pi}} e^{-(t-\mu)^2/2\sigma^2} \qquad (6.67)$$

where $\sigma = \sqrt{\operatorname{var}(t_1)^2 + \operatorname{var}(t_2)^2 + \cdots + \operatorname{var}(t_n)^2}$
$\mu = E(t_1) + E(t_2) + \cdots + E(t_n)$

and the reliability function becomes

$$R(t) = 1 - F(t) = 1 - \int_0^t \frac{1}{\sigma \sqrt{2\pi}} e^{-(t-\mu)^2/2\sigma^2} dt \qquad (6.68)$$

The normal probability integral $F(t)$ is of course extensively tabulated; therefore, Eq. (6.68) is easily evaluated.

All the standby models that have been discussed were based on constant-hazard components. One can, of course, derive similar models for time-varying hazards. If we consider a standby system composed of two components with linearly increasing hazard $z_1 = k_1 t$, $z_2 = k_2 t$, a reliability function can be derived using the technique of Sec. 5.8.4.[2] In this case

$$g_1(\tau) = k_1 \tau e^{-k_1 \tau^2/2} \qquad 0 < \tau < t$$

$$g_2(t|\tau) = \begin{cases} k_2(t - \tau)e^{-k_2(t-\tau)^2/2} & 0 < \tau < t \\ 0 & \tau > t \end{cases}$$

$$\phi(t,\tau) = g_1(\tau)g_2(t|\tau)$$

$$f(t) = \int_0^\infty \phi(t,\tau)\, d\tau = \int_0^{\tau=t} k_1 \tau e^{-k_1 \tau^2/2}\, k_2(t - \tau)e^{-k_2(t-\tau)^2/2}\, d\tau \qquad (6.69)$$

The integral in Eq. (6.69) is quite intractable, and in order to simplify it, an approximation will be made for small $t$ and small $\tau$. Expanding the exponential terms in power series and retaining the first two terms yields

$$f(t) \approx k_1 k_2 \int_0^{\tau=t} \tau(t - \tau)\left(1 - \frac{k_1}{2}\tau^2\right)\left[1 - \frac{k_2}{2}(t - \tau)^2\right] d\tau$$

$$\text{for } \frac{k_1}{2}\tau^2 < 1 \text{ and } \frac{k_2(t - \tau)^2}{2} < 1 \qquad (6.70)$$

[1] Karl Pearson, "Tables of the Incomplete Gamma Function," Cambridge University Press, New York, 1922.

[2] One can also use the technique of Sec. 5.8.5.

Expanding the polynomial, integrating, and retaining the two largest terms yields

$$f(t) \approx k_1 k_2 \left( \frac{t^3}{6} - \frac{k_2 t^5}{24} \right)$$

Computing the reliability function

$$R(t) = 1 - f(t) \approx 1 - \int_0^t k_1 k_2 \left( \frac{\xi^3}{6} - \frac{k_2 \xi^5}{24} \right) d\xi$$

$$R(t) = 1 - k_1 k_2 \left( \frac{t^4}{24} - \frac{k_2}{144} t^6 \right)$$

and when $k_1 = k_2 = k$ (6.71)

$$R(t) = 1 - \frac{k^4 t^4}{24} + \frac{k^3 t^3}{144} \qquad t^2 < \frac{2}{k}$$

For comparison purposes, the reliability function of two parallel components with linearly increasing hazard is given by

$$R(t) = e^{-k_1 t^2/2} + e^{-k_2 t^2/2} - e^{-(k_1+k_2)t^2/2}$$

When the components are identical, $k_1 = k_2 = k$,

$$R(t) = 2e^{-kt^2/2} - e^{-kt^2} \qquad (6.72)$$

If both exponential terms in Eq. (6.72) are replaced by the first four terms in the series approximation for small $t$, we obtain

$$R(t) = 1 - \frac{k^2 t^4}{4} + \frac{7k^3 t^6}{48} \qquad (6.73)$$

Comparing Eqs. (6.71) and (6.73), we see that the standby system is better for small $t$. For illustrative purposes, if $k = 10^{-4}$ and $t = 20$, the standby system has a reliability of 0.99994 and the parallel system 0.99960. To extend the region of validity of Eq. (6.71), we would have to retain more terms in the expansions which yielded Eq. (6.70) or use some other form of approximation to Eq. (6.69).

Standby systems are perhaps the most sophisticated reliability improvement scheme discussed so far and probably promise the most significant improvement except for cases in which the entire system is redesigned to operate in a simpler fashion. Up to this point we have assumed that component failures are irreversible; however, whenever a system can be repaired or replaced, large reliability improvements can often be obtained. The next section discusses reliability improvement by means of repair and/or replacement.

## 6.10 REPAIRABLE SYSTEMS

### 6.10.1 INTRODUCTION

In general, whenever the average repair cost in time and money of a piece of equipment is a fraction of the initial equipment cost, one considers system repair.  If such a system can be rapidly returned to service, the effect of the failure is minimized.  Obvious examples are such equipment as a television set, an automobile, or a radar installation.  In such a system the time between failures, repair time, number of failures in an interval, and percentage of operating time in an interval are figures of merit which must be considered along with the system reliability.  Of course, in some systems, such as those involving life support, surveillance, or safety, any failure is probably catastrophic, and repair is of no avail.

In order to describe the beneficial features of repair in a system that tolerates shutdown times, a new system function .called *availability* is introduced.  The availability function $A(t)$ is defined as the probability that the system is operating *at time t*.  By contrast, the reliability function $R(t)$ is the probability that the system has operated *over the interval* 0 *to t*.  Thus, if $A(250) = 0.95$, then if 100 such systems are operated for 250 hr, on the average, 95 will be operative when 250 hr are reached and 5 will be undergoing various stages of repairs.  The availability function contains no information on how many (if any) failure-repair cycles have occurred prior to 250 hr.  On the other hand, if $R(250) = 0.95$, then if 100 such systems are operated for 250 hr, on the average, 95 will have operated without failure for 250 hr and 5 will have failed at some time within this interval.  It is immaterial in which stage of the first or subsequent failure-repair cycles the five failed systems are.  Obviously the requirement that $R(250) = 0.95$ is much more stringent than the requirement that $A(250) = 0.95$.  Thus, in general, $R(t) \leq A(t)$.

If a *single unit* has no repair capability, then by definition $A(t) = R(t)$.  If we allow repair, then $R(t)$ does not change, but $A(t)$ becomes greater than $R(t)$.  The same conclusions hold for a *chain structure*.  The situation changes for any system involving more than one tie set, i.e., systems with inherent or purposely introduced *redundancy*.  In such a case, repair can beneficially alter both the $R(t)$ and $A(t)$ functions.  This is best illustrated by a simple system composed of two parallel units.  If a system consists of components $A$ and $B$ in parallel and no repairs are permitted, the system fails when both $A$ and $B$ have failed.  In a repairable system if $A$ fails, unit $B$ continues to operate, and the system survives.  Meanwhile, a repairman begins repair of unit $A$.  If the repairman restores $A$ to usefulness before $B$ fails, the system continues to operate.  The second component failure might be unit $B$, or unit $A$ might fail the second time in a row.  In either case there is no system failure

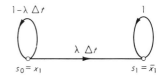

**Fig. 6.32**   Markov graph for the *reliability* of a single component with repair.

as long as the repair time is shorter than the time between failures.   In the long run, at some time a lengthy repair will be started and will be in progress when the alternate unit fails, causing system failure.   It is clear that repair will improve system reliability in such a system.   It seems intuitive that the increase in reliability will be a function of the mean time to repair divided by the MTTF.

To summarize, in a series system, repair will not affect the reliability expression; however, for a complete description of system operation we shall have to include measures of repair time and time between failures. If the system structure has any parallel paths, repair will improve reliability, and repair time and time between failures will be of importance. In some systems, e.g., an unmanned space vehicle or an undersea telephone repeater amplifier, repair may be impossible or impractical.

### 6.10.2   RELIABILITY AND AVAILABILITY FUNCTIONS

As long as the failure and repair density functions are exponential, i.e., constant hazard, we can structure Markov repair models, as done in Sec. 5.8.2.   The reliability and availability models will differ, and we must exercise great care in assigning absorbing states in a reliability model for a repairable system.

The reliability of a single component $x_1$ with constant failure hazard $\lambda$ and constant repair hazard $\mu$ can be derived easily using a Markov model. The Markov graph is given in Fig. 6.32 and the differential equations and reliability function in Eqs. (6.74) and (6.75).

$$\dot{P}_{s_0} + \lambda P_{s_0} = 0$$
$$\dot{P}_{s_1} = \lambda P_{s_0}$$ 
$$P_{s_0}(0) = 1 \qquad P_{s_1}(0) = 0$$ (6.74)
$$R(t) = P_{s_0}(t) = 1 - P_{s_1}(t) = e^{-\lambda t}$$ (6.75)

Note that repair in no way influenced the reliability computation.   Element failure $\bar{x}_1$ is an absorbing state, and once it is reached, the system never returns to $x_1$.

If we wish to study the availability, we must make a different Markov graph.   State $\bar{x}_1$ is no longer an absorbing state, since we now allow transitions from state $\bar{x}_1$ back to state $x_1$.   The Markov graph is given in Fig. 6.33 and the differential equations and state probabilities in

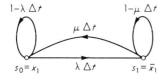

**Fig. 6.33** Markov graph for the *availability* of a single component with repair.

Eqs. (6.76) and (6.77). The corresponding differential equations are

$$\dot{P}_{s_0} + \lambda P_{s_0} = \mu P_{s_1} \qquad \dot{P}_{s_1} + \mu P_{s_1} = \lambda P_{s_0} \qquad (6.76)$$
$$\dot{P}_{s_0}(0) = 1 \qquad P_{s_1}(0) = 0$$

Solution yields the probabilities

$$P_{s_0}(t) = \frac{\mu}{\lambda + \mu} + \frac{\lambda}{\lambda + \mu} e^{-(\lambda+\mu)t}$$
$$P_{s_1}(t) = \frac{\lambda}{\lambda + \mu} - \frac{\lambda}{\lambda + \mu} e^{-(\lambda+\mu)t} \qquad (6.77)$$

By definition, the availability is the probability that the system is good, $P_{s_0}(t)$

$$A(t) = P_{s_0}(t) = \frac{\mu}{\lambda + \mu} + \frac{\lambda}{\lambda + \mu} e^{-(\lambda+\mu)t} \qquad (6.78)$$

The availability function given in Eq. (6.78) is plotted in Fig. 6.34.

An important difference between $A(t)$ and $R(t)$ is their steady-state behavior. As $t$ becomes large, all reliability functions approach zero, whereas availability functions reach some steady-state value. For the single component the steady-state availability

$$A_{ss}(t) = \lim_{t \to \infty} A(t) = \mu/(\lambda + \mu)$$

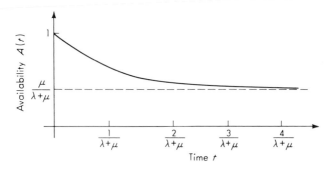

**Fig. 6.34** Availability function for a single component.

In the normal case, the mean repair time $1/\mu$ is much smaller than the time to failure $1/\lambda$, and we can expand the steady-state availability in a series and approximate by truncation

$$A_{ss}(t) = A(\infty) = \frac{1}{1 + \lambda/\mu} = 1 - \frac{\lambda}{\mu} + \frac{\lambda^2}{2\mu^2} + \cdots \approx 1 - \frac{\lambda}{\mu} \qquad (6.79)$$

The transient part of the availability function decays to zero fairly rapidly. The time at which the transient term is negligible with respect to the steady-state term depends on $\lambda$ and $\mu$. As an upper bound we know that the term $e^{-\alpha t} \leq 0.02$ for $t > 4/\alpha$; therefore, we can state that the transient term is over before $t = 4/(\lambda + \mu)$. If $\mu > \lambda$, the transient is over before $t = 4/\mu$. The interaction between reliability and availability specifications is easily seen in the following example.

Suppose a system is to be designed to have a reliability of greater than 0.90 over 1,000 hr and a minimum availability of 0.99 over that period. The reliability specification yields

$$R(t) = e^{-\lambda t} \geq 0.90 \qquad 0 < t < 1,000$$
$$e^{-1,000\lambda} \approx 1 - 10^3\lambda = 0.90 \qquad \lambda \geq 10^{-4}$$

Assuming $A(\infty)$ for the minimum value of the availability, Eq. (6.79) yields

$$A(\infty) = 1 - \frac{\lambda}{\mu} = 0.99$$
$$\mu = 100\lambda = 10^{-2}$$

Thus, we use a component with an MTTF of $10^4$ hr, a little over 1 year, and a mean repair time of 100 hr (about 4 days). The probability of any failure within 1,000 hr (about 6 weeks) is less than 10 percent. Furthermore, the probability that the system is down and under repair at any chosen time between $t = 0$ and $t = 10^3$ hr is less than 1 percent. Now to check the approximations; the transient phase of the availability function lasts for $4/(10^{-2} + 10^{-4}) \sim 400$ hr; thus the availability will be somewhat greater than 0.99 for 400 hr and then settle down at 0.99 for the remaining 600 hr. Since $\mu$ is $100\lambda$, the approximation of Eq. (6.79) is valid. Also since $\lambda t = 10^{-4} \times 10^3 = 10^{-1}$, the two-term series expansion of the exponential is also satisfactory.

The availability function has been defined as a probability function, just as the reliability function was. There is another statistical interpretation which sheds some light on the concept. Suppose that a large number of system operating hours are accumulated. This can be done either by operating one system for a long time, so that many failure and repair cycles are obtained and recorded, or by operating a large number

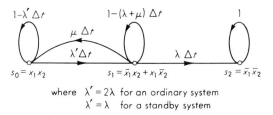

where  $\lambda' = 2\lambda$  for an ordinary system
$\lambda' = \lambda$   for a standby system

**Fig. 6.35**  Markov *reliability* model for two identical parallel elements and one repairman.

of identical systems (an ensemble) for a shorter period of time and combining the data.  If the ratio of cumulative operating time to total test time is computed, it approaches $A(\infty)$ as $t \to \infty$.  Actually the data taken during the transient period of availability should be discarded to avoid any distortions.  In fact if one wished to compute the transient phase of availability from experimental data, one would be forced to use a very large number of systems over a short period of time.  In analyzing the data one would break up the time scale into many small intervals and compute the ratio of cumulative operating time over the intervals divided by the length of the interval.

As a second example we shall consider a two-element system.  In a two-element nonseries system, the reliability function as well as the availability function is influenced by system repairs.  The Markov reliability graph of an ordinary parallel system with two components $x_1$, $x_2$ and repair capability is given in Fig. 5.13a.  If the two elements are identical, only three states are necessary, as shown in Fig. 5.13b.  If this simplification is performed, one must specify whether the system is an ordinary or a standby one at the outset.  To avoid writing separate Markov models for each new variable, $\lambda'$ is defined to assume the value $\lambda$ if the system is a standby one, and $2\lambda$ if the system is an ordinary parallel one.  Using the above notation, the Markov reliability model is that given in Fig. 6.35 for constant failure and repair hazards.  Note that the transition probability for $s_1 \to s_2$ is $\lambda$ for either an ordinary or a standby system, since in either case there is only one item which can fail.  An additional feature can be added to the model if we consider more than one repairman.  Suppose there are two repairmen.  When an item fails, they might decide to take turns in making repairs, in which case there is no change in the Markov graph.  Suppose, however, they both pitch in and work at the same time.  Then the mean service time $1/\mu$ should decrease; that is, $\mu$ should increase.  The repair time might double or might at least increase to 1.5 times[1] its normal value.  Thus, one can

---

[1] Sandler assumes that two repairmen yield $\mu' = 1.5\mu$.

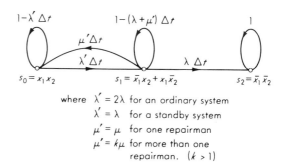

where $\lambda' = 2\lambda$ for an ordinary system
$\lambda' = \lambda$ for a standby system
$\mu' = \mu$ for one repairman
$\mu' = k\mu$ for more than one repairman. $(k > 1)$

**Fig. 6.36**  Markov *reliability* model for two identical parallel elements and $k$ repairmen.

set up a general Markov reliability graph by substituting $\mu'$ for $\mu$† (see Fig. 6.36).

The differential equations associated with Fig. 6.36 are

$$
\begin{aligned}
&\dot{P}_{s_0}(t) + \lambda P_{s_0}(t) = \mu' P_{s_1}(t) \\
&\dot{P}_{s_1}(t) + (\mu' + \lambda)P_{s_1}(t) = \lambda' P_{s_0}(t) \\
&\dot{P}_{s_2}(t) = \lambda P_{s_1}(t) \\
&P_{s_0}(0) = 1 \qquad P_{s_1}(0) = P_{s_2}(0) = 0
\end{aligned}
\tag{6.80}
$$

Taking the Laplace transform of this set of equations yields

$$
\begin{aligned}
(s + \lambda')P_{s_0}(s) - \mu' P_{s_1}(s) + 0 P_{s_2}(s) &= 1 \\
-\lambda' P_{s_0}(s) + (s + \mu' + \lambda)P_{s_1}(s) + 0 P_{s_2}(s) &= 0 \\
0 P_{s_0}(s) - \lambda P_{s_1}(s) + (s)P_{s_2}(s) &= 0
\end{aligned}
\tag{6.81}
$$

Solution via Cramer's rule yields

$$
\begin{aligned}
P_{s_0}(s) &= \frac{(s + \lambda + \mu')}{s^2 + (\lambda + \lambda' + \mu')s + \lambda\lambda'} \\
P_{s_1}(s) &= \frac{\lambda'}{s^2 + (\lambda + \lambda' + \mu')s + \lambda\lambda'} \\
P_{s_2}(s) &= \frac{\lambda\lambda'}{s[s^2 + (\lambda + \lambda' + \mu')s + \lambda\lambda']}
\end{aligned}
\tag{6.82}
$$

Solution for the roots of the denominator quadratic (the system poles) yields

$$
r_1, r_2 = \frac{-(\lambda + \lambda' + \mu') \pm \sqrt{(\lambda + \lambda' + \mu')^2 - 4\lambda\lambda'}}{2}
\tag{6.83}
$$

† If there are $n$ elements and $k < n$ repairmen, a waiting line of failed components may build up if there are many failures in a brief period. For details see M. Messinger, Ph.D. dissertation in system science, chap. 5, Polytechnic Institute of Brooklyn, New York, June 1967.

Expanding Eqs. (6.79) in partial fractions,

$$P_{s_0}(s) = \frac{(s + \lambda + \mu')}{(s - r_1)(s - r_2)} = \frac{(\lambda + \mu' + r_1)/(r_1 - r_2)}{s - r_1}$$
$$+ \frac{(\lambda + \mu' + r_2)/(r_2 - r_1)}{s - r_2} \qquad (6.84)$$

$$P_{s_1}(s) = \frac{\lambda'}{(s - r_1)(s - r_2)} = \frac{\lambda'/(r_1 - r_2)}{s - r_1} + \frac{\lambda'/(r_2 - r_1)}{s - r_2} \qquad (6.85)$$

$$P_{s_2}(s) = \frac{\lambda\lambda'}{s(s - r_1)(s - r_2)} = \frac{\lambda\lambda'/r_1 r_2}{s} + \frac{\lambda\lambda'/r_1(r_1 - r_2)}{s - r_1}$$
$$+ \frac{\lambda\lambda'/r_2(r_2 - r_1)}{s - r_2} \qquad (6.86)$$

As a check one can sum Eqs. (6.84) to (6.86). If one uses the identities

$$r_1 r_2 = \lambda\lambda'$$
$$r_1 + r_2 = -(\lambda + \lambda' + \mu')$$

the result is

$$P_{s_0}(s) + P_{s_1}(s) + P_{s_2}(s) = \frac{1}{s} \qquad (6.87)$$

Taking the inverse transforms, one obtains $P_{s_0}(t) + P_{s_1}(t) + P_{s_2}(t) = 1$. The inverse transforms of Eqs. (6.84) to (6.86) yield

$$P_{s_0}(t) = \frac{\lambda + \mu' + r_1}{r_1 - r_2} e^{r_1 t} - \frac{\lambda + \mu' + r_2}{r_1 - r_2} e^{r_2 t} \qquad (6.88)$$

$$P_{s_1}(t) = \frac{\lambda'}{r_1 - r_2} e^{r_1 t} - \frac{\lambda'}{r_1 - r_2} e^{r_2 t} \qquad (6.89)$$

$$P_{s_2}(t) = 1 + \frac{r_2}{r_1 - r_2} e^{r_1 t} - \frac{r_1}{r_1 - r_2} e^{r_2 t} \qquad (6.90)$$

Note that inspection of Eq. (6.83) shows that $r_1$ and $r_2$ are always negative real numbers; therefore, the time functions are decaying exponentials.[1] For a system composed of two series elements, the system reliability is unaffected by repair, and $R(t) = e^{-2\lambda t}$, which can be obtained by setting $\mu' = 0$ in the expression for $P_{s_0}(t)$. For a parallel system (standby or ordinary) the reliability is given by $P_{s_0}(t) + P_{s_1}(t)$. The reliability functions for several systems are compared in Table 6.13. Note that repair does not help a series system since the problem stops once there is any failure, and thus no repair can ever be attempted. In order to use repair

[1] The roots cannot be complex since the minimum value of the radical (obtained when $\mu' \to 0$) is $\sqrt{(\lambda - \lambda')^2}$.

**Table 6.13 Comparison of reliability functions for several two-element systems with repair**

| System | No. of repairmen | $\lambda'$ | $\mu'$ | For $\mu = 10\lambda$ $r_1$ | $r_2$ | Reliability function $R(t)$ | $R\left(t = \dfrac{1}{10\lambda}\right)$ | $R\left(t = \dfrac{1}{\lambda}\right)$ |
|---|---|---|---|---|---|---|---|---|
| Series | 0, 1, 2 | $2\lambda$ | 0 | $-\lambda$ | $-2\lambda$ | $e^{-2\lambda t}$ | 0.818 | 0.135 |
| Ordinary parallel | 0 | $2\lambda$ | 0 | $-\lambda$ | $-2\lambda$ | $2e^{-\lambda t} - e^{-2\lambda t}$ | 0.992 | 0.601 |
| Ordinary parallel | 1 | $2\lambda$ | $\mu$ | $-0.175\lambda$ | $-12.83\lambda$ | $1.013e^{-0.175\lambda t} - 0.013e^{-12.83\lambda t}$ | 0.9934 | 0.850 |
| Ordinary parallel | 2 | $2\lambda$ | $2\mu$ | $-0.10\lambda$ | $-22.9\lambda$ | $1.004e^{-0.10\lambda t} - 0.004e^{-22.9\lambda t}$ | 0.9936 | 0.909 |
| Standby | 0 | $\lambda$ | 0 | $-\lambda$ | $-\lambda$ | $e^{-\lambda t}(1 + \lambda t)$ | 0.9950 | 0.736 |
| Standby | 1 | $\lambda$ | $\mu$ | $-0.1\lambda$ | $-11.9\lambda$ | $1.008e^{-0.10\lambda t} - 0.008e^{-11.9\lambda t}$ | 0.9956 | 0.907 |
| Standby | 2 | $\lambda$ | $2\mu$ | $-0.05\lambda$ | $-21.95\lambda$ | $1.002e^{-0.05\lambda t} - 0.002e^{-21.95\lambda t}$ | 0.9978 | 0.952 |

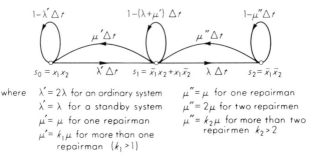

where   $\lambda' = 2\lambda$ for an ordinary system     $\mu'' = \mu$ for one repairman
        $\lambda' = \lambda$ for a standby system        $\mu'' = 2\mu$ for two repairmen
        $\mu' = \mu$ for one repairman                   $\mu'' = k_2\mu$ for more than two
        $\mu' = k_1\mu$ for more than one                repairmen $k_2 > 2$
        repairman $(k_1 > 1)$

**Fig. 6.37**   Markov *availability* graph for two identical parallel elements.

effectively as a reliability improvement tool, important sections of the system structure must form parallel systems. In the high-reliability region, $t \leq 1/10\lambda$, there is a uniform increase in reliability as the reliability effort increases. This effect does not remain uniform as time increases. For example, at $t = 1/\lambda$ it is slightly better to use an ordinary parallel system with two repairmen[1] than to use a standby system with one repairman. Thus, different systems might be chosen if one wished very high reliability for a short period or reasonably good reliability over a longer period. The choice of a specific system would of course depend on the usual engineering compromise and involve trading off reliability vs. cost, weight, size, etc.

Availability computations can be performed in a manner similar to the above reliability computations. A different Markov graph must be formulated, since by the basic definition of availability, repairs are permitted in any system state. A general two-element Markov graph for system availability computations is given in Fig. 6.37. The associated differential equations are

$$
\begin{aligned}
\dot{P}_{s_0}(t) + \lambda' P_{s_0}(t) &= \mu' P_{s_1}(t) \\
\dot{P}_{s_1}(t) + (\lambda + \mu') P_{s_1}(t) &= \lambda' P_{s_0}(t) + \mu'' P_{s_2}(t) \\
\dot{P}_{s_2}(t) + \mu'' P_{s_2}(t) &= \lambda P_{s_1}(t) \\
P_{s_0}(0) = 1 \qquad P_{s_1}(0) &= P_{s_2}(0) = 0
\end{aligned}
\tag{6.91}
$$

Computing the Laplace transforms of Eqs. (6.91) yields

$$
\begin{aligned}
(s + \lambda') P_{s_0}(s) - \mu' P_{s_1}(s) &= 1 \\
-\lambda' P_{s_0}(s) + (s + \lambda + \mu') P_{s_1}(s) - \mu'' P_{s_2}(s) &= 0 \\
-\lambda P_{s_1}(s) + (s + \mu'') P_{s_2}(s) &= 0
\end{aligned}
\tag{6.92}
$$

[1] Another way of achieving the same result is to double the repair rate with only one repairman by making his techniques more efficient or by improving system accessibility to speed up maintenance.

Solution of these equations yields

$$P_{s_0}(s) = \frac{s^2 + (\lambda + \mu' + \mu'')s + \mu'\mu''}{s[s^2 + (\lambda + \lambda' + \mu' + \mu'')s + (\lambda\lambda' + \lambda'\mu'' + \mu'\mu'')]}$$

$$P_{s_1}(s) = \frac{\lambda'(s + \mu'')}{s[s^2 + (\lambda + \lambda' + \mu' + \mu'')s + (\lambda\lambda' + \lambda'\mu'' + \mu'\mu'')]} \qquad (6.93)$$

$$P_{s_2}(s) = \frac{\lambda\lambda'}{s[s^2 + (\lambda + \lambda' + \mu' + \mu'')s + (\lambda\lambda' + \lambda'\mu'' + \mu'\mu'')]}$$

Factoring the quadratic equation in the denominator one obtains

$$r_3, r_4 =$$
$$\frac{-(\lambda + \lambda' + \mu' + \mu'') \pm \sqrt{(\lambda + \lambda' + \mu' + \mu'')^2 - 4(\lambda\lambda' + \lambda'\mu'' + \mu'\mu'')}}{2}$$

$$(6.94)$$

Partial-fraction expansion yields

$$P_{s_0}(s) = \frac{s^2 + (\lambda + \mu' + \mu'')s + \mu'\mu''}{s(s - r_3)(s - r_4)} = \frac{\mu'\mu''/r_3 r_4}{s}$$
$$+ \frac{[r_3^2 + (\lambda + \mu' + \mu'')r_3 + \mu'\mu'']/r_3(r_3 - r_4)}{s - r_3}$$
$$+ \frac{[r_4^2 + (\lambda + \mu' + \mu'')r_4 + \mu'\mu'']/r_4(r_4 - r_3)}{s - r_4}$$

$$P_{s_1}(s) = \frac{\lambda'(s + \mu'')}{s(s - r_3)(s - r_4)} = \frac{\lambda'\mu''/r_3 r_4}{s} + \frac{\lambda'(r_3 + \mu'')/r_3(r_3 - r_4)}{s - r_3} \qquad (6.95)$$
$$+ \frac{\lambda(r_4 + \mu'')/r_4(r_4 - r_3)}{s - r_4}$$

$$P_{s_2}(s) = \frac{\lambda\lambda'}{s(s - r_3)(s - r_4)} = \frac{\lambda\lambda'/r_3 r_4}{s} = \frac{\lambda\lambda'/r_3(r_3 - r_4)}{s - r_3}$$
$$+ \frac{\lambda\lambda'/r_4(r_4 - r_3)}{s - r_4}$$

The transform of the availability function for a parallel system is given by[1]

$$A(s) = P_{s_0}(s) + P_{s_1}(s)$$

Algebraic manipulation combined with the identities

$$r_3 + r_4 = -(\lambda + \lambda' + \mu' + \mu'') \qquad r_3 r_4 = (\lambda\lambda' + \lambda'\mu'' + \mu'\mu'')$$

yields

$$A(s) = \frac{1 - \lambda\lambda'/r_3 r_4}{s} - \frac{\lambda\lambda'/r_3(r_3 - r_4)}{s - r_3} - \frac{\lambda\lambda'/r_4(r_4 - r_3)}{s - r_4} \qquad (6.96)$$

[1] For a series system $A(s) = P_{s_0}(s)$.

Taking the inverse transform,

$$A(t) = \left(1 - \frac{\lambda\lambda'}{r_3 r_4}\right) - \frac{\lambda\lambda'}{r_3 - r_4}\left(\frac{e^{r_3 t}}{r_3} - \frac{e^{r_4 t}}{r_4}\right) \tag{6.97}$$

Inspection of Eq. (6.94) reveals that for $\mu'$ and $\mu'' > \lambda$ and $\lambda'$, $r_3$ and $r_4$ are approximately given by

$$r_3, \, r_4 \approx \frac{-(\mu' + \mu'') \pm \sqrt{(\mu' - \mu'')^2 - 4\lambda'\mu''}}{2}$$

The first term in Eq. (6.97) represents the constant steady-state availability and the second term a decaying transient.[1]   The time to reach steady state is no longer than $4/\mathrm{Re}\,(r_3)$ or $4/\mathrm{Re}\,(r_4)$, depending on which is longer.   The steady-state availability

$$A(\infty) = 1 - \frac{\lambda\lambda'}{\lambda\lambda' + \lambda'\mu'' + \mu'\mu''} \tag{6.98}$$

can be made close to unity by making $\mu'$ and $\mu'' \gg \lambda$.   Since $\lambda$ and $\lambda'$ have roughly the same magnitude, Eq. (6.98) reduces to[2]

$$A(\infty) \approx 1 - \frac{\lambda\lambda'}{\mu'\mu''} \tag{6.99}$$

The steady state and transient availability for several typical configurations are compared in Table 6.14 for $\mu = 10\lambda$.   Again note that an ordinary parallel system with two repairmen is slightly more effective than a standby system with one repairman.   When several repairmen are used, a fairly high reliability is obtained, and the steady state is reached in about one-fourth the MTTF of a single component.

When only the steady-state availability is of interest, a simplified computational procedure can be used.   In the steady state, all the state probabilities should approach a constant; therefore,

$$\dot{P}_{s_0}(t) = \dot{P}_{s_1}(t) = \dot{P}_{s_2}(t) = 0$$

After setting the derivatives to zero, Eqs. (6.91) become

$$\begin{align*}
\lambda P_{s_0}(\infty) - \mu' P_{s_1}(\infty) &= 0 \\
-\lambda P_{s_0}(\infty) + (\lambda + \mu')P_{s_1}(\infty) - \mu'' P_{s_2}(\infty) &= 0 \\
-\lambda' P_{s_1}(\infty) + \mu'' P_{s_2}(\infty) &= 0
\end{align*} \tag{6.100}$$

---

[1] If $(\mu' - \mu'')^2 > 4\lambda'\mu''$, the transient is a sum of two exponential decays.   If $(\mu' - \mu'')^2 < 4\lambda'\mu''$, the transient is a decaying sinusoid.

[2] If only this steady-state term is desired, one can apply the final-value theorem for Laplace transforms to Eqs. (6.93) and obtain

$$A(\infty) = \lim_{s \to 0} [sP_{s_0}(s) + sP_{s_1}(s)]$$

**Table 6.14  Comparison of availability of several two-element systems with repair**

| System | No. of repairmen | $\lambda'$ | $\mu'$ | $\mu''$ | Availability function $A(t)$ for $\mu = 10\lambda$ | $A(\infty)$ | Duration of trans less than |
|---|---|---|---|---|---|---|---|
| Series | 0 | $2\lambda$ | 0 | 0 | $P_{s_0}(t) = e^{-2\lambda t}$ | 0 | $\dfrac{2}{\lambda}$ |
| Series | 1 | $2\lambda$ | $\mu$ | $\mu$ | $P_{s_0}(t) = 0.819 + 0.079e^{-14.71\lambda t} + 0.102e^{-8.30\lambda t}$ | 0.819 | $\dfrac{0.482}{\lambda}$ |
| Series | 2 | $2\lambda$ | $2\mu$ | $2\mu$ | $P_{s_0}(t) = 0.905 + 0.0427e^{-26\lambda t} + 0.0523e^{-17\lambda t}$ | 0.905 | $\dfrac{0.235}{\lambda}$ |
| Ordinary parallel | 0 | $2\lambda$ | 0 | 0 | $P_{s_0}(t) + P_{s_1}(t) = 2e^{-\lambda t} - e^{-2\lambda t}$ | 0 | $\dfrac{4}{\lambda}$ |
| Ordinary parallel | 1 | $2\lambda$ | $\mu$ | $\mu$ | $P_{s_0}(t) + P_{s_1}(t) = 0.9836 + 0.0376e^{-8.30\lambda t} - 0.0212e^{-14.7\lambda t}$ | 0.984 | $\dfrac{0.482}{\lambda}$ |
| Ordinary parallel | 2 | $2\lambda$ | $2\mu$ | $2\mu$ | $P_{s_0}(t) + P_{s_1}(t) = 0.9955 + 0.0131e^{-17\lambda t} - 0.00854e^{-26\lambda t}$ | 0.9955 | $\dfrac{0.235}{\lambda}$ |
| Standby | 0 | $\lambda$ | 0 | 0 | $P_{s_0}(t) + P_{s_1}(t) = e^{-\lambda t}(1 + \lambda t)$ | 0 | $\dfrac{5}{\lambda}$ |
| Standby | 1 | $\lambda$ | $\mu$ | $\mu$ | $P_{s_0}(t) + P_{s_1}(t) = 0.9910 + 0.0198e^{-7.83\lambda t} - 0.0110e^{-14.17\lambda t}$ | 0.9910 | $\dfrac{0.511}{\lambda}$ |
| Standby | 2 | $\lambda$ | $2\mu$ | $2\mu$ | $P_{s_0}(t) + P_{s_1}(t) = 0.998 + 0.00675e^{-16.52\lambda t} - 0.00438e^{-25.48\lambda t}$ | 0.998 | $\dfrac{0.242}{\lambda}$ |

This set of equations cannot be solved for the steady-state probabilities, since their determinent is zero.   Any two of these equations can, however, be combined with the identity

$$P_{s_0}(\infty) + P_{s_1}(\infty) + P_{s_2}(\infty) = 1 \tag{6.101}$$

to yield a solution.   The reader can easily verify that this technique leads directly to Eq. (6.98).   Note that at no time were the initial-state probabilities $P_{s_0}(0)$, $P_{s_1}(0)$, and $P_{s_2}(0)$ used in this computation.   This means that the steady-state availability is independent of the initial state of the system and that only the transient terms change if the initial conditions are changed.   In fact the same natural frequencies will be present in the solution, and the initial conditions will affect only their amplitudes.

So far we have discussed reliability and availability computations only in one- and two-element systems.   Obviously we could set up and solve Markov models for a larger number of elements, but the complexity of the problem increases very rapidly as $n$, the number of elements, increases. (If the elements are distinct, it goes as $2^n$ and if identical as $n + 1$.)   In order to simplify the computations we shall use the approach of Sec. 5.9. All the combinatorial methods discussed in Chap. 3 are applicable to both the reliability and availability functions for systems with repair.   Thus, computing system availability in terms of component availabilities is no different from the problem of computing system reliability in terms of component reliability, except that the Markov models (made for each cluster of repairable components) may have a more complex solution because of the coupling in the equations caused by repair.

All computations up to this point have been done assuming constant failure and repair hazards.   This was primarily done for computational simplicity; however, it is now appropriate to examine the validity of these assumptions.   As has been amply discussed, a constant failure hazard is a valid assumption for a large number of practical systems but by no means all.   In the case of repair, the constant-hazard assumption is in greater doubt.

This implies that the probability of completing a repair between $t$ and $t + \Delta t$ is the same as the probability of completing a repair between $10t$ and $10t + \Delta t$.   They both are $\mu \, \Delta t$.   The conclusion is that the repairman learns nothing about what has caused the failure as his work proceeds.   One situation which does seem to satisfy these assumptions is the case of a poor repairman searching mainly by trial and error to replace plug-in modules until the correct one is found.   Such might be the case if an untrained or unskilled repairman were to try to fix a system composed of plug-in printed-circuit or integrated-circuit modules.   With an intelligent repairman who systematically tracks down errors, one

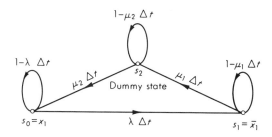

**Fig. 6.38**  Modeling a nonconstant repair using a dummy state.

would expect a rapid increase in the probability of repair as time increased. A Rayleigh, Weibull, or other increasing-repair-hazard model may be required.

If one wishes to work with nonconstant failure and/or repair hazards, there are two approaches.   One technique is to use the methods of Sec. 5.8.4 or 5.8.5 and approximate if necessary the integral solutions by power-series expansions.   The other approach is to formulate a modified Markov model with added dummy states.[1]   This allows modeling of nonconstant hazards and is best illustrated by the following example.

The availability of a single element with constant failure hazard and increasing repair hazard is modeled in Fig. 6.38.   The time till transition from state $s_1$ to state $s_0$, $\tau_{10}$, is the sum of the two transition times $\tau_{12}$ and $\tau_{20}$.   Thus $\tau_{10}$ is the sum of two other exponentially distributed random variables.   We can compute the density function of $\tau_{10}$ using Eq. (2.102).[2]   When $\mu_1 = \mu_2 = \mu_0$, we obtain a gamma distribution with a density function of the form

$$h(t_0) = \mu_0^2 t e^{-\mu_0 t} \tag{6.102}$$

We can compute the associated hazard function using Eq. (4.23)

$$z(t) = \frac{\mu_0^2 t e^{-\mu_0 t}}{1 - \mu_0^2 \int_0^t \xi e^{-\mu_0 \xi} \, d\xi} = \frac{\mu_0^2 t}{1 + \mu_0 t} \tag{6.103}$$

which is sketched in Fig. 6.39.

---

[1] E. Muth, Stochastic Theory of Repairable Systems, Ph.D. dissertation in system science, Polytechnic Institute of Brooklyn, New York, June, 1967.

[2] One can also use Theorem 4 in Table 2.12.   In this case

$\mathcal{L}\{h(t)\} = \mathcal{L}\{f_1(t)\}\mathcal{L}\{f_2(t)\}$; and $f_1(t) = \mu_0 e^{-\mu_0 t}$, $F_1(s) = \mu_0/(s + \mu_0)$,

$H(s) = \mu_0^2/(s + \mu_0)^2$.   Then $\mathcal{L}^{-1}\{\mu_0^2/(s + \mu_0)^2\}$ yields Eq. (6.102).

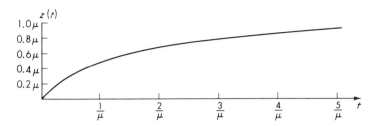

**Fig. 6.39**  Sketch of the "gamma" hazard given by Eq. (6.103).

The differential equations for the model of Fig. 6.38 (assuming that $\mu_1 = \mu_2 = \mu_0$) are

$$
\begin{aligned}
\dot{P}_{s_0} + \lambda P_{s_0} &= \mu_0 P_{s_2} \\
\dot{P}_{s_1} + \mu_0 P_{s_1} &= \lambda P_{s_0} \\
\dot{P}_{s_2} + \mu_0 P_{s_2} &= \mu_0 P_{s_1}
\end{aligned}
\qquad
\begin{aligned}
P_{s_0}(0) &= 1 \\
P_{s_1}(0) &= P_{s_2}(0) = 0
\end{aligned}
\tag{6.104}
$$

Solving Eqs. (6.104) for $P_{s_0}(s)$, the availability is given by

$$
A(s) = P_{s_0}(s) = \frac{(s + \mu_0)^2}{s[s^2 + (2\mu_0 + \lambda)s + (\mu_0^2 + 2\mu_0\lambda)]}
\tag{6.105}
$$

If we wish to compare the availability function for a constant hazard, Eq. (6.78), with that for the gamma hazard given in Fig. 6.39 [Eq. (6.105)], we must equate moments.   The mean of Eq. (6.102) is seen from Table 2.4 to be $2/\mu_0$.   For the exponential density $\mu e^{-\mu t}$ the mean is $1/\mu$. Equating the two, we have $\mu_0 = 2\mu$, and Eq. (6.105) becomes

$$
A(s) = \frac{(s + 2\mu)^2}{s[s^2 + (4\mu + \lambda)s + (4\mu^2 + 4\mu\lambda)]}
\tag{6.106}
$$

Applying the final-value theorem (Theorem 7 in Table 2.12), we obtain

$$
A(\infty) = \frac{4\mu^2}{4\mu^2 + 4\mu\lambda} = \frac{\mu}{\lambda + \mu}
$$

This agrees with Eq. (6.79).   Thus, the two problems have the same steady-state availability.   The transient term in the availability solution will be a decaying sinusoid as compared with the exponential in Eq. (6.78).

Of course, by using more dummy states and/or different values of $\mu_i$ one can obtain many different hazard functions.[1]

### 6.10.3  RENEWAL THEORY

The preceding discussion of repairable systems has developed a new figure of system performance, availability, in addition to the conventional

[1] Muth, *op. cit.*

reliability function.    As one delves deeper into the subject of repair and replacement, other measures of system performance must be developed. The availability function measures only the probability that the system is operating at some point in time.    It tells us nothing about how many failure-repair cycles have occurred.    This information is necessary if one is to plan on an ample supply of spares and to schedule the work load of repairmen.    The amount of up time and downtime is also of interest, since this allows one to compute the probability of lengthy periods of inoperation.    It is easy to conceive of cases in which five 1-hr repairs in a time interval would be acceptable but one 5-hr repair would not, even though they both represent the same cumulative downtime.

The mathematical background for further study is included in the subject of renewal theory.[1]    The theory is basically an extension of the study of the distribution of a sum of random variables which was started in Chap. 2.    Some of the simpler aspects will be discussed in the following material.

Consider a single component or unit which is in operation over a long time.    At the first failure time $t_1$, the component is immediately replaced by another identical one.    The downtime during replacement is assumed so short it can be neglected.    In this case the availability approaches unity.    [Replacement in zero time implies $\mu \to \infty$; and from Eq. (6.78) we can see that $A(t) \to 1$.]    The second element begins operation at time $t_1$, and it fails at time $t_2'$.    Thus, component 2 has operated for $t_2 = t_2' - t_1$ hr.    Component 2 is replaced by a third component, which in turn fails after operating for $t_3$ hr, etc.    The system operating time $\tau_n$ for $n - 1$ replacements (renewals) is thus given by

$$\tau_n = t_1 + t_2 + \cdots + t_n \tag{6.107}$$

which is the time of the $n$th failure.[2]    The density function of system operating times for $n$ renewals is given by $f(\tau_n)$.    This density function is computed from the individual density functions $f_1(t_1)$, $f_2(t_2)$, . . . , $f_n(t_n)$ by the multiple convolution integral, a generalization of Eq. (2.102). Use of the Laplace transform simplifies this computation since the convolution in the time domain becomes a product of Laplace transforms. [Compare Eq. (2.102) and Theorem 4 of Table 2.12.]    Thus,[3]

$$f_{\tau_n}^*(s) = f_1^*(s) f_2^*(s) \cdots f_n^*(s) \tag{6.108}$$

If the components are all identical (the only case to be treated in this

[1] D. R. Cox, "Renewal Theory," John Wiley & Sons, Inc., New York, 1962.

[2] Note that $\tau_n$ is the time of the $n$th failure, whereas $t_n$ is the time from the $(n - 1)$st failure to the $n$th failure.

[3] As explained in Chap. 2, the notation $f^*(s)$ is used for $\mathcal{L}\{f(t)\}$ in order that there be no confusion between the density function $f(t)$ and the distribution function $F(t)$.

discussion), the density functions should all be identical, and Eq. (6.108) becomes

$$f_{\tau_n}^*(s) = [f^*(s)]^n \tag{6.109}$$

The simplest and most common case to treat is that of constant-hazard components, where

$$z(t) = \lambda$$
$$f(t) = \lambda e^{-\lambda t}$$
$$f^*(s) = \frac{\lambda}{s + \lambda}$$

and

$$f_{\tau_n}^*(s) = \left(\frac{\lambda}{s + \lambda}\right)^n \tag{6.110}$$

For one and two renewals, the density functions for the renewal times are[1]

$$f_{\tau_1}(t) = \mathcal{L}^{-1}\left\{f_{\tau_1}^*(s) = \frac{\lambda}{s + \lambda}\right\} = \lambda e^{-\lambda t} \tag{6.111}$$

$$f_{\tau_2}(t) = \mathcal{L}^{-1}\left\{f_{\tau_2}^*(s) = \frac{\lambda^2}{(s + \lambda)^2}\right\} = \lambda^2 t e^{-\lambda t} \tag{6.112}$$

and the general expression for $n$ renewals is given by

$$f_{\tau_s}(t) = \mathcal{L}^{-1}\left\{\frac{\lambda^n}{(s + \lambda)^n}\right\} = \frac{\lambda(\lambda t)^{n-1}e^{-\lambda t}}{(n - 1)!} \tag{6.113}$$

The density function given by Eq. (6.113) is called the special Erlangian[2] distribution with $n$ stages.   A renewal process of this type—exponential failure-time density function and Erlangian operating-time density function—is called a *Poisson process*.   Equations (6.111) to (6.113) have the following interpretation: the MTTF for the first component is known from previous computations to be $1/\lambda$.   This could also be obtained formally by computing the expected value of $\tau_1$ using Eq. (6.111). Furthermore, the probability that the first renewal occurs on or before $t = 1/\lambda$ is given by the value of the distribution function associated with Eq. (6.111) evaluated at $t = 1/\lambda$.

$$P\left(t_1 \leq \frac{1}{\lambda}\right) = F_{\tau_1}\left(t = \frac{1}{\lambda}\right) = \int_0^{1/\lambda} \lambda e^{-\lambda t}\, dt$$
$$= 1 - e^{-1} = 0.632$$

---

[1] See transform 5, Table 2.11.
[2] A. K. Erlang worked with this distribution in studying the theory of congestion in telephone systems.

The mean time of occurrence of the second renewal is the expected value of $\tau_2$ computed from Eq. (6.111). The result is $E(\tau_2) = 2/\lambda$.

The probability of two renewals before $t = 2/\lambda$ is computed from Eq. (6.79) as

$$P\left(t_2 \leq \frac{2}{\lambda}\right) = F_{\tau_2}\left(t = \frac{2}{\lambda}\right) = \int_0^{2/\lambda} \lambda^2 t e^{-\lambda t}\, dt$$
$$= 1 - 3e^{-2} = 0.595$$

The information one can obtain from Eq. (6.113), i.e., the probability that the $m$th renewal occurs before some time $t$, is useful in planning the stock of spare parts for repairable equipment. An even more important probability function is the probability that exactly a certain number of renewals occurs in the interval 0 to $t$. The derivation of this function proceeds as follows.

Let $N(t)$ be the number of renewals in $t$ operating hours. The number of renewals is less than $n$ if $\tau_n$ is greater than $t$; thus

$$N(t) < n \qquad \text{when} \qquad \tau_n > t$$

therefore

$$P[N(t) < n] = P(\tau_n > t)$$

however,

$$P(\tau_n > t) = 1 - P(\tau_n \leq t) = 1 - F_{\tau_n}(t)$$

where $F_{\tau_n}(t)$ is given by integration of Eq. (6.113); thus

$$P[N(t) < n] = 1 - F_{\tau_n}(t)$$

However, we want the probability $P[N(t) = n]$. Since $n$ is discrete, the sequence $N(t) < n$ is given by 0, 1, 2, . . . , $n - 1$ and the sequence $N(t) < n + 1$ by 0, 1, 2, . . . , $n$; thus,

$$P[N(t) = n] = P[N(t) < n + 1] - P[N(t) \leq n]$$
$$= F_{\tau_n}(t) - F_{\tau_{n+1}}(t) \tag{6.114}$$

For the Poisson process Eq. (6.113) substituted into (6.114) yields

$$P[N(t) = n] = \int_0^t \frac{\lambda(\lambda\xi)^{n-1}e^{-\lambda\xi}}{(n-1)!}\, d\xi - \int_0^t \frac{\lambda(\lambda\xi)^n e^{-\lambda\xi}}{n!}\, d\xi \tag{6.115}$$

Using the integral table given in Appendix C, one obtains

$$F_{\tau_n}(t) = \int_0^t \frac{\lambda(\lambda\xi)^{n-1}e^{-\lambda\xi}}{(n-1)!} = 1 - \sum_{r=0}^{n-1} \frac{e^{-\lambda t}(\lambda t)^r}{r!} \tag{6.116}$$

Substituting Eq. (6.116) into Eq. (6.115) yields

$$P[N(t) = n] = \sum_{r=0}^{n} \frac{e^{-\lambda t}(\lambda t)^r}{r!} - \sum_{r=0}^{n-1} \frac{e^{-\lambda t}(\lambda t)^r}{r!} = \frac{(\lambda t)^n e^{-\lambda t}}{n!} \tag{6.117}$$

Thus, we have shown that the number of renewals has a Poisson distribution. Evaluating Eq. (6.117) for $n = 1$ yields

$$P[N(t) = 1] = \lambda t e^{-\lambda t}$$

and for $t = 1/\lambda$

$$P\left[N\left(\frac{1}{\lambda}\right) = 1\right] = 0.368$$

Another quantity of interest is the mean number of renewals, which is given by the expected value of Eq. (6.114), where the expected value is taken with respect to $n$. Since $n$ is a discrete variable, the expected-value formula is a summation rather than an integral

$$E[N(t)] = \sum_{n=0}^{\infty} nP[N(t) = n]$$

From Eq. (6.114)

$$E[N(t)] = \sum_{n=0}^{\infty} n[F_{\tau_n}(t) - F_{\tau_{n+1}}(t)]$$

Writing out a few terms in the summation leads to

$$E[N(t)] = \sum_{n=1}^{\infty} F_{\tau_n}(t) \tag{6.118}$$

One can use Eqs. (6.118) and (6.116) directly, but it is easier to deal with the Laplace transforms. Using Theorem 3 in Table 2.12,

$$F_{\tau_n}^*(s) = \mathcal{L}\left\{\int_0^t f(\tau_n)\,d\tau_n\right\} = \frac{1}{s} f_{\tau_n}^*(s)$$

Substituting from Eq. (6.109),

$$F_{\tau_n}^*(s) = \frac{[f^*(s)]^n}{s}$$

Taking the Laplace transform of Eq. (6.118) and substituting yields

$$E^*[N(s)] = \frac{1}{s}\{f^*(s) + [f^*(s)]^2 + \cdots\}$$

Using the identity $x/(1 - x) = x + x^2 + \cdots$, we obtain

$$E^*[N(s)] = \frac{f^*(s)}{s[1 - f^*(s)]} \qquad (6.119)$$

for a Poisson process $f^*(s) = \lambda/(s + \lambda)$ and

$$E^*[N(s)] = \frac{\lambda}{s^2}$$

The corresponding time function is

$$E[N(t)] = \lambda t \qquad (6.120)$$

thus, the number of renewals in a Poisson process increases linearly with time. The renewal rate is defined as the time derivative of $E[N(t)]$, which yields from Eq. (6.120)

$$\frac{dE[N(t)]}{dt} = \lambda = \text{const}$$

Of course different results are obtained for other than Poisson processes.

We have now derived several important results. The distribution of time of the $n$th renewal is given by Eq. (6.109) and for the case of a Poisson process by Eq. (6.113). The probability of $n$ renewals as a function of time is given by Eq. (6.114) and for the Poisson process by Eq. (6.117). The expected number of renewals is given by either Eq. (6.118) or Eq. (6.119), and for the Poisson process by Eq. (6.120).

In some cases Eqs. (6.109), (6.114), and (6.118) reduce to certain limiting forms independent of the density functions $f(t)$.† If we use the notation

$$E(t) = \int_0^\infty \xi f(\xi)\, d\xi = m$$
$$\text{var } t = \int_0^\infty (\xi - m)^2 f(\xi)\, d\xi = \sigma$$

we can state

1   For $n \to \infty$, the density function $f(\tau_n)$, Eq. (6.109), approaches a normal distribution in the limit. The limiting normal distribution has a mean $m$ and a variance $\sigma^2/n$. This result is a consequence of the central-limit theorem.
2   Applying similar reasoning to Eq. (6.114), as $n \to \infty$, $t \to \infty$, and $P[N(t) = n]$ becomes normally distributed with mean $t/m$ and variance $\sigma^2 t/m^3$.

† Cox, op. cit., p. 40.

3   Working with Eq. (6.119) and applying the final-value theorem of Laplace transforms, one obtains for $t \rightarrow \infty$ that

$$E[N(t)] = t/m + (\sigma^2 - m^2)/2m^2$$

This also implies that in the limit the renewal rate becomes

$$dE[N(t)]/dt = 1/m$$

So far the mathematics and derivations have treated the renewal of only a single component. In general we are interested in the replacement (renewal) problem for a system with many components, some of which will be identical, but many will differ. Thus, we are in practice really interested in the *superposition* of renewal processes. The easiest quantity to deal with first is the number of renewals. If we have a three-component unit, the total number of renewals will be given by

$$N_T(t) = N_1(t) + N_2(t) + N_3(t) \tag{6.121}$$

The density function for the total number of renewals $f_{N_T}$ is given by the convolution of $f_{N_1}$, $f_{N_2}$, and $f_{N_3}$. Or in terms of the Laplace transforms

$$f_{N_T}^*(s) = f_{N_1}^*(s)f_{N_2}^*(s)f_{N_3}^*(s) \tag{6.122}$$

To compute $f_{N_1}^*(s)$ one takes the Laplace transform of Eq. (6.114), makes use of the theorem

$$\mathcal{L}\left\{ \int_0^t f(t)\,dt \right\} = \frac{1}{s} f^*(s)$$

and substitutes from Eq. (6.109), obtaining

$$f_{N_1}^*(s) = \frac{[f_1^*(s)]^{n_1}}{s}[1 - f_1^*(s)] \tag{6.123a}$$

Thus, Eq. (6.122) becomes

$$f_{N_T}^*(s) = \frac{[f_1^*(s)]^{n_1}[f_2^*(s)]^{n_2}[f_3^*(s)]^{n_3}}{s^3}[1 - f_1^*(s)][1 - f_2^*(s)][1 - f_3^*(s)] \tag{6.123b}$$

Inversion of Eq. (6.123b) will give $f_{N_T}(t)$.

Since we are now dealing with the superposition of sums of random variables, the arguments for using the central-limit theorem and obtaining limiting forms are even stronger. Specifically one can state[1] that

---

[1] Cox, *op. cit.*, pp. 73, 77–79.

for $k$ superposed (*pooled*) processes:

1   If each process is Poisson with parameter $\lambda$, the pooled process is Poisson with parameter $k\lambda$.
2   For arbitrary processes, if a large number is pooled, the output approaches a Poisson process.
3   As $k$ becomes large, the time between renewals approaches an exponential distribution with parameter $k\lambda$.
4   The distribution of the $n$th failure time of the pooled process becomes normal asymptotically with mean $nm/r$ and variance $n\sigma^2/r^2$.
5   The distribution of the number of renewals $N_T(t)$ becomes asymptotically normal with mean $rt/m$ and variance $r\sigma^2 t/m$.

Having briefly discussed some of the mathematics of replacement, we shall now turn to repair processes. This subject can be treated as an alternating renewal process with failure 1 followed by repair 1 followed by failure 2, etc. By analogy to Eq. (6.107) one can write

$$\begin{aligned}
\tau_n &= t_1 + T_1 + t_2 + T_2 + \cdots + t_n + T_n \\
&= (t_1 + t_2 + \cdots + t_n) + (T_1 + T_2 + \cdots + T_n)
\end{aligned} \qquad (6.124)$$

where $t_1, t_2, \ldots, t_n$ = operating times
$\quad T_1, T_2, \ldots, T_n$ = repair times
It is convenient to introduce two new variables, the system downtime $D_n$ and the system up time $U_n$, which are defined by

$$\begin{aligned}
U_n &= t_1 + t_2 + \cdots + t_n \\
D_n &= T_1 + T_2 + \cdots + T_n \\
\tau_m &= U_n + D_n
\end{aligned} \qquad (6.125)$$

Letting $f_1(t), f_2(t), \ldots, f_n(t)$ be the failure density functions, as before, and $g_1(t), g_2(t), \ldots, g_n(t)$ the repair density functions, we obtain

$$f_{U_n}^*(s) = f_1^*(s)f_2^*(s) \cdots f_n^*(s) \qquad (6.126)$$
$$f_{D_n}^*(s) = g_1^*(s)g_2^*(s) \cdots g_n^*(s) \qquad (6.127)$$
$$f_{\tau_m}^*(s) = f_1^*(s)g_1^*(s)f_2^*(s)g_2^*(s) \cdots f_n^*(s)g_n^*(s) \qquad (6.128)$$

These equations allow one (after taking inverse transforms) to find the distribution of system up time, the distribution of system downtime, and the time to the $n$th system renewal (repair completion). If we wish the time to the $n$th system *failure*, we must use $f_{\tau_m}^*(s)/g_n^*(s)$, that is, leave the last repair out of Eq. (6.128). We can use the preceding results in conjunction with Eq. (6.114) to compute the distribution of the number of failures or repairs. Also Eq. (6.119) can be used to calculate the expected number.  To compute the *expected number of repairs* if both failure and repair densities are exponential, we have

$$f_1^*(s) = \frac{\lambda}{s + \lambda} \qquad g_1^*(s) = \frac{\mu}{s + \mu}$$

Substituting in Eq. (6.119),

$$f^*(s) = f_1^*(s)g_1^*(s) = \frac{\lambda\mu}{(s + \lambda)(s + \mu)}$$

therefore

$$E^*[N(s)] = \frac{\lambda\mu/[(s + \lambda)(s + \mu)]}{s\left[1 - \dfrac{\lambda\mu}{(s + \lambda)(s + \mu)}\right]} = \frac{\lambda\mu}{s^2(s + \lambda + \mu)}$$

$$= \frac{\lambda\mu/(\lambda + \mu)}{s^2} - \frac{\lambda\mu/(\lambda + \mu)^2}{s} + \frac{\lambda\mu/(\lambda + \mu)^2}{s + \lambda + \mu}$$

$$E[N(t)] = \frac{\lambda\mu}{\lambda + \mu}t - \frac{\lambda\mu}{(\lambda + \mu)^2}(1 - e^{-(\lambda+\mu)t}) \tag{6.129}$$

To compare the *expected number of failures*

$$\frac{E^*[N(s)]}{g(s)} = \frac{\lambda(s + \mu)}{s^2(s + \lambda + \mu)}$$

Partial-fraction expansion and inversion yields the expected number of failures

$$\frac{\lambda\mu}{\lambda + \mu}t + \frac{\lambda^2}{(\lambda + \mu)^2}(1 - e^{-(\lambda+\mu)t}) \tag{6.130}$$

One may also relate up time and downtime to availability.  Remembering the frequency interpretation of availability we write,

$$A(\infty) = \lim_{t \to \infty} \frac{U(t)}{U(t) + D(t)} \tag{6.131}$$

or more specifically

$$A(\infty) = \frac{\lim\limits_{t \to \infty} E[U(t)]}{\lim\limits_{t \to \infty} E[U(t) + D(t)]} = \frac{\lim\limits_{t \to \infty} E[U(t)]}{\lim\limits_{t \to \infty} E[U(t)] + E[D(t)]}$$

Applying asymptotic results

$$A(\infty) = \frac{nm_u}{nm_u + nm_d} \tag{6.132}$$

where $m_u \equiv$ mean up time and
$\qquad m_d \equiv$ mean downtime

If the uptime and downtime are exponentially distributed with parameters $\lambda$ and $\mu$, respectively, then $m_u = 1/\lambda$, and $m_d = 1/\mu$. Thus,

$$A(\infty) = \frac{n/\lambda}{n/\lambda + n/\mu} = \frac{\mu}{\lambda + \mu} \tag{6.133}$$

which checks with Eq. (6.79).

The further study of system downtime generates several useful measures of system performance. The maintainability of a system $M(t)$ is generally defined as the probability that a failed system will be repaired within $t$ hr. Thus

$$M(t) = \int_0^t g(\xi)\, d\xi$$

The expected value of repair time $E[g(t)]$ is called the mean time to repair, MTTR. For an exponential repair distribution this yields MTTR $= E(\mu e^{-\mu t}) = 1/\mu$ hr. Another important measure is the distribution of cumulative downtime $D(t)$, where $t$ is the time of system operation. This function is independent of the number of renewals $n$. For the case of exponential failure and repair[1]

$$P[D(t) < x] = e^{-\lambda(t-x)} \left[ 1 + \sqrt{\lambda\mu(t-x)} \int_0^x e^{-\mu z} z^{-\frac{1}{2}} I_1(2\sqrt{\lambda\mu(t-x)z})\, dz \right]$$
$$\tag{6.134}$$

where $I_1$ is a Bessel function of the first kind and order one. In the limit, as $t \to \infty$ one can show that[2] $D(t)$ is normally distributed with mean

$$\lim_{t \to \infty} E[D(t)] \to \frac{m_r}{m_f + m_r} t \tag{6.135}$$

where $m_r \equiv$ mean of $g(t)$
$\quad\quad m_f \equiv$ mean of $f(t)$
and the variance is given by

$$\lim_{t \to \infty} \text{var}\,[D(t)] \to \frac{(m_r^2\sigma_f^2 + m_f^2\sigma_r^2)t}{(m_f + m_r)^3} \tag{6.136}$$

Where $\sigma_r \equiv$ variance of $g(t)$
$\quad\quad \sigma_f \equiv$ variance of $f(t)$
A complete discussion and derivation of these last two equations as well as the other material in this section on repair appears in Muth's work.[3]

---

[1] R. E. Barlow and L. C. Hunter, Reliability Analysis of a One Unit System, *J. Operations Res. Soc. Am.*, vol. 9, no. 2, March–April, 1961.

[2] L. Takacs, On Certain Sojourn Time Problems in the Theory of Stochastic Processes, *Acta Math. Hung.*, 1957, p. 169.

[3] Muth, *op. cit.*

## PROBLEMS

6.1   Make a structural model for a monaural and a stereo high-fidelity system. Using the information given in Fig. 1.2 and Figs. 4.5 to 4.15, estimate the reliability functions for the two devices.

6.2   Repeat Prob. 6.1 for a black and white and a color television set.

6.3   The circuit shown in the figure represents a simple one-stage transistor amplifier. Assume that each component is necessary for proper circuit operation. Compare the reliability of design $A$, where all components operate at maximum ratings, with design $B$, where a 50 percent derating factor is used. Comment on size, weight, cost, etc.

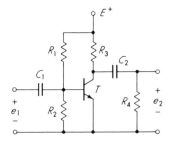

**Fig. P 6.3**

6.4   A motor drives a load through a gear train as shown. The load torque is fixed at $T_2 = 0.1$ ft-lb, but the load speed $\omega_2$ can be varied over a wide range. Assume that when $\omega_1 = 5,000$ rpm and $T_2$ is 0.1 ft-lb the motor is operating at one-half power. Sketch load power $T_2\omega_2$ vs. gear ratio $d_2/d_1$. Use Fig. 4.14 and sketch on the same graph the reliability for 1 year of operation as a function of $d_2/d_1$.

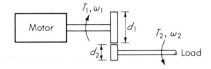

**Fig. P 6.4**

6.5   In designing an electric automobile many features would be changed from the present state of the art because of inherent differences in the two devices. List as many as you can. How would they effect reliability? Whenever such a major design change is undertaken, there is ample opportunity to discard previous design concepts which have been unchallenged and accepted as state of the art. List several changes which could be instituted at such a time and which would improve automobile reliability.

6.6   Repeat Prob. 6.3 using the failure rates for Minuteman parts and ordinary parts quoted in Table 6.2.

    ($a$)  Compare MTTF for both amplifiers and the time $t_1$ at which the reliability drops to 0.9.

(b) Compare the ratios of the two MTTF values and the two values of $t_1$. Comment.

(c) Comment on size, weight, cost, etc.

6.7 How would you set a reliability standard for a transportation vehicle such as an automobile, train, or plane in which vehicle failure might endanger human lives?

6.8 Explain how you could apply redundancy on the component or unit level to the circuit of Prob. 6.3.

(a) Compute the reliability gain using unit redundancy.

(b) Compute the reliability gain using component redundancy for those components where it is feasible.

(c) Discuss any assumptions or additional information which you would need for complete solution of this problem.

6.9 Repeat Prob. 6.8 for the system of Prob. 6.4.

6.10 We wish to remodel the braking systems shown in Fig. 6.2 to include leakage failures. Assume that each component has a leakage failure mode as well as a blocked failure mode.

(a) Formulate a reliability graph for each of the four systems given in Fig. 6.2.

(b) Compute the reliability of perfect and safe braking.

(c) Assume all components are independent and identical and have a probability of leakage failure of $q_l$ and an equal probability of open failures $q_o$.

6.11 The series system shown has the success probabilities indicated. We desire an overall system with a reliability of 0.99.

(a) Compute the amount of unit reliability needed to raise $R$ to the desired value.

(b) Repeat part $a$ for the case of component redundancy.

(c) Suppose units $A$, $B$, and $C$ cost \$1,000, \$3,000, and \$5,000, respectively. Would this change your approach any in parts $a$ and $b$?

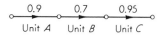

**Fig. P 6.11**

6.12 Redundant diodes might be placed either in series or parallel, depending on the ratio of open to short failures. Let $p$ be the probability a diode is good, $q_o$ be the probability of an open failure, and $q_s$ the probability of a short failure.

(a) How should one apply redundancy if $q_o + q_s = 0.1$ and $q_o/q_s = 0$, 0.25, 0.50, 0.75, 1.00?

(b) What is the maximum system reliability for each of these cases [see Eq. (6.35)]?

6.13 Compare the improvement obtained using component and unit redundancy to raise the reliability of this structure.

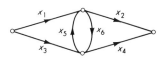

**Fig. P 6.13**

6.14   Repeat Prob. 6.13 for transmission path $AB$ in the graph.   Also calculate the results for path $AC$.

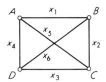

**Fig. P 6.14**

6.15   Describe several actual engineering devices or systems which require high reliability and which would benefit from redundancy.   Describe how you would employ redundancy and discuss any associated practical problems.

6.16   Look up a standard circuit for a transistor audio preamplifier.   Predict its reliability using discrete components by using the data given in Figs. 4.5 to 4.15. Compare this with the expected reliability of an integrated circuit using the model associated with Table 6.3.

6.17†   We wish to reinvestigate the redundant half-adder circuit given in Fig. 6.12.

    (a)   Assume that when a gate fails, it produces the complement of the correct output.   On the basis of this assumption, analyze the circuit of Fig. 6.12 and compute its reliability.

    (b)   Assume a three-state model for gate failures where the gate can fail stuck zero or stuck one and compute the probability of a correct transmission.

6.18†   We wish to compare the effect of using a majority voter constructed using the logic of Fig. 6.20 and one using the circuit of Fig. 6.22.   Compare the voter reliabilities using the reliability data for resistors and transistors from Chap. 4, for three, five, and seven circuit voters.   Over what time period will the voters satisfy the minimum voter reliability given in Table 6.6?

6.19†   Compute the reliability of a two-bit parallel binary *full-adder*, which uses a minimum number of NAND gates.   (Assume that the input numbers are $x_2x_1$ and $y_2y_1$ and that $x_1$, $\bar{x}_1$, $x_2$, $\bar{x}_2$, $y_1$, $\bar{y}_1$, $y_2$, $\bar{y}_2$ are available as inputs.)

6.20†   Compute the improvement obtained if a three-element voter is used to improve the reliability of the full-adder described in Prob. 6.19.

    (a)   Assume a perfect voter.

    (b)   Include the voter reliability.

6.21†   (a)   Compute the reliability of the circuit given in Fig. 6.24d.

    (b)   Plot the result as a function of $q_o/q_s$ and compare with a single switch.

    (c)   If $q_o + q_s = 0.01$, plot the reliability function vs. $q_o/q_s$.

    (d)   Compare the results of part $c$ with the bounds given by Eqs. (6.50) to (6.52).

6.22†   Repeat Prob. 6.21 for the circuit given in Fig. 6.24e.

6.23   (a)   For system $A$ compute the value of $t_1$ for which $R_A(t_1) = 0.90$.

    (b)   Choose $\lambda_2$ and $\lambda_3$ so that $R_B(t_1) = 0.9$; also choose $\lambda_4$ and $\lambda_5$ so that $R_C(t_1) = 0.9$.

    (c)   Sketch $R_A(t)$, $R_B(t)$, and $R_C(t)$ over the range $0 < t < 2t_1$.

    (d)   Suppose the switch in system $C$ is not perfect.   How large can $\lambda_s$ be if $R_C(t) \geq R_B(t)$ over the range $0 < t < t_1$?

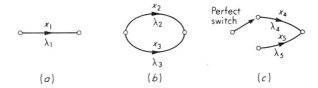

**Fig. P 6.23**

6.24* We wish to study further the standby-system model with an imperfect switch which resulted in the reliability function given in Eq. (6.62). State $s_5 = \bar{x}_1 x_2 \bar{x}_3$ represents failure of the on-line unit and the standby unit. If the switch fails first, this is system failure, and if the switch fails second, we are already using the good off-line component, and the system succeeds. To account for this we can split $s_5$ into two ordered states: $s_5' = \bar{x}_1 x_2 \bar{x}_3$ (where $\bar{x}_1$ fails first), which is a successful state, and $s_5'' = \bar{x}_3 x_2 \bar{x}_1$ (where $\bar{x}_3$ fails first), which is a failed state. Now all the branches which entered $s_5$ must enter either $s_5'$ or $s_5''$. The *sequence* of failures determines how the branches are connected. The branches leaving $s_5'$ and $s_5''$ must be the same as those which left $s_5$. Compute the reliability function for this model and compare with Eq. (6.62).

6.25 Assume that we are to apply standby redundancy to an $n$-stage transistor amplifier, where each stage is similar to the one given in Prob. 6.3. Suppose that the failure detection circuit contains two transistors and the failure switching circuit two transistors. The total complexity of the "switch" is roughly 4 times that given by the circuit in Prob. 6.3. What is the minimum value of $n$ if the standby circuit is to improve the basic amplifier reliability?

6.26† Can you devise a failure-detection and switching circuit similar to that described in Prob. 6.25? Explain and discuss any assumptions.

6.27 For a single component with repair $R(t)$ and $A(t)$ are given by Eqs. (6.75), (6.78), and (6.79). If we specify that $R(t_1) = 0.9$,

(a) What can you say about $A(t_1)$?

(b) How are $\lambda$ and $\mu$ constrained if $A(t_1) \geq 0.99$?

6.28 Refer to the reliability functions given in Table 6.13.

(a) Use a series expansion to sketch and compare these reliability functions in the high-reliability region.

(b) Compute a *few* points and sketch these functions over a wider region.

6.29 Repeat Prob. 6.28 for the availability functions given in Table 6.14.

6.30 We wish to examine the approximations for Eq. (6.94).

(a) Derive the approximate root expression if $\mu'$ and $\mu'' > \lambda$ and $\lambda'$.

(b) When are the roots real, when are they complex?

(c) When are $r_3$ and $r_4$ complex conjugates with equal real and imaginary parts? Sketch $A(t)$ for this case.

6.31 By setting the state probability derivatives equal to zero solve for $A(\infty)$ for each case given in Table 6.14. Verify the values for $A(\infty)$ given in the table.

CHAPTER
7

# drift failures, component tolerances, and parameter variations

## 7.1 INTRODUCTION

The preceding chapters have considered catastrophic failures, where the part in question underwent a radical change that characterized its failure. A simple example is an electrical resistor which fails as a short or open circuit. Similarly a mechanical disk clutch might jam and lock, or the plates might separate so that no torque could be transmitted. There are modes of failure other than catastrophic ones. If a resistor neither shorts nor opens but changes in value either up or down by a large amount, it may cause significant enough changes in circuit performance to constitute a failure.

For example, suppose the output of a photocell in a sensitive photographic exposure meter is to be amplified by a transistor amplifier and read on a meter. If the resistor in question affects the gain of the amplifier, it also affects the meter calibration. If a change in resistance results in an increase in gain, it will indicate more light than is actually present and result in underexposure, whereas the converse effect would lead to overexposure. The tolerable change in calibration might be set by experiment, accuracy claimed for the meter, or engineering judgment. Sometimes the standard of good or bad, operative or inoperative, is highly subjective. In the case of a clutch, if it is part of an automobile power train, it must satisfy the driver; for if the owner returns the car for service during the warranty period because he feels clutch slippage, the part has failed.

Failures such as these may occur for a variety of reasons. If the initial tolerance on parts is too large, many items will fail inspection tests after assembly or soon after being put into use. Similarly, the variance for a particular parameter distribution will change with time and use. Most commonly the drift of the parameters will be such as to increase the spread, increasing the parameter variance. Thus, the percentage of extreme values which now appear in the tails of the distributions will increase and cause an increased probability of drift failures. A gradual drift of the mean in either direction can cause similar results. If environmental conditions radically change component parameters either in a reversible or irreversible fashion, the system will experience a temporary or permanent drift failure.

If the system in question is a missile system or navigation system, the performance function of interest is generally the system accuracy. An analytical or computer description of how system accuracy varies as parameters vary is often called an *error analysis* or *accuracy analysis*. The methods and techniques are virtually the same as those used in a reliability analysis. The main difference is that an accuracy analysis is done to determine whether the system operates well or only in a mediocre fashion. (It is assumed that the engineering was competent enough to rule out poor operation.) In the case of reliability analysis one wishes to answer the questions how often or what percentage of the time will the system be successful? Unsuccessful?

Another interesting point regards environmental effects. Some people argue that if the environmental variation is due to some well-known parameter such as temperature, the variations in the components and the respective variations in system performance are predictable in a deterministic sense, and probabilistic techniques are not needed. This is, of course true only as long as the temperature is known. If only the range of temperature is known, then temperature is a random variable, and probabilistic methods are required. Of course, if the temperature was controlled to within a fraction of a degree, there would be negligible component variation due to temperature. This would merely mean that the temperature effect would not contribute significantly to the parameter variations caused by other sources.

The overall reliability of a system is the probability that the system experiences neither a catastrophic nor a marginal system failure. If the two failure modes are independent, this is simply the product of the catastrophic reliability and the marginal reliability. Since the former has already been established in the preceding chapters, this chapter will focus on the computation of marginal reliability based on models for the parameter statistics.

Several deterministic (nonprobabilistic) approaches to this problem are first discussed. The general probabilistic approach is then discussed to cast the problem in its correct theoretical framework. Unfortunately, only a small percentage of practical problems have a simple solution. The majority result in an integral which cannot be reduced to simplified form. Those problems which do result in an elementary solution are tabulated. In addition to these solutions, the exact formulation clearly reveals the assumptions which are inherent in the deterministic approaches (but are seldom stated).

Fortunately, if we assume that parameter variations in a well-designed system are small, simple approximations are possible. This approach yields accurate results as well as some physical feeling for the manner in which the individual parameter variations combine to yield system variations.

The latter sections of the chapter relate the approximate statistical approach to sensitivity calculations, which have been popular for some time in circuit and control-system analysis. Several circuit and system examples are given to illustrate how such computations can be made in practice. Of course, the beneficial effect of negative feedback in reducing parameter variations is apparent in the examples.

The mathematical background for the material covered in this chapter appears in Sec. 6.9.

## 7.2 MARGINAL AND CATASTROPHIC FAILURES

Obviously for a system to be successful, it must experience neither a catastrophic nor a marginal failure. If we let $x_s$ represent the event system success and $x_c$ and $x_m$ the events no catastrophic failure and no marginal failure, respectively, then

$$R(t) = P(x_s) = P(x_c x_m) \tag{7.1}$$

If we assume that marginal and catastrophic failures are independent,[1] then $R(t) = P(x_c)P(x_m)$. Defining $P(x_c) = R_c(t)$ and $P(x_m) = R_m(t)$, we have

$$R(t) = R_c(t)R_m(t) \tag{7.2}$$

---

[1] One might reason that there is dependence if one can show that poor components fail quickly via marginal or catastrophic means whereas good components seem to last a long while before either effect causes failure. Thus, in such a case $P(x_m|x_c)$ or $P(x_c|x_m)$ may be larger than $P(x_m)$ and $P(x_c)$ after a period of time.

Using Eqs. (4.16) and (4.17), we obtain

$$f(t) = \dot{R}(t) = R_c(t)\dot{R}_m(t) + \dot{R}_c(t)R_m(t)$$
$$z(t) = \frac{f(t)}{R(t)} = \frac{\dot{R}_m(t)}{R_m(t)} + \frac{\dot{R}_c(t)}{R_c(t)}$$

If we let

$$\dot{R}_c(t) = f_c(t) \qquad \dot{R}_m(t) = f_m(t)$$
$$\frac{\dot{R}_c(t)}{R_c(t)} = z_c(t) \qquad \frac{\dot{R}_m(t)}{R_m(t)} = z_m(t)$$

we obtain

$$f(t) = R_c(t)f_m(t) + R_m(t)f_c(t) \tag{7.3}$$

and

$$z(t) = z_c(t) + z_m(t) \tag{7.4}$$

Thus, we see that the density function is a weighted sum of the individual densities, whereas the hazard function is simply the sum of the catastrophic and marginal failures. This implies that in analyzing failure data, it is easier to separate the two effects if one deals with the hazard rather than the density function. Equation (7.2) tells us that we can use the techniques of the preceding chapters to compute $R_c(t)$ and deal separately with $R_m(t)$ using the techniques of this chapter.

## 7.3 MARGINAL FAILURES IN TIME

In the preceding section we saw how one can treat marginal failures as a separate probability function. In this section we shall concentrate on how this probability function changes in time.

We assume that some system performance or goodness parameter $G$ is related to several internal system parameters $x_1, x_2, \ldots, x_n$. The density function of $G$, $f_G(t)$, is a time function and is related to the density functions for the internal parameters $f_{x_1}(t), f_{x_2}(t), \ldots, f_{x_n}(t)$, which are also time functions. Following sections of this chapter treat the problem of relating $f_c(t)$ to $f_{x_1}(t), f_{x_2}(t), \ldots, f_{x_n}(t)$ or relating probability statements about $f_G(t)$ to equivalent statements about $f_{x_1}(t), f_{x_2}(t), \ldots, f_{x_n}(t)$. We assume that this problem is already solved and that we know either exactly or roughly the shape of $f_G(t)$ and its first and second moments and that in a large number of cases $f_G$ will be normal.

The marginal reliability can be simply related to $f_G$. If we assume that the system succeeds if $G_l < G < G_u$, then

$$R_m(t) = P_s(t) = P(G_l < \mathbf{G} \leq G_u) = \int_{G_l}^{G_u} f_G(\xi,t) \, d\xi \qquad (7.5)$$

$$1 - R_m(t) = P_f(t) = P(\mathbf{G} < G_l \text{ or } \mathbf{G} > G_u) = \int_0^{G_l} f_G(\xi,t) \, dt$$
$$+ \int_{G_u}^{\infty} f_G(\xi,t) \, dt \quad (7.6)$$

Of course if the $G$ function has more than one acceptable region, $R_m(t)$ is the sum of several integrals, one for each region. As time increases, the shape and location of $f_G(G,t)$ change, and therefore so does $R_m(t)$. (One may also wish to let $G_l$ and $G_u$ be functions of $t$, as discussed in the following section.)

In general, one would attempt to adjust $f_G(G,t)$ by choosing appropriate initial values of the parameters $x_1(0)$, $x_2(0)$, . . . , $x_n(0)$ so that $R_m(0)$ is a maximum (close to unity). This initial choice of values will be called the *initial-tolerance problem* in the remainder of this chapter. As time increases, one would expect that the changes in the internal parameters, i.e., the parameter drifts due to aging, temperature, etc., would be reflected in slow changes in $f_G(G,t)$. In almost all situations these drifts would be expected to reduce the area under $f_G(G,t)$ between $G_l$ and $G_u$ and consequently reduce $R_m(t)$.[1]

One can think of these drifts as manifesting themselves in four different ways:

1   The mean shifts up or down.
2   The variance increases.
3   A combination of effects 1 and 2.
4   A change in the shape of the distribution, alone or accompanied by effects 1 to 3.

If we argue that $f_G(G,t)$ will probably be normal because of the effects of the central-limit theorem, we have every reason to believe that the distribution will remain so as drift occurs. In general, a system is designed so that $R_m(t) \approx 1$. This means that Eq. (7.6) represents the sum of the areas in the tails of the distributions. If the distribution is reduced to the unit variance, zero mean normal, then the area can be approximated by a series expansion for large values of the variable (see Appendix C, integral 6)

$$\frac{1}{\sqrt{2\pi}} \int_x^{\infty} e^{-\xi^2/2} \, d\xi = \frac{1}{\sqrt{2\pi}} \frac{e^{-x^2/2}}{x} \left[ 1 - \frac{1}{x^2} + \frac{1(3)}{x^4} - \frac{1(3)(5)}{x^6} \cdots \right]$$
$$\approx \frac{1}{\sqrt{2\pi}} \frac{e^{-x^2/2}}{x} \qquad \text{for } x \text{ large} \qquad (7.7)$$

---

[1] One exception to this is a parameter that is purposely biased initially so that as things age, it will drift through its optimum value. Such is the case in the initial

The actual area under the tail of the unit-normal probability density is compared with the approximate value given by $e^{-x^2/2}/\sqrt{2\pi}$ in Fig. 7.1. Although the error decreases slowly, it is about 25 percent for $x \approx 1.5$, 10 percent for $x \approx 3$, and 1 percent for $x \approx 5$. The approximate expression is an upper bound, i.e., an optimistic result.

design of the picture width in a television set without a width control. Initially the picture is wider than the screen, but as the set ages, it just fits the tube, and as old age sets in, the picture shrinks so that it no longer fills the screen.

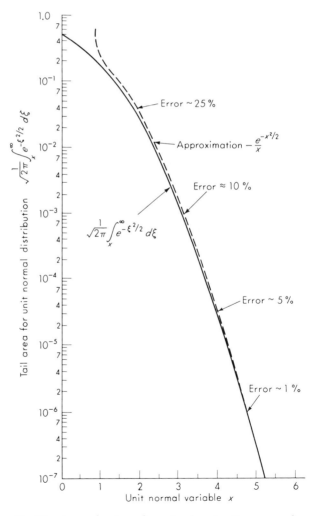

**Fig. 7.1** Approximate and exact values for the area under the tail of the normal distribution.

For example, if we require that for some range $0 < t < t_1$, $R_m(t) \geq 0.99$, we can compute the required maximum value of $x$. Assuming a normal distribution and symmetrical values of $G_l$ and $G_u$, half the probability is in each tail, and we require

$$\frac{1}{\sqrt{2\pi}} \int_x^\infty e^{-\xi^2/2} \, d\xi \leq 0.005$$

From Fig. 7.1 we see that $x \leq 3.3$ and that if the approximation were used, the error would be above 9 percent.

## 7.4  WEIGHTING FUNCTIONS AND MARGINAL FAILURES

In the previous section we assumed that our goodness function was acceptable over a certain range and unacceptable outside this range. This is a rather arbitrary criterion and is illogical in many cases. For example, suppose the goodness criterion happened to be the system accuracy; then it would be unreasonable to set this at 10 percent and consider a 9 percent accuracy as acceptable and an 11 percent accuracy as unacceptable. A more logical procedure is to weight the errors so that a 9 percent error receives a better score than 11 percent error yet both contribute to the overall scoring. This, of course, is the principle behind the circular rings on a pistol or archery target.

For a more sophisticated example we might consider the accuracy associated with an inertial guidance system used to guide a rocket designed to place a satellite in a parking orbit around the earth. Additional thrust rockets will be used to boost the satellite from the parking orbit into another working orbit. Obviously there is some best parking orbit which requires the least additional energy (fuel) to make the orbit change to the working orbit. This orbit can be rated maximum. There are also those parking orbits which require more than the available fuel and which should be rated zero. The family of orbits between these two extremes should be weighted between the maximum and zero in some manner inversely proportioned to the required orbit-change fuel expenditure. Thus, either accuracy or fuel expenditure could be used with an appropriate weighting function as the measure of goodness. A few typical weighting functions are given in Fig. 7.2.

If we let $W(G,t)$ be the system weighting function, the *weighted* marginal reliability becomes

$$R_{Wm}(t) = \int_{G_l}^{G_u} W(\xi,t) f_G(\xi,t) \, d\xi \tag{7.8}$$

The choice of what shape weighting function to use and the normalization of its parameters depend on the application. In some cases the weighting

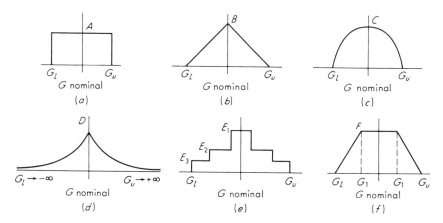

**Fig. 7.2** Typical weighting functions.  (a) Constant;  (b) linearly decreasing;  (c) quadrically decreasing;  (d) exponentially decreasing;  (e) stepwise decreasing;  (f) constant plus linearly decreasing.

function remains constant in time, whereas in others the shape and/or size may change.

## 7.5  DETERMINISTIC APPROACHES

The simple first approach to the problems discussed in the preceding sections is to ignore the probabilistic nature of the problem and attempt a deterministic solution.   Three common techniques that approach the problem in this manner are called *stacking up the tolerances, worst-case analysis,* and *parameter plots.*   These methods are discussed in this section.   Although deterministic in nature, all three approaches have an approximate probabilistic interpretation, which is discussed in Sec. 7.6.1. In each case the technique relates the deviation or tolerance, as the goodness criterion, to the internal parameter tolerances.

### 7.5.1  STACKING UP THE TOLERANCES

This technique was probably an outgrowth of the methods used in engineering drawing to compute the overall tolerance on a device knowing the tolerance on each part.   The procedure is to merely take the sum of the individual tolerances and use this as the system tolerance.   This is best illustrated by an example.

Figure 7.3 shows a voltage divider consisting of three parts, the input voltage source $e_1$, resistor $R_1$, and resistor $R_2$.   The goodness parameter, or performance index, is simply the percentage change in the output

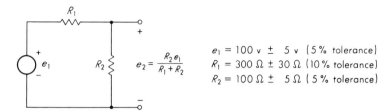

$e_1 = 100 \text{ v} \pm 5 \text{ v}$ (5% tolerance)

$R_1 = 300 \ \Omega \pm 30 \ \Omega$ (10% tolerance)

$R_2 = 100 \ \Omega \pm 5 \ \Omega$ (5% tolerance)

**Fig. 7.3**   Voltage-divider network.

voltage $e_2$.   The nominal value of the output voltage $e_2$ is 25 volts.   To use the method known as stacking up the tolerances we would say that the tolerance on $e_2$ is the sum of the tolerances on $e_1$, $R_1$, and $R_2$, that is, 20 percent.   Thus $e_2$ would be $25 \pm 5$ volts.   This is a conservative but rather naïve approach to the problem.   Somewhat more insight is shown in the worst-case-analysis approach.

### 7.5.2   WORST-CASE ANALYSIS

This technique makes an honest attempt to determine how much change there will be in the performance parameter if all the constituent parts are at their extremes and combine in the worst possible manner. Again referring to the example of Fig. 7.3, the idea is to relate the minimum and maximum values of $e_2$ to the minimum and maximum values of $e_1$, $R_1$, and $R_2$.   A little thought shows that these values are given by

$$(e_2)_{\max} = \frac{(e_1)_{\max}}{1 + (R_1)_{\min}/(R_2)_{\max}} \tag{7.9}$$

$$(e_2)_{\min} = \frac{(e_1)_{\min}}{1 + (R_1)_{\max}/(R_2)_{\min}} \tag{7.10}$$

Substitution of numerical values of 105 and 95 volts, 330 and 270 and 105 and 95 ohms for the maximum and minimum values of $e_1$, $R_1$, and $R_2$ respectively into Eqs. (7.9) and (7.10) yields $(e_2)_{\max} = 28.4$ volts, and $(e_2)_{\min} = 21.2$ volts.   Thus, $(e_2)_{\text{nom}} = 25$ volts ($+13.6$ percent, $-15.2$ percent).   This method gives a somewhat more accurate solution than the previous one, and although strictly a deterministic approach, the method has a probabilistic interpretation, which will be discussed later.

If the performance index is a rather complicated function involving many parameters, it may be hard to decide by inspection which combination of values gives a maximum and minimum value of the index.   In such cases, approximating the performance index by the first few terms of a Taylor series expansion will simplify the problem.   The general form for a Taylor series expansion of a function of $n$ variables, $h(x_1, x_2, \ldots, x_n)$, is

$$h(x_1 + \Delta x_1, x_2 + \Delta x_2, \ldots, x_n + \Delta x_n) = \sum_{k=0}^{\infty} \frac{1}{k!} \left[ \left( \Delta x_1 \frac{\partial}{\partial x_1} \right. \right.$$
$$\left. \left. + \Delta x_2 \frac{\partial}{\partial x_2} + \cdots + \Delta x_n \frac{\partial}{\partial x_n} \right)^k h \right]_{op} \quad (7.11)$$

where all partial derivatives are to be evaluated at the expansion point or operating point, op. For illustrative purposes, we give the expansion of a function of three variables

$$h(x_1 + \Delta x_1, x_2 + \Delta x_2, x_3 + \Delta x_3) = h(x_1, x_2, x_3)$$
$$+ \frac{1}{1!} \left( \frac{\partial h}{\partial x_1} \Delta x_1 + \frac{\partial h}{\partial x_2} \Delta x_2 + \frac{\partial h}{\partial x_3} \Delta x_3 \right)_{op}$$
$$+ \frac{1}{2!} \left( \frac{\partial^2 h}{\partial x_1^2} \Delta x_1^2 + \frac{\partial^2 h}{\partial x_2^2} \Delta x_2^2 + \frac{\partial h^2}{\Delta x_3^2} \partial x_3^2 \right.$$
$$+ 2 \frac{\partial^2 h}{\partial x_1 \partial x_2} \Delta x_1 \Delta x_2 + 2 \frac{\partial^2 h}{\partial x_1 \partial x_3} \Delta x_1 \Delta x_3 + 2 \frac{\partial^2 h}{\partial x_2 \partial x_3} \Delta x_2 \Delta x_3 \Bigg)_{op}$$
$$+ \cdots \quad (7.12)$$

For the purposes of worst-case analysis it should be sufficient to retain the constant and the first-order terms.[1]

Returning to the voltage-divider example,

$$e_2(e_1 + \Delta e_1, R_1 + \Delta R_1, R_2 + \Delta R_2) = (e_2)_{op}$$
$$+ \left( \frac{\partial e_2}{\partial e_1} \right)_{op} \Delta e_1 + \left( \frac{\partial e_2}{\partial R_1} \right)_{op} \Delta R_1 + \left( \frac{\partial e_2}{\partial R_2} \right)_{op} \Delta R_2 + \cdots \quad (7.13)$$

where $e_2$ and its derivatives are evaluated at the nominal values of $e_1$, $R_1$, and $R_2$ and $\Delta e_1$, $\Delta R_1$, and $\Delta R_2$ are the variations from their nominal values. Evaluation of the first four terms in Eq. (7.13) yields

$$e_2 = \frac{R_2 e_1}{R_1 + R_2} = 25$$
$$\frac{\partial e_2}{\partial e_1} = \frac{1}{1 + R_1/R_2} = \frac{1}{4}$$
$$\frac{\partial e_2}{\partial R_1} = \frac{-e_1}{R_2(1 + R_1/R_2)^2} = -\frac{1}{16}$$
$$\frac{\partial e_2}{\partial R_2} = \frac{e_1 R_1}{R_2^2(1 + R_1/R_2)^2} = +\frac{3}{16}$$

[1] Computer circuit-analysis programs generally include worst-case-analysis options. See H. Wall, Circuit Analysis by Computer, *Electro-Technology*, November, 1966, for a description of the IBM ECAP program.

Substituting these values into Eq. (7.13), we obtain

$$e_2(e_1 + \Delta e_1, R_1 + \Delta R_1, R_2 + \Delta R_2) \approx 25$$
$$+ \tfrac{1}{4}\Delta e_1 - \tfrac{1}{16}\Delta R_1 + \tfrac{3}{16}\Delta R_2 \quad (7.14)$$

Again using worst-case techniques, $(e_2)_{max}$ occurs when $\Delta e_1 = +5$ volts, $\Delta R_1 = -30$ ohms, $\Delta R_2 = +5$ ohms, and $(e_2)_{min}$ occurs when $\Delta e_1 = -5$ volts, $\Delta R_1 = +30$ ohms, and $\Delta R_2 = -5$ ohms. The resulting values are $(e_2)_{max} = 29.06$ ($+16.2$ percent) and $(e_2)_{min} = 20.94$ ($-16.2$ percent). Of course for the simple example chosen, the exact equations given by Eqs. (7.9) and (7.10) are preferred; however, in a complex problem involving many parameters the Taylor series expansion may be the only feasible approach.

### 7.5.3 PARAMETER PLOTS (SCHMOO PLOTS)

A group of engineering techniques which have been used in particular situations and appear to have some general usefulness have been classified under the titles *marginal checking*[1] and *Schmoo plots*.[2] Marginal checking is perhaps most directly a technique for testing an existing system to determine its present state of performance and to judge whether degradation has occurred. An example will illustrate the procedure.

Anyone with a television set has probably noticed that a new and well-designed set has a large range over which the horizontal-hold control can be varied and still obtain a well-synchronized picture; in fact in most cases this is the entire range of adjustment. As the set ages, the range of lock-in reduces, and more critical adjustments are necessary. In fact, a disturbance such as airplane flutter or channel switching may throw the picture out. A set owner who does his own servicing would know that this reduction in range of lock-in signal is caused by aging of the set components, most probably a reduction in gain of a tube in the horizontal-synchronizing circuit. Assuming normal reluctance to bother opening the rear of a set, the replacement would probably wait until other maintenance was needed because of a catastrophic failure or until the picture completely went out of synchronization. On the other hand, this sort of a test would be simple to perform in any scheduled maintenance procedure and would be far more accurate than a simple tube checker in spotting incipient failures. Obviously, tests such as this could be done after assembly to check on the initial tolerance problem.

Taylor's paper[1] goes one step further and actually applies this technique at the breadboard stage to generate design curves. The particular parameter or parameters to be varied must be left to the ingenuity of the

[1] N. H. Taylor, Designing for Reliability, *Proc. IRE*, June, 1957.

[2] J. A. Connor in R. M. Meyers et al. (eds.), "Reliability Engineering for Electronic Systems," chap. 4, John Wiley & Sons, Inc., New York, 1964.

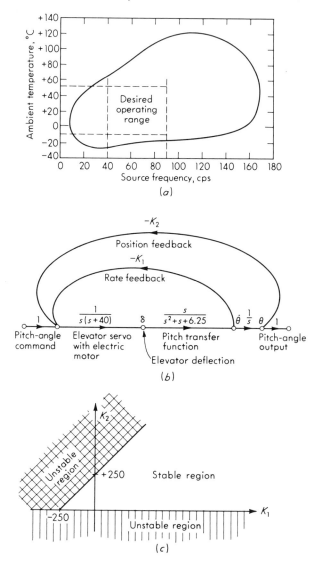

**Fig. 7.4**   Schmoo and non-Schmoo characteristics for an ac bridge network and a position control system.   (a) Parameter plot for an ac bridge network which exhibits the characteristic Schmoo shape; (b) crude representation of a pitch-axis aircraft autopilot, with position and rate feedback; (c) a parameter plane plot for a control system which has an open shape.   (*Part a from J. A. Connor, chap. 4 in R. M. Myers et. al. (eds.), "Reliability Engineering for Electronic Systems," John Wiley & Sons, Inc., New York, 1964; parts b and c from M. L. Shooman, "Stability Analysis of Two Parameter Control Systems," PIB-MRI 920-61, Polytechnic Institute of Brooklyn, Brooklyn, N.Y., 1961.*)

designer.   These ideas can be extended to the case of many parameters varying simultaneously by agreeing to treat the parameters in pairs, holding all others fixed.   Some performance or goodness parameter $G$ is chosen, the two parameters in question $x$ and $y$ are varied (either analytically or experimentally), and $G$ is measured.   A design curve is drawn from this information.

As an example consider an ac bridge network where the balance point is subject to variations in source frequency and environmental temperature.   The results of such an analysis are given in Fig. 7.4$a$.   The acceptable region is the locus of operating points with null shifts of less than 10 $\mu$v as frequency and temperature change.   Note that the desired operating region originally chosen should probably be shifted up and to the right to allow for adequate safety margins.   Taylor stated that such an analysis leads often to closed curves, and Connor suggests that the closed curve is commonly of the shape shown in Fig. 7.4$a$.   Those curves have been nicknamed Schmoo plots after the characters shaped like a bowling pin which appear from time to time in Al Capp's cartoon strip.   This reader must disagree with the statement that such a curve shape is common.

Figure 7.4$b$ depicts a case in which stability of a control system is the goodness measure and rate feedback $K_1$ and position feedback $K_2$ are the parameters.   Many other examples of this nature connected with control systems fail to portray this Schmoo-like behavior.   Furthermore, letting our goodness figure of merit be of the form $|G - G_{nom}|$ and plotting it along the $z$ axis with parameters $x$ and $y$ along the $x$ and $y$ axes, we find that $|G - G_{nom}| = 0$ when $x = x_{nom}$ and $y = y_{nom}$.   The surface described by this relation is above the $z = 0$ plane.   Parameter plane shapes represent the intersection of this surface with cutting planes perpendicular to the $z$ axis.   There is no reason to believe that in general this intersection will result in a closed curve.

Although one can make no general statement about the shape of parameter plane plots, they are obviously useful as a design tool to choose a good circuit operating point.   In fact, the distances from any operating point to the boundary measured parallel to the axes can be used to evaluate approximately the first partial derivatives needed in Eq. (7.11).

## 7.6  PROBABILISTIC APPROACHES

### 7.6.1  INTRODUCTION

The marginal system reliability was related to a goodness density function by Eq. (7.5).   Thus, a knowledge of $f_G(G,t)$ contains all the information necessary to compute the marginal reliability.   This section directly tackles the problem of how to compute $f_G(G,t)$ from the statistics of the parameters which $G$ depends on. It is important to note that exact solution of this problem requires complete information about the internal random variables $x_1(t)$, $x_2(t)$, . . . , $x_n(t)$. This means that we must know the distribution of each $x_i$, the parameters of the distribution, and how changes occur as a function of time. Some of the approximate approaches of Sec. 7.6 will require less information about the $x_i$'s.

The amount of information required for the exact solution generally will not be available. Also if the goodness function involves products, quotients, or any other nonlinear operations, solution in closed form is generally not possible. These are of course the reasons why the next section discusses approximations. Even though there are only a limited number of problems for which the exact approach is practical, it provides insight into the basis of the other techniques.

The performance parameter characterizing system operation is a function of $n$ parameters in general. The region(s) of satisfactory performance is therefore a hypervolume(s) in $n$-dimensional space. The deterministic techniques are really just statements about the extent of this region. A probabilistic approach answers the more realistic question of how probable it is that the system is satisfactory. If the points were evenly spaced in this volume, it would be easy to take just the ratios of good volume to total volume. Unfortunately the points have a variable density within the volume. What we are really interested in is the mass in the volume which will be obtained by integrating the mass density function.

### 7.6.2 PROBABILISTIC TRANSFORMATION OF VARIABLES

*One variable* The mathematical foundations of this method are discussed in detail in Chap. 2, and examples are given in this section which illustrate the main features of the technique. For example, one might wish to relate fluid flow to the area of an oil port in a hydraulic system. In simple cases the flow would be equal to a constant times the pressure times the area, flow = $KPA$. If the constant and the pressure were both fixed quantities and $KP = 1$, then the flow would be equal to the port area, which is a random variable. If the distribution of the hole diameter produced by the drill press used in fabricating the port is known, the problem is to find the area distribution from the known diameter distribution. One could then intelligently specify a tolerance on drilling diameter which would yield a desired area (flow) tolerance.

The change-of-variables theorem for one random variable is given by

$$h(u) = \left| \frac{dx}{du} \right| f[x(u)] \tag{2.93a}$$

where $\mathbf{x}$ = original random variable
$\mathbf{u}$ = transformed random variable

$f(x)$ = density function of $x$ (known)

$h(u)$ = density function of $u$ (quantity to be found)

$x(u)$ = formula relating $x$ to $u$

$\left| \dfrac{dx}{du} \right|$ = *absolute value* of the derivative of $x$ with respect to $u$

In the above problem $x$ = diameter $D$, $u$ = area $A$. These variables are related by $A = (\pi/4)D^2$, and the inverse of this formula is

$$D = \pm \sqrt{4A/\pi}$$

which is $x(u)$. The derivative $dx/du$ is $dD/dA$, which equals $\sqrt{1/A\pi}$. Thus to find $h(u)$ one substitutes $\sqrt{4A/\pi}$ for $x$ in the density function $f(x)$. Actually since there are two roots, one takes the sum of $f(+\sqrt{4A/\pi})$ and of $f(-\sqrt{4A/\pi})$. Multiplying this by $\sqrt{1/A\pi}$ yields $h(u)$, which is $h(A)$

$$h(A) = \sqrt{\frac{1}{A\pi}} \left[ f\left(\sqrt{\frac{4A}{\pi}}\right) + f\left(-\sqrt{\frac{4A}{\pi}}\right) \right] \tag{7.15}$$

To complete the problem the density function of $D$ must be given. If $D$ has a rectangular distribution

$$f(D) = \begin{cases} \dfrac{1}{b-a} & 0 < a < D < b \\ 0 & \text{elsewhere} \end{cases}$$

then substitution into (7.15) yields[1]

$$h(A) = \frac{1}{\sqrt{\pi}} A^{-\frac{1}{2}} \left( \frac{1}{b-a} + 0 \right) = \frac{1}{\sqrt{\pi}\,(b-a)} A^{-\frac{1}{2}}$$

$$\frac{\pi}{4} a^2 < A < \frac{\pi}{4} b^2 \tag{7.16}$$

A pictorial representation of this transformation is shown in Fig. 7.5a. If the hole diameter is represented by a normal density function, then

$$f(D) = \frac{1}{\sigma\sqrt{2\pi}} e^{-(D-\mu)^2/2\sigma^2} \qquad -\infty < D < +\infty$$

Substitution into Eq. (7.15) yields

$$h(A) = \sqrt{\frac{1}{A\pi}} \frac{1}{\sqrt{2\pi}\,\sigma} \left\{ \exp\left[ -\frac{(\sqrt{4A/\pi} - \mu)^2}{2\sigma^2} \right] \right.$$

$$\left. + \exp\left[ -\frac{(-\sqrt{4A/\pi} - \mu)^2}{2\sigma^2} \right] \right\} \tag{7.17}$$

[1] The function $f(D = +\sqrt{4A/\pi})$ is just the constant $1/(b-a)$. The function $f(D = -\sqrt{4A/\pi}) = 0$, since $f(D)$ is zero for all negative $D$.

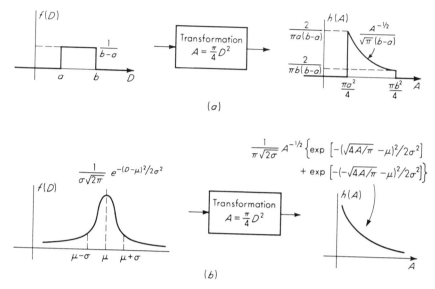

**Fig. 7.5**   Transformation of diameter density functions into area density functions. (a) Uniform diameter density function; (b) normal diameter density function.

Both roots of $D$ contribute to $h(A)$ in this example.   The normal distribution is defined over the range $-\infty < D < +\infty$.   Since negative diameters are logically inadmissible, the reader may question the validity of the model.   If $\mu > \sigma$, then the area under the normal curve for $D < 0$ is small, and little error will be introduced.   This will be the case in all the practical situations we shall discuss.

The effect of a transformation is to change the shape of the density function, which in turn changes the probabilities in the problem.   For example, in the case of the uniform density function intuition would tell us that the average area should be given by averaging the largest and smallest areas

$$A_{\text{av}} = \frac{(\pi/4)a^2 + (\pi/4)b^2}{2} = \frac{\pi}{8}(a^2 + b^2) \tag{7.18}$$

Actually we should compute the mean of the transformed distribution given in Eq. (7.16)

$$\mu_A = \int_{A_1}^{A_2} A h(A)\,dA = \int_{\pi a^2/4}^{\pi b^2/4} \frac{A^{\frac{1}{2}}}{\sqrt{\pi}\,(b-a)}\,dA$$

$$= \frac{\pi}{12}(a^2 + ab + b^2) \tag{7.19}$$

If $a \approx b$, then both equations (7.18) and (7.19) approach the quantity $(\pi/4)b^2$ and thereby yield the same answer. However, if $a \ll b$, then Eq. (7.18) becomes $(\pi/8)b^2$, and Eq. (7.19) becomes $(\pi/12)b^2$. The results differ by 30 percent. Equation (7.19) is, of course, the correct result, and Eq. (7.18) only an approximate solution motivated by intuition.

Equation (7.17) is somewhat cumbersome, and it is not at all clear how $h(A)$ varies with $A$. The situation is somewhat like the first encounter a student has with the normal distribution. Quantitative interpretation is difficult until one consults tables of the normal probability integral. Of course with modern-day digital computers, tabulation of such a function and its area are simple tasks.

As an aid to the reader, the form of the density function for 11 common transformations is given in Table 7.1.

*Several variables*   If two or more variables are involved in a transformation, a similar change-of-variables formulation is used. For example, suppose that two linear springs with spring constants $K_1$ and $K_2$ are connected in parallel so that the total spring constant is $K_T = K_1 + K_2$. Assuming the distribution of $K_1$ and $K_2$ is known, we wish to find the distribution of $K_T$.

The mathematical solution to this problem will involve a transformation of two random variables, which is defined by

$$\psi(u,v) = \phi[x(u,v),y(u,v)]|J| \tag{2.100}$$

$$J = \begin{vmatrix} \dfrac{\partial x}{\partial u} & \dfrac{\partial x}{\partial v} \\ \dfrac{\partial y}{\partial u} & \dfrac{\partial y}{\partial v} \end{vmatrix} \equiv \text{Jacobian} \tag{2.99}$$

where   $\mathbf{x}, \mathbf{y}$ = original random variables
   $\mathbf{u}, \mathbf{v}$ = transformed random variables
   $\phi(x,y)$ = original joint density function
   $\psi(u,v)$ = transformed joint density function
   $u(x,y), v(x,y)$ = transformation equations
   $x(u,v), y(u,v)$ = inverses of transformation equations
   $|J|$ = *magnitude* of Jacobian

As discussed in Sec. 2.9.6, this technique holds as stated for one-to-one transformations[1] of random variables. Also the transformation takes two original random variables into two transformed random variables.

[1] For the discussion of the case where the mapping is not one to one, see A. Papoulis, "Probability, Random Variables, and Stochastic Processes," p. 201, McGraw-Hill Book Company, New York, 1965.

**Table 7.1   Transformations of a single random variable (distributions unspecified)**

| No. | Transformation $u$ | Resulting density function $h(u)$ |
|---|---|---|
| 1 | $ax$ | $\left\|\dfrac{1}{a}\right\| f\left(\dfrac{u}{a}\right)$ |
| 2 | $a + x$ | $f(u - a)$ |
| 3 | $\sqrt{x}$ | $2\|u\|f(x = u^2) \qquad x > 0\dagger$ |
| 4 | $x^2$ | $\dfrac{1}{2\sqrt{u}}\,[f(x = +\sqrt{u}) + f(x = -\sqrt{u})]$ |
| 5 | $(x)^{1/n}$ | $\|nu^{n-1}\|f(x = u^n) \qquad x > 0\dagger$ |
| 6 | $x^n$ | $\left\|\dfrac{1}{n} u^{(1/n)-1}\right\| \displaystyle\sum_{i=1}^{n} f(x_i) \quad$ where $x_1, x_2, \ldots, x_n \equiv n$ roots of $x = (u)^{1/n}$ |
| 7 | $\dfrac{1}{x}$ | $\dfrac{1}{u^2} f\left(x = \dfrac{1}{u}\right)$ |
| 8 | $e^x$ | $\left\|\dfrac{1}{u}\right\| f(x = \ln u)$ |
| 9 | $e^{ax}$ | $\left\|\dfrac{1}{au}\right\| f(x = \ln u^{1/a})$ |
| 10 | $e^{ax^n}$ | $\left\|\dfrac{1}{nau}(\ln u^{1/a})^{(1/n)-1}\right\| x \displaystyle\sum_{i=1}^{n} f(x_i) \quad$ where $x_1, x_2, \ldots,$ $x_n \equiv n$ roots of $x = (\ln u^{1/a})^{1/n}$ |
| 11 | $\ln x$ | $e^u f(x = e^u) \qquad x > 0\dagger$ |

† A negative value of $x$ would yield an imaginary value of the random variable $u$, which is inadmissible.

Thus we can either do two transformations at once, or simply let $u$ be the transformation and $v$ a convenient dummy random variable.   In such a case we want the marginal density function for $u$ associated with the joint density $\psi(u,v)$, which is given by

$$h(u) = \int_v \psi(u,v)\,dv \tag{7.20}$$

Of course this technique can be generalized to fit the case of an $n$-variable transformation.

*Sum of two independent normal variables* Returning to the parallel-spring example, $x = K_1$ and $y = K_2$, $u = K_T = K_1 + K_2$. If we were also interested in series springs, we might define $K_T' = K_1 K_2 (K_1 + K_2)^{-1}$ and let this be $v$; however, we assume this is not of interest, and therefore no function $v(x,y)$ exists. Because the form of Eq. (2.100) requires it, a dummy function $v(x,y)$ will be chosen. A simple choice such as $v = x$ is generally convenient since it simplifies the computation.[1] Thus, $v = x = K_1$. The transformation equations and their inverses are

$$u(x,y) = x + y \qquad x(u,v) = v$$
$$v(x,y) = x \qquad y(u,v) = u - v$$

and the partial derivatives required in the Jacobian are

$$\frac{\partial x}{\partial u} = 0 \qquad \frac{\partial x}{\partial v} = 1 \qquad \frac{\partial y}{\partial u} = 1 \qquad \frac{\partial y}{\partial v} = -1$$

Substitution in the Jacobian yields

$$|J| = \begin{Vmatrix} 0 & 1 \\ 1 & -1 \end{Vmatrix} = |-1| = 1$$

Note that one takes the *magnitude* of the Jacobian, which is itself a *determinant*.

The transformed joint density function is given by substitution in Eq. (2.100)

$$\psi(u,v) = \phi(v,\, u - v) \qquad\qquad (7.21)$$

and the marginal density function is given by

$$h(u) = \int_v \phi(v,\, u - v)\, dv \qquad\qquad (7.22)$$

If the original random variables **x** and **y** are independent, the original joint density function $\phi(x,y)$ is a product of the marginal density functions for **x** and **y**, $\phi(x,y) = f(x)g(y)$. Thus, Eq. (7.22) simplifies, yielding

$$h(u) = \int_v f(v)g(u - v)\, dv \qquad\qquad (7.23)$$

---

[1] At this point the reader might think that an arbitrary choice for $v(x,y)$ is silly. As long as we are doing the problem, why not find a useful by-product such as

$$K_T = K_1 K_2 (K_1 + K_2)^{-1}$$

To some extent this is valid reasoning; however, the choice $v = x$ might result in a much simpler computation.

To further evaluate Eq. (7.23) we must specify the density functions $f(x)$ and $g(y)$.

Returning to our spring example, we add the necessary information to solve the problem. Suppose that the two spring values $K_1$ and $K_2$ are independent and both have a normal distribution; then

$$\phi(x,y) = f(x)g(y) = \frac{1}{2\pi\sigma_1\sigma_2} \exp\left[-\frac{(x-\mu_1)^2}{2\sigma_1^2}\right] \exp\left[-\frac{(y-\mu_2)^2}{2\sigma_2^2}\right] \quad (7.24)$$

Thus, Eq. (7.21) becomes

$$\psi(u,v) = \frac{1}{2\pi\sigma_1\sigma_2} \exp\left[-\frac{(v-\mu_1)^2}{2\sigma_1^2}\right] \exp\left[-\frac{(u-v-\mu_2)^2}{2\sigma_2^2}\right] \quad (7.25)$$

The actual quantity of interest is $h(u)$, which can be obtained from the joint density function in Eq. (7.23) by integrating over the entire range of $v$. The range of this integral must be carefully chosen. Since $v = x$, the range on $v$ is the same as the range on $x$, that is, $-\infty < v < +\infty$. In this case the range computation is straightforward, but at times it requires care to avoid errors. (If the $v$ function were chosen to have any meaning, one would repeat the procedure by integrating $\psi(u,v)$ over all values of $u$ to find the marginal density function for $v$.) Equation (7.23) becomes

$$h(u) = \int_{-\infty}^{+\infty} \frac{1}{2\pi\sigma_1\sigma_2} \exp\left[-\frac{(v-\mu_1)^2}{2\sigma_1^2}\right] \exp\left[-\frac{(u-v-\mu_2)^2}{2\sigma_2^2}\right] dv$$

Defining $\lambda = \mu_2 - u$, algebraic manipulation yields

$$h(u) = \frac{1}{2\pi\sigma_1\sigma_2} \exp\left[-\frac{1}{2\sigma_1^2\sigma_2^2}(\sigma_2^2\mu_1^2 + \sigma_1^2\lambda^2)\right]$$
$$\int_{-\infty}^{+\infty} \exp\left\{-\frac{(\sigma_1^2+\sigma_2^2)}{2\sigma_1^2\sigma_2^2}\left[v^2 + 2\frac{(\sigma_1^2\lambda - \sigma_2^2\mu_1)}{\sigma_1^2+\sigma_2^2}v\right]\right\} dv$$

Completing the square on the term in brackets yields

$$h(u) = \frac{1}{2\pi\sigma_1\sigma_2} \exp\left[-\frac{(\sigma_1^2\lambda - \sigma_2^2\mu_1)^2 - (\sigma_1^2+\sigma_2^2)(\sigma_2^2\mu_1^2 + \sigma_1^2\lambda^2)}{2\sigma_1^2\sigma_2^2(\sigma_1^2+\sigma_2^2)}\right]$$
$$\int_{-\infty}^{+\infty} \exp\left\{\frac{-[v + (\sigma_1^2\lambda - \sigma_2^2\mu_1)/(\sigma_1^2+\sigma_2^2)]^2}{2\sigma_1^2\sigma_2^2/(\sigma_1^2+\sigma_2^2)}\right\} dv$$

This integral is related to the integral of the normal density function

$$\frac{1}{\sqrt{2\pi}\,b} \int_{-\infty}^{+\infty} \exp\left[-\frac{(x-a)^2}{2b^2}\right] dx = 1$$

Although $b$ is a very complicated expression, as long as it is independent of $v$, the area is still unity; thus

$$h(u) = \frac{1}{\sqrt{2\pi} \sqrt{\sigma_1^2 + \sigma_2^2}} \exp\left[-\frac{(\sigma_1^2\lambda - \sigma_2^2\mu_1)^2 - (\sigma_1^2 + \sigma_2^2)(\sigma_2^2\mu_1^2 + \sigma_1^2\lambda^2)}{2\sigma_1^2\sigma_2^2(\sigma_1^2 + \sigma_2^2)}\right]$$

Substitution of $\lambda = \mu_2 - u$, expansion, and factoring yields

$$h(u) = \frac{1}{\sqrt{2\pi} \sqrt{\sigma_1^2 + \sigma_2^2}} \exp\left\{-\frac{[u - (\mu_1 + \mu_2)]^2}{2(\sigma_1^2 + \sigma_2^2)}\right\} \qquad (7.26)$$

The transformed distribution given in Eq. (7.26) is also normal with a new mean equal to the sum of the means for $x$ and $y$ and a variance equal to the sum of the two variances.[1]

If the original density function $\phi(x,y)$ was other than normal (either through assumption or on the basis of data), a different result would be expected. As previously stated, in some cases setting the range for the integral in Eq. (7.23) is rather tricky, but it only requires practice and care. The real difficulty in using this approach occurs when the resulting integral cannot be evaluated in closed form. There are two recourses in this case: tabulation of the function and approximation. The first requires tabulation and study of the new integral in much the same way a new student in probability theory tackles the normal probability integral. Of course the accessibility of a modern digital computer does much to dispel any difficulties here. The above example was carried through in detail to illustrate how transformations involving several random variables can be performed. If the integral of Eq. (7.23) cannot be expressed in simple form, the second approach is to approximate the integrand by a truncated series. In other cases, numerical methods and a digital computer are required. As an aid in performing other common transformations the integral form of $h(u)$ is listed for six cases in Table 7.2.

*Sum of two dependent normal variables*    If the variables $x$ and $y$ are not independent, the original joint density function $\phi(x,y)$ is not simply the product of $f(x)$ and $g(y)$ but must be formulated to account for the dependency. Returning for the sake of discussion to the spring example, we might expect independence if $K_1$ and $K_2$ were picked at random from a box of several hundred springs. If, however, the springs were a matched pair selected by pairing successive items from the same production run, then in all probability their spring constants would differ only by a few percent, and we would expect $K_1$ and $K_2$ to be dependent random variables.

[1] For this particular problem, the method of Sec. 2.9.8 is much simpler since it avoids much of the algebra.

**Table 7.2 Transformation of two random variables (distributions unspecified)**

| No. | Transformation $u$† | | Resulting density function $h(u)$ |
|---|---|---|---|
| 1 | $x + y$ | convolution | $\displaystyle\int_{\text{over } v} f(v)g(u - v)\, dv$ |
| 2 | $xy$ | | $\displaystyle\int_{\text{over } v} \left\lvert \frac{1}{v} \right\rvert f(v)g\left(\frac{u}{v}\right) dv$ |
| 3 | $\dfrac{x}{y}$ | | $\displaystyle\int_{\text{over } v} \left\lvert \frac{v}{u^2} \right\rvert f(v)g\left(\frac{v}{u}\right) dv$ |
| 4 | $x^2 + y^2$ | | $\displaystyle\int_{\text{over } v} \left\lvert \frac{1}{2\sqrt{u - v^2}} \right\rvert f(v)g(\sqrt{u - v^2})\, dv$ |
| 5 | $\sqrt{x^2 + y^2}$ | | $\displaystyle\int_{\text{over } v} \left\lvert \frac{u}{\sqrt{u^2 - v^2}} \right\rvert f(v)g(\sqrt{u^2 - v^2})\, dv$ |
| 6 | $\tan^{-1}\dfrac{y}{x}$ | | $\displaystyle\int_{\text{over } v} \left\lvert \frac{v}{\csc^2 u} \right\rvert f\left(\frac{v}{\tan u}\right) g(v)\, dv$ |

† The variables $x$ and $y$ are independent with density functions $f(x)$ and $g(y)$. Also the dummy variable $v$ is chosen for simplicity to be $v = x$.

To construct a joint dependent density function we postulate a $\phi(x,y)$ function with an additional dependence parameter. In the case of the normal distribution, the parameter is $\rho$, the correlation coefficient, and the distribution is given by

$$\phi(x,y) = \frac{1}{2\pi\sigma_1\sigma_2\sqrt{1 - \rho^2}}\, e^{-w(x,y;\mu_1,\mu_2,\sigma_1,\sigma_2,\rho)}$$

$$w = \frac{1}{2(1 - \rho^2)}\left[\left(\frac{x - \mu_1}{\sigma_1}\right)^2 - 2\rho\,\frac{x - \mu_1}{\sigma_1}\frac{y - \mu_2}{\sigma_2} + \left(\frac{y - \mu_2}{\sigma_2}\right)^2\right] \quad (7.27)$$

The marginal density functions are independent of $\rho$ and turn out to be normal, as one would expect

$$f(x) = \int_{-\infty}^{+\infty} \phi(x,y)\, dy = \frac{1}{\sqrt{2\pi}\,\sigma_1}\exp\left[-\frac{1}{2}\left(\frac{x - \mu_1}{\sigma_1}\right)^2\right] \quad (7.28)$$

$$g(y) = \int_{-\infty}^{+\infty} \phi(x,y)\, dx = \frac{1}{\sqrt{2\pi}\,\sigma_2}\exp\left[-\frac{1}{2}\left(\frac{y - \mu_2}{\sigma_2}\right)^2\right] \quad (7.29)$$

The conditional density function is

$$g(y|x) = \frac{1}{\sqrt{2\pi}\,\sigma_2\sqrt{1-\rho^2}}\,e^{-w_1(x,y;\mu_1,\mu_2,\sigma_1,\sigma_2,\rho)}$$

$$w_1 = \frac{1}{2}\left\{\frac{y-[\mu_2+\rho(\sigma_2/\sigma_1)(x-\mu_1)]}{\sigma_2\sqrt{1-\rho^2}}\right\}^2$$

If Eq. (7.27) is plotted in cartesian coordinates $x = x$, $y = y$, and $\phi(x,y) = z$, a bell-shaped surface is obtained.

Now if we repeat our spring problem assuming dependence, we replace Eq. (7.24) with Eq. (7.27); then Eq. (7.22) becomes

$$h(u) = \int_{-\infty}^{+\infty}\frac{1}{2\pi\sigma_1\sigma_2\sqrt{1-\rho^2}}\,e^{-w_2(u,v;\mu_1,\mu_2,\sigma_1,\sigma_2,\rho)}\,dv \qquad (7.30)$$

$$w_2 = \frac{1}{2(1-\rho^2)}\left[\left(\frac{v-\mu_1}{\sigma_1}\right)^2 - 2\rho\frac{v-\mu_1}{\sigma_1}\frac{u-v-\mu_2}{\sigma_2} + \left(\frac{u-v-\mu_2}{\sigma_2}\right)^2\right]$$

Algebraic manipulation of the variable $w$ becomes very cumbersome. The results are that $\mu$ is normally distributed with mean

$$E(u) = \mu_1 + \mu_2 \qquad (7.31)$$

and variance[1]

$$\text{var } u = \sigma_1^2 + 2\rho\sigma_1\sigma_2 + \sigma_2^2 \qquad (7.32)$$

As discussed in Chap. 2, the correlation coefficient $\rho$ is limited to the range $-1 < \rho < +1$. When $\rho = 0$, Eqs. (7.31) and (7.32) yield the same result as for the independent case. To illustrate the application of the results derived above, a simple example follows.

*Design example*   One often wishes to keep the current in a particular circuit constant. Suppose our circuit is the field winding of a dc motor. The simplest technique is to connect the winding across a dc voltage source $V$. The voltage source is assumed to be very accurately known, i.e., the tolerance is very close, and therefore $\sigma$ is very small and variations can be neglected. The field current $I$ is given by $V/R_w$, where $R_w$ is the dc resistance of the winding. If the winding could be manufactured with very close tolerance on $R_w$, the problem would be solved. If data show that the manufacturing procedure yields a normal distribution for $R_w$, or if we decide to assume this fact, the distribution of $I$ can be computed.

---

[1] One can make an interesting interpretation of this result by analogy with the law of cosines in trigonometry. Let var $u$ be the area of the square constructed on the unknown side. Then $\sigma_1$ and $\sigma_2$ are the known legs, and $\rho = -\cos\theta$, where $\theta$ is the angle opposite the unknown side. If $\rho = 0$, one has a right triangle, and the Pythagorean theorem holds. As $\rho \to +1$, the angle is very acute, and a small area is obtained. If $\rho \to -1$, the angle approaches $180°$, and the maximum area occurs.

We must start with the parameters of the normal distribution, $\mu$ and $\sigma$. These are easy to obtain if we have data on the spread of $R$ values, but in most situations all that is available is a nominal value of $R$ and a certain tolerance on this value. It is reasonable to assume that $\mu =$ the nominal value and that the tolerance is a certain number of $\sigma$ units. The exact choice of $\sigma$ in terms of the tolerance is a matter of judgment when data are not present. Table 7.3 suggests a rationale for this choice. If $R_w$ is nominally 100 ohms $\pm$ 10 percent and we assume case 2 of Table 7.3, then $\sigma = 5$ ohms. We shall defer our computation of the distribution of $I$ from $R_w$ and try to decrease the variance of $R$ using several schemes.

Assuming that it is too difficult or too costly to decrease the variance on $R_w$, we might try constructing the field winding with two series-connected coils. Each coil would have a nominal value of 50 ohms $\pm$ 10 percent, and we would have $R_T = R_{w_1} + R_{w_2}$. Thus, we have the addition of two normal random variables with means of 50 ohms each and identical variances of 2.5 ohms. If we assume no correlation between the windings, Eq. (7.26) shows the mean value of $R_T$ to be 100 ohms and the standard deviation to be

$$\sigma_T = \sqrt{\sigma_1{}^2 + \sigma_2{}^2} = \sqrt{2.5^2 + 2.5^2} = 3.53 \text{ ohms}$$

Thus, by putting the windings in series we have reduced the standard deviation from 5 to 3.5 ohms.

Another technique might be to measure the winding resistance of each 50-ohm coil and only keep those falling within, say, a 1 percent rather than a 10 percent tolerance band. This technique is illustrated in Fig.

**Table 7.3  Relationship between tolerance and standard deviation†**

| No. | Type of component and manufacturer | Relationship |
|---|---|---|
| 1 | High-quality military component in mature development stage; reputable, conservative manufacturer with much experience | Choose $\mu = N, 3\sigma = TN$ (1% normal consumer risk)‡ |
| 2 | Average situation somewhere between 1 and 3 | Choose $\mu = N, 2\sigma = TN$ (5% normal consumer risk)‡ |
| 3 | Ordinary commercial component, early development stages; manufacturer little known or has poor reputation and little experience | Choose $\mu = N, \sigma = TN$ (37% normal consumer risk)‡ |

† $\mu \equiv$ mean, $N \equiv$ nominal value, $\sigma \equiv$ standard deviation, and $T \times 100\% \equiv \%$ tolerance.

‡ Based on a normal distribution this represents the percentage of out-of-tolerance components in any purchased batch.

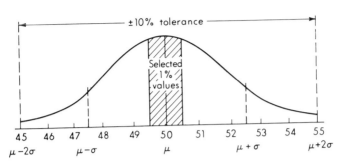

**Fig. 7.6**  Selection from a normal distribution.

7.6, but it may be economically unfeasible since only 16 percent of the windings are kept and the remainder are rejected. The distribution is approximately a uniform one with $49.5 < R < 50.5$ and

$$\mu = \frac{49.5 + 50.5}{2} = 50 \qquad \sigma^2 = \frac{(50.5 - 49.5)^2}{12} = \frac{1}{12}$$

This technique is often used by resistor manufacturers to obtain precision resistors. In this case it is economically feasible, since resistors are fairly cheap, and the rejected resistors can simply be sold at a lower price as resistors with a wider tolerance. An example of this is illustrated by Fig. 7.7. If such a selection process is used, it is a poor idea to use a normal model for the components. For the case shown in Fig. 7.7b it seems as if a rectangular distribution would be a good model. Returning to our example, the 1 percent selection process would result in a much smaller standard deviation; however, we assume that the cost of individual testing is too high. An alternate test procedure is to measure each resistance value and mark it with some code as low, medium, or high. Then when the motor is assembled, the coils would be matched so that one high and one low were paired or two mediums were paired. The random variables $R_{w_1}$ and $R_{w_2}$ would now have smaller variances, as would the sum $R_{w_1} + R_{w_2}$.

Another technique could be to separate the output of two machines, one which produced consistently large values of $R_w$ and the other consistently small values. If we joined one resistor from each batch, the two resistors would be correlated. If we assume that each winding has nominal resistance of 50 ohms $\pm$ 10 percent and the correlation coefficient obtained is $\rho = -0.5$, Eq. (7.32) yields

$$\sigma_T = \sqrt{\sigma_1{}^2 + \sigma_2{}^2 - 2\rho\sigma_1\sigma_2}$$
$$= \sqrt{2.5^2 + 2.5^2 - 2 \times 0.5 \times 2.5 \times 2.5} = 2.5$$

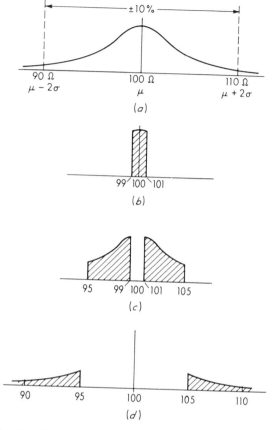

**Fig. 7.7** Precision resistors selected from a normal population. (*a*) Original population; (*b*) selected 1 percent resistors; (*c*) selected 5 percent resistors; (*d*) remaining resistors, 10 percent.

This reduces the variance to 2.5 ohms, and if $\rho \to -1$, $\sigma_T$ would be even smaller.

Another approach which is often used in such a situation is to increase the supply voltage to 10 volts and connect a precision resistor, $R_p = 9R$, in series with the winding. Since the precision resistor is large compared to $R_w$, most of the variation of $R_w$ will be swamped out. For $R_w = 100$ ohms $\pm$ 10 percent and $R_p = 900$ ohms $\pm$ 1 percent we have

$$\mu_T = 100 + 900 = 1{,}000$$
$$\sigma_T = \sqrt{5^2 + 4.5^2} = \sqrt{45.25} = 6.72 \text{ ohms}$$

The best way to compare the results of the various techniques for reduc-

**Table 7.4   Comparison of various means for reducing variation of circuit resistance**

| No. | Circuit | Distribution of $R_T$ | Coefficient of variation |
|-----|---------|----------------------|--------------------------|
| 1 | One winding, $R_w = 100 \ \Omega$ $\pm 10\%$ | Normal $\mu = 100 \ \Omega, \sigma = 5 \ \Omega$ | 0.050 |
| 2 | Two series windings, $R_{w_1} = R_{w_2} = 50 \ \Omega \pm 10\%$ | Normal $\mu = 100 \ \Omega, \sigma = 3.5 \ \Omega$ | 0.035 |
| 3 | One winding selection of $R_w = 100 \ \Omega \pm 1\%$ | Approximately rectangular $\mu = 100 \ \Omega, \sigma = 1/\sqrt{3} \ \Omega$ | 0.0058 |
| 4 | Two series windings, $R_{w_1} = R_{w_2} = 50 \ \Omega \pm 10\%$; winding matched so that $\rho = -0.5$ | Normal $\mu = 100 \ \Omega, \sigma = 2.5 \ \Omega$ | 0.025 |
| 5 | One winding, $R_w = 100 \ \Omega \pm$ 10% in series with a 900 $\Omega \pm 1\%$ resistor | Normal $\mu = 1{,}000 \ \Omega, \sigma = 6.7 \ \Omega$ | 0.0067 |

ing the variance of the circuit resistance is to compute the coefficient of variation $\sigma/\mu$, which is sort of a normalized standard deviation. Such a comparison appears in Table 7.4.

Circuits 3 and 5 are seen to be the most effective, but they are probably the most costly. The former requires a large production run of windings with a small yield and the latter a high-voltage ($9V$) source, which may be expensive depending on the value of $V$. If the motor winding could be designed with a nominal resistance of 10 ohms, then a series precision resistor of 90 ohms could be used with the same source voltage $V$. If neither 3 nor 5 proves feasible, one could return to technique 4 and try to match windings so as to obtain a value of $\rho$ closer to $-1$.

A sixth technique also must be mentioned since it could yield the best results, at least on first consideration. One could make a single winding of 90 ohms $\pm$ 10 percent and place it in series with an adjustable 25-ohm resistor and adjust each circuit by hand to obtain a tolerance as small as the accuracy of the measuring equipment would permit. Of course the situation changes when we allow $V$ to vary and allow all the parameters to change with time, temperature, etc. In such a case a more detailed analysis is called for, and much engineering judgment needed to arrive at the "best" design.

At the beginning of the discussion, we postponed consideration of a solution for the circuit current in order to concentrate on the circuit resistance and schemes for reducing its coefficient of variation.    Now we turn to the distribution of $I = V/R$.    Since $V$ is assumed to be a constant, the main task is to find the distribution of $1/R$ given the distribution of $R$.    We must solve this problem for a rectangular distribution, case 3 of Table 7.4, and a normal distribution, cases 1, 2, 4, and 5 of Table 7.4.    For the rectangular-distribution case, using case 7 of Table 7.1,

$$u = 1/R \qquad f(R) = \frac{1}{b-a} \qquad a < R < b$$

$$h(u) = \frac{1}{u^2}\frac{1}{b-a} \qquad \frac{1}{b} < u < \frac{1}{a} \tag{7.33}$$

The transformation given by Eq. (7.33) is depicted in Fig. 7.8a.
The mean and variance are given by

$$E(u) = \int_{1/b}^{1/a} u h(u)\, du = \frac{1}{b-a}\int_{1/b}^{1/a} u\,\frac{1}{u^2}\, du = \frac{1}{b-a}\ln\frac{b}{a}$$

$$\operatorname{var} u = E(u^2) - [E(u)]^2$$

$$E(u^2) = \int_{1/b}^{1/a} u^2 h(u)\, du = \frac{1}{b-a}\int_{1/b}^{1/a} u^2\,\frac{1}{u^2}\, du = \frac{1}{ab}$$

$$\operatorname{var} u = \frac{1}{ab} - \left(\frac{1}{b-a}\ln\frac{b}{a}\right)^2$$

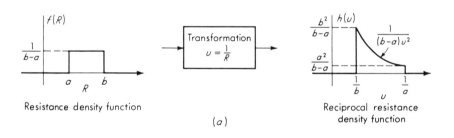

Resistance density function

Reciprocal resistance density function

(a)

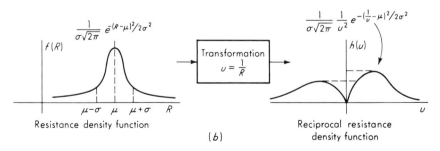

Resistance density function

Reciprocal resistance density function

(b)

**Fig. 7.8**    Reciprocal transformations of uniform and normal densities.    (a) Uniform density function; (b) normal density function.

Substituting numerical values from Table 7.4, case 3 yields

$$a = 99 \qquad b = 101$$

$$E(u) = \frac{1}{2} \ln \frac{101}{99} = 0.009995$$

$$\text{var } u = \frac{1}{99(101)} - 0.009995^2 = 1.1 \times 10^{-7}$$

Suppose one wished to avoid the details of the transformation procedure and look for an approximate shortcut. Intuition might have told us that $1/R$ is still approximately uniformly distributed with a range $\frac{1}{101} < R < \frac{1}{99}$. Estimating $E(u)$ and var $u$ by computation on such a distribution yields

$$E(u) \approx \frac{\frac{1}{99} + \frac{1}{101}}{2} = 0.01005$$

$$\text{var } u \approx \frac{(\frac{1}{99} - \frac{1}{101})^2}{12} = \frac{1}{3} \times 10^{-8}$$

Note that intuition yields a good estimate of the mean but a poor one for the variance. Using the correct values, the coefficient of variation for $u$ becomes $\sqrt{1.1 \times 10^{-7}}/0.009995 = 0.0332$. Thus, the coefficient of variation of $1/R$ is about 6 times as large as that of $R$ itself.

The final step in our transformation procedure is to compute $I$ as the product of the constant $V$ and $1/R$. By inspection, or direct application of case 1 of Table 7.1, we see that $I$ has the same distributions as $1/R$ with a scale factor of $V$. This means that $E(I) = VE(1/R)$ and var $I = V^2$ var $(1/R)$; thus the coefficient of variation is still 0.0332.

Before we draw any conclusions on how to minimize variations in $I$ from Table 7.4, we had better find the reciprocal transformation for a normal distribution, as is needed for cases 1, 2, 4, and 5. Application of case 7 of Table 7.1 to a normal distribution yields

$$u = \frac{1}{R} \qquad f(R) = \frac{1}{\sqrt{2\pi}\,\sigma} \exp\left[ -\frac{(R - \mu)^2}{2\sigma^2} \right] \qquad -\infty < R < +\infty$$
$$\tag{7.34}$$
$$h(u) = \frac{1}{\sqrt{2\pi}\,\sigma} \exp\left[ -\frac{(1/u - \mu)^2}{2\sigma^2} \right] \qquad -\infty < u < +\infty$$

The integrals required to compute the mean and variance of $u$ appear intractable. Numerical techniques and a digital computer are necessary to study $h(u)$ and compute $E(u)$ and var $u$.

The approximation techniques which are discussed in Sec. 7.6 will allow fairly easy solution of this problem and many others. However, before going on to approximate techniques the next three sections will discuss and tabulate many problems which are known to have a simple closed-form solution.

### 7.6.3 TABULATED TRANSFORMATIONS

As demonstrated by the example of the last section, probability transformations for physical problems may work out simply but generally lead to considerable difficulty and complication. Each particular situation depends on the details of the transformation and the distributions involved in the problem. The form of the transformation is fixed by the problem; i.e., in the previous example Ohm's law relates current to resistance. One can, however, approximate this function by expressions which are simpler to deal with. These approximation techniques are discussed in Sec. 7.7.6; therefore, in this section we shall assume that the form of the transformation is fixed. The choice of distribution models is another matter and involves much engineering judgment, since seldom are there sufficient data on hand to reduce it to a problem of statistics. One should choose a distribution model which best fits the available data and information. If more than one distribution seems to be a reasonable model (this is often the case when scant data are available), the analyst may choose the one which yields a simpler transformation computation.

It is tempting to look for one or more models of probability distributions which transform in a simple and well-known manner when subject to addition, reciprocation, multiplication, and division. Unfortunately one can find a few models which work well under certain of these transformations but fall down in one or two operations so that their use is not general. Three basic models, the normal, the Cauchy, and the uniform distribution, possess many of these properties and are discussed below along with many other miscellaneous transformations.

A large number of probability transformations have been studied and computed as examples of the theory of transformations in probability texts and as by-products of various statistical procedures. A number of these are given in Table 7.5 so that the reader need not recompute well-known results which appear in various places in the literature.

Transformations 1 and 2 in Table 7.5 are scale-factor and scale-shift transformations and apply to any distribution; transformation 3 is merely a simplified statement of the central-limit theorem. A careful study of what requirements must be placed on the $x$'s for convergence of the central-limit theorem becomes complicated.

A sufficient set of conditions for convergence of the central-limit theorem are the Laplace-Liapounoff conditions, which state that a *sufficient* condition for convergence is that

$$\lim_{n \to \infty} \left[ (\text{var } u)^{-\frac{3}{2}} \sum_{i=1}^{n} E(|x_i - \mu_i|^3) \right] = 0$$

**Table 7.5 Transformations of random variables (distributions specified)**

| No. | Transformation $u$ | Original distribution | Final distribution |
|---|---|---|---|
| 1 | Multiplication by a constant $ax$ | Any distribution | $\mu_u = a\mu_x \qquad \sigma_u^2 = a^2\sigma_x^2$<br>Scale factor, form unchanged |
| 2 | Addition of a constant $a + x$ | Any distribution | $\mu_u = a + \mu_x \qquad \sigma_u^2 = \sigma_x^2$<br>Scale shifted, form unchanged |
| 3 | Sum of $n$ variables $x_1 + x_2 + \cdots + x_n$ | Distribution unspecified as to shape; variables independent; see text for further limitations | Approaches gaussian rapidly as $n$ becomes large, i.e., becomes the same as case 4; approximation good for $n > 4$ or 5 (see case 13) |
| 4 | Sum of $n$ variables $x_1 + x_2 + \cdots + x_n$ | $x$'s normal and independent; mean $= \mu_i$ variance $= \sigma_i^2$ | $u$ has a normal distribution with<br>$\mu = \mu_1 + \mu_2 + \cdots + u_n \qquad \sigma^2 = \sigma_1^2 + \sigma_2^2 + \cdots + \sigma_n^2$ |
| 5 | $\dfrac{x_1}{x_2}$ | $x_1, x_2$ independent unit normal variables $(\mu = 0, \sigma = 1)$ | $u = $ Cauchy<br>$h(u) = \dfrac{(1 + u^2)^{-1}}{\pi} \qquad -\infty < u \leq +\infty$ |
| 6 | $\dfrac{x_1}{x_2}$ | $x_1, x_2$ have a joint normal distribution with zero mean, variances $\sigma_1$ and $\sigma_2$, and correlation $\rho$ | $u = $ Cauchy<br>$h(u) = \dfrac{1}{\dfrac{\pi\sigma_1\sigma_2}{\sqrt{1-\rho^2}}\left[\left(\dfrac{u}{\sigma_1} - \dfrac{\rho}{\sigma_2}\right)^2 + \dfrac{\sqrt{1-\rho^2}}{\sigma_1^2}\right]} \qquad -\infty < u \leq +\infty$ |
| 7 | $\dfrac{1}{x}$ | $x$ normal variable with mean $\mu$ and variance $\sigma^2$ | $h(u) = \dfrac{1}{\sqrt{2\pi}\,\sigma}\dfrac{1}{u^2}\exp\left[\dfrac{-(1/u - \mu)^2}{2\sigma^2}\right] \qquad -\infty < u \leq +\infty$ |
| 8 | Sum of squares $x_1^2 + x_2^2 + \cdots + x_n^2$ | $x$'s independent unit normal variables $(\mu = 0, \sigma = 1)$ | $u = $ chi square with $n$ degrees of freedom<br>$h(u) = \dfrac{1}{(2)^{n/2}\Gamma(n/2)}e^{-u/2}u^{(n/2)-1} \qquad 0 < u \leq \infty$ |

# Table 7.5 Transformations of random variables (distributions specified) (Continued)

| No. | Transformation $u$ | Original distribution | Final distribution |
|---|---|---|---|
| 9 | $\sqrt{x_1^2 + x_2^2}$ | $x_1, x_2$ independent normal distributions with zero mean and the same $\sigma$ | $u$ = Rayleigh $\quad h(u) = \dfrac{u}{\sigma^2} e^{-u^2/2\sigma^2} \quad 0 < u \leq \infty$ |
| 10 | $\sqrt{x_1^2 + x_2^2}$ | $x_1, x_2$ independent normal distributions with means $\mu_1$ and $\mu_2$ and the same $\sigma$ | $h(u) = \dfrac{u}{\sigma^2} e^{-(u^2+\mu^2)/2\sigma^2} I_0\left(\dfrac{u\mu}{\sigma^2}\right)$ $\mu = \sqrt{\mu_1^2 + \mu_2^2}$ $I_0$ = modified Bessel function of order zero $\quad 0 < u \leq \infty$ |
| 11 | $x^2$ | $x$ normal with zero mean | $h(u) = \dfrac{1}{\sigma\sqrt{2\pi u}} e^{-u/2\sigma^2} \quad 0 < u \leq \infty$ |
| 12 | Sum of two variables $x_1 + x_2$ | $x$'s rectangular and independent. Mean = $\mu_1 = \dfrac{b_1 + a_1}{2}$. Variance = $\sigma_1^2 = \dfrac{(b_1 - a_1)^2}{12}$ [diagram: height $1/(b_1-a_1)$ between $a_1$ and $b_1$] | Trapezoidal when $b_1 - a_1 < b_2 - a_2$; Triangular when $b_1 - a_1 = b_2 - a_2$. [trapezoidal diagram: height $1/(b_1-a_1)$; x-labels $a_1+a_2$, $a_1+b_2$, $a_2+b_1$, $b_1+b_2$] [triangular diagram: height $1/(b_1-a_1)$; x-labels $a_1+a_2$, $b_1+b_2$] |
| 13 | Sum of three variables $x_1 + x_2 + x_3$ | Same as 12 | For $b_1 - a_1 = b_2 - a_2 = b_3 - a_3$: [bell-shaped diagram; x-labels $a_1+a_2+a_3$, $b_1+b_2+b_3$] |

**Table 7.5 Transformations of random variables (distributions specified) (Continued)**

| No. | Transformation $u$ | Original distribution | Final distribution |
|---|---|---|---|
| 14 | $\dfrac{1}{x}$ | $x$ rectangular $\quad a < x \leq b$ | $h(u) = \dfrac{1}{b-a}\,\dfrac{1}{u^2} \qquad \dfrac{1}{b} < u \leq \dfrac{1}{a}$ |
| 15 | $x^2$ | $x$ rectangular $\quad a < x \leq b$ | $h(u) = \dfrac{1}{b-a}\,\dfrac{1}{\sqrt{u}} \qquad a^2 < u \leq b^2$ |
| 16 | $-2 \ln x$ | $x$ rectangular over range $(0,1)$ | $u$ = chi square with $\nu = 2$ <br> $h(u) = \tfrac{1}{2} e^{-u/2} \qquad 0 < u \leq \infty$ |
| 17 | $x_1 + x_2 + \cdots + x_n$ | $x_i$'s all Cauchy distributions with parameters $\theta_i$ and $\alpha_i$ <br><br> $f(x) = \dfrac{\alpha_i/\pi}{(x-\theta_i)^2 + \alpha_i^2}$ | $h$ = Cauchy <br><br> $h(u) = \dfrac{\alpha/\pi}{(x-\theta)^2 + \alpha^2} \qquad -\infty < u \leq +\infty$ <br><br> $\alpha = \alpha_1 + \alpha_2 + \cdots + \alpha_n$ <br> $\theta = \theta_1 + \theta_2 + \cdots + \theta_n$ |
| 18 | $\dfrac{1}{x}$ | $x$ Cauchy with parameters $\theta$, $\alpha$ | $u$ = Cauchy <br><br> $h(u) = \dfrac{\alpha'/\pi}{(x-\theta')^2 + \alpha'^2} \qquad -\infty < u \leq +\infty$ <br><br> $\theta' = \dfrac{\theta}{\alpha^2 + \theta^2} \qquad \alpha' = \dfrac{\alpha}{\alpha^2 + \theta^2}$ |
| 19 | $xy$ | $x, y$ Cauchy with <br> $\theta_1 = \theta_2 = 0,\ \alpha_1 = \alpha_2 = 1$ | $h(u) = \dfrac{2}{\pi}\,\dfrac{\log u}{u^2 - 1} \qquad -\infty < u \leq +\infty$ |
| 20 | $\dfrac{x}{y}$ | Same as 19 | Same as 19 |

**Table 7.5 Transformations of random variables (distributions specified)** *(Continued)*

| No. | Transformation $u$ | Original distribution | Final distribution |
|---|---|---|---|
| 21 | $x_1 + x_2 + \cdots + x_n$ | $x$'s independent exponential distributions with same $\beta$ $$f(x) = \frac{1}{\beta} e^{-x/\beta}$$ | $u$ = gamma distribution $$h(u) = \frac{1}{\beta^{\alpha+1}\Gamma(\alpha+1)} u^{\alpha} e^{-u/\beta} \quad 0 < u \leq \infty$$ $\alpha = n - 1$ |
| 22 | $x_1 + x_2 + \cdots + x_n$ | $x$'s independent gamma variates with same $\beta$ and $\alpha_1, \alpha_2, \ldots, \alpha_n$ | $u$ = gamma distribution with same $\beta$ and $\alpha = \alpha_1 + \alpha_2 + \cdots + \alpha_n + (n-1)$ |
| 23 | $x_1 + x_2$ | $x_1, x_2$ independent exponentials with unequal $\beta$ | $$h(u) = \frac{1}{\beta_2 - \beta_1} (e^{-u/\beta_1} - e^{-u/\beta_2}) \quad \beta_2 > \beta_1; \; 0 < u \leq +\infty$$ |
| 24 | $x_1 + x_2$ | $x$'s independent exponentials with $\beta = 1$ | $u$ = exponential $$h(u) = u e^{-u} \quad 0 < u \leq \infty$$ |
| 25 | $\dfrac{x_1}{x_2}$ | $x$'s independent exponentials with $\beta = 1$ | $$h(u) = \frac{1}{(1+u)^2} \quad 0 < u \leq \infty$$ |
| 26 | $\dfrac{x_1/\nu_1}{x_2/\nu_2}$ | $x_1, x_2$ independent chi-square distributions with $\nu_1$ and $\nu_2$ degrees of freedom | $u$ = $F$ distribution $$h(u) = \frac{\Gamma[(\nu_1+\nu_2)/2]}{\Gamma(\nu_1/2)\Gamma(\nu_2/2)} u^{(\nu_1/2)-1}(1-u)^{(\nu_2/2)-1} \quad 0 < u \leq \infty$$ |
| 27 | $\dfrac{x_1}{\sqrt{x_2/\nu}}$ | $x_1$ unit normal and $x_2$ has a chi-square distribution with $\nu$ degrees of freedom; $x_1, x_2$ independent | $u$ = $t$ distribution $$h(u) = \frac{\Gamma[(\nu+1)/2]}{\Gamma(\nu/2)} \left(1 + \frac{u^2}{\nu}\right)^{-(\nu+1)/2} \quad -\infty < u \leq +\infty$$ |

TABLE 7.5 SOURCES:
1   A. Papoulis, "Probability, Random Variables, and Stochastic Processes," McGraw-Hill Book Company, New York, 1964.
2   J. E. Freund, "Mathematical Statistics," Prentice-Hall, Inc., Englewood Cliffs, N.J., 1962.
3   M. E. Monroe, "Theory of Probability," McGraw-Hill Book Company, New York, 1951.
4   P. G. Hoel, "Introduction to Mathematical Statistics," John Wiley & Sons, Inc., New York, 1954.
5   G. P. Wadsworth and J. G. Bryan, "Introduction to Probability and Random Variables," McGraw-Hill Book Company, New York, 1960.
6   H. Freeman, "Introduction to Statistical Inference," Addison-Wesley Publishing Company, Inc., Reading, Mass., 1963.

provided that each $x_i$ is independent and possesses a third moment. Notice that the criterion involves a ratio. The numerator of the ratio is the sum of quantities which are similar to the third moment about the mean (the absolute-value signs make this different from the third moment). The denominator is the variance of $u$ raised to the $\frac{3}{2}$ power. If the ratio approaches zero as $n \to \infty$, the central-limit theorem holds. Since this is only a sufficient condition, if the test fails, we must investigate further; nothing is certain. One classic example of the failure of the central-limit theorem is the Cauchy distribution. Referring to transformation 17 of Table 7.5, we see that no matter how many Cauchy random variables are added, the resulting distribution remains Cauchy. A complete discussion of various necessary and sufficient conditions for the convergence of the central-limit theorem can be found in Munroe.[1]

Transformations 4 to 11 all deal with the normal distribution. Although the linear transformations of the normal distribution are simple, all nonlinear operations give rise to new distributions, only some of which have been studied and tabulated. Thus, the use of a normal model in transformations with nonlinear operations is limited. Transformations 12 to 16 apply to the rectangular distribution. In this case, the nonlinear operations yield fairly simple results; however, the summation of terms given by the convolution integral keeps changing shape for the first three or four summations until it begins to approach a normal distribution (see transformation 3). In some cases, the Cauchy distribution works quite well, as illustrated by transformations 17 to 20. The use of the Cauchy distribution as a model is discussed below with other examples to illustrate the use of the transformation table.

*Example 1*   In the previous section we discussed the problem of finding the distribution of $I = V/R$ given that $V$ is a constant and $R$ a random

[1] M. E. Munroe, "The Theory of Probability," McGraw-Hill Book Company, New York, 1951.

variable.   We used a normal distribution and a rectangular distribution model for $R$.   The results could of course have been predicted immediately using transformations 7 and 14 from Table 7.5.   In this case only the rectangular model led to a distribution which was easy to handle. If we had chosen a Cauchy model for $R$, we could have used transformation 18 and known immediately that the current also had a Cauchy distribution.   Although the Cauchy distribution has no mean or variance, the median $\theta$ and the spread parameter $\alpha$ can be used in their place.

The Cauchy, normal, and rectangular distributions are compared in Fig. 7.9.   Both the normal and rectangular distributions are plotted with zero mean value, and the Cauchy is plotted with zero median.   The spread parameters are equated such that the standard deviation of the normal distribution $\sigma$ is equal to the standard deviation of the rectangular $(b - a)/2\sqrt{3}$, which in turn is equal to twice the spread parameter of

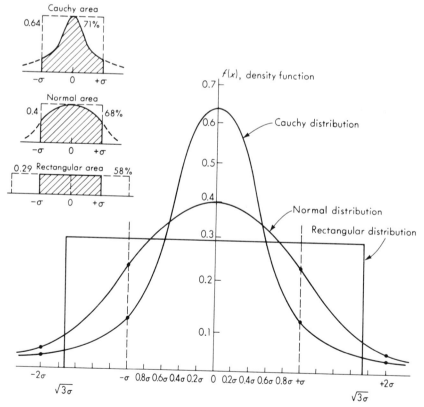

**Fig. 7.9**   Normalized comparison of the Cauchy, normal, and rectangular distributions.

the Cauchy $2\alpha$. When this normalization is done, the area under $-\sigma < x < +\sigma$ represents 68 percent of the area for a normal distribution, 71 percent of the area for a Cauchy distribution, and 58 percent for a rectangular distribution. Although the three distributions shown in the figure are similar in that the central areas of the distributions are equal, each has a distinct shape.

The normal distribution might be expected to hold as a good model in many cases. Since manufacture may be viewed as a multistep procedure with a different distribution for each step, the central-limit theorem may be invoked and a normal distribution model used. In the case where there is appreciable measurement and selection or go and no-go gaging, one might expect a rectangular distribution. The physical model which accompanies the Cauchy distribution involves the intensity of radiation produced by a point source measured along a line illuminated by this source. Unfortunately, this does not suggest any natural manufacturing steps which might give rise to the Cauchy distribution.

*Example 2*    Another simple problem which is easy to solve with a Cauchy model is the distribution of parallel resistances.[1] If one connects resistors $R_1$ and $R_2$ in parallel, elementary circuit theory tells us that the total resistance is given by

$$R_T = \frac{1}{1/R_1 + 1/R_2} = \frac{R_1 R_2}{R_1 + R_2} \tag{7.35}$$

If we use the first algebraic form for $R_T$ involving reciprocals and sums, the solution is straightforward. The distributon of $R_1$ is assumed Cauchy with parameters $\theta_1$ and $\alpha_1$, that is, $f(R_1) = C(\theta_1, \alpha_1)$. The reciprocal distribution is

$$f_1\left(\frac{1}{R_1}\right) = C\left(\frac{\theta_1}{\theta_1^2 + \alpha_1^2}, \frac{\alpha_1}{\theta_1^2 + \alpha_1^2}\right)$$

The sum of reciprocals is

$$f_2\left(\frac{1}{R_1} + \frac{1}{R_2}\right) = C\left[\left(\frac{\theta_1}{\theta_1^2 + \alpha_1^2} + \frac{\theta_2}{\theta_2^2 + \alpha_2^2}\right), \left(\frac{\alpha_1}{\theta_1^2 + \alpha_1^2} + \frac{\alpha_2}{\theta_2^2 + \alpha_2^2}\right)\right]$$

Lastly, the reciprocal is Cauchy

$$f_3(R_T) = f_3\left(\frac{1}{1/R_1 + 1/R_2}\right) = C(\theta', \alpha') \tag{7.36}$$

[1] M. V. Menon, Problems Arising in Considering the Distribution of Equivalent Resistance, *IBM Gen. Prod. Develop. Lab. Tech. Rept.* 02.163, June 26, 1961.

where

$$\theta' = \frac{[\theta_1/(\theta_1{}^2 + \alpha_1{}^2)] + [\theta_2/(\theta_2{}^2 + \alpha_2{}^2)]}{[\theta_1/(\theta_1{}^2 + \alpha_1{}^2) + \theta_2/(\theta_2{}^2 + \alpha_2{}^2)]^2 + [\alpha_1/(\theta_1{}^2 + \alpha_1{}^2) + \alpha_2/(\theta_2{}^2 + \alpha_2{}^2)]^2}$$

$$\alpha' = \frac{[\alpha_1/(\theta_1{}^2 + \alpha_1{}^2)] + [\alpha_2/(\theta_2{}^2 + \alpha_2{}^2)]}{[\theta_1/(\theta_1{}^2 + \alpha_1{}^2) + \theta_2/(\theta_2{}^2 + \alpha_2{}^2)]^2 + [\alpha_1/(\theta_1{}^2 + \alpha_1{}^2) + \alpha_2/(\theta_2{}^2 + \alpha_2{}^2)]^2}$$

One could also have started with the second algebraic form of Eq. (7.35). The denominator would then be Cauchy, since $R_1$ and $R_2$ are summed. The numerator product would not be Cauchy and would have to be derived. Finally, the ratio of numerator to denominator would be computed. In this last step the numerator and denominator would be dependent. The end result would of course be Eq. (7.36), but the computation would be very much harder. Thus, in tackling multiple transformation problems it is wise to consider alternate approaches and plan judiciously.

The remaining distributions in Table 7.5, transformations 21 to 27, are a miscellaneous collection which may be of use in special cases.

The next section discusses a further simplification of the transformation problem.

### 7.6.4   MOMENT CALCULATIONS

As seen in the preceding examples, exact solution of the probability-transformation problem can become very difficult. One way of relaxing some of the computational difficulties is simply to ask for less information. The transformed density function tells the complete story and contains all the information about the problem. Often one is satisfied with knowing a little less about the problem if such information can be obtained more easily. This is especially true when one is unsure about the accuracy of the model for the original distribution because only a few data are available or because only limited information about tolerance and nominal values can be obtained. In such a situation, information about the moments of the distribution is generally sufficient for engineering purposes. In fact, in most cases, the mean and variance of the distribution are adequate. The mean and the variance alone are enough to make statements on the probability that the random variables lie within a certain range. Since the distribution is unknown, we can bound the probabilities using Chebyshev's or Gauss' bound, Eqs. (2.136) and (2.137).

Computational formulas for moments of a distribution were discussed in Chap. 2. The appropriate integral relationships are repeated here. If we are interested in a single variable $x$ with a density function $f(x)$ that undergoes a transformation specified by the equation $u(x)$, then the $k$th moment of the transformed variable $u$ about the origin is given by

$$\mu_k = E[u^k(x)] = \int_{-\infty}^{+\infty} u^k(x)f(x)\, dx \tag{7.37}$$

In general the two most important moments are the mean, the first origin moment

$$\text{Mean} = \mu_1 = E[u(x)] = \int_{-\infty}^{+\infty} u(x)f(x)\, dx \tag{7.38}$$

and the variance, the second moment about the mean

$$\text{Variance} = \sigma^2 = E[u^2(x)] - E^2[u(x)] \tag{7.39}$$

Thus, the variance can always be computed from the first and second origin moments.

If the problem involves many random variables, where the original density function is $\phi\ (x_1, x_2, \ldots, x_n)$ and the transformation equation is $u(x_1, x_2, \ldots, x_n)$, then the $k$th origin moment is

$$\begin{aligned}
\mu_k &= E[u^k(x_1, x_2, \ldots, x_n)] \\
&= \int_{-\infty}^{+\infty} \cdots \int_{-\infty}^{+\infty} u^k(x_1, x_2, \ldots, x_n)\phi(x_1, x_2, \ldots, x_n)\, dx_1\, dx_2 \cdots dx_n
\end{aligned} \tag{7.40}$$

The computation given in Eq. (7.40) is identical with Eq. (7.37), except that a multiple integration is called for. The same analogy will hold for the mean and variance of $u(x_1, x_2, \ldots, x_n)$ when compared with Eqs. (7.37) and (7.40).

It is also of considerable interest to deal with moments of several random variables when the variables are considered pairwise. Specifically, the special moment called the covariance is of interest whenever the variables are not independent

$$\begin{aligned}
\text{cov}\ (x_i, x_j) &= E[(x_i - \mu_i)(x_j - \mu_j)] \\
&= \iint_{-\infty}^{+\infty} (x_i - \mu_i)(x_j - \mu_j)h(x_i, x_j)\, dx_i\, dx_j
\end{aligned} \tag{7.41}$$

where

$$h(x_i, x_j) = \underbrace{\int_{-\infty}^{+\infty} \cdots \int_{-\infty}^{+\infty}}_{n-2\ \text{times}} \phi(x_1, x_2, \ldots, x_n)\, dx_1\, dx_2 \cdots dx_n$$
$$\quad dx_i\ \text{and}\ dx_j\ \text{omitted}$$

also

$$\text{cov}\ (x_i, x_j) = E(x_i x_j) - E(x_i)E(x_j) \tag{7.42}$$

Thus, the covariance depends on three pieces of information, the mean of each variable and the mean of their product. In addition to the covariance, one defines the correlation coefficient, a sort of normalized covariance, as

$$\rho(x_i,x_j) = \frac{\text{cov}\ (x_i,x_j)}{\sigma(x_i)\sigma(x_j)} \tag{7.43}$$

Sometimes it is more convenient to determine $\rho$ than the covariance; therefore we can use the inverse relation

$$\text{cov}\ (x_i,x_j) = \rho(x_i,x_j)\sigma(x_i)\sigma(x_j) \tag{7.44}$$

Thus, for two random variables $x_1$ and $x_2$ which undergo a transformation $u(x_1,x_2)$ one can compute the mean and variance of $u$ and the covariance and correlation of the two variables from $E[u(x_1,x_2)]$, $E[u^2(x_1,x_2)]$, and the given data $\mu_{x_1}$, $\mu_{x_2}$, $E(x_1{}^2)$, $E(x_2{}^2)$, $E(x_1x_2)$. For three variables, more work and more given data are required since three covariances and three correlation coefficients are of interest.

The particular forms that the mean and variance take for some specific transformations of interest are given in Table 7.6. In many cases, the transformations require only the mean, variance, and covariance of the variables. In some cases, fourth-order moments or other special moments are required. It is important to note the difference between independent random variables and uncorrelated random variables. If two random variables $x_1$ and $x_2$ are independent, we can write

$$\phi(x_1,x_2) = f_1(x_1)f_2(x_2)$$

In the case of uncorrelated variables, we know that $\rho = 0$, and from Eq. (7.44) for finite $\sigma_1$ and $\sigma_2$ this implies that cov $(x_1,x_2) = 0$. Using Eq. (7.42), we find that for uncorrelated variables

$$E(x_1x_2) = E(x_1)E(x_2)$$

The conclusion is that independence is a stronger requirement than uncorrelation and therefore that independent variables are uncorrelated; however, the converse need not be true.

One can place some bounds on some of these moment relations even if cov $(x_i,x_j)$ is unknown by making use of the following inequality

$$-1 \leq \rho \leq +1 \tag{7.45}$$

which implies that

$$-\sigma_i\sigma_j \leq \text{cov}\ (x_i,x_j) \leq \sigma_i\sigma_j \tag{7.46}$$

**Table 7.6  Moments of transformed variables**

| No. | Transformation $u$ | Restriction | Transformed mean and variance |
|---|---|---|---|
| 1 | $ax$ | $a = \text{const}$ <br> $E(x) = \mu$ <br> $\text{var } x = \sigma^2$ | $E(u) = a\mu$ <br> $\text{var } u = a^2\sigma^2$ |
| 2 | $a + x$ | $a = \text{const}$ <br> $E(x) = \mu$ <br> $\text{var } x = \sigma^2$ | $E(u) = a + \mu$ <br> $\text{var } u = \sigma^2$ |
| 3 | $a_1 x_1 + a_2 x_2 + a_3 x_3$ | $a_1, a_2, a_3 = \text{const}$ <br> $E(x_1) = \mu_1 \quad E(x_2) = \mu_2 \quad E(x_3) = \mu_3$ <br> $\text{var } x_1 = \sigma_1^2 \quad \text{var } x_2 = \sigma_2^2 \quad \text{var } x_3 = \sigma_3^2$ <br> $\text{cov } (x_i, x_j) \text{ is known}$ | $E(u) = a_1\mu_1 + a_2\mu_2 + a_3\mu_3$ <br> $\text{var } u = a_1^2\sigma_1^2 + a_2^2\sigma_2^2 + a_3^2\sigma_3^2 + 2a_1a_2 \text{ cov } (x_1,x_2)$ <br> $\qquad\qquad + 2a_1a_3 \text{ cov } (x_1,x_3) + 2a_2a_3 \text{ cov } (x_2,x_3)$ |
| 4 | $a_1 x_1 + a_2 x_2 + \cdots + a_n x_n$ | $a_1, a_2, \ldots, a_n = \text{const}$ <br> $E(x_i) = \mu_i$ <br> $\text{var } x_i = \sigma_i^2$ <br> $\text{cov } (x_i, x_j) \text{ is known}$ | $E(u) = a_1\mu_1 + a_2\mu_2 + \cdots + a_n x_n$ <br> $\text{var } u = \displaystyle\sum_{i=1}^{n} a_i^2\sigma_i^2 + \sum_{i \neq j} a_i a_j \text{ cov } (x_i, x_j)$ |
| 5 | $a_1 x_1 + a_2 x_2 + \cdots + a_n x_n$ | Same as 4 except the random variables are either independent or pairwise uncorrelated (see text for discussion) | $E(u) = a_1\mu_1 + a_2\mu_2 + \cdots + a_n\mu_n$ <br> $\text{var } u = a_1^2\sigma_1^2 + a_2^2\sigma_2^2 + \cdots + a_n^2\sigma_n^2$ |
| 6 | $x_1 x_2$ | $E(x_1) = \mu_1 \quad E(x_2) = \mu_2$ <br> $\text{var } x_1 = \sigma_1^2 \quad \text{var } x_2 = \sigma_2^2$ <br> $\text{cov } (x_1, x_2) \text{ known}$ <br> A fourth moment must also be known <br> $\text{cov } (x_1^2, x_2^2) \text{ or } E(x_1^2 x_2^2)$ | $E(u) = \text{cov } (x_1, x_2) + \mu_1\mu_2$ <br> $\text{var } u = E(x_1^2 x_2^2) - E^2(u)$ <br> $\qquad = \text{cov } (x_1^2, x_2^2) + (\sigma_1^2 + \mu_1^2)(\sigma_2^2 + \mu_2^2) - E^2(u)$ |

**Table 7.6 Moments of transformed variables (Continued)**

| No. | Transformation $u$ | Restriction | Transformed mean and variance |
|---|---|---|---|
| 7 | $x_1 x_2$ | Same as 6 except random variables $x_1$, $x_2$ either independent or $\text{cov}\,(x_1,x_2) = \text{cov}\,(x_1^2,x_2^2) = 0$ | $E(u) = \mu_1 \mu_2$ <br> $\text{var}\,u = (\sigma_1^2 + \mu_1^2)(\sigma_2^2 + \mu_2^2) - \mu_1^2 \mu_2^2$ <br> $\quad\quad = \sigma_1^2 \sigma_2^2 + \mu_1^2 \sigma_2^2 + \mu_2^2 \sigma_1^2$ |
| 8 | $x_1 x_2 \cdots x_n$ | $E(x_i) = \mu_i$ <br> $\text{var}\,x_i = \sigma_i^2$ <br> Random variables independent | $E(u) = \mu_1 \mu_2 \cdots \mu_n$ <br> $\text{var}\,u = \displaystyle\prod_{i=1}^{n}(\sigma_i^2 + \mu_i^2) - \prod_{i=1}^{n}\mu_i^2$ |
| 9 | $x_1^2 + x_2^2$ | $E(x_1) = \mu_1$ <br> $E(x_2) = \mu_2$ <br> $\text{var}\,x_1 = \sigma_1^2$ <br> $\text{var}\,x_2 = \sigma_2^2$ <br> The fourth moments $E(x_1^4)$, $E(x_2^4)$ must be known | $E(u) = E(x_1^2) + E(x_2^2)$ <br> $\quad\quad = \sigma_1^2 + \mu_1^2 + \sigma_2^2 + \mu_2^2$ <br> $\text{var}\,u = E(x_1^4) + E(x_2^4) - E^2(u)$ |
| 10 | $\sqrt{x_1^2 + x_2^2}$ | Same as 9 except moment $E(\sqrt{x_1^2 + x_2^2})$ must be known | $E(u) = E(\sqrt{x_1^2 + x_2^2})$ <br> $\text{var}\,u = (\sigma_1^2 + \mu_1^2) + (\sigma_2^2 + \mu_2^2) - E^2(u)$ |
| 11 | $\dfrac{x_1}{x_2}$ | $E(x_1) = \mu_1$ <br> $E(x_2) = \mu_2$ <br> $\text{var}\,x_1 = \sigma_1^2$ <br> $\text{var}\,x_2 = \sigma_2^2$ <br> Random variables independent; moments $E\left(\dfrac{1}{x_2}\right)$, $E\left(\dfrac{1}{x_2^2}\right)$ must be known | $E(u) = \mu_1 E\left(\dfrac{1}{x_2}\right)$ <br> $\text{var}\,u = (\sigma_1^2 + \mu_1^2)E\left(\dfrac{1}{x_2^2}\right) - \mu_1^2 E^2\left(\dfrac{1}{x_2}\right)$ |

Applying (7.46) to case 6 of Table 7.6 one obtains

$$\mu_1\mu_2 - \sigma_1\sigma_2 \leq E(x_1x_2) \leq \mu_1\mu_2 + \sigma_1\sigma_2$$

Similarly for case 3 of the table

$$(a_1\sigma_1 - a_2\sigma_2 - a_3\sigma_3)^2 \leq \text{var } (a_1x_1 + a_2x_2 + a_3x_3) \leq (a_1\sigma_1 + a_2\sigma_2 + a_3\sigma_3)^2$$

where $\sigma_1 > \sigma_2 > \sigma_3$.

The moment-transformations given in Table 7.6 simplify when a specific density function is chosen. Table 7.7 tabulates many of the specific results for normal and rectangular distributions. Again the reciprocal transformation which occurs in case 3 causes difficulty if the distribution is normal because of the intractability of $\int_a^b \frac{1}{x} e^{-x^2} dx$. The use of moment calculations will be illustrated by the following two examples.

*Example 1*    In many mechanical devices several small pieces are assembled and fitted into a larger piece. It is important to know how the subassembly tolerance relates to the individual part tolerances. Assuming a normal distribution for each part and a 10-part subassembly, $u = x_1 + x_2 + \cdots + x_{10}$. Using case 1 of Table 7.7 with $a_1 = a_2 = \cdots = a_n = 1$,

$$E(\mu) = \mu_1 + \mu_2 + \cdots + \mu_{10}$$
$$\text{var } u = \sigma_1{}^2 + \sigma_2{}^2 + \cdots + \sigma_{10}{}^2$$

If we assume all the parts are the same size, we have $\mu_1 = \mu_2 = \cdots = \mu_{10}$, and if all the tolerances are equal, $\sigma_1 = \sigma_2 = \cdots = \sigma_{10}$. Thus, the coefficient of variation of each part is $\sigma/\mu$ and for the subassembly

$$E(u) = 10\mu$$
$$\sigma_u = \sqrt{10}\ \sigma$$
$$\frac{\sigma_u}{E(u)} = \frac{\sqrt{10}\ \sigma}{10\mu} = \frac{1}{\sqrt{10}} \frac{\sigma}{\mu}$$

The coefficient of variation and the associated tolerance have been decreased to about one-third the initial value.

*Example 2*    As a second example, consider a three-stage transistor amplifier. The current gain of the amplifier (in the midband)[1] is deter-

---

[1] Midband means a frequency high enough so that the large series capacitors in the circuit are shorts and low enough so that the small parallel capacitors are open circuits. This leads to a simplified model.

**Table 7.7 Transformed moments for rectangular and normal distributions**

| No. | Transformation $u$ (all $x_i$'s independent) | Normal distribution $E(x) = \mu$  $\operatorname{var} x = \sigma^2$ | Rectangular distribution |
|---|---|---|---|

The normal distribution column shows a bell curve $f(x)$ with markings at $\mu - \sigma$, $\mu$, $\mu + \sigma$ on the $x$ axis.

The rectangular distribution column shows a rectangle of height $1/(B-A)$ between $A$ and $B$, with

$$\mu = \frac{A+B}{2} \qquad \sigma^2 = \frac{(B-A)^2}{12}$$

---

**1**   $a_1 x_1 + a_2 x_2 + \cdots + a_n x_n$

$$E(u) = a_1\mu_1 + a_2\mu_2 + \cdots + a_n\mu_n$$
$$\operatorname{var} u = (a_1\sigma_1)^2 + (a_2\sigma_2)^2 + \cdots + (a_n\sigma_n)^2$$

$$E(u) = \frac{1}{2}\sum_{i=1}^{n} a_i(B_i + A_i)$$
$$\operatorname{var} u = \frac{1}{12}\sum_{i=1}^{n}(B_i - A_i)^2$$

---

**2**   $\displaystyle\prod_{i=1}^{n} x_i$

$$E(u) = \prod_{i=1}^{n}\mu_i$$
$$\operatorname{var} u = \prod_{i=1}^{n}(\sigma_i^2 + \mu_i^2) - \prod_{i=1}^{n}\mu_i^2$$

$$E(u) = \left(\frac{1}{2}\right)^n \prod_{i=1}^{n}(A_i - B_i)$$
$$\operatorname{var} u = \left(\frac{1}{3}\right)^n \prod_{i=1}^{n}(A_i^2 + A_iB_i + B_i^2) - \mu_u^2$$

---

**3**   $\dfrac{x_1}{x_2}$

Integrals difficult to evaluate (see text)

$$E(u) = \mu_1 \frac{\ln B - \ln A}{B - A}$$
$$\operatorname{var} u = \frac{2(\sigma_1^2 + \mu_1^2)(B^2 + AB + A^2)}{A^3 B^3}$$

---

**4**   $x^n$   $n$ integer $> 0$

For $\mu_x = 0$:
$$E(u) = E(x^n)$$
$$\operatorname{var} u = E(x^{2n}) - E^2(x^n)$$
where
$$E(x^n) = \begin{cases} 0 & n \text{ odd} \\ [1 \times 3 \times 5 \times \cdots \times (n-1)]\sigma^n & n \text{ even} \end{cases}$$

$$E(u) = \frac{B^{n+1} - A^{n+1}}{(n+1)(B+A)}$$
$$\operatorname{var} u = \frac{B^{2n+1} - A^{2n+1}}{(2n+1)(B-A)} - \mu_u^2$$

---

**5**   $e^{ax}$

$$E(u) = e^{a\mu + a^2\sigma^2/2}$$
$$\operatorname{var} u = e^{2a\mu + 2a^2\sigma^2} - e^{(a\mu + a^2\sigma^2/2)^2}$$

$$E(u) = \frac{1}{a}(e^{aB} - e^{aA})$$
$$\operatorname{var} u = \frac{1}{2a}(e^{2aB} - e^{2aA}) - E^2(u)$$

---

407

mined by the current gain of each transistor $\beta$ and a current-divider relationship among the circuit resistors, which we shall call $K$. The amplifier gain is thus given by $K_1 K_2 K_3 \beta_1 \beta_2 \beta_3$. In practice, the tolerance on $\beta$ is large, and if we assume the resistors to have fairly narrow tolerances, we can approximate $K_1$, $K_2$, and $K_3$ by constants. Using case 2 of Table 7.6,

$$E(u) = K_1 K_2 K_3 \mu_1 \mu_2 \mu_3$$
$$\text{var } u = (K_1 K_2 K_3)^2 [(\sigma_1{}^2 + \mu_1{}^2)(\sigma_2{}^2 + \mu_2{}^2)(\sigma_3{}^2 + \mu_3{}^2) - \mu_1{}^2 \mu_2{}^2 \mu_3{}^2]$$

In the case of identical components

$$\frac{\sigma_u}{E(u)} = \frac{\sigma \sqrt{3}}{\mu} \sqrt{1 + \frac{\sigma^2}{\mu^2} + \frac{\sigma^4}{3\mu^4}} \approx \sqrt{3} \frac{\sigma}{\mu}$$

In this case the coefficient of variation has increased by approximately $\sqrt{3}$. A number of problems of practical significance can be solved exactly using the methods of Sec. 7.6. In complicated problems, especially those involving several parameters, the solution reduces to a complicated numerical integration problem. In general a solution can be obtained, but it yields no insight, only a numerical answer. In such cases, the approximation techniques discussed in the next section are more practical.

### 7.7 APPROXIMATION TECHNIQUE

Four different types of approximations will be discussed in this section. First we shall examine the deterministic techniques of Sec. 7.5 and discuss their probabilistic interpretation. The second approach will be to perform an inverse mapping of $u$ into the parameter space of the $x$'s. The third technique involves linearization of the transformation equation by expansion in a truncated Taylor series. The last technique is to apply Monte Carlo methods either in the laboratory or on a computer. The types of problems best suited to each technique are discussed in each section.

### 7.7.1 PROBABILISTIC INTERPRETATION OF DETERMINISTIC APPROACHES

As a prelude to the approximation techniques to be discussed we shall first give a probabilistic explanation to the deterministic techniques discussed in Sec. 7.5. We can interpret worst-case analysis in the following manner. Suppose that there are three random variables $x_1$, $x_2$, and $x_3$ and that we are interested in some function of these three variables $u(x_1, x_2, x_3)$. If the three random variables *exist only over a finite range*[1]

---

[1] More precisely one refers to the *domain* of the $x$'s and the *range* of $u$.

of values $x_{1,\min} \leq x_1 \leq x_{1,\max}$, etc., then these ranges are statistics of interest in the problem.    The transformed variable will also exist over a certain range $u_{\min} \leq u(x_1,x_2,x_3) \leq u_{\max}$.    The range of $u$ is again an interesting statistic.    In the case where the transformation $u$ produces a *one-to-one mapping* between the variables $x_1$, $x_2$, $x_3$, and $u$, the technique of worst-case analysis allows one to find $u_{\min}$ and $u_{\max}$ in a simple manner. Thus, if the $x$ parameters are limited in range and the transformation from the $x_i$'s to $u$ is a one-to-one mapping, then the range of $u$ is given by worst-case analysis.

Stacking up the tolerances also has a probabilistic interpretation.    If the $x$ parameters are limited in range and $u$ is the sum of the $x_i$'s, then the distribution of $u$ is limited in range.    The end points of the $u$ distribution are given by stacking up the tolerances.

Thus, the deterministic approaches give us some information about the range of the transformed random variable if the assumptions hold.    (If the assumptions do not hold, they may still serve as an approximation to the range.    However, they shed no light on the distribution within this range.)

### 7.7.2  INVERSE MAPPING

Often the problem is simplified if we invert the mapping, i.e., map $u$ into a parameter space of the $x_i$'s.    Consider the two parameters to be $x_1$ and $x_2$ and the performance function to be $u(x_1,x_2)$.    We define the performance parameter $u$ to be satisfactory if it falls between two limits $a$ and $b$, that is, $a \leq u \leq b$.    One then maps in the $x_1$ vs. $x_2$ plane the following two curves $u(x_1,x_2) = a$ and $u(x_1,x_2) = b$.    The area between these two curves represents pairs of points which satisfy the performance criterion.    If one knows the joint density function $\phi(x_1,x_2)$ [in the case where $x_1$ and $x_2$ are independent this is given by $\phi(x_1,x_2) = f_1(x_1)f_2(x_2)$], the probability of an acceptable system is given by

$$\text{Probability of a successful system} = \iint\limits_{\substack{\text{domain}\\ =\text{ function}\\ \text{of } a \text{ and } b}} \phi(x_1,x_2)\, dx_1\, dx_2 \qquad (7.47)$$

Clearly this technique is a probabilistic extension of the methods of Sec. 7.4.3.

For example, suppose that the performance index $u$ is $Kx_1x_2$.    (This could correspond to the gain of a two-stage transistor amplifier where $\beta_1$ and $\beta_2$ are analogous to $x_1$ and $x_2$.)    The limits on the performance would logically be $u_{\min} \leq Kx_1x_2 \leq u_{\max}$.    (In some problems $u_{\max}$ might be $+\infty$.)    The $x_1x_2$-plane plot would be as shown in Fig. 7.10.    The area between the two equilateral hyperbolas represents a good system.

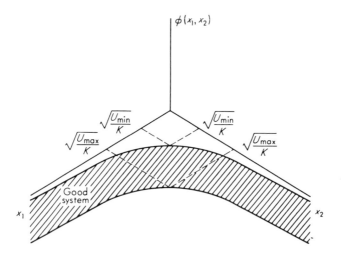

**Fig. 7.10**   A two-parameter plot for the function $u = Kx_1x_2$.

If one plotted $\phi(x_1,x_2)$ along the remaining axis in this figure, it would form a surface above the $x_1x_2$ plane representing the joint density function. The *nomalized volume* under the surface between the two parabolic curves would be the probability in question. If $\phi(x_1,x_2)$ is a parallelepiped or the surface has a flat plateau in the region of interest, one can project the top of the box down to the $x_1x_2$ plane and compute the probability as the ratio of the area between the two hyperbolas to the total rectangular area. The area computations could be done by integration or making an accurate graph and counting small grid squares. One must take care in using this technique to include all the areas in the mapping. For example, in the problem in question, the mapping is not one to one, since there are two other equilateral hyperbolas in the $-x_1,-x_2$ quadrant. In this problem there is no physical significance to $-\beta_1,-\beta_2$, and therefore the function $\phi(x_1,x_2)$ should have area only in the first quadrant and the third quadrant region can be neglected. One can obtain much information of significance by fixing a range of $u$ values and computing the corresponding probability for this range. Repeating this computation for seven ranges, one can plot a curve of probability vs. range. By varying each parameter $x_i$ in turn, one can obtain a series of design curves giving the tolerance on $x_i$ for a confidence interval in $u$.

### 7.7.3 TAYLOR SERIES EXPANSION

If one treats problems in which the tolerances are small or moderate, the density function $\phi(x_1,x_2, \ldots ,x_n)$ will have a central peak and will be concentrated near this peak. In this case $u(x_1,x_2, \ldots ,x_n)$ may change slowly in the vicinity of this peak, and the function can be expanded in a Taylor series which can be truncated after a few terms. Approximations based on this principle[1] will be developed for single- and multiple-variable functions.

*Single-variable expansion*   For a single-variable function, one is interested in transformations of the form $u(x)$. The function $u$ can be expanded in a Taylor series about the point $a$

$$u(x + a) = u(x)\Big|_{x=a} + \dot{u}(x)\Big|_{x=a}(x - a) + \ddot{u}(x)\Big|_{x=a}\frac{(x - a)^2}{2!}$$
$$+ \cdots + u^n(x)\Big|_{x=a}\frac{(x - a)^n}{n!} + \cdots \quad (7.48)$$

The logical point to expand about is the mean of the original density function $\mu = E(x)$, that is, $a = \mu$. Rewriting Eq. (7.48) with notational simplification yields

$$u(\Delta x) = u(\mu) + \dot{u}(\mu)\,\Delta x + \ddot{u}(\mu)\frac{\Delta x^2}{2!} + \cdots + u^n(\mu)\frac{\Delta x^n}{n!} + \cdots \quad (7.49)$$

where $u^n(\mu) \equiv m$th derivative of $u(x)$ evaluated at $\mu$
   $\Delta x^n \equiv (x - \mu)^n$
The first few terms in Eq. (7.49) will be used as an approximation of $u(x)$ to simplify the transformation problem and the moment-calculation problem.

Before we begin to truncate the series, we should inquire over what range of $x$ our truncated series approximation should hold. The best way to estimate this is to inspect the behavior of $u(x)$ compared with $f(x)$, as shown in Fig. 7.11. We know that the density function is concentrated within a few $\sigma$ units of the mean, therefore, if $u(x)$ has a fairly smooth variation over this range, $u(x)$ can be approximated by the first few terms of the series. Using a two-term (constant plus linear) approximation to Eq. (7.49) we obtain

$$u(\Delta x) = u(\mu) + \dot{u}(\mu)\,\Delta x$$

To emphasize that $u(\mu)$ and $\dot{u}(\mu)$ are merely constants we rename them $a$ and $b$, respectively, and obtain

$$u(\Delta x) = a + b\,\Delta x \quad (7.50)$$

The inverse function is

$$\Delta x = \frac{u - a}{b}$$

[1] M. Shooman, Determination of Variations in System Performance Resulting from Component Variations, *Sperry Gyroscope Co., Tech. Mem.* 314034, July, 1957; Papoulis, *op. cit.;* M. Shooman, Mathematical Models for Drift Failure Analysis, *Nat. Symp. Reliability Quality Control,* vol. R-15, no. 2, 1965.

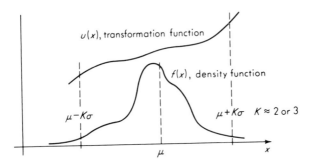

**Fig. 7.11**  Comparison of $u(x)$ with $f(x)$ near the point $x = \mu$.

and

$$\frac{d\,\Delta x}{du} = \frac{1}{b}$$

Using transformation 1 of Table 7.1, we obtain

$$h(u) \approx \frac{1}{b} f\left(\frac{u - a}{b}\right) \tag{7.51}$$

Thus, the constant term $a$ merely serves as a shifting factor translating the distribution. The linear coefficient $b$ is a scale factor for the new distribution. Note that the two-term approximation has not predicted any change in shape. The mean and variance transformations associated with Eq. (7.51) are seen from Table 7.6 to be

$$E(u) = a + b\mu \qquad \operatorname{var} u = b^2\sigma^2 \tag{7.52}$$

Taking an additional term in the approximation adds further insight

$$u(\Delta x) = u(\mu) + \dot{u}(\mu)\,\Delta x + \frac{\ddot{u}(\mu)}{2!}\,\Delta x^2$$

which becomes

$$u(\Delta x) = a + b\,\Delta x + c\,\Delta x^2 \tag{7.53}$$

The inverse relation of course is a quadratic equation with roots

$$r_1, r_2 = \frac{-b \pm \sqrt{b^2 - 4c(a - u)}}{2c}$$

To obtain $dx/du$ we compute it from Eq. (7.53) by implicit differentiation

$$\left|\frac{dx}{du}\right| = \frac{1}{|du/dx|} = \frac{1}{|b + (c\,\Delta x)/2|}$$

The transformed distribution becomes

$$h(u) = \frac{1}{b + (c\,\Delta x)/2}\,[f(r_1) + f(r_2)] \tag{7.54}$$

It is difficult to interpret the bracketed term unless one substitutes numerical values and solves for $r_1$ and $r_2$. However, if $c$ is small, the behavior should be almost the same as $f[(u - a)/b]$ in Eq. (7.52). The term $b + (c\,\Delta x)/2$ can be interpreted more easily. The behavior of this term for the case where $b$ and $c$ have like signs and unlike signs is sketched in Fig. 7.12. Thus, if the first and second derivatives of $u$ have the same sign, the transformation tends to concentrate the distributions, whereas if they differ in sign, the distribution is further dispersed.

The new mean and variance are easily computed from Eq. (7.53). The mean is given by

$$
\begin{aligned}
E(u) &= \int_{-\infty}^{+\infty} [a + b(x - \mu) + c(x - \mu)^2]f(x)\,dx \\
&= a\int_{-\infty}^{+\infty} f(x)\,dx + b\int_{-\infty}^{+\infty} xf(x)\,dx - b\mu\int_{-\infty}^{+\infty} f(x)\,dx \\
&\quad + c\int_{-\infty}^{+\infty} x^2f(x)\,dx - 2c\mu\int_{-\infty}^{+\infty} xf(x)\,dx + c\mu^2\int_{-\infty}^{+\infty} f(x)\,dx \\
&= a + b\mu - b\mu + cE(x^2) - 2c\mu^2 + c\mu^2 = a + c[E(x^2) - \mu^2] \\
&= a + c\sigma^2
\end{aligned}
\tag{7.55}
$$

The variance is computed as follows:

$$
\begin{aligned}
\text{var}\,(u) &= E(u^2) - E^2(u)\cdot \\
E(u^2) &= \int_{-\infty}^{+\infty} [a + b(x - \mu) + c(x - \mu)^2]^2 f(x)\,dx \\
&= a^2\int_{-\infty}^{+\infty} f(x)\,dx + b^2\int_{-\infty}^{+\infty} (x - \mu)^2 f(x)\,dx \\
&\quad + c^2\int_{-\infty}^{+\infty} (x - \mu)^4 f(x)\,dx + 2ab\int_{-\infty}^{+\infty} (x - \mu)f(x)\,dx \\
&\quad + 2ac\int_{-\infty}^{+\infty} (x - \mu)^2 f(x)\,dx + 2bc\int_{-\infty}^{+\infty} (x - \mu)^3 f(x)\,dx \\
&= a^2 + b^2\sigma^2 + 2ac\sigma^2 + 2bcE[(x - \mu)^3] + c^2E[(x - \mu)^4] \\
\text{var}\,(u) &= a^2 + b^2\sigma^2 + 2ac\sigma^2 + 2bcE[(x - \mu)^3] + c^2E[(x - \mu)^4] \\
&= b^2\sigma^2 + 2bcE[(x - \mu)^3] + c^2E[(x - \mu)^4] - c^2\sigma^4
\end{aligned}
\tag{7.56}
$$

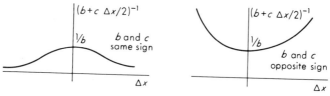

**Fig. 7.12**  Behavior of term $1/[b + (c\,\Delta x/2)]$.

The inclusion of the quadratic term $c$ in the series expansion has shifted the mean slightly, either up or down depending on the sign of $c$. Interpretation of the variance is a bit more complicated. Since $c^2 < b^2$, we can neglect the $E[(x - \mu)^4]$ and $\sigma^4$ terms. The remaining term should be small since $2bc < b^2$ but still larger than the fourth-order terms. In many cases, the third moment $E[(x - \mu)^3]$ will be zero. This is always so if $f(x)$ is symmetrical about $\mu$ and may also be so in some cases if $f(x)$ is asymmetrical. If the third moment is nonzero and positive, the change in variance (increase or decrease) is governed by the signs of $b$ and $c$ as previously described. In most cases, the third and fourth moments will be small, and as a practical matter they may be unknown. Thus, it is not unreasonable to approximate var $u$ with only the first term

$$\text{var } u \approx b^2 \sigma^2 \tag{7.57}$$

The series approximations discussed above will be illustrated by the following example.

*Example*  Earlier in this chapter the computation of the current distribution in terms of a fixed voltage and the distribution of resistance was discussed. The solution became difficult when $R$ was assumed to have a normal distribution. This can be simply solved by the above techniques, by expanding the function $V/R$ in a series. Computing the derivatives of the system, one obtains

$$u(x) = \frac{1}{x} \qquad u(\mu) = \frac{1}{\mu} = a$$

$$\dot{u}(x) = -\frac{1}{x^2} \qquad \ddot{u}(\mu) = -\frac{1}{\mu^2} = b$$

$$\ddot{u}(x) = \frac{2}{x^3} \frac{\ddot{u}(\mu)}{2} = \frac{1}{\mu^3} = c$$

The moments of the normal distribution are $\mu$, $\sigma$, $E[(x - \mu)^3] = 0$, and $E[(x - \mu)^4] = 3\sigma^4$ (see Chap. 2). Substitution in Eqs. (7.55) and (7.56) yields

$$E(u) = \frac{1}{\mu}\left(1 + \frac{\sigma^2}{\mu^2}\right) \qquad \text{var } u = \frac{\sigma^2}{\mu^4}\left(1 + \frac{2\sigma^2}{\mu^2}\right)$$

Obviously, if the coefficient of variation, $\sigma/\mu < 1$, then $E(u) = 1/\mu$ and var $u = \sigma^2/\mu^4$.

*Multivariable expansion*  The series approximation technique described above is very useful and quite accurate. The preceding development dealt with one variable, but it is easy to apply this technique to a function of many variables as well. If one begins with a transformation function

$u(x_1, x_2, \ldots, x_n)$ and wishes to calculate $h(u)$, the same series-expansion techniques can be used. The expansion of $u(x_1, x_2, \ldots, x_n)$ in a multi-dimensional Taylor series can be computed from the general operational form

$$u(x_1 + x_{10}, x_2 + x_{20}, \ldots, x_n + x_{n0}) = \sum_{K=0}^{\infty} \frac{1}{K!} \left\{ \left[ (x_1 - x_{10}) \frac{\partial}{\partial x_1} \right. \right.$$
$$\left. \left. + (x_2 - x_{20}) \frac{\partial}{\partial x_2} + \cdots + (x_n - x_{n0}) \frac{\partial}{\partial x_n} \right]^K u(x_1, x_2, \ldots, x_n) \right\} \quad (7.58)$$

Expanding Eq. (7.58) and retaining only the first- and second-order terms yields

$$u(\Delta x_1, \Delta x_2, \ldots, \Delta x_n) = u_{op} + \left[ \left( \frac{\partial u}{\partial x_1} \right)_{op} \Delta x_1 + \left( \frac{\partial u}{\partial x_2} \right)_{op} \Delta x_2 \right.$$
$$+ \cdots + \left( \frac{\partial u}{\partial x_n} \right)_{op} \Delta x_n \left] + \frac{1}{2} \right[ \left( \frac{\partial^2 u}{\partial x_1^2} \right)_{op} \Delta x_1^2$$
$$+ \left( \frac{\partial^2 u}{\partial x_2^2} \right)_{op} \Delta x_2^2 + \cdots + \left( \frac{\partial^2 u}{\partial x_n^2} \right)_{op} \Delta x_n^2 \right]$$
$$+ \left[ \left( \frac{\partial^2 u}{\partial x_1 \, \partial x_2} \right)_{op} \Delta x_1 \, \Delta x_2 + \left( \frac{\partial^2 u}{\partial x_1 \, \partial x_3} \right)_{op} \Delta x_1 \, \Delta x_3 \right.$$
$$\left. + \cdots + \left( \frac{\partial^2 u}{\partial x_i \, \partial x_j} \right)_{\substack{op \\ i \neq j}} \Delta x_i \, \Delta x_j \right] \quad (7.59)$$

where $\Delta x_1^n \equiv (x_1 - \mu_1)^n$, $\mu_1$ is $E(x_1)$, and

$$\left( \frac{\partial u}{\partial x_1} \right)_{op} \qquad \left( \frac{\partial^2 u}{\partial x_1^2} \right)_{op} \qquad \left( \frac{\partial^2 u}{\partial x_1 \, \partial x_2} \right)_{op}$$

are partial derivatives[1] of $u$ evaluated at the operating point, $x_1 = \mu_1$, $x_2 = \mu_2$, etc., with $\mu_i = E(x_i)$. For simplicity and to emphasize that the partial derivatives are constants we write Eq. (7.59) as

$$u(\Delta x_1, \Delta x_2, \ldots, \Delta x_n) = a + \sum_{i=1}^{n} b_i \, \Delta x_i + \frac{1}{2} \sum_{i=1}^{n} c_i \, \Delta x_i^2$$
$$+ \sum_{i=1}^{n} \sum_{\substack{j=1 \\ i \neq j}}^{n} d_{ij} \, \Delta x_i \, \Delta x_j \quad (7.60)$$

[1] When the function $u$ is complex or does not possess a derivative, one can compute ratios of differences instead of derivatives. These differences can be computed in the laboratory by actually varying system parameters throughout a small range or by a similar variation in the coefficients of a computer model. For example, such partial-derivative calculations are generally included in computer circuit-analysis programs. See, for example, Wall, *op. cit.*

It is difficult to draw any conclusions from this as to the form of $h(u)$; therefore, we shall go to the computation of first and second moments. Computing $E(u)$ from Eq. (7.60) yields

$$E(u) = a + \frac{1}{2} \sum_{i=1}^{n} c_i \sigma_i^2 + \sum_{\substack{i=1 \ j=1 \\ i \neq j}}^{n} \sum^{n} d_{ij} \, \mathrm{cov} \, (x_i, x_j) \qquad (7.61)$$

The computation of variance is much more involved. For two variables $x_1$ and $x_2$ we proceed by computing $E(u^2) - E^2(u)$. The $E(u)$ is given by

$$u = a + b_1 \, \Delta x_1 + b_2 \, \Delta x_2 + \tfrac{1}{2} c_1 \, \Delta x_1^2 + \tfrac{1}{2} c_2 \, \Delta x_2^2 + d_{12} \, \Delta x_1 \, \Delta x_2$$
$$E(u) = a + \tfrac{1}{2} c_1 \sigma_1^2 + \tfrac{1}{2} c_2 \sigma_2^2 + d_{12} \, \mathrm{cov} \, (x_1, x_2)$$

The quantity $E^2(u)$ contains 10 terms, and the $E(u^2)$ has 19 nonzero terms. Their difference after cancellation contains 21 terms, which can be grouped as shown below

$$\begin{aligned}
\mathrm{var} \; u = E(u^2) - E^2(u) = \; & b_1^2 \sigma_1^2 + b_2^2 \sigma_2^2 + 2b_1 b_2 \, \mathrm{cov} \, (x_1, x_2) \\
& + b_1 c_1 E(\Delta x_1^3) + b_2 c_2 E(\Delta x_2^3) \\
& + (2b_1 d_{12} + b_2 c_1) E(\Delta x_1^2 \, \Delta x_2) \\
& + (2b_2 d_{12} + b_1 c_2) E(\Delta x_1 \, \Delta x_2^2) \\
& + \tfrac{1}{4} c_1^2 [E(\Delta x_1^4) - \sigma_1^4] + \tfrac{1}{4} c_2^2 [E(\Delta x_2^4) - \sigma_2^4] \\
& + 2 d_{12}^2 [E(\Delta x_1^2 \, \Delta x_2^2) - \mathrm{cov}^2 \, (x_1, x_2)] \\
& + \tfrac{1}{2} c_1 c_2 [E(\Delta x_1^2 \, \Delta x_2^2) - \sigma_1^2 \sigma_2^2] \\
& + c_1 d_{12} [E(\Delta x_1^3 \, \Delta x_2) - \sigma_1^2 \, \mathrm{cov} \, (x_1, x_2)] \\
& + c_2 d_{12} [E(\Delta x_1 \, \Delta x_2^3) - \sigma_2^2 \, \mathrm{cov} \, (x_1, x_2)]
\end{aligned}$$

This expression must be simplified to make it useful as a computational tool. If one assumes independence, $\mathrm{cov} \, (x_1, x_2) = 0$,

$$E(\Delta x_1 \, \Delta x_2^n) = E(\Delta x_1) E(\Delta x_2^n) = 0$$

and $E(\Delta x_1^2 \, \Delta x_2^2) = \sigma_1^2 \sigma_2^2$, the expression reduces to

$$\begin{aligned}
\mathrm{var} \; u = \; & b_1^2 \sigma_1^2 + b_2^2 \sigma_2^2 + b_1 c_1 E(\Delta x_1^3) + b_2 c_2 E(\Delta x_2^3) \\
& + \tfrac{1}{4} c_1^2 [E(\Delta x_1^4) - \sigma_1^4] + \tfrac{1}{4} c_2^2 [E(\Delta x_2^4) - \sigma_2^4] + 2 d_{12}^2 \sigma_1^2 \sigma_2^2
\end{aligned}$$

Furthermore, if the distribution is symmetrical, $E(\Delta x_1^3) = E(\Delta x_2^3) = 0$. Another useful simplification is to assume that the $c$ and $d$ coefficients are smaller than the $b$ coefficients and that the third- and fourth-order moments are smaller than the second, which yields

$$\mathrm{var} \; u = b_1^2 \sigma_1^2 + b_2^2 \sigma_2^2 + 2b_1 b_2 \, \mathrm{cov} \, (x_1, x_2)$$

If we agree to neglect higher than second-order moments for the above reasons, var $u$ can be written in general as

$$\text{var } u = \sum_{i=1}^{n} b_i^2 \sigma_i^2 + 2 \sum_{i=1}^{n} \sum_{\substack{j=1 \\ i \neq j}}^{n} b_i b_j \text{ cov } (x_i, x_j) \tag{7.62}$$

The following example will illustrate these calculations.

*Example*  Two resistors $R_1$ and $R_2$ are to be connected in parallel to form a new resistance $R_p$

$$R_p = \frac{R_1 R_2}{R_1 + R_2}$$

The resistors $R_1$ and $R_2$ are 200 ohms $\pm$ 10 percent. Assuming that the tolerance represents $2\sigma$ units, we obtain $\mu_1 = \mu_2 = 200$ ohms and $\sigma_1 = \sigma_2 = 10$ ohms. If we assume that $R_1$ and $R_2$ are independent random variables, cov $(R_1, R_2) = 0$. In this case $u(R_1, R_2) = R_p$, and the required derivatives are

$$u_{op} = \frac{R_1 R_2}{R_1 + R_2} \bigg|_{R_1 = R_2 = 200} = 100 \text{ ohms} = a$$

$$\left(\frac{\partial u}{\partial R_1}\right)_{op} = \frac{R_2^2}{(R_1 + R_2)^2} \bigg|_{R_1 = R_2 = 200} = \frac{1}{4} = b_1$$

$$\left(\frac{\partial u}{\partial R_2}\right)_{op} = \frac{R_1^2}{(R_1 + R_2)^2} \bigg|_{R_1 = R_2 = 200} = \frac{1}{4} = b_2$$

$$\left(\frac{\partial^2 u}{\partial R_1^2}\right)_{op} = \frac{-2R_2^2}{(R_1 + R_2)^3} \bigg|_{R_1 = R_2 = 200} = -\frac{1}{8} \times 10^{-2} = c_1$$

$$\left(\frac{\partial^2 u}{\partial R_2^2}\right)_{op} = \frac{-2R_1^2}{(R_1 + R_2)^3} \bigg|_{R_1 = R_2 = 200} = -\frac{1}{8} \times 10^{-2} = c_2$$

$$\left(\frac{\partial^2 u}{\partial R_1 \, \partial R_2}\right)_{op} = \frac{2R_1 R_2}{(R_1 + R_2)^3} \bigg|_{R_1 = R_2 = 200} = \frac{1}{8} \times 10^{-2} = d_{12}$$

Since the covariance of $R_1$ and $R_2$ is zero, substitution in Eq. (7.52) yields

$$E(u) = 100 + \tfrac{1}{2}(-\tfrac{1}{8} \times 10^{-2} \times 10^2 - \tfrac{1}{8} \times 10^{-2} \times 10^2)$$
$$= 100 - \tfrac{1}{8} = 99.875 \text{ ohms}$$

Similarly substitution in Eq. (7.53) gives

$$\text{var } u = [(\tfrac{1}{4})^2 \times 10^2 + (\tfrac{1}{4})^2 \times 10^2] = 12.5$$

The coefficient of variation was originally $10/200 = 0.05$, and the coefficient of variation for $R_p$ is $\sqrt{12.5}/100 = 0.035$, which is an improvement.

Thus, using the approximation of Eq. (7.58), one can obtain simple solutions to fairly complex problems. In addition, the magnitude of the coefficients $a$, $b$, $c$, and $d$ yields valuable insight into the relative importance of the system parameters as to how they affect marginal failure. The following two sections will apply the preceding results to various circuit and control problems of interest.

### 7.7.4 MONTE CARLO SIMULATION

If the shape of the transformed distribution is of importance but exact methods are untenable, Monte Carlo techniques can be used. One can either replicate a physical experiment in the laboratory or a model experiment on a computer.

Suppose one wished to evaluate the distribution of the gain of a transistor amplifier containing three transistors and several resistors and capacitors. The laboratory approach would be to build a breadboard amplifier with clip-type terminals so that components are easily replaceable. One would then obtain three boxes, each filled with a "large" number of transistors, resistors, and capacitors. In each case one would use the same type of component to be used in construction of the circuit. The numbers of each component must be large enough so that the sample fairly represents the manufacturing distribution of such components. In case of doubt the component values can be measured and the empirical distribution examined. The first circuit would be built by random selection of sufficient components from each component box. The gain of amplifier 1 would then be measured in the laboratory and recorded. The parts from amplifier 1 would then be returned to their boxes and mixed, and a new set would be drawn for amplifier 2. The gain of amplifier 2 would be measured and recorded. This process would be repeated $n$ times and the empirical gain distribution plotted.

The accuracy of the empirical points will depend on how many gain points are clustered in each interval $n_i$. The expected number of data points will be

$$n_i = f_i n$$

where $f_i$ is the mean value for the ordinate of the interval in question. The variance of the empirical points will have a standard deviation which varies as $1/\sqrt{n_i} = 1/\sqrt{f_i n}$. Thus, the accuracy with which we determine any point on the curve will increase as $n$ increases. Also the points on the tails of the curve will be less accurate than the center points, since the value of $f_i$ is smaller at the tails than in the center.

If one wishes to perform Monte Carlo analysis on a digital computer, a model must be chosen for each component distribution. Each of these distributions is generated on the computer, using the techniques described in Sec. 5.10.4. An analytical gain expression is then obtained for the circuit. A set of random numbers for the parameters is then substituted into the gain expression and the sample value of gain obtained.    This is repeated for $n$ trials.    As in the experimental case, the empirical distribution must be plotted, and the standard deviation varies with $1/\sqrt{f_i n}$.

## 7.8  CIRCUIT APPLICATIONS

This section will apply the principles developed in the preceding sections to various circuit problems.    The discussion will begin with a few simple resistive network examples and then treat the application to impedance and transfer functions for networks containing frequency-sensitive elements.    In the latter context, several theorems regarding the sum of the sensitivities in a network will be discussed.    Although the examples included are electrical in nature, the techniques may also be applied to hydraulic, mechanical, thermal, and pneumatic problems if a lumped-circuit (either active or passive) model can be structured for the problem.

### 7.8.1  CIRCUIT EXAMPLES

This section will discuss how component tolerances interact to yield circuit tolerances in several simple circuit examples.    In each case the network will not be frequency-dependent; i.e., only sources and resistances appear.

*Series and parallel resistors*   In the preceding sections examples concerning two resistors in series and two in parallel have been discussed. In both cases the coefficient of variation of the combined structure was smaller than that of a single resistor (assuming the same tolerance on all components).    Turning from analysis to design, we pose the following problem: if one wishes to achieve a network resistance with a small tolerance by combining resistors with larger tolerances, should these resistors be combined in series or parallel?    Let us compare three different cases:

1   A single resistor with a nominal value $R$ and a fractional tolerance $T$
2   Two independent series resistors $R_1$ and $R_2$ which have nominal values $KR$ and $(1 - K)R$ respectively, each with fractional tolerance $T$
3   Two independent parallel resistors $R_3$ and $R_4$ which have nominal values $R/K$ and $R/(1 - K)$, respectively, each with fractional tolerance $T$

In case 1 we shall assume that $2\sigma = TR$.    Therefore, $\sigma = TR/2$, and the coefficient of variation is $\sigma/R = T/2$.

In case 2 we have not chosen equal resistors with values $R/2$ but have only required that the series combination add up to $R$.    Thus, we are free to minimize the resultant tolerance with respect to $K$ and choose the best series configuration. Since the network resistance is given by $R_N = R_1 + R_2$, $E(R_N) = E(R_1) + E(R_2) = KR + (1 - K)R = R$, the variance is given by

$$\text{var } R_N = \sigma_1{}^2 + \sigma_2{}^2 \tag{7.63}$$

Assuming that both $R_1$ and $R_2$ have identical tolerances of $T$ and that $2\sigma = TR$, we obtain

$$\sigma_1{}^2 = \left(\frac{TKR}{2}\right)^2 \quad \text{and} \quad \sigma_2{}^2 = \left(\frac{T(1 - K)R}{2}\right)^2$$

$$\text{var } R_N = \frac{T^2R^2}{4}[K^2 + (1 - K)^2] \tag{7.64}$$

Minimizing var $R_N$ with respect to $K$ yields

$$\frac{\partial \text{ var } R_N}{\partial K} = \frac{T^2R^2}{4}[2K - 2(1 - K)] = 0$$

The resulting solution is $K = \frac{1}{2}$, which is just what intuition would have told us. Thus the best policy is to make $R_1 = R_2 = R/2$. Substituting $K = \frac{1}{2}$ in Eq. (7.64) yields

$$\text{var } R_N = \frac{T^2R^2}{8}$$

$$\sigma R_N = \frac{TR}{2\sqrt{2}}$$

Therefore, the series configuration has reduced the standard deviation and coefficient of variation by roughly 30 percent.

For case 3 we proceed in a manner similar to case 2. The network resistance is

$$R_N = \frac{1}{1/R_3 + 1/R_4} = \frac{R_3R_4}{R_3 + R_4}$$

The $E(R_N)$ is computed from Eq. (7.61) with $u = R_N$. The solution for the $E(R_N)$ for parallel resistors was obtained in the previous section where it was shown that

$$E(R_N) = \frac{R_3R_4}{R_3 + R_4}\bigg|_{\text{op}} + \frac{1}{2}\left[\frac{-2R_4{}^2}{(R_3 + R_4)^3}\bigg|_{\text{op}}\sigma_3{}^2 - \frac{2R_3{}^2}{(R_3 + R_4)^3}\bigg|_{\text{op}}\sigma_4{}^2\right]$$

Substituting $E(R_3) = R/K$ and $E(R_4) = R/(1 - K)$ yields

$$E(R_N) = R - \left[\frac{K^3(1 - K)}{R}\sigma_3{}^2 + \frac{K(1 - K)^3}{R}\sigma_4{}^2\right] \tag{7.64a}$$

We notice as before that the mean is decreased somewhat from the desired value of $R$. Assuming that this is a small effect, we continue to compute the variance

$$\text{var } R_N = \left[ \frac{R_4{}^2}{(R_3 + R_4)^2} \Big|_{op} \right]^2 \sigma_3{}^2 + \left[ \frac{R_3{}^2}{(R_3 + R_4)^2} \Big|_{op} \right]^2 \sigma_4{}^2$$

Substitution of $E(R_3)$ and $E(R_4)$ gives

$$\text{var } R_N = K^4 \sigma_3{}^2 + (1 - K)^4 \sigma_4{}^2$$

Substituting $\sigma_3{}^2 = (TR/2K)^2$ and $\sigma_4{}^2 = \left[ \dfrac{TR}{2(1-K)} \right]^2$

$$\text{var } R_N = \frac{T^2 R^2 K^2}{4} + \frac{T^2 R^2 (1 - K)^2}{4} = \frac{T^2 R^2 (2K^2 - 2K + 1)}{4} \tag{7.65}$$

Minimizing $\text{var } R_N$ by setting $(\partial \text{ var } R_N)/\partial K = 0$ yields

$$\frac{\partial \text{ var } R_N}{\partial K} = \frac{T^2 R^2}{4}(4K - 2) = 0$$
$$\therefore K = \tfrac{1}{2}$$

Substitution in (7.65) gives

$$\sigma_{R_N} = \frac{TR}{2\sqrt{2}}$$

Thus, the variance is approximately the same as in the series case. To compute the mean shift, we substitute $K = \tfrac{1}{2}$, $\sigma_3{}^2 = \sigma_4{}^2 = T^2 R^2$ in Eq. (7.5) to obtain

$$E(R_N) = R\left(1 - \frac{T^2}{8}\right)$$

The mean shift is entirely negligible, since for $T = 0.10$ the shift is on the order of $10^{-3}$, and even for $T = 0.5$ the correction term is $\sim 0.03$.

These results show that both the series and parallel cases are the same as far as reducing variance. At first thought it would appear that the two methods are equivalent, but this is not the case. Careful consideration reveals that either case worsens the probability of catastrophic failures. In fact replacing a single resistor with a series or parallel combination to reduce variance makes sense only if the catastrophic-failure rate of these components is low. If the circuit which remains after one resistor failure is still considered operable, then there is a choice between the series and the parallel arrangements on the basis of catastrophic failures. If resistors fail mainly as open circuits, the parallel circuit is better, and if the converse is true, then the series circuit should be used.

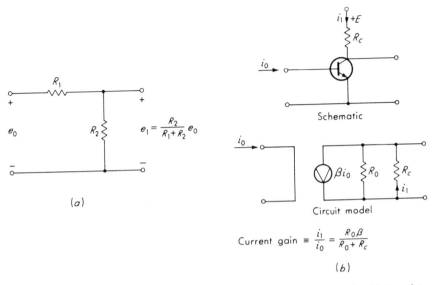

**Fig. 7.13**  Two common electronic circuits.  (a) Voltage-divider circuit; (b) transistor amplifier.

*Divider circuit*  A circuit which occurs frequently in electronic systems is the voltage-divider[1] circuit shown in Fig. 7.13a.  For the case where $e_1 = 100$ volts $\pm 5$ percent, $R_1 = 300$ ohms $\pm 10$ percent, and

$$R_2 = 100 \text{ ohms } \pm 5 \text{ percent}$$

the Taylor series expansion is given by the following terms.  The constant term is

$$e_2 = \frac{e_1}{1 + R_1/R_2} = +25$$

The first-order partials are

$$\frac{\partial e_2}{\partial e_1} = \frac{1}{1 + R_1/R_2} = +\frac{1}{4}$$

$$\frac{\partial e_2}{\partial R_2} = \frac{-e_1}{R_2(1 + R_1/R_2)^2} = -\frac{1}{16}$$

$$\frac{\partial e_2}{\partial R_2} = \frac{e_1 R_1}{R_2{}^2(1 + R_1/R_2)^2} = +\frac{3}{16}$$

[1] The reader familiar with vacuum-tube circuit analysis might reflect that the functional form of the voltage divider occurs quite frequently in conventional grounded cathode amplifiers, generally with the voltage gain $\mu$ as a multiplier in the numerator.

The second-order partials are

$$\frac{\partial^2 e_2}{\partial e_1{}^2} = 0$$

$$\frac{\partial^2 e_2}{\partial R_1{}^2} = \frac{2e_1}{R_1 R_2 (1 + R_1/R_2)^3} = \frac{1}{9,600}$$

$$\frac{\partial^2 e_2}{\partial R_2{}^2} = \frac{2e_1 R_1}{R_2{}^3 (1 + R_1/R_2)^3} = \frac{-3}{3,200}$$

If we assume independence, the second-order *cross* partials are not needed.[1] Assuming that $TN = 2\sigma$; $\sigma_{e_1} = 2.5$, $\sigma_{R_1} = 15$, $\sigma_{R_2} = 2.5$, from Eqs. (7.61) and (7.62)

$$E(e_2) = 25 + \frac{1}{2}\left(\frac{1}{9,600} \times 15^2 \frac{3}{3,200} 2.5^2\right) \approx 25 - 0.016 = 25$$

$$\text{var } e_2 = \tfrac{1}{4}{}^2(2.5^2) + (-\tfrac{1}{16})^2(15^2) + (\tfrac{3}{16})^2 (2.5^2) = 1.473$$

$$\sigma_{e_2} = 1.21$$

Defining the overall tolerance on $e_2$ as twice the coefficient of variation of $e_2$ yields $T_{e2} = 2 \times 1.2 \times 100/26 = 9.7$ percent.

*Transistor amplifier*  The schematic and circuit model of a transistor amplifier are shown in Fig. 7.13b. If $R_o = 10,000$ ohms $\pm 20$ percent, $R_c = 10,000$ ohms $\pm 10$ percent, and $\beta = 100 \pm 50$ percent, then $\sigma_{Ro} = 1,000$ ohms, $\sigma_{Rc} = 500$ ohms, and $\sigma_\beta = 25$. The partial derivatives are

$$G = \frac{R_o}{R_o + R_c}\beta = 50$$

$$\frac{\partial G}{\partial R_o} = \frac{\beta R_c}{R_o{}^2(1 + R_c/R_o)^2} = \frac{1}{4} \times 10^{-2}$$

$$\frac{\partial G}{\partial R_c} = \frac{-\beta}{R_o(1 + R_c/R_o)^2} = -\frac{1}{4} \times 10^{-2}$$

$$\frac{\partial G}{\partial \beta} = \frac{R_o}{R_o + R_c} = \frac{1}{2}$$

$$\frac{\partial^2 G}{\partial R_o{}^2} = \frac{-2\beta R_c}{R_o{}^3(1 + R_c/R_o)^3} = -\frac{1}{4} \times 10^{-6}$$

$$\frac{\partial^2 G}{\partial R_c{}^2} = \frac{2\beta}{R_c R_o(1 + R_c/R_o)^3} = \frac{1}{4} \times 10^{-6}$$

$$\frac{\partial^2 G}{\partial \beta^2} = 0$$

---

[1] The assumption of independence implies that the covariance is zero, and the *cross* partials are multiplied by covariance terms, see Eqs. (7.61) and (7.62).

Assuming independence, the cross partials are not necessary

$$E(G) = 50 + \tfrac{1}{2}(-\tfrac{1}{4} \times 10^{-6} \times 10^6 + \tfrac{1}{4} \times 10^{-6} \times 500^2) \approx 50 - 0.1 \approx 50$$

$$\text{var } G = (\tfrac{1}{4} \times 10^{-2})^2(10^3)^2 + (-\tfrac{1}{4} \times 10^{-2})^2(500^2) + (\tfrac{1}{2})^2(25^2) = 164$$

$$\sigma_G = 12.8$$

$$T_G = \frac{2\sigma_G \times 100\%}{E(G)} = 51.2\%$$

As is well known to any transistor-circuit designer, the large spread (tolerance) on $\beta$ predominates the entire problem. This is one of the primary reasons why feedback is used in transistor amplifier circuits.

### 7.8.2 SENSITIVITY AND COEFFICIENT OF VARIATION

If one considers circuits with frequency-sensitive elements, capacitance, inductance, mass, springs, thermal capacitance, etc., there are several network functions of interest. If one takes the Laplace transform of the circuit equations and forms the ratio of output over input parameters (the ratio might be voltage/voltage, current/current, or mixed parameters), one obtains a ratio of polynomials called a *transfer function*.[1] The numerator polynomial roots are called *zeros*, and the denominator polynomial roots are called *poles*. The quantities of interest in analysis and utilization of such circuits are generally the pole and zero values, and the magnitude and phase of the transfer function for sinusoidal excitations. These problems of course are not different from those already discussed, except that the form of the equation in the case of magnitude and phase is generally more complex, and if the circuit has many poles and zeros, the calculations become numerous.[2] To simplify things a bit, a sensitivity function is defined, and certain sensitivity theorems are developed.

In the previous two examples, the importance of a particular parameter variation was not immediately obvious upon inspection of the partial derivatives, since these derivatives were multiplied by incremental changes, the $\Delta x$'s, in the equations, and one had to inspect the products to be sure of the effects of each in the mean and variance expressions. The sensitivity of function $u$ with respect to parameter $x$ is defined as the limit of the fractional change in $u$ divided by the fractional change in $x$ as $\Delta x$ and $\Delta u$ become small

$$S_x^u = \lim_{\substack{\Delta x \to 0 \\ \Delta u \to 0}} \frac{\Delta u/u}{\Delta x/x} = \frac{du/u}{dx/x} \tag{7.66}$$

$$S_x^u = \frac{d(\ln u)}{d(\ln x)} = \frac{u}{x}\frac{du}{dx} \tag{7.67}$$

[1] The initial conditions must either be zero or treated as additional input variables.
[2] If the number of poles and zeros becomes too large, the analyst must retain only the significant ones or focus on the magnitude and phase alone.

Solving Eq. (7.58) for the fractional change in $u$ yields

$$\frac{du}{u} = S_x{}^u \frac{dx}{x} \tag{7.68}$$

If $u$ is a function of several variables, we can write the total differential of $u$ as

$$du = \frac{\partial u}{\partial x_1} dx_1 + \frac{\partial u}{\partial x_2} dx_2 + \cdots + \frac{\partial u}{\partial x_n} dx_n$$

Dividing by $u$ yields

$$\frac{du}{u} = \frac{\partial u}{\partial x_1} \frac{dx_1}{u} + \frac{\partial u}{\partial x_2} \frac{dx_2}{u} + \cdots + \frac{\partial u}{\partial x_n} \frac{dx_n}{u} \tag{7.69}$$

If we replace $du/dx$ with $\partial u/\partial x$ in Eq. (7.67) because $u$ is a function of several variables and substitute into Eq. (7.69), we obtain

$$\frac{du}{u} = S_{x_1}{}^u \frac{dx_1}{x_1} + S_{x_2}{}^u \frac{dx_2}{x_2} + \cdots + S_{x_n}{}^u \frac{dx_n}{x_n} \tag{7.70}$$

This equation is extremely handy, since each sensitivity appears as a weighting factor which tells whether the effect of fractional changes in $x$ are subdued or magnified when they are included in the summation of Eq. (7.70). In fact this result allows another interpretation of the method of stacking up the tolerance previously discussed. This is precisely the calculation which would ensue if

$$S_{x_1}{}^u = S_{x_2}{}^u = \cdots = S_{x_n}{}^u = 1$$

We can also modify Eq. (6.70) to describe the case where the variations in $dx_1, dx_2, \ldots, dx_n$ are related, since the variations are all due to some environmental parameter such as temperature $T$. If we let $x_i = f_i(T)$ (where $T$ stands for any coupling parameter), then using the chain rule,

$$\frac{dx_i}{x_i} = \frac{dx_i}{dT} \frac{dT}{x_i} \tag{7.71}$$

Multiplying the right-hand side of Eq. (7.71) by $T/T$, we can combine it with Eq. (7.67) to yield

$$\frac{dx_i}{x_i} = S_{x_i}{}^T \frac{dT}{T} \tag{7.72}$$

Substituting Eq. (7.72) in Eq. (7.70) yields

$$\frac{du}{u} = (S_{x_1}{}^u S_{x_1}{}^T + S_{x_2}{}^u S_{x_2}{}^T + \cdots + S_{x_n}{}^u S_{x_n}{}^T) \frac{dT}{T} \tag{7.73}$$

If each parameter has the same dependence on the external parameter, that is, $x_1(T) = x_2(T) = \cdots = x_n(T) = f(T)$, then Eq. (7.73) becomes

$$\frac{du}{u} = (S_{x_1}{}^u + S_{x_2}{}^u + \cdots + S_{x_n}{}^u) S_x{}^T \frac{dT}{T} \tag{7.74}$$

One must remember that Eqs. (7.70) and (7.74) are correct in the limit; however, in a practical problem we are interested in $\Delta u/u$, which is approximately equal to $du/u$ if all the increments are small. The computation given in Eqs. (7.70) and (7.74) is deterministic; however, there should be some similarity to the results of Eqs. (7.60) and (7.61).

Precisely we can ask: Is $\sigma_u/E(u)$, the coefficient of variation of $u$, in some way similar to $du/u$? From Eqs. (7.60) and (7.61) we have for the case of *independent* parameters

$$\frac{\sigma_u}{E(u)} = \frac{\sqrt{\displaystyle\sum_{i=1}^{n} b_i{}^2 \sigma_i{}^2}}{a + \frac{1}{2}\displaystyle\sum_{i=1}^{n} c_i{}^2 \sigma_i{}^2} \tag{7.75}$$

If we limit ourselves to first-derivative terms in the series expansion, $c_1 = c_2 = \cdots = c_i = 0$, then the denominator becomes $a = u_{\mathrm{op}}$. In the numerator we express $b_i = \partial u/\partial x_i \big|_{\mathrm{op}}$ in terms of sensitivity, using Eq. (7.67),

$$b_i = \frac{\partial u}{\partial x_i}\bigg|_{\mathrm{op}} = \frac{u}{x_i} S_{x_i}{}^u$$

Using these two substitutions, Eq. (7.75) becomes

$$\frac{\sigma_u}{E(u)} = \frac{\sqrt{u^2 \displaystyle\sum_{i=1}^{n} \left(S_{x_i}{}^u \frac{\sigma_i}{x_i}\right)^2}}{u} = \sqrt{\displaystyle\sum_{i=1}^{n} \left(S_{x_i}{}^u \frac{\sigma_i}{x_i}\right)^2}$$

If we let the variation in the parameter $x_i$ be $\Delta x_i$ and equate this to one $\sigma_i$ unit, we obtain

$$\frac{\sigma_u}{E(u)} = \sqrt{\left(S_{x_1}{}^u \frac{\Delta x_1}{x_1}\right)^2 + \left(S_{x_2}{}^u \frac{\Delta x_2}{x_2}\right)^2 + \cdots + \left(S_{x_n}{}^u \frac{\Delta x_n}{x_n}\right)^2} \tag{7.76}$$

The expressions of Eqs. (7.70) and (7.76) are basically quite different, since one is a sum of terms and the other a square root of the sum of squares of the same terms.

In some cases these two expressions are equivalent.  If we assume that each contribution to $\Delta u/u$, that is, each $S_{x_i}{}^u \, \Delta x_i/x_i$ term is positive, then the two expressions correlate well.  Assuming that all the terms are positive and that the $j$th term predominates over the others,

$$\frac{\Delta u}{u} \approx \frac{\sigma_u}{E(u)} = S_{x_j}{}^u \frac{\Delta x_j}{x_j}$$

Similarly, if all the terms are approximately equal in magnitude, then

$$\frac{\Delta u}{u} = n S_x{}^u \frac{\Delta x}{x}$$

$$\frac{\sigma_u}{E(u)} = \sqrt{n} \, S_x{}^u \frac{\Delta x}{x}$$

and the two results differ by $\sqrt{n}$.  In fact, if there are $K$ significant terms out of $n$, the results differ by approximately $\sqrt{K}$.  If not all the terms add in Eq. (7.70), we can get cancellation and obtain far different results.  Equation (7.70) is really a deterministic interpretation of a probabilistic problem.  One has no reason to believe that the particular set of $\Delta x_i$ which occurs in any analysis will have algebraic signs which match up with the associated sensitivities to produce cancellation.  Thus, Eq. (7.70) should be interpreted in the worst-case sense and should be written

$$\left| \frac{\Delta u}{u} \right|_{\max} = \left| S_{x_1}{}^u \frac{\Delta x_1}{x_1} \right| + \left| S_{x_2}{}^u \frac{\Delta x_2}{x_2} \right| + \cdots + \left| S_{x_i}{}^u \frac{\Delta x_i}{x_i} \right| \tag{7.77}$$

In this case Eqs. (7.75) and (7.77) differ by approximately $\sqrt{K}$ with no restrictions on algebraic signs of sensitivities or increment terms.

Thus, if one is trying to obtain a system which is insensitive to independent random variations in components, one must make the magnitude of each sensitivity small.  There is no advantage to making some sensitivities positive and some negative in an attempt to cancel things.  Of course, this latter approach will work if one agrees to test components and separate them into two batches, that is, $\Delta x_i > 0$, large values, and $\Delta x_i < 0$, small values.  Then if all sensitivities were of the same algebraic sign, one could alternate large and small component values.  If the sensitivities alternated in sign, one would wish to use either all large or all small components.  Equation (7.76) establishes that the improvement is due to a reduction of the variances of the variables.  The reduction is obtained by measurements and separation.

Another case is the one in which two or more variables depend on an external variable. In such a case Eq. (7.74) holds. Assuming a series network of two resistors, the sensitivities with respect to $r$ are positive. If one connects two resistors in series, one with a positive temperature coefficient and one with a negative temperature coefficient, then the overall resistance might stay constant over a wide range of temperatures. The probabilistic nature of this problem is the stochastic aspects of how the total resistance vs. temperature is related to the distributions of each temperature coefficient. This will tell one how good a temperature match one could obtain with random selection of temperature coefficients rather than by measurement and matching.

Thus, Eq. (7.64) or Eq. (7.77) can be used to predict system variability. The labor in the computation involves the calculation of the set of system sensitivities. This can of course be accomplished by computing the required partial derivatives; however, there are a few techniques which yield considerable simplification in particular cases.

### 7.8.3 NETWORK SENSITIVITIES

As previously stated, network design generally deals with either the gain and phase of the governing transfer function or the location of the poles and zeros of such a transfer function. Several examples will be discussed below to illustrate how such computations are made in specific cases, and the general results are derived.

Several important sensitivity theorems have been developed by Belove[1] for two- and three-element networks. They are given in Table 7.8. They allow one to slightly reduce the number of sensitivity computations, or they act as a check on the consistency of the computations. The first row in Table 7.8 pertains to networks containing only resistances and capacitances (or dashpots and masses, etc.). The term $S_R{}^{S_0}$ is the sensitivity of a pole (or zero) to changes in resistor $R_K$. We see that the sum of the resistor (capacitor) sensitivities equals $-1$. The third column tells us that any increase in a network $R$ or $C$ causes a decrease in the pole values. The fourth column tells us that $RC$ sensitivities always lie between $-1$ and $0$. The last column tells us that the fractional change in the roots is equal to the sum of the fractional changes in $C$ and $R$. Similar results appear in the table for $RL$ and $LC$ networks. These theorems will be illustrated in the examples computed below.

*RC network example* As a simple example of computing pole sensitivities consider the circuit given in Fig. 7.14. The transfer function for this circuit has a single pole at $\omega_p = 1/RC$. Computation of $\partial \omega_p / \partial R$

[1] C. Belove, The Sensitivity Function in Variability Analysis, *IEEE Trans. Reliability*, vol. R-15, no. 2, 1966.

**Table 7.8 Sensitivity relations for two-element-kind networks**

| Network type | Sensitivity sums | Direction of root shift as elements change [applies to roots of $D(s)$, the denominator polynomial] | Sensitivity bounds, roots of $D(s)$ | Root shift for all elements of one kind varying alike $\frac{dR}{R} = \alpha \quad \frac{dC}{C} = \beta$ $\frac{dL}{L} = \gamma$ |
|---|---|---|---|---|
| RC | $\sum_{k=1}^{r} S_{R_k}^{s_0} = -1$ <br> $\sum_{k=1}^{c} S_{C_k}^{s_0} = -1$ | $D(s) = (s + \omega_1)(s + \omega_2) \cdots (s + \omega_n)$ <br> $\frac{\partial \omega_i}{\partial R_j} < 0$   any $R$ in network <br> $\frac{\partial \omega_i}{\partial C_j} < 0$   any $C$ in network | $-1 \leq S_{R_i}^{s_0} \leq 0$ <br> $-1 \leq S_{C_i}^{s_0} \leq 0$ | $\frac{ds_0}{s_0} = -(\alpha + \beta)$ |
| RL | $\sum_{k=1}^{l} S_{L_k}^{s_0} = -1$ <br> $\sum_{k=1}^{r} S_{R_k}^{s_0} = +1$ | $D(s) = (s + \omega_1)(s + \omega_2) \cdots (s + \omega_n)$ <br> $\frac{\partial \omega_i}{\partial L_j} < 0$   any $L$ <br> $\frac{\partial \omega_i}{\partial R_j} > 0$   any $R$ | $-1 \leq S_{L_i}^{s_0} \leq 0$ <br> $0 \leq S_{R_i}^{s_0} \leq 1$ | $\frac{ds_0}{s_0} = -(\gamma - \alpha)$ |
| LC | $\sum_{k=1}^{l} S_{L_k}^{s_0} = -\frac{1}{2}$ <br> $\sum_{k=1}^{c} S_{C_k}^{s_0} = -\frac{1}{2}$ | $D(s) = (s^2 + \omega_1^2)(s^2 + \omega_2^2) \cdots (s^2 + \omega_n^2)$ <br> $\frac{\partial \omega_i}{\partial L_j} < 0$   any $L$ <br> $\frac{\partial \omega_i}{\partial C_j} < 0$   any $C$ | $-\frac{1}{2} \leq S_{L_i}^{s_0} \leq 0$ <br> $-\frac{1}{2} \leq S_{C_i}^{s_0} \leq 0$ | $\frac{ds_0}{s_0} = -\frac{1}{2}(\beta + \gamma)$ |

SOURCE: Charles Belove, The Sensitivity Function in Variability Analysis, *IEEE Trans. on Reliability*, vol. R-15, no. 2, August, 1966.

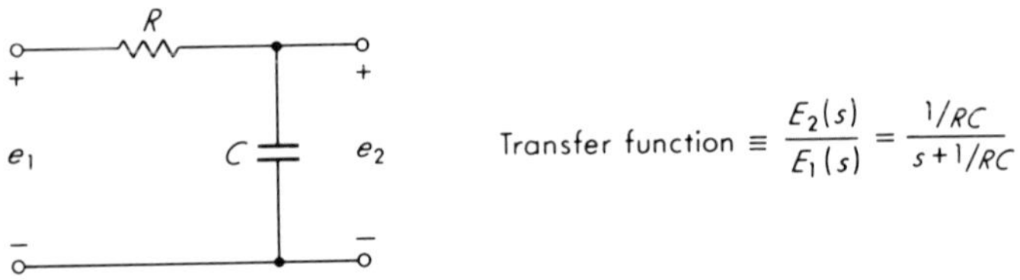

**Fig. 7.14** Transfer function of $RC$ filter.

and $\partial \omega_p / \partial C$ yields

$$\frac{\partial \omega_p}{\partial R} = \frac{\partial}{\partial R} \frac{1}{RC} = -\frac{1}{R^2 C} \qquad \frac{\partial \omega_p}{\partial C} = \frac{\partial}{\partial C} \frac{1}{RC} = -\frac{1}{RC^2}$$

Computation of the pole location sensitivities with respect to $R$ and $C$ gives

$$S_R^{\omega_p} = \frac{R}{\omega_p} \frac{\partial \omega_p}{\partial R} = -1 \qquad S_C^{\omega_p} = \frac{C}{\omega_p} \frac{\partial \omega_p}{\partial C} = -1$$

Inspection of Table 7.8 shows that for an $RC$ network, the sum of the pole (or zero) sensitivities with respect to the resistors equals $-1$. In this example there is only one resistor; therefore, the one sensitivity is $-1$ by inspection. A similar result holds for the one sensitivity with respect to the single circuit capacitance.

*General transfer-function sensitivities* For a general network example, one could state the transfer function in the form

$$
\begin{aligned}
T(s) &= K \frac{N(s)}{D(s)} \\
&= K \left\{ \frac{(s + \omega_{z_1}) \cdots (s + \omega_{z_n})}{(s + \omega_{p_1}) \cdots (s + \omega_{p_n})} \right. \\
&\quad \times \left. \frac{[(s^2 + 2\sigma_{z_1}s + \omega_{z_1}{}^2) \cdots (s^2 + 2\sigma_{z_u}s + \omega_{z_u}{}^2)]}{[(s^2 + 2\sigma_{p_1}s + \omega_{p_1}{}^2) \cdots (s^2 + 2\sigma_{z_v}s + \omega_{z_v}{}^2)]} \right\}
\end{aligned}
\tag{7.78}
$$

where the system has $n$ real zeros, $u$ complex zeros, $m$ real poles, and $v$ complex poles. Then for each zero $\omega_{z_i}$ and each pole $\omega_{p_i}$ a set of sensitivity relations can be written. One of the theorems of Table 7.8 then applies, depending on the type of network in question. The sensitivity theorems can be used to reduce by one the number of sensitivity calculations involved in a problem or, more importantly, can be used as a check on computational accuracy.[1]

In addition to the pole and zero locations, one is often interested in the magnitude and phase of the transfer function as a function of frequency

[1] Note that this check is a necessary but not sufficient condition for correctness.

$$|T(j\omega)| = K \left\{ \frac{(\omega^2 + w_{z_1}{}^2) \cdots (\omega^2 + \omega_{z_m}{}^2)}{(\omega^2 + \omega_{p_1}{}^2) \cdots (\omega^2 + \omega_{p_n}{}^2)} \right.$$

$$\left. \times \frac{[(\omega_{z_1}{}^2 - \omega^2)^2 + (2\sigma_{z_1}\omega)^2] \cdots [(\omega_{z_u}{}^2 - \omega^2)^2 + (2\sigma_{z_u}\omega)^2]}{[(\omega_{p_1}{}^2 - \omega^2)^2 + (2\sigma_{p_1}\omega)^2] \cdots [(\omega_{p_v}{}^2 - \omega^2)^2 + (2\sigma_{p_v}\omega)^2]} \right\}^{\frac{1}{2}}$$

$$(7.79)$$

$$T(j\omega) = \left( \tan^{-1} \frac{\omega}{\omega_{z_1}} + \cdots + \tan^{-1} \frac{\omega}{\omega_{z_m}} \right)$$

$$+ \left( \tan^{-1} \frac{2\sigma_{z_1}\omega}{\omega_{z_1}{}^2 - \omega^2} \cdots \tan^{-1} \frac{2\sigma_{z_u}\omega}{\omega_{z_u}{}^2 - \omega^2} \right)$$

$$- \left( \tan^{-1} \frac{\omega}{\omega_{p_1}} + \cdots + \tan^{-1} \frac{\omega}{\omega_{p_n}} \right)$$

$$- \left( \tan^{-1} \frac{2\sigma_{p_1}\omega}{\omega_{p_1}{}^2 - \omega^2} \cdots \tan^{-1} \frac{2\sigma_{p_v}\omega}{\omega_{p_v}{}^2 - \omega^2} \right) \qquad (7.80)$$

The corresponding partial derivatives are

$$\frac{\partial |T(j\omega)|}{\partial K} = \frac{N(j\omega)}{D(j\omega)} \qquad (7.81)$$

$$\frac{\partial |T(j\omega)|}{\partial \omega_{z_i}} = + \frac{\omega_{z_i}}{\omega^2 + \omega_{z_i}{}^2} |T(j\omega)|$$

$$\frac{\partial |T(j\omega)|}{\partial \omega_{p_j}} = - \frac{\omega_{p_j}}{\omega^2 + \omega_{p_j}{}^2} |T(j\omega)|$$

$$\frac{\partial |T(j\omega)|}{\partial \sigma_{z_i}} = \frac{2\omega}{(\omega_{z_i}{}^2 - \omega^2)^2 + (2\sigma_{z_i}\omega)^2} |T(j\omega)|$$

$$\frac{\partial |T(j\omega)|}{\partial \omega_{z_i}} = \frac{2\omega_{z_i}(\omega_{z_i}{}^2 - \omega^2)}{(\omega_{z_i}{}^2 - \omega^2)^2 + (2\sigma_{z_i}\omega)^2} |T(j\omega)| \qquad (7.82)$$

$$\frac{\partial |T(j\omega)|}{\partial \sigma_{p_j}} = \frac{-2\omega}{(\omega_{p_i}{}^2 - \omega^2)^2 + (2\sigma_{p_i}\omega)^2} |T(j\omega)|$$

$$\frac{\partial T(j\omega)}{\partial \omega_{p_j}} = \frac{2\omega_{p_j}(\omega_{z_j}{}^2 - \omega^2)}{(\omega_{p_j}{}^2 - \omega^2)^2 + (2\sigma_{p_j}\omega)^2} |T(j\omega)|$$

$$\frac{\partial \angle T(j\omega)}{\partial \omega_{z_i}} = + \frac{\omega}{\omega^2 + \omega_{z_i}{}^2}$$

$$\frac{\partial \angle T(j\omega)}{\partial \omega_{p_j}} = - \frac{\omega}{\omega^2 + \omega_{p_i}{}^2}$$

$$\frac{\partial \angle T(j\omega)}{\partial \sigma_{z_i}} = \frac{2\omega(\omega_{z_i}{}^2 - \omega^2)}{(\omega_{z_i}{}^2 - \omega^2)^2 + (2\sigma_{z_i}\omega)^2}$$

$$\frac{\partial \angle T(j\omega)}{\partial \omega_{z_i}} = \frac{-4\omega\sigma_{z_i}\omega_{z_i}}{(\omega_{z_i}{}^2 - \omega^2)^2 + (2\sigma z_i\omega)^2} \qquad (7.83)$$

$$\frac{\partial \angle T(j\omega)}{\partial \sigma_{p_i}} = \frac{-2\omega(\omega_{p_i}{}^2 - \omega^2)}{(\omega_{p_i}{}^2 - \omega^2)^2 + (2\sigma_{p_i}\omega)^2}$$

$$\frac{\partial \angle T(j\omega)}{\partial \omega_{p_i}} = \frac{-4\omega\sigma_{p_i}\omega_{p_i}}{(\omega_{p_i}{}^2 - \omega^2)^2 + (2\sigma_{p_i}\omega)^2}$$

Using Eqs. (7.81) to (7.83), the corresponding sensitivities for the real poles[1] are given by

$$S_K^{|T(j\omega)|} = \frac{K}{|T(j\omega)|} \frac{\partial |T(j\omega)|}{\partial K} = 1 \qquad (7.84)$$

$$S_{\omega_{z_i}}^{|T(j\omega)|} = \frac{\omega_{z_i}}{|T(j\omega)|} \frac{\partial |T(j\omega)|}{\partial \omega_{z_i}} = \frac{\omega_{z_i}^2}{\omega^2 + \omega_{z_i}^2}$$

$$S_{\omega_{p_i}}^{|T(j\omega)|} = \frac{\omega_{p_i}}{|T(j\omega)|} \frac{\partial |T(j\omega)|}{\partial \omega_{p_i}} = -\frac{\omega_{p_i}^2}{\omega^2 + \omega_{p_i}^2} \qquad (7.85)$$

$$S_{\omega_{z_i}}^{\angle T(j\omega)} = \frac{\omega_{z_i}}{\angle T(j\omega)} \frac{\partial \angle T(j\omega)}{\partial \omega_{z_i}} = -\frac{\omega \omega_{z_i}}{\omega^2 + \omega_{z_i}^2} \frac{1}{\angle T(j\omega)}$$

$$S_{\omega_{p_j}}^{\angle T(j\omega)} = \frac{\omega_{p_j}}{\angle T(j\omega)} \frac{\partial \angle T(j\omega)}{\partial \omega_{p_j}} = \frac{\omega \omega_{p_j}}{\omega^2 + \omega_{p_j}^2} \frac{1}{\angle T(j\omega)} \qquad (7.86)$$

Similar expressions of course hold for the complex poles.

In many cases one is interested in how the magnitude and phase of the transfer function change as the network elements vary. These sensitivities can be computed from the set of sensitivities given in Eqs. (7.84) to (7.86) and the element sensitivities, or by direct calculation. Both techniques will be illustrated below.

For the example given in Fig. 7.12 the following sensitivity relations hold (see chain rule of partial differentiation)

$$S_R^{|T(j\omega)|} = S_K^{|T(j\omega)|} S_R^K + S_{\omega_p}^{|T(j\omega)|} S_R^{\omega_p}$$
$$S_C^{|T(j\omega)|} = S_K^{|T(j\omega)|} S_C^K + S_{\omega_p}^{|T(j\omega)|} S_C^{\omega_p}$$
$$S_R^{\angle T(j\omega)} = S_{\omega_p}^{\angle T(j\omega)} S_R^{\omega_p}$$
$$S_C^{\angle T(j\omega)} = S_{\omega_p}^{\angle T(j\omega)} S_C^{\omega_p}$$

Combining the above relations with Eq. (7.77) yields the magnitude relation

$$\frac{\Delta |T(j\omega)|}{|T(j\omega)|} = \left| S_K^{|T(j\omega)|} S_R^K \frac{\Delta R}{R} + S_{\omega_p}^{|T(j\omega)|} S_R^{\omega_p} \frac{\Delta R}{R} \right|$$
$$+ \left| S_K^{|T(j\omega)|} S_C^K \frac{\Delta C}{C} + S_{\omega_p}^{|T(j\omega)|} S_C^{\omega_p} \frac{\Delta C}{C} \right| \qquad (7.87)$$

For the example we find

$$S_K^{|T(j\omega)|} = 1 \qquad S_R^{\omega_p} = -1 \qquad S_C^{\omega_p} = -1$$

---

[1] In the case of a repeated pole or zero of multiplicity $m$, Eqs. (7.82) and (7.83) are multiplied by the number $m$.

Also since

$$K = \frac{1}{RC} = \omega_p$$

we have

$$S_R{}^K = S_R{}^{\omega_p} = -1 \qquad S_C{}^K = S_C{}^{\omega_p} = -1$$

Computation of the remaining sensitivity $S_{\omega_p}^{|T(j\omega)|}$ from Eq. (7.85) gives

$$S_{\omega_p}^{|T(j\omega)|} = - \frac{1/R^3C^3}{(\omega^2 + 1/R^2C^2)^{\frac{3}{2}}}$$

Thus, Eq. (7.87) becomes

$$\begin{aligned}
\frac{\Delta|T(j\omega)|}{|T(j\omega)|} &= \left| \frac{\dfrac{1}{R^2C^2}}{\left(\omega^2 + \dfrac{1}{R^2C^2}\right)^{-1}} \right| \left( \left| \frac{\Delta R}{R} \right| + \left| \frac{\Delta C}{C} \right| \right) \\
&= \frac{R^2C^2\omega^2}{1 + R^2C^2\omega^2} \left( \left| \frac{\Delta R}{R} \right| + \left| \frac{\Delta C}{C} \right| \right)
\end{aligned} \qquad (7.88)$$

At high frequencies, the frequency-sensitive term approaches unity. At $\omega = 1/RC$ it is $\frac{1}{2}$ in magnitude, and it becomes very small for small $\omega$. A similar expression can be written for the phase variations

$$\frac{\Delta\angle T(j\omega)}{\angle T(j\omega)} = \left| S_{\omega_p}^{\angle T(j\omega)} S_R{}^{\omega_p} \frac{\Delta R}{R} \right| + \left| S_{\omega_p}^{\angle T(j\omega)} S_C{}^{\omega_p} \frac{\Delta C}{C} \right| \qquad (7.89)$$

since $S_R{}^{\omega_p} = S_C{}^{\omega_p} = -1$ and from Eq. (7.86)

$$S_{\omega_p}^{\angle T(j\omega)} = \frac{\omega/RC}{\omega^2 + 1/R^2C^2} \frac{1}{\tan^{-1} \omega RC}$$

Substitution yields

$$\begin{aligned}
\frac{\Delta\angle T(j\omega)}{\angle T(j\omega)} &= \left| \frac{\omega/RC}{\omega^2 + 1/R^2C^2} \frac{1}{\tan^{-1} \omega RC} \right| \left( \left| \frac{\Delta R}{R} \right| + \left| \frac{\Delta C}{C} \right| \right) \\
&= \left| \frac{\omega RC}{(\omega^2R^2C^2 + 1) \tan^{-1} \omega RC} \right| \left( \left| \frac{\Delta R}{R} \right| + \left| \frac{\Delta C}{C} \right| \right)
\end{aligned} \qquad (7.90)$$

For large values of $\omega$, the frequency-sensitive term approaches zero, at $\omega = 1/RC$ the coefficient is $2/\pi$, and at low frequencies the coefficient becomes unity.

One can simplify the computation of pole sensitivities with respect to parameter changes. In order to avoid complicated partial differentiation

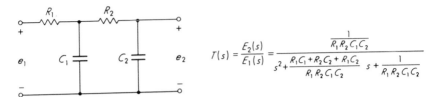

$$T(s) = \frac{E_2(s)}{E_1(s)} = \frac{\dfrac{1}{R_1 R_2 C_1 C_2}}{s^2 + \dfrac{R_1 C_1 + R_2 C_2 + R_1 C_2}{R_1 R_2 C_1 C_2}\, s + \dfrac{1}{R_1 R_2 C_1 C_2}}$$

**Fig. 7.15**   Ladder filter network.

when the polynomials $N(s)$ and $D(s)$ are second-order or higher, the following chain rule for partial derivatives can be used[1]

$$S_{x_1}^{\omega_1} = \frac{x_1}{\omega_1}\frac{\partial \omega_1}{\partial x_1} = \frac{x_1\,[\partial D(s)/\partial x_1]_{s=-\omega_1}}{\omega_1\,[\partial D(s)/\partial \omega_1]_{s=-\omega_1}} \tag{7.91}$$

where $\omega_1$ is one of the roots of the denominator polynomial $D(s)$ and $x_1$ is a network element which is contained in the expression for $\omega_1$.

As an example the ladder filter network of Fig. 7.15 will be used. For the element values $R_1 = R_2 = 10^4$ ohms and $C_1 = C_2 = 10^{-6}$ farad, the transfer function becomes

$$T(s) = \frac{10^4}{(s+262)(s+38.5)} = \frac{10^4}{(s+\omega_1)(s+\omega_2)}$$

If we wish to calculate the pole sensitivities to $R_1$ and $R_2$, the following partial derivatives are necessary

$$\left.\frac{\partial D(s)}{\partial \omega_1}\right|_{s=-\omega_1} = (s+\omega_2)_{s=-\omega_1} = (-262+38.5) = -223.5$$

$$\left.\frac{\partial D(s)}{\partial \omega_2}\right|_{s=-\omega_2} = (s+\omega_1)_{s=-\omega_2} = (-38.5+262) = +223.5$$

$$\frac{\partial D(s)}{\partial R_1} = \frac{\partial}{\partial R_1}\left[s^2 + \frac{C_1 + C_2 + (R_2/R_1)C_2}{C_1 R_2 C_2}\, s + \frac{1}{R_1 R_2 C_1 C_2}\right]$$

$$= -\left(\frac{s}{R_1^2 C_1} + \frac{1}{R_1^2 R_2 C_1 C_2}\right)$$

$$\left.\frac{\partial D(s)}{\partial R_1}\right|_{s=\omega_1} = +1.62 \qquad \left.\frac{\partial D(s)}{\partial R_1}\right|_{s=\omega_2} = -0.615$$

$$\frac{\partial D(s)}{\partial R_2} = \frac{\partial}{\partial R_2}\left\{s^2 + \frac{[R_1(C_1 + C_2)/R_2] + C_2}{R_1 C_1 C_2}\, s + \frac{1}{R_1 R_2 C_1 C_2}\right\}$$

$$= -\left[\frac{(C_1 + C_2)s}{R_2^2 C_1 C_2} + \frac{1}{R_2^2 R_1 C_1 C_2}\right]$$

$$\left.\frac{\partial D(s)}{\partial R_2}\right|_{s=\omega_1} = +4.24 \qquad \left.\frac{\partial D(s)}{\partial R_2}\right|_{s=\omega_2} = -0.23$$

[1] Belove, *op. cit.*

The sensitivity computations are given by

$$S_{R_1}{}^{\omega_1} = \frac{R_1}{\omega_1}\frac{\partial D(s)/\partial R_1|_{s=\omega_1}}{\partial D(s)/\partial \omega_1|_{s=\omega_1}} = \frac{10^4}{262}\frac{1.62}{(-223.5)} = -0.276$$

$$S_{R_2}{}^{\omega_1} = \frac{R_2}{\omega_1}\frac{\partial D(s)/\partial R_2|_{s=\omega_1}}{\partial D(s)/\partial \omega_1|_{s=\omega_1}} = \frac{10^4}{263}\frac{4.24}{(-223.5)} = -0.725$$

$$S_{R_2}{}^{\omega_2} = \frac{R_1}{\omega_2}\frac{\partial D(s)/\partial R_1|_{s=\omega_2}}{\partial D(s)/\partial \omega_2|_{s=\omega_2}} = \frac{10^4}{38.5}\frac{(-0.615)}{223.5} = -0.715$$

$$S_{R_2}{}^{\omega_2} = \frac{R_2}{\omega_2}\frac{\partial D(s)/\partial R_2|_{s=\omega_2}}{\partial D(s)/\partial \omega_2|_{s=\omega_2}} = \frac{10^4}{38.5}\frac{(-0.23)}{223.5} = -0.268$$

Similar sensitivities can be calculated with respect to the circuit capacitances. As a check from Table 7.8 we see that the sensitivities in an $RC$ network should sum to $-1$

$$S_{R_1}{}^{\omega_1} + S_{R2}{}^{\omega_2} = 1.001 \qquad +0.1\% \text{ error}$$
$$S_{R_1}{}^{\omega_2} + S_{R2}{}^{\omega_2} = 0.983 \qquad -1.7\% \text{ error}$$

Both results check within slide-rule accuracy.

In the above calculations we have computed magnitude and phase sensitivities with respect to parameter variations in two steps. The first step was to compute the sensitivities of $|T|$ and $\angle T$ with respect to the poles and zeros and then combine with the pole and zero sensitivities with respect to the parameters. If we are not interested in how the poles and zeros change but are interested only in changes in $|T|$ and $\angle T$, we can make use of the following relations

$$T(s) = \frac{N(s)}{D(s)}$$

$$|T| = \frac{|N|}{|D|}$$

$$\angle T = \angle N - \angle D$$

$$S_x{}^{|T|} = S_x{}^{|N|} - S_x{}^{|D|} \tag{7.92}$$

$$S_x{}^{\angle T} = \frac{\angle N}{\angle T}S_x{}^{\angle N} - \frac{\angle D}{\angle T}S_x{}^{\angle D} \tag{7.93}$$

If the analytical computations indicated above become too complex, a simple experiment can be performed. The system can be built in the laboratory from lumped-circuit components or simulated on an analog or digital computer. Small changes are then made in the circuit parameters or computer constants, and the resulting changes in the transmission expression are noted. The increment ratios are then used to approximate the appropriate derivatives.

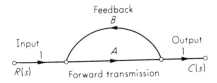

Fig. 7.16   Typical feedback flow graph.

## 7.9  APPLICATIONS TO CONTROL-SYSTEM ANALYSIS

One can apply the sensitivity computations detailed in the previous section to control problems.  If one begins by examining the system transfer function one has precisely the problem defined by Eq. (7.78) and the material that follows.

One of the main purposes of feedback is to reduce the sensitivity of a system transmission to certain parameter variations.  Again one could use the system transfer function to depict these effects; however, we shall use the pictorial diagram (signal flow graph) commonly used in control-system work.  The transfer function and sensitivities for the typical feedback structure given in Fig. 7.16 are given by

$$T(s) = \frac{C(s)}{R(s)} = \frac{A}{1 - AB} \qquad (7.94)$$

$$S_A{}^T = \frac{A}{T} \frac{\partial T}{\partial A} = \frac{1}{1 - AB} \qquad (7.95)$$

$$S_B{}^T = \frac{B}{T} \frac{\partial T}{\partial B} = \frac{AB}{1 - AB} \qquad (7.96)$$

The sensitivity of the system depends to a great extent on the magnitude of $AB$ and the algebraic sign of $AB$.  If $AB$ is positive, the system is said to possess *positive feedback*, and if $AB$ is negative, the configuration is called a *negative-feedback system*.  The amount of feedback $|AB|$ which one can use is limited by system stability.  In general the following results are obtained.  A small amount of positive feedback increases the system gain $|T(s)|$ and increases the system sensitivities, which can become greater than unity.  (In some systems any positive feedback no matter how small results in instability, leading some people to the erroneous conclusion that positive feedback should always be avoided.)  A larger amount of positive feedback generally leads to system instability.  A small amount of negative feedback reduces both the system gain and sensitivities somewhat.  A moderate amount of negative feedback reduces the gain quite a bit, decreases the forward-transmission sensitivity $S_A{}^T \approx 1/AB$ by a large amount, and has little effect on $S_B{}^T \approx 1$.  If a large amount of negative feedback is used, the system generally

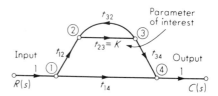

**Fig. 7.17**   Equivalent flow graph for sensitivity calculations.

becomes unstable.   The conclusions are that if one wishes to make a system insensitive to changes in a forward-transmission parameter, one uses as large an amount of feedback as stability will permit.   In such a case the sensitivity of the transmission to changes in feedback gain $AB$ are large, $S_B{}^T \approx 1$.   These results apply to any feedback structure of the form given in Fig. 7.16.

For a more complex structure one can proceed in a straightforward manner involving partial differentiation of more complex functions or employ flow-graph manipulations.   One can always manipulate a parameter $K$ in a signal flow graph so that it is present in a single branch, and the effects of feedback on $K$ are evident.[1]   In the general case, the structure one obtains is of the form given in Fig. 7.17.   One can view Fig. 7.16 as a special case of Fig. 7.17 where $t_{14} = 0$, $t_{12} = t_{34} = 1$, $K = A$, and $t_{32} = B$.   The transfer function and sensitivity of the graph of Fig. 7.17 are given by

$$T(s) = \frac{C(s)}{R(s)} = t_{14} + \frac{t_{12}Kt_{34}}{1 - Kt_{32}} = t_{14} + \frac{t_{12}t_{34}K}{F_K} \tag{7.97}$$

$$S_K{}^T = \frac{t_{12}Kt_{34}}{T(1 - Kt_{32})^2} = \frac{1}{F_K}\left(1 - \frac{t_{14}}{T}\right) \tag{7.98}$$

where

$$F_K \equiv \text{return difference} \equiv 1 - \text{loop gain} = 1 - Kt_{32}$$

Thus, if $t_{14}/T < 1$, the sensitivity with respect to $K$ is the reciprocal of the return difference.   In this case signal flow-graph manipulation is traded for partial differentiation.

### 7.10  SUMMARY

This chapter has discussed a variety of approaches to marginal-failure analysis.   The deterministic techniques are generally simple and can be

[1] J. G. Truxal, "Control Engineers' Handbook," p. 4-47, McGraw-Hill Book Company, New York, 1958.

applied at the beginning of a problem even though they yield only limited insight.   If the particular problem happens to be one with a known analytical solution, such as those given in Table 7.5, the problem is solved.   In general any sizable engineering problem will not have a simple exact probabilistic solution, and numerical solution or Taylor series approximation must be used.   The sensitivity calculations discussed in the latter portion of the chapter are most useful in the design of circuits or devices.   In such cases, they allow the designer to gain insight into how the parameters affect the system.   Such information will allow him to redesign a circuit or device so as to minimize sensitivity or to contribute a marginal figure of merit to a broad evaluation of competitive designs.

## PROBLEMS

7.1   Assuming that the system reliability is the product of the marginal and catastrophic reliability $R_s = R_m R_c$, plot a set of design curves for constant $R_m$ with $R_c$ along the $x$ axis and $R_m$ along the $y$ axis.   Let $R_m = 0.99, 0.9$, and $0.5$.

7.2   The tuning frequency in a radio receiver is essentially given by $\omega = 1/\sqrt{LC}$. The inductor $L$ and capacitor $C$ are assumed to drift by the same percentage as a result of heating.   Use worst-case analysis to predict the allowable choice in $L$ and $C$ if a circuit tuned to 1,000 kilohertz is only allowed to shift by 1 kilohertz.

7.3   Check the even-numbered transformations given in Table 7.1.

7.4   Check the odd-numbered transformations given in Table 7.1.

7.5   If $x$ has a rectangular distribution, sketch $u$ for cases 3 and 7 in Table 7.1.

7.6   Check the even-numbered transformations given in Table 7.2.

7.7   Check the odd-numbered transformations given in Table 7.2.

7.8   Sketch $u$ for the first three cases given in Table 7.2 if $x$ and $y$ have independent rectangular distribution, that is, $a < \mathbf{x} \le b, c < \mathbf{y} \le d$.

7.9†  An analog-computer adder performs the addition $z = x + y$.   Assume that the voltages $x$ and $y$ are rectangularly distributed with a standard deviation equal to 1 percent of the mean.   Compute the error in $z$, the output, where we define error as $\sigma_z/E(z) \times 100$ percent.

7.10† Repeat Prob. 7.9 for an analog-computer multiplier.

7.11  Check any five of the transformations in Table 7.5.

7.12  Repeat Prob. 7.11 for Table 7.6.

7.13  Repeat Prob. 7.11 for Table 7.7.

7.14  Two resistors are connected in series so that $R = R_1 + R_2$.   Compute the coefficients of variation of $R$ for the following two cases and compare.   Explain.

    (a)  $R_1$ and $R_2$ have independent normal distributions with $E(R_1) = \mu_1$, $E(R_2) = \mu_2$, var $R_1 = \sigma_1$, var $R_2 = \sigma_2$.

    (b)  $R_1$ and $R_2$ have independent rectangular distributions with the same means and variances.

7.15  Using the Taylor series approximation method, solve Prob. 7.2.   Compare the results and explain.

7.16  Using the Taylor series approximation method solve Probs. 7.9 and 7.10. Compare and explain the results.

7.17* Compute the transfer functions for the following two networks:

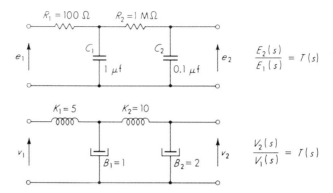

**Fig. P 7.17**

Compute $S^{|T|}$ and $S^{\angle T}$ with respect to each circuit parameter. Use the theorems given in Table 7.8 to check the results. Which parameters are most critical?

7.18    Show that the transfer functions of problems $A$ and $B$ are given by

(a)   $T_a = \dfrac{A_1 A_2 A_3}{1 - (-A_1 B_1 - A_2 B_2 - A_3 B_3) + A_1 B_1 A_2 B_2 - A_1 A_2 B_3 B_4}$

(b)   $T_b = \dfrac{\alpha_1 \alpha_2 \alpha_3}{1 - (-\alpha_1 \beta_1 - \alpha_3 \beta_2 - \alpha_1 \alpha_2 \alpha_3 \beta_3) + \alpha_1 \beta_1 \alpha_3 \beta_2}$

Compute all the transmission sensitivities with respect to each forward and each feedback parameter. If we adjust the parameters so that $T_a = T_b$, which system has the smallest sensitivity? Explain.

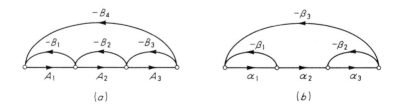

(a)                                        (b)

**Fig. P 7.18**

CHAPTER

# *8*

# *reliability physics models and statistical parameter estimation*

## 8.1 INTRODUCTION

The title of this chapter seems to imply the union of two disjoint ideas, physics of failure and parameter estimation. Actually these ideas must be considered at the same time whenever one tries to obtain numerical values for the parameters of the models discussed. In many respects, the preferred method is to use failure physics to predict hazard parameters for each particular part or item in question. This is especially attractive since, given a complete physical model, the parameters will be determined as functions of the particular environmental conditions such as temperature and humidity. Thus, one can obtain a general picture of how the environment affects part failures as well as good numerical values for the nominal environment.

Unfortunately, too few physical failure models are known, and therefore only a small number of components can be treated in this manner. The situation should improve in the future. Although physics of failure is a difficult and elusive subject, much effort is being expended in this area.

Since one must have numbers for any engineering problem, life testing and field-failure reporting are used in practice to obtain failure data. The data are then analyzed as suggested in Chap. 3 by plotting histograms of $z_d(t)$. Appropriate models are chosen, and parameters are estimated. In Chap. 3 the model was chosen on the basis of experience, intuition, and inspection of the $z_d(t)$ histogram. The second part of this chapter will develop some more refined and precise techniques which will help in choosing a good model and in evaluating accurately the parameters of the model.

The main difficulties with life-testing procedures are their cost and length of time. The cost is measured in terms of parts used plus labor expended. The latter is generally large, since it is difficult to set up a controlled-environment test. The cost of parts is unimportant in the life test of, say, 1,000 ten-cent resistors, but this is not true if the 1,000 components are $10,000 inertial gyros. The former test is feasible; the latter too expensive to contemplate.

In addition the numbers obtained will not apply for different environments. Also, the time necessary for a life test may be prohibitive regardless of the cost factor. For example, if a constant-hazard part has a hazard of $\lambda = 10^{-6}$ per hr, then the MTTF $= 10^6$ hr $\approx 12$ years. Even if the test were to last for a fraction of $\lambda$, several years would be required if the sample size were small. As an alternative one may test at a more severe environmental level, knowing that this will increase the hazard and shorten the test. Then one uses either hypothesis or a simple physical failure model to obtain a relation between the hazard at elevated environment and that at normal environment. These techniques are called *accelerated testing*.

The mathematical background for the reliability physics portion of Chap. 8 appears in Sec. 2.9.6, and the background material on parameter estimation is discussed in Sec. 2.10.

## 8.2 STRESS–STRENGTH MODELS

If one agrees to characterize a component by a $z(t)$ function and to evaluate the hazard parameters by testing, the result is a macroscopic model. Such a model is not concerned with what happens inside the black box containing the part but only with the statistics of the past performance. To delve inside the box one must postulate various hypotheses about the microscopic behavior of the device and test them to prove validity.

One general model of this sort is to assume that a part has a certain strength $y$. This part is subject to certain stresses $x$. As long as $y > x$, the part endures; but when $y < x$, the part fails. If we visualize the part as made up of many elementary building blocks, the strength of the part is dependent on the configuration of these building blocks and their strengths. Since imperfections and nonuniformity occur in the building blocks, the strengths of a group of parts are statistically distributed.[1] If we assume that many different and independent factors fix the part strength and each of these factors has an associated distribution, we might suppose that the central-limit law would hold for almost all combinations of distributions and that the distribution of part strengths $f(y)$ would be normal.[2]

In a similar manner the magnitude of the stress applied will vary over a considerable range in practice because of the stochastic nature of stresses in an actual application. For example, electric input signals into a capacitor in a filter circuit are stochastic in nature, as are the mechanical stresses applied to a structural part in a spacecraft during its entire mission. Again we shall assume a normal distribution for the stresses applied, that is, $g(x)$ is normally distributed, and later generalize the model for any $g(x)$ density function. A graphical picture of this model appears in Fig. 8-1. In Fig. 8-1a, we assume[3] that the part strength is known to be equal to $y_1$. In this case the stresses which are large enough to cause failure are shown shaded in Fig. 8-1a. The probability of failure in this case is simply the area under the $g(x)$ curve to the right of $y_1$, that is,

$$p_f(y_1) = \int_{y_1}^{\infty} g(x)\, dx \tag{8.1}$$

Similarly, the probability of success is

$$p_s(y_1) = 1 - p_f(y_1) = \int_{-\infty}^{y_1} g(x)\, dx \tag{8.2}$$

The fact that both $f(y)$ and $g(x)$ exist for negative $x$ and $y$ can cause some conceptual problems if the physical variables $x$ and $y$ are nonnegative. In the usual case the coefficient of variation $\sigma/\mu$ for $x$ and $y$ is small enough so that the area of $g(x)$ and $f(y)$ between $-\infty$ and $0$ is negligible. If this is not so, one can use truncated normal distributions or some other distributions for $x$ and $y$.[4]

When the part strength $y$ is unknown, one must treat the success and failure probabilities in Eq. (8.1) and (8.2) as functions of the random variable $y$ and then integrate over all values of $y > x$. A more direct procedure is to define a new variable $z = y - x$ such that if $z > 0$, the

---

[1] There is some experimental justification for models of this kind in describing the strength of metals and materials.

[2] An assumption of normality for $f(y)$ will be used in the derivation even though this is not essential to the models, which will hold equally well for other strength distributions.

[3] We assume that a particular part is selected and its strength is measured as $y_1$ by some nondestructive test.

[4] For a complete discussion of the use of other distributions, see reference to R. L. Disney et al., in bibliography for Chap. 8, page 516.

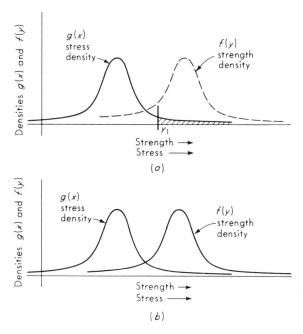

**Fig. 8.1** Stress-strength models. (a) Stress-strength models for a part of known strength $y_1$; (b) stress-strength models for a part of unknown strength. The strength density $f(y)$ is known.

part succeeds, and if $z < 0$, the part fails. If $f(y)$ and $g(x)$ are normal, the density function for $z$, $\phi(z)$, is normal with $E(z) = E(x) - E(y)$ and var $z =$ var $x +$ var $y$. The probabilities of success and failure are

$$p_f = \int_{-\infty}^{0} \phi(z)\, dz \tag{8.3}$$

$$p_s = \int_{0}^{\infty} \phi(z)\, dz \tag{8.4}$$

To be more precise, let us restate the above model in terms of a specific part. Suppose we assume that we are interested in the reliability of a capacitor in an electric filter network. It is reasonable to assume that the dielectric breakdown voltage $V_b$ (strength) might have a normal distribution $g(V_b)$ centered about some value $E(V_b)$. If we also assume that the input-signal amplitude $e_{in}$ will have a normal distribution, then $f(e_{in})$ is normal. If we select a particular capacitor for our filter from a box of, say, 100 and measure its breakdown voltage as $V_{b_1}$ by some nondestructive test, the probability of success or failure on any *one* applied stress is given in Eqs. (8.1) and (8.2) with $y_1$ replaced by $V_{b_1}$ and

$x$ by $e_{in}$. If we do not bother to test a selected capacitor and pick one out of the box of 100 at random, the probability of success or failure for any *one* applied stress is given by Eqs. (8.3) and (8.4) with $x$ and $y$ replaced by $e_{in}$ and $V_b$. If we buy a very high-quality tight-tolerance capacitor for this application, it is reasonable to assume that the density function $f(y)$ will be tall and thin. In fact, in many cases we could replace $f(y)$ by an impulse $u_0(y_\mu)$, where $y_\mu = E(y)$. In such a case, Eqs. (8.3) and (8.4) essentially degenerate to Eqs. (8.1) and (8.2) with $y_1 = y_\mu$.

In any practical case we would like to make $p_f$ small. To do this we use a safety factor and make the smallest expected value of $y$ larger than the largest expected value of $x$. If we assume that the distributions for $x$ and $y$ extend only $3\sigma$ units on either side of their mean, then we should require, if feasible with respect to size, cost, weight, etc., that $E(y) - 3\sigma_y > E(x) + 3\sigma_x$. Using the above model, we can begin to relate probabilities of success and failure to the statistical nature of the part parameters; however, the very crucial factor of time has been ignored. The following section will complete the model and insert the necessary time dependence.

## 8.3 STRESS, STRENGTH, TIME MODELS

In the previous section we derived a model which allows one to evaluate the probability of success or failure when any one stress was applied to a part. It is obvious that many stresses will occur when a part is used in a system and that the average frequency of occurrence and spacing between stress occurrences is of importance. Thus, it is appropriate to discuss various models for the stochastic behavior of the part stress.

Several patterns of stress variation are shown in Fig. 8.2. Associated with each of these behaviors there is a stochastic model which approximates the time behavior of the signal. For example, in Fig. 8.2$d$ the stresses occur at random, and we may let $h(t)$ represent the density function for time of occurrence. The amplitude distribution of the stresses is still given by $g(x)$. We might assume a Poisson distribution for the probability of stress occurrence in Fig. 8.2$d$

$$h(n,t) = \frac{(\lambda t)^n e^{-\lambda t}}{n!} \qquad (8.5)$$

If we assume that the random variables **x**, **y**, and **t** are independent, we can write the probability that the part does not fail (success), as

$$P_s(t) = [P \ (0 \ \text{stresses})] \ [P \ (\text{surviving 0 stresses})]$$
$$+ \ [P \ (1 \ \text{stress})] \ [P \ (\text{surviving 1 stress})]$$
$$+ \ [P \ (2 \ \text{stresses})] \ [P \ (\text{surviving 2 stresses})] + \cdots \qquad (8.6)$$

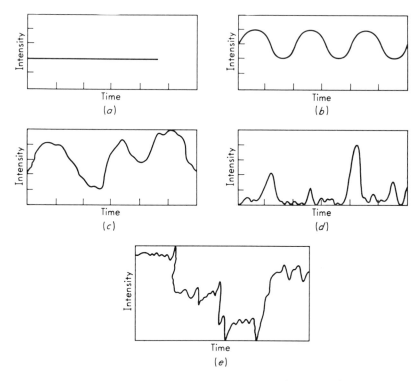

**Fig. 8.2**   Pattern of stress variation in time.   (a) Constant value; (b) cyclic value; (c) strong persistence value; (d) irregular value; (e) stepped value. (*R. P. Haviland "Engineering Reliability and Long Life Design," D. Van Nostrand Company, Inc., Princeton, N.J., 1964.*)

Substituting the occurrence probabilities of 0, 1, 2, . . . , $n$ stresses as given by Eq. (8.5), and the probability of survival as given by Eq. (8.4) into Eq. (8.6) yields

$$P_s(t) = e^{-\lambda t}1 + \frac{\lambda t e^{-\lambda t}}{1!} p_s + \frac{(\lambda t)^2 e^{-\lambda t}}{2!} p_s^2 + \cdots$$
$$+ \frac{(\lambda t)^n e^{-\lambda t}}{n!} p_s^n + \cdots \quad (8.7)$$

Factoring yields

$$P_s(t) = e^{-\lambda t}\left[1 + \frac{\lambda t p_s}{1!} + \frac{(\lambda t p_s)^2}{2!} + \cdots + \frac{(\lambda t p_s)^n}{n!} + \cdots\right]$$

This series is just the expansion of $e^{+\lambda p_s t}$; thus

$$P_s(t) = e^{-\lambda t}e^{+\lambda p_s t} = e^{-(1-p_s)\lambda t} = e^{-p_f \lambda t} \qquad R(t) = e^{-p_f \lambda t} \qquad (8.8)$$

Equation (8.8) is an exponential reliability function with an

$$\text{MTTF} = 1/p_f\lambda$$

If the lowest strength of the part, $\sim[E(y) - 3\sigma_y]$, is larger than the largest stress, $\sim[E(x) + 3\sigma_x]$, then $p_s \to 1$, and $p_f \to 0$. This means that the MTTF $\to \infty$, or, in words, if the average part strength is much larger than the average part stress, it takes a long while before a freakish large stress occurs to fail the part. On the other hand, if $[E(y) + 3\sigma_y]$ is smaller than $[E(x) - 3\sigma_x]$, then $p_s \to 0$. In this case the MTTF $\to 1/\lambda$. This means that the part is weak enough compared to the stress for it to fail on almost every stress occurrence. Thus, the reliability function is governed by the input distribution to a great extent.

Having investigated the model and found that it makes sense and is reasonable in several respects, one should inquire what sort of part reliabilities are represented by this model. The most common first approximation to a reliability model is a constant hazard, i.e., an exponential reliability function. At first one might think that since Eq. (8.8) is also an exponential function, there is agreement with a constant-hazard model. However, the constant-hazard data collected from laboratory tests are probably all the result of constant-stress-level testing. This is, of course, far different from the random type of stress model which was assumed in the derivation of Eq. (8.8). Furthermore, Eq. (8.8) predicts a hazard value which varies directly with $\lambda$, the parameter of the Poisson distribution. Thus, the model does not appear to fit very well what is known about failures of electronic parts.

Intuition seems to suggest some sort of failure mechanism which decreases the part strength with time. Such a mechanism would yield a small initial probability of failure, which would increase as time increased.

If we return to the stress-strength model shown in Fig. 8.1a, a constant stress at level $x$ would be modeled by an impulse stress distribution at $x_1$, as shown in Fig. 8.3a. The probability of success is given by the area of $f(y)$ under the curve for $y > x_1$

$$p_s(x_1) = \int_{x_1}^{+\infty} f(y) \, dy \tag{8.9}$$

and similarly the probability of failure[1] is

$$p_f(x_1) = \int_{-\infty}^{x_1} f(y) \, dy \tag{8.10}$$

Our hypothesis of part deterioration would imply that $\mu_y$ is a function of time and decreases as time increases such that $p_s(x_1)$ becomes smaller

---

[1] As previously stated $p_f(x_1) \approx \int_0^{x_1} f(y) \, dy$ since $\int_{-\infty}^0 f(y) \, dy \approx 0$.

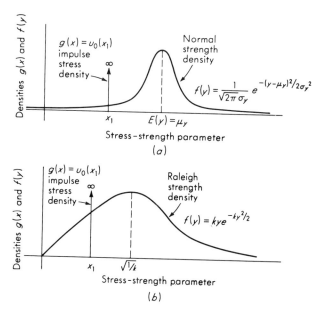

**Fig. 8.3** A stress-strength model for constant applied stress. (a) Normal strength model; (b) Rayleigh strength model.

with advancing time. It may also be reasonable to assume that $\sigma_y$ increases with time; however, this probably acts as a second-order effect in most cases. To continue with a normal model for the part strength becomes questionable. As time advances and $\mu_y$ decreases, more and more of the density function $f(y)$ slides over into the negative stress region, which has no physical meaning. In Fig. 8.3b a Rayleigh strength density function is used. This model is actually simpler than the normal model since it possesses only one parameter $K$, as opposed to the two parameters associated with the normal distribution, $\mu$ and $\sigma$. The Rayleigh has the desirable property that the distribution is defined only for $0 < t < +\infty$. The undesirable asymmetry about the peak in the Rayleigh distribution will be ignored initially and discussed later in the development. Substitution of the Rayleigh model for $y$ in Eqs. (8.9) and (8.10) yields

$$p_s(x_1) = \int_{x_1}^{\infty} Kte^{-Kt^2/2}\, dt = e^{-Kx_1^2/2} \tag{8.11}$$

$$p_f(x_1) = \int_{0}^{x_1} Kte^{-Kt^2/2}\, dt = 1 - e^{-Kx_1^2/2} \tag{8.12}$$

To inject strength deterioration with time in this model we merely cause $K$ to increase with time. Somewhat arbitrarily we shall allow $K$

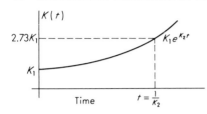

**Fig. 8.4**  Exponential growth with time of the parameter $K$.

to vary exponentially[1] with time, as shown in Fig. 8.4.  This will be shown shortly to have considerable physical significance.  Substitution of this time variation for $K$ into Eq. (8.11) gives

$$R(t,x_1) = \exp\left(-\frac{K_1 e^{K_2 t} x_1^2}{2}\right) \tag{8.13}$$

In order to interpret Eq. (8.13) we can expand $e^{K_2 t}$ in a series

$$e^{K_2 t} = 1 + K_2 t + \frac{K_2^2 t^2}{2!} + \frac{K_2^3 t^3}{3!} + \cdots \tag{8.14}$$

For $K_2 t$ small we retain only the unity term in the series and obtain

$$R_1(t,x_1) = e^{-K_1 x_1^2/2} \qquad K_2 t \ll 1 \tag{8.15}$$

This says that initially the system reliability is roughly constant and dependent on the square of the applied stress $x_1^2$.  Retaining another term of the series yields

$$R_2(t,x_1) = \exp\left[-\frac{K_1(1 + K_2 t)x_1^2}{2}\right] = \exp\left[-\left(\frac{K_1 x_1^2}{2} + \frac{K_1 K_2 x_1^2 t}{2}\right)\right]$$
$$K_2 t > \frac{K_2^2 t^2}{2} \tag{8.16}$$

Including a third term gives

$$R_3(t,x_1) = \exp\left[-\frac{K_1(1 + K_2 t + K_2^2 t^2/2!)x_1^2}{2}\right]$$
$$= \exp\left[-\left(\frac{K_1 x_1^2}{2} + \frac{K_1 K_2 x_1^2 t}{2} + \frac{K_1 K_2^2 x_1^2 t^2}{4}\right)\right]$$
$$\frac{K_2^3 t^3}{6} < \frac{K_2^2 t^2}{2} \tag{8.17}$$

The reliability functions given in Eqs. (8.13) and (8.15) to (8.17) can be easily interpreted if we compute the associated hazard.  Since

$$R(t) = e^{-Z(t)} = \exp\left(-\int_0^t z(\xi)\,d\xi\right)$$
$$Z(t) = \int_0^t z(\xi)\,d\xi$$

[1] One could achieve much the same results by assuming a polynomial model for $K$ of the form $K = a_0 + a_1 t + a_2 t^2 + \cdots$

and

$$z(t) = \frac{dZ(t)}{dt}$$

Thus, for the four reliability functions in question[1]

$$z(t) = \frac{d}{dt} \frac{K_1 e^{K_2 t} x_1^2}{2} = \frac{K_1 K_2 x_1^2}{2} e^{K_2 t} \tag{8.18}$$

$$z_1(t) = \frac{d}{dt} \left[ \frac{K_1 x_1^2}{2} u_1(t) \right] = \frac{K_1 x_1^2}{2} u_0(t) \tag{8.19}$$

$$z_2(t) = \frac{d}{dt} \left[ \frac{K_1 x_1^2}{2} u_{-1}(t) + \frac{K_1 K_2 x_1^2}{2} t \right] = \frac{K_1 x_1^2}{2} u_0(t) + \frac{K_1 K_2 x_1^2}{2} \tag{8.20}$$

$$z_3(t) = \frac{d}{dt} \left[ \frac{K_1 x_1^2}{2} u_{-1}(t) + \frac{K_1 K_2 x_1^2 t}{2} + \frac{K_1 K_2^2 x_1^2 t^2}{4} \right]$$
$$= \frac{K_1 x_1^2}{2} u_0(t) + \frac{K_1 K_2 x_1^2}{2} + \frac{K_1 K_2^2 x_1^2 t}{2} \tag{8.21}$$

The growth models for $K$ and their associated hazard and reliability functions are compared in Fig. 8.5a to c.

The models given in Eq. (8.18) have considerable justification. It has been observed that some physical processes have exponential hazard rates,[2] which agrees with the assumption of an exponential growth for $K$. It is obvious that constant and linearly increasing hazard models are good approximations to the exponential for small $t$.

The hazard impulse at the origin represents those systems which fail almost immediately upon being energized. If we assume burned-in components or discard the initial failures from consideration, this can be dropped.

The hazard model parameters are all proportional to the square of the input stress. In the case of a resistor, if the input stress were voltage or current, then the hazards would be proportional to power dissipation. In the case of a spring, if the input stress were either a force or displacement (compression or elongation), the hazards would be proportional to stored mechanical energy. It would therefore seem that this model predicts hazards proportional to input power for dissipative elements and proportional to potential energy for energy-storage elements. If these physically appealing relations are invalid for a particular part, one can postulate that $K_1$ and/or $K_2$ are functions of input stress, $K_1(x_1)$ and

[1] Equation (8.19) is actually not a constant but a step function, and therefore its derivative is an impulse.

[2] D. K. Lloyd and M. Lipow, "Reliability: Management, Method, Mathematics," p. 140, Prentice-Hall, Inc., Englewood Cliffs, N.J., 1962; R. P. Haviland, "Engineering Reliability and Long Life Design," p. 57, D. Van Nostrand Company, Inc., Princeton, N.J., 1964.

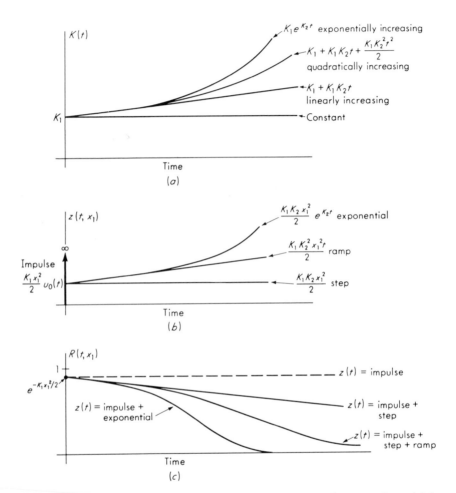

**Fig. 8.5**  Comparison of strength-deterioration models.   (a) Time growth model for Rayleigh parameter $K$; (b) hazard models associated with the $K$ models of part $a$; (c) reliability models for the hazards of part $b$.

$K_2(x_1)$, and obtain a wide variety of stress dependencies in the reliability model.   The real proof of the utility of the strength-deterioration models postulated must await a critical evaluation in light of experimental data.[1]

The above model does have one drawback common to all single-parameter models: the mean and variance of the distribution cannot be

[1] The models seem to fit well some data on capacitor and light bulb failures.   See S. Aranoff, "Derivation of a Stress-Strength Reliability Model for Electronic Components with Application to Accelerated Life Tests," M.S. thesis, Polytechnic Institute of Brooklyn, June, 1968.

independently adjusted. Thus, one must be satisfied with a rather approximate fit of a Rayleigh model to experimental data which determine $f(y)$. A better procedure is to start with a two-parameter model, in which case the mean and variance are separately adjustable. One can use a variety of two-parameter distributions. A convenient choice is the Weibull distribution, which is defined by the density function

$$f(y) = Ky^m e^{-Ky^{m+1}/(m+1)}$$

(8.22)

Note that in Chap. 4 the random variable associated with the Weibull distribution was time $t$, whereas in Eq. (8.22) it is part strength $y$. The family of different density functions obtainable by choice of $K$ and $m$ in the Weibull distribution are shown in Fig. 4.19. In every case the distribution is defined only for $y > 0$. Using this distribution, Eq. (8.9) becomes

$$p_s(x_1) = \int_{x_1}^{\infty} Ky^m e^{-Ky^{m+1}/(m+1)} \, dy = e^{-Kx_1^{m+1}/(m+1)}$$

(8.23)

and assuming that $K$ varies exponentially as before

$$R(t,x_1) = \exp\left(-\frac{K_1 e^{K_2 t}}{m+1} x_1^{m+1}\right)$$

(8.24)

Of course for $m = 1$ we have the Rayleigh distribution previously used. If $K_1$ is considered independent of stress input $x_1$, then the parameter $m$ determines the power to which $x_1$ is raised in the hazard expression. If $K_1$ is allowed to vary with $x_1$, then $K_1(x_1)x_1^{m+1}$ determines the dependence on input stress. For example, the Rayleigh model coupled with a $K_1$ parameter independent of strength produces a $x_1^2$ variation. One could also choose $m = 3$ in order to fit the $f(y)$ curve and $K_1(x_1) \sim 1/x_1^2$ and still obtain an $x_1^2$ variation. Physical measurements of the initial hazard determine $K_1(x_1)x_1^{m+1}$ but do not specify each function in the product. Thus, one is free to choose $m$ and $K$ to match the $f(y)$ distribution and then set the $K_1(x_1)$ function to agree with experimental data on how the initial hazard value varies with the input stress.

As an aid to picking suitable values of $K$ and $m$ in Eq. (8.22) which fit physical data, one can refer to the normalized Weibull curves of Chap. 4 or match the mean and variance of the Weibull distribution to physical data. The mean and variance for a Weibull distribution are

$$E(y) = \Gamma\left(\frac{m+2}{m+1}\right)\left(\frac{K}{m+1}\right)^{1/(m+1)}$$

(8.25)

$$\text{var } y = \left(\frac{K}{m+1}\right)^{2/(m+1)} \left[\Gamma\left(\frac{m+3}{m+1}\right) - \Gamma^2\left(\frac{m+2}{m+1}\right)\right]$$

(8.26)

Other models could be proposed which would be representative of the other stress patterns in Fig. 8.2.   One might guess that they would have features which lie somewhere between the constant-value model, Eq. (8.24), and the irregular-value model, Eq. (8.8).

One can also generalize Eq. (8.23) for situations in which more than one stress acts.   This can be done in many different ways.   One possibility is where the stresses are additive, e.g., if $x_1 = z_1 + z_2$, or where the stresses are multiplicative, $x_1 = z_1 z_2$.

## 8.4   ACCELERATED TESTING

Several models were proposed in the previous section to describe how reliability varies with applied stress.   Such models are useful for a variety of reasons:

1   They focus attention on particular failure mechanisms within a part, furnishing the designer with a qualitative and quantitative picture which should help him in improving the part.
2   They allow the system designer to operate the part at low stress levels and to make an intelligent estimate of the expected increase in reliability.
3   They make possible meaningful life tests to determine the part hazard function in short periods of time by testing at a high stress level.[1]

The third model is commonly called accelerated testing, the idea being to reduce the extent, duration, and cost of the test by taking data at a high stress level and extrapolating to compute what the hazard function would be at a normal stress level.   For example if the model given in Eq. (8.16) holds, the hazard is proportional to $x_1^2$, thus a three-fold increase in $x_1$ leads to a ninefold increase in $z(t)$.   This is equivalent to a shorter test.   In fact one can compare the effect of operating a component at stress $x_1$ for time $t_1$ with that of operation at stress $x_2$ for time $t_2$.   To make such a comparison one equates the reliability functions obtained under the two sets of conditions

$$R(t_1, x_1) = \exp\left[ -\left( \frac{K_1 x_1^2}{2} + \frac{K_1 K_2}{2} x_1^2 t_1 \right) \right] = R(t_2, x_2)$$
$$= \exp\left[ -\left( \frac{K_1 x_2^2}{2} + \frac{K_1 K_2 x_2^2 t_2}{2} \right) \right] \quad (8.27)$$

We may simplify Eq. (8.27) by assuming that the probability of failure at time $t = 0$ is very low.   This could be achieved in practice if one burned-in the components in question.   Also if the initial failures

---

[1] This requires an accurate model if accurate results are desired.

which occur when the parts are energized are treated separately, we eliminate any failures at $t = 0$.[1]   Under these conditions

$$R(0,x_1) = e^{-K_1 x_1^2/2} \approx 1 \qquad R(0,x_2) = e^{-K_1 x_2^2/2} \approx 1$$

Therefore Eq. (8.27) simplifies to

$$e^{-K_1 K_2 x_1^2 t_1/2} = e^{-K_1 K_2 x_2^2 t_2/2}$$

Taking logarithms of both sides and solving for $t_1$ yields

$$t_1 = \left(\frac{x_2}{x_1}\right)^2 t_2 \tag{8.28}$$

The quantity $(x_2/x_1)^2$ is called an *acceleration factor* and represents the time scaling achieved by testing the components at a higher stress level. Since this is proportional to the square of the $x_2/x_1$ ratio, a $3:1$ ratio results in a $9:1$ time scaling.   This means if we test at $x_2 = 3x_1$ and compute a constant hazard $\lambda_2 = K_1 K_2 x_2^2/2$, we can estimate the constant hazard $\lambda_1$ which would be obtained at normal stress level $x_1$ by

$$\lambda_1 = \left(\frac{x_1}{x_2}\right)^2 \lambda_2$$

The stress levels must be accurately controlled, since small changes in $x_1/x_2$ result in larger changes in the ratio $(x_1/x_2)^2$.   In general the acceleration factor is given by solution of the relationship between the hazard functions at normal and at increased stress.   The function involved may be more complex than that indicated in Eq. (8.28).[2]

## 8.5  RATE PROCESS MODELS

The failure models already discussed in this chapter have all been built upon a stress-strength hypothesis.   These are physical models in the sense that the stresses and strengths involved are physical quantities in the problem.   They are not specifically identified; therefore, the constants in the model must be evaluated from test data.   Since researchers are beginning to learn more about failure mechanisms, some specific failure mechanisms are being postulated.   Specific causes of part failure

[1] Actually one could use the failures at time $t = 0$ to estimate some parameters of the model.   For a population of $N$ items with $n_0$ initial failures for stress level $x_1$ and $n_{02}$ for stress level $x_2$ one can equate $n_{01}/N = e^{-K_1 x_1^2/2}$ and $n_{02}/N = e^{-K_1 x_2^2/2}$.   Solving for $K_1$, we get two independent estimates of this parameter

$$K_1 = \frac{2 \ln (N/n_{01})}{x_1^2} \qquad \text{and} \qquad K_1 = \frac{2 \ln (N/n_{02})}{x_2^2}$$

[2] G. J. Blakemore, On the Use of Weibull Sampling Plans, *Proc. Conf. Reliability Assurance Tech. Semicond. Specifications*, Washington, D.C., 1961.

such as material evaporation or diffusion, oxidation, mechanical fracture due to internal stresses, etc., have been proposed.[1]  These allow further insight into how the part fails and should be most valuable in improving part reliability and planning life tests.  Most of these investigations have dealt with resistors, capacitors, diodes, and transistors.  This is probably due to their low cost, standardization, and wide use.  The general conclusion which is usually drawn from these studies is that the failure mechanisms should be treated like chemical rate processes.

An extensive amount of work has been done on rate processes by chemists and physicists.[2]  The two equations used to explain the time rate of change $\dot{Q}'$ of a quantity $Q$ are the Arrhenius model and the Eyring model.  The Arrhenius equation

$$\dot{Q}(x) = \frac{dQ(x)}{dt} = e^{A - B/x} = e^A e^{-B/x} \tag{8.29}$$

was empirically derived in 1880 from observations of chemical reaction rates.  The quantity changing is $Q$, and its time derivative is $\dot{Q}$; $x$ is a particular stress parameter which fixes $\dot{Q}$.  The constants in the equation are $A$ and $B$.  From a chemical point of view, the most obvious stress parameter encountered is temperature $T$, and Eq. (8.29) is found to be a good model for many cases where $x$ is the absolute temperature.  If experimental data for $\dot{Q}$ vs. $1/x$ are plotted on semilog paper, a straight line is obtained with $A$ the intercept and $B$ the slope.

The Eyring model is derived from quantum-mechanical concepts for the stress parameter $T$

$$\dot{Q}(x) = \alpha T e^{-\beta/kT} \tag{8.30}$$

If the range of absolute-temperature changes is small, one can replace the $\alpha T$ term by its average value and treat it as a constant, that is, $k = \alpha T_{av}$.  Under these circumstances, Eq. (8.30) becomes Eq. (8.29) with $k = e^A$ and $B = \beta/k$.

Two fundamental questions must be answered before Eqs. (8.29) and (8.30) can be applied successfully (or replaced by more general models).  First it is not clear that either Eq. (8.29) or (8.30) will hold if temperature is replaced by other physical stresses such as pressure, humidity, voltage, power, heat, etc.  Second, even if these models are shown to hold for a wide range of types of stress $x$, there is no reason to believe a priori that the hazard function should be proportional to $\dot{Q}$ or $Q$.

[1] D. W. Levinson and R. G. Pohl, in M. F. Goldberg (ed.), "Physics of Failure in Electronics," p. 108, Spartan Books, Inc., Baltimore, 1963.

[2] S. Glasstone, K. Laidler, and H. Eyring, "The Theory of Rate Processes," McGraw-Hill Book Company, New York, 1941; and Haviland, *op. cit.*

If we do assume that $z(t) \sim Q$ and use Eq. (8.29) for $\dot{Q}$, we obtain

$$z(t) = kQ = k\int \dot{Q}\, dt = z_0 + k e^A e^{-B/x} t \tag{8.31}$$

This result is in some ways similar to Eq. (8.21) if we drop the impulse term $u_0(t)$. However, in Eq. (8.31), the constant $z_0$ is unspecified, and the hazard slope is constrained to vary with $x$ in only one particular fashion, that is, $e^A e^{-B/x}$.

Until more physical-failure data are scrutinized and more failure mechanisms are developed, the physical-failure approach will only supplement life testing as a means of determining the parameters of hazard models.

## 8.6  HUMAN OPERATOR MODELS

As discussed in Sec. 6.8, most of the quantitative engineering studies of the human being as a system component have focused on his performance in a control application. The dynamic behavior of a pilot flying an aircraft (or spacecraft) has been extensively studied. Little work has been done on the problem of describing human reliability. For example, suppose an operator has to monitor a display of gages and meters and initiate manual commands after interpreting their readings. The operator may fail by misreading, misinterpreting, or misreacting to the readings and initiating wrong action or by taking too long to react and thereby failing in one of his appointed tasks.

The gage-reading problem may be discussed in terms of two typical situations. In one the gages generally stay at some nominal value but occasionally deviate, requiring the person to interpret accurately and react promptly to the large amount of new information he is exposed to. In the other situation the gages are constantly changing, and he responds by initiating frequent actions.

The range of human responses is very large; however, we shall focus on two typical situations. In the first situation the operator is required to throw various toggle switches in response to visual information. In the second case the operator must control a vehicle in response to meter readings. In both these situations attempts have been made to utilize the mathematics of information theory[1] to measure the information content of a display and the information-handling capacity of a human being.

---

[1] A good introduction to information theory is given in M. Schwartz, "Information Transmission, Modulation, and Noise," McGraw-Hill Book Company, New York, 1959.

The use of an information-theory model to describe a control-tracking situation is currently under investigation,[1] and the applicability of the model is uncertain. In the case of the toggle-switching problem, some results have been reported.[2]

The unit of information used in information theory is the *bit*, defined by

$$H = \log_2 n \tag{8.32}$$

where $H \equiv$ information in bits

$n \equiv$ number of equiprobable, independent, alternative readings of the display

In the case of constant meter readings which occasionally fluctuate, Eq. (8.32) must be modified, since the readings are not equiprobable.[3] (If any one reading predominates, the information content goes down.) One model for the time required for the human being to process information in such a situation is

$$\tau = a + bH \tag{8.33}$$

where $\tau$ = reaction time, sec

$a$ = lower limit of human response time = 0.2 sec

$b$ = reciprocal of the information-handling rate (human information-handling rate here is typically 15 bits per sec)

$H$ = display information in bits

Little seems to have been done in relating error rate[4] to $H$; it is hoped that research will confirm the hypothesis (which seems logical) that error rate and $H$ are related.

## 8.7 INTERPRETATION OF LIFE-TEST DATA

The preceding sections in this chapter have discussed some of the results of reliability physics. Although these models contribute to our understanding of failure, they are not complete enough to replace an

[1] L. Young and R. Winblade, M.I.T.–NASA Working Conference on Manual Control, *IEEE Spectrum*, November, 1966, p. 88.

[2] G. Cole et al., Study of Pilot-Controller Integration for Emergency Conditions, *Wright-Patterson Air Force Base Tech. Doc. Rept.* RTD-TDR-63-4092, p. 40, January, 1964.

[3] Schwartz, *op. cit.*, pp. 8, 13.

[4] The author remembers an undergraduate experiment in an experimental psychology laboratory which measured the error rate in tracing paths on an oscilloscope screen (a simplified model of the air-traffic-controller problem). The results showed that the error rate was related to the log of the number of paths, which would predict an error rate proportional to $H$. There is also counter evidence, see reference to S. Kornblum in bibliography, Chap. 8, page 516.

ordinary or accelerated life test as the primary source of failure-rate numbers.

The basic treatment of failure-rate data was discussed in Chap. 4. The histograms for $z_d(t)$ and $f_d(t)$ were introduced and discussed. No formal discussion was included on the choice of an appropriate model or the determination of model parameters. Most of the remaining sections of this chapter will center on these two topics.

A word of common sense is in order before we delve into the mathematics. If only two or three items are tested for a short time, little in the way of *accurate* quantitative conclusions can be drawn. No matter how powerful or sophisticated the statistical technique employed, it cannot make up for scant data. At the other extreme if thousands of items have been tested over a long interval, any logical and valid technique for analyzing the data should yield accurate results. Modern statistical techniques of data analysis will probably be most beneficial in the intermediate range when, say, 20 to 100 items have been tested. They will help extract the most information from such a situation.

The initial procedure in the choice of a model is to plot the histogram for $z_d(t)$ from the failure data. The general shape of this empirical function is perhaps the best clue as to what sort of model should be chosen. For example, it is clear that a constant-hazard model will fit the data of Fig. 4.1b fairly well. The situation in Fig. 4.2 is less clear-cut; however, one might choose a constant failure rate between 0 and 3 hr and a linearly increasing model for the remainder of the curve. (Another choice might be to use a constant model plus a Weibull model with $m$ equal to 2 or 3.) To fit the data of Fig. 4.3, a decreasing-failure-rate model should be chosen. A Weibull model with $-1 < m < 0$ or a two-region piecewise-linear model might also be used. In each of the preceding cases, a judgment was made by inspection of the $z_d(t)$ function as to what sort of model might be suitable.

Any graphical or analytical curve-fitting procedure applied to the hazard curve directly yields a model for $z(t)$ which implies an associated model for $R(t)$. Such curve-fitting procedures should be supplemented by engineering judgment. For example, if the last three life tests on a certain electronic component yielded constant-hazard data, it is a good assumption to try a constant-hazard model first in analyzing the fourth batch of failure data on the same component.

## 8.8 PROBABILITY GRAPH PAPER

The use of engineering judgment in connection with inspection of the hazard curve should lead to a proper choice of a model in most cases.

In some instances a better test is needed, and various graphical and analytical procedures exist.   The simplest graphical procedure is to use probability paper.[1]   Probability graph paper is specially constructed with a nonlinear time scale along the abscissa and a nonlinear scale for plotting the value of the distribution function along the ordinate.   In each case the nonlinear scales are chosen so that if the data taken truly belong to the type of model being tested, the probability-paper plot will be a straight line.   In simple cases, one of the scales may be linear.   An example will clarify how probability paper is constructed and used.

Starting with the basic relation between $R(t)$ and $z(t)$, we write

$$R(t) = 1 - F(t) = \exp\left(- \int_0^t z(\xi)\, d\xi\right)$$

$$\frac{1}{1 - F(t)} = \exp\left(+ \int_0^t z(\xi)\, d\xi\right)$$

$$\ln \frac{1}{1 - F(t)} = \int_0^t z(\xi)\, d\xi \tag{8.34}$$

In the case of a constant hazard rate, $z(t) = \lambda$, and Eq. (8.34) becomes

$$\ln \frac{1}{1 - F(t)} = \lambda t \tag{8.35}$$

If the variable $1/[1 - F(t)]$ is plotted on a natural-logarithmic scale[2] and time along a linear scale, Eq. (8.35) will appear as a straight line with slope $\lambda$.

The basic data to be plotted are a set of failure times for the $n$ items which have failed within the duration of the test period.   The original population contained $N$ items.   Since $F(t)$ is not available, the best value to use instead is $E[F(t_i)]$, where the $t_i$ values are the failure times

$$E[F(t_i)] = \sum_{i=1}^{n} \frac{i}{N + 1} \tag{8.36}$$

Intuition would predict that $F(t_3)$, the probability of failure by time $t_3$, would be given by $3/N$, that is, the fractional number of item failures. Thus intuition would predict

$$F(t_i) = \sum_{i=1}^{n} \frac{i}{N}$$

---

[1] E. Pieruschka, "Principles of Reliability," chap. 14, Prentice-Hall, Inc., Englewood Cliffs, N.J., 1963.

[2] Actually any logarithmic scale can be used to rectify the function, but the constant $\lambda$ will then no longer be the slope directly.

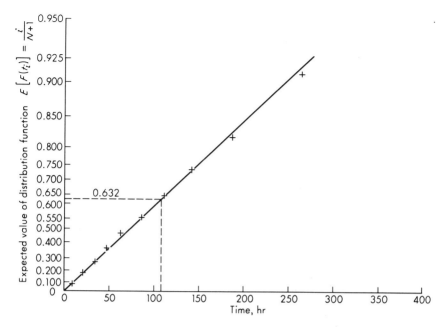

**Fig. 8.6**  Exponential probability paper.

which agrees well for large $N$ with the *better*[1] statistical result containing $N + 1$ in the denominator.  Substitution of Eq. (8.36) into Eq. (8.35) yields

$$\ln \frac{N + 1}{N + 1 - \sum_{i=1}^{n} i} = \int_0^t z(\xi) \, d\xi \tag{8.37}$$

Thus, in the case of constant hazard rate, Eq. (8.37) reduces to

$$\ln \frac{N + 1}{N + 1 - \sum_{i=1}^{n} i} = \lambda t \tag{8.38}$$

Equation (8.38) is the basis for using the exponential probability (natural-log) paper shown in Fig. 8.6.

The graph has vertical scale points spaced at a distance $\ln [1/(1 - F)]$ apart, as indicated in Eq. (8.35); however, the values of the ordinate

---

[1] See J. H. K. Kao, A Summary of Some New Techniques for Failure Analysis, *Proc. Sixth Natl. Symp. Reliability*, Washington, D.C., January, 1960, p. 193.

scale are in units of $F$.   This is for plotting convenience so that the user need merely calculate $E[F(t_i)] = i/(N + 1)$ and plot this value directly. The nonlinear ordinate scale in effect subtracts this value from unity, forms the reciprocal, and then takes the natural logarithm.[1]   The following example illustrates the use of exponential probability paper.

The data from Table 4.1 are plotted in Fig. 8.6.   As predicted, the points fall along a straight line.   The slope of the straight line is of course related to the time constant of the exponential; however, a simpler procedure for determining the time constant will be used.   When $t = 1/\lambda$, that is, one time constant, then Eq. (8.35) reduces to

$$\frac{1}{1 - F(t)} = e$$

$$F(t) = 1 - \frac{1}{e} = 0.632$$

This point is shown as the dotted horizontal line on the probability paper.   For the example plotted $1/\lambda = 107$ hr, and $\lambda = 0.94 \times 10^{-2}$. This compares favorably with the visual estimate of $1.1 \times 10^{-2} \pm 20$ percent obtained by inspection of Fig. 4.1$b$.   Obviously the data are well fitted by an exponential model.

One can also construct Weibull probability paper in a similar manner. For the Weibull distribution Eq. (8.37) becomes

$$\ln \frac{N + 1}{N + 1 - \sum_{i=1}^{n} i} = \frac{K}{m + 1} t^{m+1} \tag{8.39}$$

Unfortunately this will not result in a straight-line plot unless a second transformation is performed.

If the single transformation is used, one finds that the two parameters $K$ and $m$ are "bound together" in the expression.   One could plot a family of probability papers for various values to $m$ and thus "separate" the parameters; however, it would be necessary to define a transformed time scale $\tau = t^{m+1}$ for each member of the family.   To use the curves, one would have to guess an appropriate value of $m$, choose the corresponding paper, and plot the data.   It would probably be necessary to try larger and smaller values of $m$ and use interpretation to arrive at the final parameter values.   A better method is to use a second logarithmic

---

[1] For the ordinate values $F = 0.1, 0.2, 0.3, 0.4, 0.5, 0.55, 0.60, 0.65, 0.7, 0.75, 0.8,$ $0.85, 0.9, 0.925, 0.950$ in Fig. 8.6, the corresponding spacings given by $\ln [1/(1 - F)]$ are $0.104, 0.223, 0.357, 0.510, 0.694, 0.798, 0.916, 1.05, 1.21, 1.39, 1.61, 1.89, 2.30,$ $2.59, 3.00$.

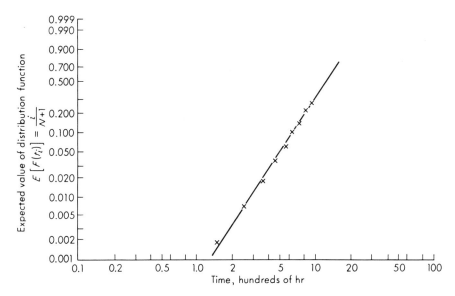

**Fig. 8.7**   Weibull probability paper.

transformation on Eq. (8.39).   Taking the natural logarithm of both sides of Eq. (8.39),

$$\ln\left[\ln F(t)\right] = \ln\left(\frac{K}{m+1}\, t^{m+1}\right)$$

$$\ln\left[\ln \frac{N+1}{N+1-\sum\limits_{i=1}^{n} i}\right] = \ln \frac{K}{m+1} + (m+1)\ln t \qquad (8.40)$$

Equation (8.40) will plot as a straight line on probability paper with a vertical ln-ln scale and a horizontal ln scale.   An example of Weibull probability paper[1] appears in Fig. 8.7.   The following example illustrates its use.

The data given in Table 8.1 are from a failure process which has in the past been accurately described by a Weibull model.   The data are plotted on Weibull probability paper in Fig. 8.7.   The values of $i/1{,}001$ are plotted along the vertical scale vs. midpoints of the time intervals, that is, 0.5, 1.5, 2.5, etc., plotted along the horizontal scale.   The resulting values of $K$ and $m$ are $K = 2.47 \times 10^{-3}$, $m = 1.74$.

In the previous two cases we chose to curve-fit the data for the cumula-

[1] Kao, *op. cit.*

**Table 8.1  Failure data for a process suspected to be Weibull (number on test = 1,000)**

| Time interval, hr | Number failed | Hazard $z(t)$ $\times 10^{-3}$ | $\dfrac{1}{N+1} = \dfrac{i}{1,001}$ |
|---|---|---|---|
| 0–1 | 0 | 0 | 0 |
| 1–2 | 2 | 2 | 0.002 |
| 2–3 | 6 | 6.0 | 0.008 |
| 3–4 | 12 | 12.1 | 0.020 |
| 4–5 | 20 | 20.4 | 0.040 |
| 5–6 | 29 | 30.2 | 0.069 |
| 6–7 | 39 | 42.0 | 0.108 |
| 7–8 | 50 | 56.1 | 0.158 |
| 8–9 | 61 | 72.4 | 0.219 |
| 9–10 | 71 | 91.0 | 0.290 |

tive failure distribution function. This was rather arbitrary, and we could have started with the $f(t)$ or $z(t)$ function. In fact, for Weibull distributions it is much easier to fit the $z(t)$ function. A simple technique is to graph the hazard data on log-log paper. Thus if

$$z(t) = Kt^m$$

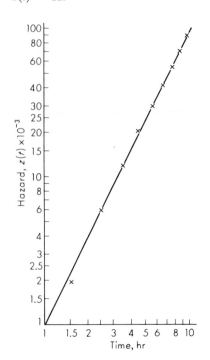

**Fig. 8.8**  Log-log plot of Weibull hazard data.

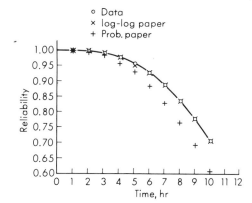

**Fig. 8.9** Comparison of graphical models.

then

$$\log z(t) = \log K + m \log t$$

The slope yields the parameter $m$, and the $t = 1$ intercept gives the value of $K$. Such a plot is shown in Fig. 8.8. The computed values of $z(t)$ are again plotted at the center of the time intervals. The resulting values are $K = 10^{-3}$ and $m = 2$.

The two techniques are compared with the experimental data in Fig. 8.9, where it is seen that the log-log estimate is a better fit than the Weibull paper estimate. This is a fortunate situation in which the simpler technique gives the better result.

Other statistical tests which help choose a model are available in the literature.[1]


## 8.9 STATISTICAL ESTIMATION OF HAZARD DATA

### 8.9.1 INTRODUCTION

We now turn to the statistical techniques which can be used to efficiently process data and obtain "best" repeatable values for model parameters. In this section we shall be concerned with point and interval estimates. A point estimate of a parameter is a single number which is our "best" estimate of the parameter. If we are somewhat

---

[1] B. Epstein, Tests for the Validity of the Assumption that the Underlying Distribution of Life Is Exponential, *Dept. of Defense Tech. Rept.*, November, 1960 (reprint of papers in February and May 1960 issues of *Technometrics*); and Pieruschka, *op. cit.*, pp. 258–263. Also for parametric and nonparametric goodness of fit tests see J. Freund, "Mathematical Statistics," chaps. 12 and 13, Prentice-Hall, Inc., Englewood Cliffs, N.J., 1962; also I. Miller and J. Freund, "Probability and Statistics for Engineers," chaps. 8–11, 13, Prentice-Hall, Inc., Englewood Cliffs, N.J., 1965.

more realistic, we may wish to quote an interval, i.e., an interval estimate, in which the parameter probably falls. Statistics being what it is, the wider we make the interval, the "surer" we are that we have bracketed the parameter. To be more precise we measure our sureness by the probability that the parameter falls within the interval. This probability is called the *confidence* or *confidence coefficient*.

The three techniques we shall study, least-square estimates, moment estimates, and maximum-likelihood estimates, all use a different "best" criterion. The author feels that the maximum-likelihood technique is the most flexible but that the other two merit consideration in certain situations. A more complete discussion of estimation criteria is given in Sec. 2.10. $p\ 80$

### 8.9.2 LEAST-SQUARES ESTIMATES

Most engineers are familiar with the least-squares method of fitting a straight line to experimental data. Actually, least-squares estimates belong to the class of techniques known as *regression analysis*. Regression analysis deals with the fitting of a certain regression model to a set of data by solving for the model coefficient. Linear regression deals with straight-line models and curvilinear regression with nonlinear models. The goodness-of-fit criterion that is generally used is least squares. The derivation of linear regression equations appears in Sec. 2.10.7 and is not repeated in the following material.

Linear models, of course, include constant-hazard and piecewise-linear models. If a linear model for $z(t)$ is assumed,

$$z(t) = a(t - \bar{t}) + b \tag{8.41}$$

where $\bar{t}$ is the mean value of the observed times to failure, that is,

$$\bar{t} = \frac{\sum\limits_{i=1}^{n} t_i}{n}$$

Applying least squares results in an estimate of $a$ and $b$ given by[1]

$$\tilde{b} = \bar{z} = \frac{\sum\limits_{i=1}^{n} z_i}{n} \tag{8.42}$$

$$\tilde{a} = \frac{\sum\limits_{i=1}^{n} (t_i - \bar{t}) z_i}{\sum\limits_{i=1}^{n} (t_i - \bar{t})^2} = \frac{\sum\limits_{i=1}^{n} t_i z_i - \bar{t}_i \sum\limits_{i=1}^{n} z_i}{\sum\limits_{i=1}^{n} t_i^2 - n\bar{t}^2} \tag{8.43}$$

---

[1] See Eqs. (2.132). The simple formula for $\tilde{b}$ in Eq. (8.42) is due to the fact that Eq. (8.41) was written about $\bar{t}$.

where the tilde over a parameter means a least-squares estimate and the bar over a quantity indicates the mean value of the quantity.

In the case of a constant-hazard model, $b = 0$, and only Eq. (8.43) need be evaluated. The following examples will illustrate the computations required.

*Example 1*    To fit a model to the data given in Table 4.2 and Fig. 4.1 we examine Fig. 4.1*b* and choose a constant-hazard model, $z(t) = \lambda$. From Eqs. (8.41) and (8.42) we obtain

$$\tilde{b} = \tilde{\lambda} =$$
$$\frac{1.25 + 0.93 + 0.96 + 1.19 + 0.98 + 0.87 + 1.00 + 1.11 + 1.11 + 1.25}{10}$$
$$\times 10^{-2} = 1.065 \times 10^{-2}$$

The numerical result compares well with a visual estimation from Fig. 4.1*b*.

*Example 2*    For the example given in Fig. 4.2*a* and Table 4.3 the hazard curve suggests a constant model up to 3,000 hr and a linear increasing one thereafter. Since our estimates are written for an equation written about the mean [see Eq. (8.4.1)], we shall write a separate hazard model for each region. In region 1, $z(t) = b_1 + a_1(t - \bar{t})$, and in region 2, $z(\tau) = b_2 + a_2(\tau - \bar{\tau})$, where

$$\bar{t} = \frac{1}{3} \sum_{i=1}^{3} t_i$$
$$\tau = t - 3{,}000$$
$$\bar{\tau} = \frac{1}{t - 3{,}000} \sum_{i=4}^{n} (t_i - 3{,}000)$$

Thus, the first three data points will be used to determine $b_1$ ($a_1$ is of course zero). Since the data are grouped, the failure times $t_i$ will be considered to occur at the center of the interval.[1]    For the first interval

$$\tilde{b}_1 = \frac{(59 \times 3.43 + 24 \times 2.12 + 29 \times 3.26) \times 10^{-4}}{112} = 3.10 \times 10^{-4}$$

In region 1, $z(t) = 3.10 \times 10^{-4}$. In region 2, both parameters $a_2$ and $b_2$ must be calculated. Since the time origin is to start at $t = 3{,}000$ hr, $t_4$, $t_5$, and $t_6$ are replaced by $\tau_4 = (3{,}500 - 3{,}000) = 500$,

$$\tau_5 = (4{,}500 - 3{,}000) = 1{,}500$$

---

[1] This was discussed in Sec. 4.1. In statistical terms the intervals are called the *class intervals* and the center of the interval the *class mark*.

and

$$\tau_6 = (5,500 - 3,000) = 2,500$$

Therefore

$$\bar{\tau} = \frac{30 \times 500 + 17 \times 1,500 + 13 \times 2,500}{30 + 17 + 13} = 1,220$$

$$\tilde{a}_2 = \frac{30(500 - 1,220)5 \times 10^4 + 17(1,500 - 1,220)5.69 \times 10^4 + 13(2,500 - 1,220)10.00 \times 10^4}{30(500 - 1,220)^2 + 17(1,500 - 1,220)^2 + 13(2,500 - 1,220)^2}$$
$$= 2.24 \times 10^{-7}$$

$$\tilde{b}_2 = \frac{30 \times 5 \times 10^{-4} + 17 \times 5.69 \times 10^{-4} + 13 \times 10 \times 10^{-4}}{30 + 17 + 13}$$
$$= 6.28 \times 10^{-4}$$

Thus, in region 2, $z(\tau) = 6.28 \times 10^{-4} + 2.24 \times 10^7(\tau - 1,220)$.

Least-squares estimates need not be restricted to linear models. The same technique can be applied to develop estimation formulas for curvilinear regression. If $z(t)$ is assumed to be a third-order polynomial in $t$,

$$z(t) = a_0 + a_1t + a_2t^2 + a_3t^3 \tag{8.44}$$

Again using least squares, a set of four regression equations is obtained[1]

$$a_0n + a_1 \sum_{i=1}^n t_i + a_2 \sum_{i=1}^n t_i^2 + a_3 \sum_{i=1}^n t_i^3 = \sum_{i=1}^n z_i$$

$$a_0 \sum_{i=1}^n t_i + a_1 \sum_{i=1}^n t_i^2 + a_2 \sum_{i=1}^n t_i^3 + a_3 \sum_{i=1}^n t_i^4 = \sum_{i=1}^n t_iz_i$$

$$a_0 \sum_{i=1}^n t_i^2 + a_1 \sum_{i=1}^n t_i^3 + a_2 \sum_{i=1}^n t_i^4 + a_3 \sum_{i=1}^n t_i^5 = \sum_{i=1}^n t_i^2z_i \tag{8.45}$$

$$a_0 \sum_{i=1}^n t_i^3 + a_1 \sum_{i=1}^n t_i^4 + a_2 \sum_{i=1}^n t_i^5 + a_3 \sum_{i=1}^n t_i^6 = \sum_{i=1}^n t_i^3z_i$$

The method indicated by Eqs. (8.44) and (8.45) can of course be extended to higher-order polynomial approximations. As seen by inspection of Eqs. (8.45), the regression equations are linear in the polynomial constants and may be solved by Cramer's rule or other techniques applicable to linear equations. Some computation time is saved if $t$ is replaced by $t - \bar{t}$ in the equations since $\sum_{i=1}^n (t_i - \bar{t})^m = 0$ for $m$ odd.

[1] P. G. Hoel, "Introduction to Mathematical Statistics," p. 132, John Wiley & Sons, Inc., New York, 1954.

This reduces the above set of $n$ simultaneous equations to two sets of equations, one set for the even-subscript coefficients and one set for the odd-subscript coefficients.

Regression functions other than polynomial or linear may be used; however, often when this is done, the resulting regression equations are nonlinear or transcendental. The nonlinear regression equations for the Weibull model are derived as follows. For the Weibull distribution, the deviation of the model value from the data point is given by

$$\Delta z_i = z_i - z_i' = z_i - Kt_i^m \tag{8.46}$$

where $\Delta z_i = i$th deviation
$\quad\quad\ z_i =$ value of hazard at $i$th point in time $t_i$
$\quad\quad\ z_i' =$ hazard value predicted by model at time $t_i$
The error function is given by

$$\epsilon(K,m) = \sum_{i=1}^{n} (\Delta z_i)^2 = \sum_{i=1}^{n} (z_i - Kt_i^m)^2$$

$$= \sum_{i=1}^{n} z_i^2 - 2 \sum_{i=1}^{n} Kz_it_i^m + \sum_{i=1}^{n} K^2t_i^{2m} \tag{8.47}$$

Minimizing the error function with respect to $K$ and $m$ yields

$$\frac{\partial \epsilon}{\partial K} = -2 \sum_{i=1}^{n} z_it_i^m + 2K \sum_{i=1}^{n} t_i^{2m} = 0$$

$$\frac{\partial \epsilon}{\partial m} = -2K \sum_{i=1}^{n} z_imt_i^{m-1} + \sum_{i=1}^{n} K^22mt_i = 0$$

Solution of the above equations yields least-squares estimates for $K$ and $m$

$$\tilde{K} = \frac{\displaystyle\sum_{i=1}^{n} z_it_i^{\tilde{m}}}{\displaystyle\sum_{i=1}^{n} t_i^{2\tilde{m}}} \tag{8.48}$$

$$\frac{\displaystyle\sum_{i=1}^{n} z_it_i^{\tilde{m}}}{\displaystyle\sum_{i=1}^{n} z_it_i^{\tilde{m}-1}} = \frac{\displaystyle\sum_{i=1}^{n} t_i^{2\tilde{m}}}{\displaystyle\sum_{i=1}^{n} t_i^{2\tilde{m}-1}} \tag{8.49}$$

Equation (8.49) must be solved by trial and error for $\tilde{m}$. The simplest way to accomplish this is to plot the left-hand side of the equation vs. $m$ on the same graph paper as a plot of the right-hand side vs. $m$. The intersection of these two curves determines the least-squares estimate $\tilde{m}$.

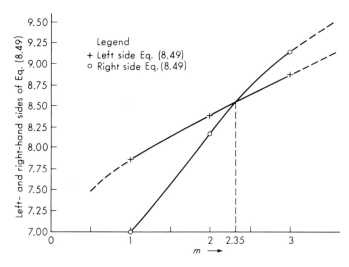

**Fig. 8.10**  Determination of parameter $m$ by graphical solution of Eq. (8.49).

Substitution of this value of $\tilde{m}$ in Eq. (8.48) yields the value of $\tilde{K}$. The technique is illustrated in the following example.

*Example*  The data in Table 8.2 may be represented by a Weibull model. The values of $t_i$ are estimated by the class marks, 0.25, 1.0, 2.0, 3.0, etc., and the values of $z_i$ are estimated by those stated in Table 8.2. The left- and right-hand sides of Eq. (8.49) are plotted in Fig. 8.10 as described above.

**Table 8.2  Failure data hypothesized to be Weibull**

| $t$, hr | $z_d(t) \times 10^{-3}$ |
|---|---|
| 0  – 0.5 | 0 |
| 0.5– 1.5 | 1.1 |
| 1.5– 2.5 | 3.9 |
| 2.5– 3.5 | 8.8 |
| 3.5– 4.5 | 17.0 |
| 4.5– 5.5 | 24.0 |
| 5.5– 6.5 | 37.0 |
| 6.5– 7.5 | 50.0 |
| 7.5– 8.5 | 63.0 |
| 8.5– 9.5 | 83.0 |
| 9.5–10.5 | 98.0 |

The graphical solution yields $\tilde{m} = 2.35$.  Substitution of this value and the data values into Eq. (8.48) yields $\tilde{K} = 5.06 \times 10^{-4}$.  As the reader may easily verify, the above solution requires considerable computation.  Another technique is to first "linearize" the hazard equation.  Starting with the Weibull hazard function $z(t) = Kt^m$, one may linearize this function by taking the logarithm of both sides of the equation

$$\log z = \log K + m \log t \tag{8.50}$$

This equation is linear and forms the basis for a different least-squares estimate.  Proceeding in the conventional manner,

$$\Delta \log z = \log z_i - \log z_1' = \log z_i - \log K - m \log t_i$$

$$\epsilon(K,m) = \sum_{i=1}^{n} (\Delta \log z)^2 = \sum_{i=1}^{n} (\log z_i - \log K - m \log t_i)^2$$

$$= \sum_{i=1}^{n} (\log z_i)^2 + \sum_{i=1}^{n} (\log K)^2 + \sum_{i=1}^{n} (m \log t_i)^2$$

$$- 2 \sum_{i=1}^{n} (\log z_i)(\log K) - 2 \sum_{i=1}^{n} (\log z_i)(m \log t_i)$$

$$+ 2 \sum_{i=1}^{n} (\log K)(m \log t_i)$$

$$\frac{\partial \epsilon}{\partial K} = 2 \sum_{i=1}^{n} \log K \frac{1}{K} - 2 \sum_{i=1}^{n} \log z_i \frac{1}{K} + 2 \sum_{i=1}^{n} m \log t_i \frac{1}{K} = 0$$

$$\frac{\partial \epsilon}{\partial m} = 2 \sum_{i=1}^{n} m (\log t_i)^2 - 2 \sum_{i=1}^{n} (\log z_i)(\log t_i) + 2 \sum_{i=1}^{n} (\log K)(\log t_i) = 0$$

Solution of the above equations yields

$$\widetilde{\log K} = \frac{\sum_{i=1}^{n} (\log z_i) \sum_{i=1}^{n} (\log t_i)^2 - \sum_{i=1}^{n} \log t_i \sum_{i=1}^{n} (\log t_i)(\log z_i)}{\sum_{i=1}^{n} (\log t_i)^2 - \left( \sum_{i=1}^{n} \log t_i \right)^2} \tag{8.51}$$

$$\tilde{m} = \frac{\sum_{i=1}^{n} (\log z_i)(\log t_i) - \left( \sum_{i=1}^{n} \log z_i \right) \left( \sum_{i=1}^{n} \log t_i \right)}{\sum_{i=1}^{n} (\log t_i)^2 - \left( \sum_{i=1}^{n} \log t_i \right)^2} \tag{8.52}$$

Substitution of data in Eqs. (8.51) and (8.52) yields least-squares estimates of $K$ and $m$.  No graphical solutions are necessary; however, one must deal with the logarithms of the data, and Eqs. (8.51) and (8.52) are a little more complex then Eqs. (8.48) and (8.49).  The numerical estimates will differ slightly. The following section discusses another type of statistical parameter estimation, moment estimates.

### 8.9.3  MOMENT ESTIMATES

Moment-estimate techniques are another classical means of point estimation. They lead to simpler equations than mean-square techniques and have an intuitive appeal, but are less flexible than the maximum-likelihood estimations discussed in Sec. 8.9.4. Moment estimates are introduced in Sec. 2.6.5. The general technique is to match the moments of the data to the moments of the hypothesized distribution. The moments of the data are given by

$$m_k = \frac{1}{n} \sum_{i=1}^{n} t_i^k \tag{8.53}$$

The moments of the hypothesized distribution are given by

$$\mu_k = \int_0^\infty t^k f(t)\, dt \tag{8.54}$$

If the hypothesized distribution has a single parameter, $m_1$ is equated to $\mu_1$, and solution of the resulting equation yields the moment estimate of the parameter. If the distribution model has two parameters, $m_1$ is equated to $\mu_1$ to form one equation, and $m_2$ is equated to $\mu_2$ to form the other equation. The simultaneous solution of these two equations yields estimator formulas for the two parameters.[1] The extension of this technique to three or more parameter distributions is obvious. No more than the minimum number of equations should be formulated, since a greater number becomes redundant and forms ambiguous solutions. Several examples of moment estimates are given below.

*Example* 1   In the case of a constant hazard distribution only one parameter need be estimated. The density function is

$$f(t) = \lambda e^{-\lambda t}$$

and the first moment given by

$$m_1 = \int_0^\infty t\lambda e^{-\lambda t}\, dt = \frac{1}{\lambda}$$

---

[1] One might also work with moments about the mean rather than moments about the origin. Thus instead of matching $\mu_1 = m_1$ and $\mu_2 = m_2$, one could match $\mu_1 = m_1$ and $\sigma_1 = m_2 - m_1^2$ (see Lloyd and Lipow, *op. cit.*, p. 173). Actually origin moments are preferable, since one is more interested in the reliability function in the region $1 > R > 0.5$ than in the region $0.5 > R > 0$. Therefore, data fitting about the origin is better than data fitting about the mean for this kind of problem.

Equating this to $m_1$,

$$m_1 = \frac{\sum\limits_{i=1}^{n} t_i}{n} = \frac{1}{\lambda} = \mu_1$$

$$\therefore \check{\lambda} = \frac{n}{\sum\limits_{i=1}^{n} t_i} \tag{8.55}$$

where the symbol $\check{\lambda}$ indicates the moment estimate of the parameter $\lambda$.

*Example 2*   For a linearly increasing hazard rate

$$f(t) = Kte^{-Kt^2/2}$$

Utilizing the integrals listed in Appendix C, one obtains

$$\mu_1 = \int_0^\infty tKte^{-Kt^2/2}\, dt = \sqrt{\frac{\pi}{2K}}$$

Equating $\mu_1$ to $m_1$ and solving for $K$ yields

$$\check{K} = \frac{\pi/2n^2}{\left(\sum\limits_{i=1}^{n} t_i\right)^2} \tag{8.56}$$

*Example 3*   The estimation formula for the case of the Weibull distribution is somewhat more complex.   The density function is given by

$$Kt^m e^{-Kt^{m+1}/(m+1)}$$

The $k$th moment about the origin is given by

$$\mu_k = \int_0^\infty t^k Kt^m e^{-Kt^{m+1}/(m+1)}\, dt \qquad \text{from (8.54)}$$

Again using the integrals in Appendix C, one obtains

$$\mu_k = \left(\frac{K}{m+1}\right)^{-k/(m+1)} \Gamma\left(\frac{k+m+1}{m+1}\right) \tag{8.57}$$

The first and second moments are

$$\mu_1 = \left(\frac{K}{m+1}\right)^{-1/(m+1)} \Gamma\left(\frac{m+2}{m+1}\right)$$

$$\mu_2 = \left(\frac{K}{m+1}\right)^{-2/(m+1)} \Gamma\left(\frac{m+3}{m+1}\right)$$

which are equated to $m_1$ and $m_2$ to yield

$$\frac{1}{n} \sum_{i=1}^{n} t_i = \left( \frac{K}{m+1} \right)^{-1/(m+1)} \Gamma \left( \frac{m+2}{m+1} \right) \tag{8.58}$$

$$\frac{1}{n} \sum_{i=1}^{n} t_i^2 = \left( \frac{K}{m+1} \right)^{-2/(m+1)} \Gamma \left( \frac{m+3}{m+1} \right) \tag{8.59}$$

The left-hand sides of Eqs. (8.58) and (8.59) are merely numbers, the average of the failure times and the average of the squares of the failure times. However, the right-hand sides prevent a closed-form solution. A simple iterative procedure is to solve both (8.58) and (8.59) for $K$

$$K = (m+1) \left[ \frac{\Gamma \left( \dfrac{m+2}{m+1} \right)}{\dfrac{1}{n} \displaystyle\sum_{i=1}^{n} t_i} \right]^{m+1} \qquad K' = (m+1) \left[ \frac{\Gamma \left( \dfrac{m+3}{m+1} \right)}{\dfrac{1}{n} \displaystyle\sum_{i=1}^{n} t_i^2} \right]^{(m+1)/2}$$

By substituting various values of $m$ in the above equations, a solution is reached when $K = K'$. A graphical procedure similar to that shown in Fig. 8.10 simplifies such a computation.

It is interesting to investigate what happens in the moment equations for the Weibull when $m$ is equal to 0 and 1. These are the constant and linearly increasing hazard distributions which are special cases of the Weibull and have already been solved [see Eqs. (8.55) and (8.56)]. Substituting $m = 0$ into Eqs. (8.58) and (8.59) yields the two estimates

$$K = \frac{2n}{\displaystyle\sum_{i=1}^{n} t_i} \qquad K^2 = \frac{6n}{\displaystyle\sum_{i=1}^{n} t_i^2}$$

Neither of these estimates agrees with Eq. (8.55); thus one should deal with the specific distribution to be estimated rather than substituting known information into a more general estimator formula. The basic problem in this case is that the Weibull estimator is a two-parameter case, whereas constant-hazard estimation contains only one parameter. Similar difficulties arise if $m = 1$, etc., is substituted.

### 8.9.4   MAXIMUM-LIKELIHOOD ESTIMATES

The most flexible and powerful of modern estimation techniques is the *maximum-likelihood method*. The estimation formulas are similar in complexity to moment estimates but possess most of the desirable good properties discussed in Sec. 2.10.2. Furthermore, it is a simple matter to compute an overall estimate when data are combined from several tests.   Life tests are often terminated (truncated) before all items have failed, or failed items are replaced with good units as they fail.   Both these effects are easily described by maximum-likehood theory.

The mathematical procedure for computing a maximum-likelihood estimate (MLE), was discussed in Sec. 2.10.6. The procedure is to formulate a joint density function (likelihood function $L$) depending on the failure times of the components $t_1$, $t_2$, . . . , $t_n$ and the density-function parameters $\theta_1$, $\theta_2$, . . . .   One then maximizes $L$ by setting $\partial L/\partial \theta_1 = \partial L/\partial \theta_2 = \cdots = 0$.   The likelihood function is given by

$$L(x_1, x_2, \ldots , x_n; \theta) = f(x_1; \theta) f(x_2; \theta) \cdots f(x_n; \theta) \qquad (2.122a)$$

where  $\theta$ = parameter to be estimated

$\qquad x_n$ = $n$th data value ($n$th time to failure)

$\qquad f(x, \theta)$ = density function containing parameter $\theta$

$\qquad L$ = likelihood function

The method is best illustrated by the following examples.

*Example* 1   For the constant hazard distribution, the hazard and density functions are

$$z(t) = \lambda \qquad f(t) = \lambda e^{-\lambda t}$$

and the likelihood function is

$$L(t_1, t_2, \ldots , t_n; \lambda) = (\lambda e^{-\lambda t_1})(\lambda e^{-\lambda t_2}) \cdots (\lambda e^{-\lambda t_n})$$

$$= \lambda^n \exp\left(-\lambda \sum_{i=1}^{n} t_i\right) \qquad (8.60)$$

The maximum-likelihood estimate is obtained by maximizing $L$ with respect to $\lambda$.   In general it is easier to maximize $\ln L$, which has the same maxima as $L$

$$\ln L(t_1, t_2, \ldots , t_n; \lambda) \equiv \mathcal{L}(t_1, t_2, \ldots , t_n; \lambda) = n \ln \lambda - \lambda \sum_{i=1}^{n} t_i \qquad (8.61)$$

Maximizing gives

$$\frac{\partial \mathcal{L}}{\partial \lambda} = \frac{n}{\lambda} - \sum_{i=1}^{n} t_i = 0 \qquad (8.62)$$

Solution of (8.62) yields

$$\hat{\lambda} = \frac{n}{\displaystyle\sum_{i=1}^{n} t_i} \qquad (8.63)$$

which is the MLE for a constant hazard.   The symbol $\hat{\lambda}$ indicates the

MLE of the parameter $\lambda$. Thus, both the moment estimate, Eq. (8.55), and the MLE, Eq. (8.63), are identical for a constant-hazard model. In general this is not true, as the next example will illustrate.

*Example 2*   For a linearly increasing hazard model

$$z(t) = Kt \qquad f(t) = Kte^{-Kt^2/2}$$

Formulating the likelihood function,

$$L(t_1,t_2, \ldots ,t_n;K) = (Kt_1e^{-Kt_1^2/2})(Kt_2e^{-Kt_2^2/2}) \cdots (Kt_ne^{-Kt_n^2/2})$$

$$= K^n \left( \prod_{i=1}^{n} t_i \right) \left[ \exp\left( -\frac{K}{2} \sum_{i=1}^{n} t_i^2 \right) \right]$$

$$\mathcal{L}(t_1,t_2, \ldots ,t_n;K) = n \ln K + \sum_{i=1}^{n} \ln t_i - \frac{K}{2} \sum_{i=1}^{n} t_i^2$$

Maximization yields

$$\frac{\partial \mathcal{L}}{\partial K} = \frac{n}{K} - \frac{1}{2} \sum_{i=1}^{n} t_i^2 = 0$$

Solving for $K$,

$$\hat{K} = \frac{2n}{\displaystyle\sum_{i=1}^{n} t_i^2} \tag{8.64}$$

In this case the moment estimate, Eq. (8.56), and the MLE, Eq. (8.64), differ, because they are based on different criteria.

Both of the examples derived above involve a single parameter, and only one maximized equation results. In the case of multiple-parameter distributions a set of maximization equations results, one for each parameter, which must be solved simultaneously.

*Example 3*   In the case of the two-parameter Weibull distribution

$$z(t) = Kt^m \qquad f(t) = Kt^me^{-Kt^{m+1}/(m+1)}$$

The likelihood function is

$$L(t_1,t_2, \ldots ,t_n;K,m) = (Kt_1^me^{-Kt_1^{m+1}/(m+1)})(Kt_2^me^{-Kt_2^{m+1}/(m+1)}) \cdots$$
$$(Kt_n^me^{-Kt_n^{m+1}/(m+1)})$$

$$= K^n \left( \prod_{i=1}^{n} t_i^m \right) \left[ \exp\left( -\frac{K}{m+1} \sum_{i=1}^{n} t_i^{m+1} \right) \right]$$

$$\mathcal{L}(t_1,t_2, \ldots ,t_n;K,m) = n \ln K + m \sum_{i=1}^{n} \ln t_i - \frac{K}{m+1} \sum_{i=1}^{n} t_i^{m+1}$$

Maximizing with respect to $K$ and $m$,

$$\frac{\partial \mathcal{L}}{\partial K} = \frac{n}{K} - \frac{1}{m+1} \sum_{i=1}^{n} t_i^{m+1} = 0$$

$$\frac{\partial \mathcal{L}}{\partial m} = \sum_{i=1}^{n} \ln t_i + \frac{K}{(m+1)^2} \sum_{i=1}^{n} t_i^{m+1} - K \sum_{i=1}^{n} t_i^m = 0$$

The first equation can be solved for $K$

$$\hat{K} = \frac{n(m+1)}{\displaystyle\sum_{i=1}^{n} t_i^{m+1}} \qquad (8.65)$$

Substitution of Eq. (8.65) into the second maximization equation and algebraic manipulation yield

$$\frac{\displaystyle\sum_{i=1}^{n} t_i^m}{\displaystyle\sum_{i=1}^{n} t_i^{m+1}} = \frac{1}{(m+1)^2} + \frac{\displaystyle\sum_{i=1}^{n} \ln t_i}{n(m+1)} \qquad (8.66)$$

Equation (8.66) may be solved graphically for $m$ by plotting both the left- and the right-hand sides vs. $m$, as done previously. This value for $m$ may be inserted in Eq. (8.65) to obtain $\hat{K}$.

*Truncated estimates*  Up till now we have discussed MLE for complete tests to failure, where the test is allowed to run long enough so that all items fail. In many cases this is impossible, and the test is terminated (truncated) before all items have failed. The following example illustrates the procedure for truncated tests.

*Example*  Suppose that 100 items are placed on life test, and after 1 year (8,760 hr) 10 of them have failed. For several practical reasons the test must be discontinued before the remaining 90 have failed. A sketch of the hazard function indicates that a constant-hazard model would be appropriate. If Eq. (8.63) is used to estimate $\lambda$, a wrong result is obtained. The mean failure time of the associated reliability function is $1/\hat{\lambda}$. Since the 10 failures have occurred within the year, the mean failure time given by $1/\hat{\lambda}$ is somewhat less than 8,760 hr, say 6,000 hr. But 90 percent of the items have survived 1 year; thus, if the tests were carried to completion (until all items have failed), the mean failure time would be greater than 1 year. The problem is that the data are truncated, and therefore the statistics must be altered to account for this. In simpler words, some credit must be given in the statistical estimation formula for the 90 items which have operated for 1 year without failure.

It is a simple matter to derive the maximum-likelihood function for a truncated test. Assume that from a population of $n$ items in time $T$, $r$ (where $r < n$) have failed with failure times $t_1, t_2, \ldots, t_r$. The density function governing failures of these items is $f(t;\theta)$. The probability that item 1 fails at $t_1$ hr is $f(t_1,\theta)\, dt_1$. The probability that item 1 fails at $t_1$ hr, item 2 at $t_2$ hours, $\ldots$, and item $r$ at $t_r = T$ hr and that the remaining $n - r$ items survive the test is the joint probability

$$f(t_1,\theta)\, dt_1\, f(t_2,\theta)\, dt_2, \ldots, f(t_r,\theta)\, dt_r\, [1 - F(T)]^{n-r}$$

since all these events are independent. However, the failure times $t_1, \ldots, t_r$ could have been assigned to the $n$ items in any one of the $n!/(n - r)!$ different possible permutations. Since each is a mutually exclusive event, the joint probability must be their product

$$\phi(t_1,t_2, \ldots, t_n;\theta)\, dt_1\, dt_2 \cdots dt_n = \frac{n!}{(n - r)!} \prod_{i=1}^{n} f(t_i)\, dt_i\, [1 - F(T)]^{n-r}$$

The likelihood function is the associated density function

$$L(t_1,t_2, \ldots, t_n;\theta) = \frac{n!}{(n - r)!} \prod_{n=1}^{n} f(t_i)[1 - F(T)]^{n-r} \tag{8.67}$$

Truncated MLEs are illustrated by the following examples.

*Example 1*   For a constant hazard, $f(t) = \lambda e^{-\lambda t}$ and $1 - F(T) = e^{-\lambda T}$. Substitution of these functions into Eq. (8.67) and performance of the familiar minimization process yields

$$\lambda = \frac{r}{\sum_{i=1}^{r} t_i + (n - r)T} \tag{8.68}$$

A denominator term $(n - r)T$ includes the effect of the $n - r$ components that survived for the $T$ hr of the test. In fact they are included in the same manner as if they had all failed suddenly during the last test hour.

*Example 2*   If the hazard function is best fitted by a Weibull model, then

$$f(t) = K t^m e^{-K t^{m+1}/(m+1)} \qquad \text{and} \qquad 1 - F(T) = e^{-K T^{m+1}/(m+1)}$$

the MLE are

$$\hat{K} = \frac{r(m+1)}{\sum\limits_{i=1}^{r} t_i^{m+1} + (n-r)T^{m+1}} \tag{8.68a}$$

$$\hat{m} + 1 = \frac{r}{K\left[\sum\limits_{i=1}^{r} t_i^{\hat{m}} + (n-r)T^{\hat{m}}\right] - \sum\limits_{i=1}^{r} \ln t_i} \tag{8.69}$$

Again the resulting formulas are the same as one would predict from the untruncated theory if all remaining survivors failed at the end of the test. The truncated results, Eqs. (8.68a) and (8.69), reduce to the untruncated results, Eqs. (8.65) and (8.66), when $r \to n$. To solve Eqs. (8.68a) and (8.69) one eliminates between the two to obtain

$$\frac{\sum\limits_{i=1}^{n} t_i^m + (n-r)T^m}{\sum\limits_{i=1}^{r} t_i^{m+1} + (n-r)T^{m+1}} = \frac{1}{(m+1)^2} + \frac{\sum\limits_{i=1}^{n} \ln t_i}{r(m+1)}$$

This equation is solved graphically for $m$ as in the untruncated case, and the resulting value of $\hat{m}$ is substituted into Eq. (8.68) to obtain $\hat{K}$.

*Example 3* The truncated nature of a piecewise linear model (Fig. 8.11) will now be treated. Region 1 is simply a case of a truncated constant-hazard problem, and the estimate for $\lambda$ is given by Eq. (8.68). If all the items have not failed by time $T_2$, the end of the test, then the data in region 2 are also truncated. In region 2

$$z(t) = \lambda + K(t - T_1)$$
$$f(t) = [\lambda + K(t - T_1)] \exp\left\{-\left[\frac{K}{2}(t - T_1)^2 + \lambda(t - T_1)\right]\right\}$$
$$1 - F(t) = \exp\left\{-\left[\frac{K}{2}(t - T_1)^2 + \lambda(t - T_1)\right]\right\}$$

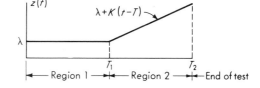

**Fig. 8.11**  A two-region piecewise linear model.

If $s$ additional items fail in region 2 between $T_1$ and $T_2$, then

$$\mathcal{L}(t_r, t_{r+1}, \ldots, t_{r+s}; \lambda, K, T_1) = \ln \frac{(n-r)!}{(n-r-s)!} + \sum_{i=r}^{r+s} \ln \left[ \lambda + K(t_i - T_1) \right]$$

$$- \frac{K}{2} \sum_{i=r}^{r+s} (t_1 - T_1)^2 - \lambda \sum_{i=r}^{r+s} (t_i - T_1)$$

$$- (n-r-s) \left[ \frac{K}{2} (T_2 - T_1)^2 \right.$$

$$\left. + \lambda(T_2 - T_1) \right] \quad (8.70)$$

Equation (8.70) contains three parameters, $\lambda$, $K$, and $T_1$. The parameter $T_2$ is an experimental constant, i.e., the duration of the test. One could minimize Eq. (8.70) with respect to parameters $T$, $K$, and $T_1$, respectively, and then solve the resulting three simultaneous equations for the estimates. However, in the case of the parameter $\lambda$, a good estimate has already been obtained from the data in region 1, and it seems reasonable to use this value. Also the parameter $T_1$ has already been determined in the solution for region 1, probably by inspection of the histogram of the data for $z(t)$. Thus, one need only minimize Eq. (8.70) with respect to the parameter $K$. This results in the expression

$$\sum_{i=r}^{r+s} \frac{\tau_i}{\lambda + K\tau_i} = \frac{1}{2} \left[ \sum_{i=r}^{r+s} \tau_i^2 + (n-r-s)(T_2 - T_1)^2 \right] \quad (8.71)$$

where

$$\tau_i = (t_1 - T_1)$$

This equation can be solved graphically by substituting various appropriate values for $K$. The above solution can be extended to a three- (or more) region piecewise-linear problem. One could also write piecewise-linear density and distribution functions for the entire problem and then minimize with respect to each parameter and solve the resulting equations.

*Combined data*   An important practical situation arises when data from two or more independent tests must be combined to obtain parameter estimates. To illustrate how a combined estimate can be obtained in such situations, the estimate will be derived for the case of a constant hazard. If test 1 runs for $T_1$ hr, producing $r_1$ failures out of $n_1$ items and test 2 lasts for $T_2$ hr, producing $r_2$ failures out of $n_2$ items, the individual likelihood functions are

$$L_1(t_1,t_2, \ldots ,t_{r_1};\lambda,T_1) = \frac{n_1!}{(n_1 - r_1)!} \prod_{i=1}^{r_1} f(t_1)[1 - F(T_1)]^{n_1-r_1}$$

$$L_2(t_1',t_2', \ldots ,t_{r_2}';\lambda,T_2) = \frac{n_2!}{(n_2 - r_2)!} \prod_{i=1}^{r_2} f(t_i')[1 - F(T_2)]^{n_2-r_2}$$

Since the two tests are independent, the overall likelihood function $L$ can be written as a product of $L_1$ and $L_2$, that is, $L = L_1 L_2$. Furthermore,

$$\mathcal{L} = \mathcal{L}_1 + \mathcal{L}_2$$

Setting $\partial \mathcal{L}/\partial \lambda = 0$ yields

$$\hat{\lambda} = \frac{r_1 + r_2}{\displaystyle\prod_{i=1}^{r_1} t_i + \prod_{i=1}^{r_2} t_i' + (n_1 - r_1)T_1 + (n_2 - r_2)T_2} \tag{8.72}$$

If several tests are involved, the estimator $\hat{\lambda}$ is simply the total number of failures divided by the total number of hours of operation. Of course similar estimators can be derived for Weibull and other hazard models.

*Tests with replacement* In many situations life tests are not limited by cost of items expended but by setup costs, monitoring costs, and especially time. One way of increasing the life-test data without changing the test size or test time is to replace failed components with new items as they fail. MLEs for tests with replacement can be derived as follows.

One can view a test with replacement as a sequence of tests. Defining

$$t_1, t_2, \ldots , t_n = \text{failure times}$$
$$n_i = \text{number of test items}$$
$$n = \text{original number of items}$$
$$T_i = \text{length of truncated test}$$
$$r_i = \text{number of failures in interval } 0 < t \leq T$$

we now decompose a test to replacement into a series of tests with

$$
\begin{array}{lll}
n_1 = n & r_1 = 1 & T_1 = t_1 \\
n_2 = n & r_2 = 1 & T_2 = t_2 - t_1 \\
\cdots & \cdots & \cdots \\
n_r = n & r_r = 1 & T_r = t_r - t_{r-1}
\end{array}
$$

Since each step is independent, we can write

$$L = L_1 L_2 \cdots L_r$$

and

$$\mathcal{L} = \mathcal{L}_1 + \mathcal{L}_2 + \cdots + \mathcal{L}_r$$

Using Eq. (8.67) and the previous definitions, we have

$$
\mathcal{L} = \frac{n!}{(n-1)!} + \ln f(t_1, \theta) + (n-1) \ln R(t_1) + \frac{n!}{(n-1)!}
$$
$$
+ \ln f(t_2 - t_1, \theta) + (n-1) \ln R(t_2 - t_1) + \cdots
$$
$$
+ \frac{n!}{(n-1)!} + \ln f(t_r - t_{r-1}, \theta) + (n-1) \ln R(t_r - t_{r-1}) \quad (8.73)
$$

For the case of a constant hazard

$$f(t,\lambda) = \lambda e^{-\lambda t} \qquad R(t) = e^{-\lambda t}$$

$$\mathcal{L} = \frac{rn!}{(n-1)!} + r \ln \lambda - n\lambda t_r$$

Maximizing by setting $\partial \mathcal{L}/\partial \lambda = 0$, we obtain

$$\hat{\lambda} = \frac{r}{nt_r} \tag{8.74}$$

It is simple to show how the data from two tests with replacement can be combined. If test 1 has parameter $r_1$, $t_{r_1}$, $n_1$ and test 2 parameters $r_2$, $t_{r_2}$, $n_2$, then

$$\mathcal{L} = \mathcal{L}_1 + \mathcal{L}_2 = \frac{n_1!}{(n_1-1)!} + \frac{n_2!}{(n_2-1)!} + (r_1 + r_2) \ln \lambda - (n_1 t_{r_1} + n_2 t_{r_2})\lambda$$

Maximizing, one obtains

$$\hat{\lambda} = \frac{r_1 + r_2}{n_1 t_{r_1} + n_2 t_{r_2}} \tag{8.75}$$

## 8.10 INTERVAL ESTIMATES

### 8.10.1 INTRODUCTION

The preceding sections have all discussed point estimates; however, it always conveys more information if one gives an interval estimate (confidence interval) and the associated probability (confidence coeffi-cient). This serves a role similar to a tolerance value: it gives the analyst some idea of how accurate the estimate is. In such a case the MLE is clearly the best choice since it is the only estimation which allows a simple computation of variance.

### 8.10.2 VARIANCE OF A MLE

For MLEs a simple formula exists, in the case of *large* $n$, for the variance (see Sec. 2.10.6). If $\hat{x}$ is the maximum likelihood estimate of $x$, then

$$\text{var } \hat{x} \xrightarrow[n \to \infty]{} - \frac{1}{\partial^2 \mathcal{L}/\partial x^2} \qquad (2.126)$$

Thus for $n$ (the number of test items) large, one need only take the second derivative of the natural log of the likelihood function and substitute it into Eq. (8.76). The following examples illustrate the computation.

*Constant hazard, MLE variance*  In the case of a constant hazard

$$f(t) = \lambda e^{-\lambda t}$$

$$L(t_1, t_2, \ldots, t_n; \lambda) = \prod_{i=1}^{n} \lambda e^{-\lambda t_i} = \lambda^n \exp\left(-\lambda \sum_{i=1}^{n} t_i\right)$$

$$\mathcal{L}(t_1, t_2, \ldots, t_n; \lambda) = n \ln \lambda - \lambda \sum_{i=1}^{n} t_i$$

$$\frac{\partial \mathcal{L}}{\partial \lambda} = \frac{n}{\lambda} - \sum_{i=1}^{n} t_i$$

$$\frac{\partial^2 \mathcal{L}}{\partial \lambda^2} = - \frac{n}{\lambda^2}$$

$$\text{var } \hat{\lambda} \approx \frac{\lambda^2}{n} \approx \frac{\hat{\lambda}^2}{n} \qquad (8.76)$$

Of course, since we do not know $\lambda^2$, we use $\hat{\lambda}^2$ instead.[1] This makes sense since the variance should of course decrease as we accumulate more data on which to base the estimate.

[1] The careful reader will question this statement on theoretical grounds even though it may seem correct on practical grounds. Actually one would have to compute the MLE for $\lambda^2$. This means setting $(\partial/\partial \lambda^2)\mathcal{L}(t_1, t_2, \ldots, t_n; \lambda^2) = 0$ and solving. Actually there is a theorem on invariance (see Sec. 2.10.6) that says that if $\hat{\lambda}$ is the MLE of $\lambda$, the MLE of some function of $\lambda$, $u(\lambda)$, is given by $u(\hat{\lambda})$. This is a very convenient feature of MLEs and fully justifies the substitution used.

*Constant hazard, truncated MLE*   In a truncated test with a constant hazard

$$f(t) = \lambda e^{-\lambda t}$$
$$1 - F(t) = e^{-\lambda t}$$

$$L(t_1, t_2, \ldots, t_r; \lambda, T) = \frac{n!}{(n - r)!} \prod_{i=1}^{r} \lambda e^{-\lambda t_i} (e^{-\lambda T})^{n-r}$$

$$\mathcal{L}(t_1, t_2, \ldots, t_r; \lambda, T) = \ln \frac{n!}{(n - r)!} + r \ln \lambda - \lambda \sum_{i=1}^{r} t_i - (n - r)\lambda T$$

$$\frac{\partial \mathcal{L}}{\partial \lambda} = \frac{r}{\lambda} - \sum_{i=1}^{r} t_i - (n - r) T$$

$$\frac{\partial^2 \mathcal{L}}{\partial \lambda^2} = -\frac{r}{\lambda^2}$$

$$\text{var } \hat{\lambda} \approx \frac{\hat{\lambda}^2}{r} \tag{8.77}$$

Thus, only the number of failed items contribute to narrowing the variance.

*Weibull hazard, MLE*   For the Weibull distribution

$$f(t) = K t^m e^{-K t^{m+1}/(m+1)}$$

$$\mathcal{L}(t_1, t_2, \ldots, t_n; K, m) = n \ln K + m \sum_{i=1}^{n} \ln t_i - \frac{K}{m + 1} \sum_{i=1}^{n} t_i^{m+1}$$

$$\text{var } \check{K} \approx \frac{\check{K}^2}{n} \tag{8.78}$$

$$\text{var } \hat{m} \approx \frac{1}{\dfrac{2n}{(m + 1)^2} - \dfrac{K}{m + 1} \displaystyle\sum_{i=1}^{n} t_i^m + mK \sum_{i=1}^{n} t_i^{m-1}} \tag{8.79}$$

*Weibull hazard truncated MLE*

$$f(t) = K t^m e^{-K t^{m+1}/(m+1)}$$
$$1 - F(t) = e^{-K t^{m+1}/(m+1)}$$

$$\mathcal{L}(t_1, t_2, \ldots, t_n; K, m, T) = \ln \frac{n!}{(n - r)!} + r \ln K + m \sum_{i=1}^{n} \ln t_i$$

$$- \frac{K}{m + 1} \sum_{i=1}^{r} t_i^{m+1} - \frac{K(n - r)}{m + 1} T^{m+1}$$

$$\text{var } \hat{K} \approx \frac{\hat{K}^2}{r} \tag{8.80}$$

$$\text{var } \hat{m} \approx \cfrac{1}{\cfrac{2r}{(m+1)^2} - \cfrac{K}{m+1}\left[\sum_{i=1}^{r} t_i{}^m + (n-r)T^m\right] + mK\left[\sum_{i=1}^{r} t_i{}^{m-1} + (n-r)T^{m-1}\right]} \qquad (8.81)$$

Now knowing the mean[1] and the variance of the distribution, one can start to make some intelligent probability-interval statements. An inequality due to Chebyshev predicts the probability that a random variable $\xi$ of *unspecified distribution* lies in an interval. Chebyshev's inequality states

$$P\big(|\xi - \mu| \geq K\sigma\big) \leq \frac{1}{K^2} \qquad (2.136)$$

where $\xi \equiv$ random variable with an arbitrary distribution
$\quad \mu \equiv E(\xi)$
$\quad \sigma^2 \equiv \text{var } \xi$

If one knows that the density function $f(\xi)$ has one maximum which occurs at the mean, then the sharper Gauss inequality can be used

$$P(|\xi - \mu| \geq K\sigma) \leq \frac{4}{9K^2} \qquad (2.137)$$

If one knows the form of the distribution, say that it is normal, a much better interval estimate can be made (see Sec. 2.10.8).

Although Eq. (2.126) has been used to compute the variance of the MLE's, nothing has been mentioned about the distribution.[2] In the discussion in Sec. 2.10.6 it was stated that the distribution of a MLE becomes approximately normal for $n$ large. Thus, one can make the following confidence statements:

1  One can be 68 percent confident that the true value of $x$ lies between $\hat{x} + \sigma_{\hat{x}}$ and $\hat{x} - \sigma_{\hat{x}}$.

2  For a 95 percent confidence band, $\hat{x} - 2\sigma_{\hat{x}} \leq x \leq \hat{x} + 2\sigma_{\hat{x}}$.

3  Only 0.3 percent of the time will the parameter $x$ lie outside $\hat{x} \pm 3\sigma_{\hat{x}}$.

[1] It is not strictly correct to assume that $\hat{x} = E(x)$. In fact the MLE is often biased and must be modified to $\hat{x}'$ in order that $\hat{x}' = E(x)$. The modification factor is often $n/(n+1)$; therefore, unless $n$ is small or a peculiar case is encountered, it is acceptable to use $\hat{x}$ for $E(x)$. The fact that the estimate $\hat{x}$ is not always unbiased is an annoying, but not serious, bad property of MLEs.

[2] Epstein has shown that for a constant hazard (exponential density) twice the accumulated test hours divided by the MTTF has a chi-square distribution with $2K$ degrees of freedom (see Miller and Freund, *op. cit.*, p. 373).

Note that statements 1 to 3 are worded slightly differently to illustrate the different ways of stating an interval estimate.

### 8.10.3  CONFIDENCE INTERVALS FOR RELIABILITY FUNCTIONS

Actually in many cases the interval estimate of the *hazard parameters* is only a first step in computing an interval estimate for the *part* reliability, which is in turn an intermediate step in solving the real problem of formulating an interval estimate for the *system* reliability. The latter is a difficult problem which is currently being studied. A good summary of the present state of the art is given by Rosenblatt.[1] The problem of how to relate a *hazard* confidence interval to a *part* confidence interval is treated below.

If one is dealing with an MLE for any sizable $n$, it is reasonable to assume that the estimate has a normal distribution. For illustration consider a constant hazard. In this case $R(t) = e^{-\lambda t}$, $\lambda$ is normally distributed, and we wish to find the probability density function for $R(t)$. This is a simple problem, but it results in a distribution which is not easily identifiable in terms of simpler well-known distributions. Instead of this problem, the transformed mean and variance will be found. This reduces to the problem of computing $E(e^{ax})$, where $x$ is normally distributed

$$E(e^{ax}) = \int_{-\infty}^{+\infty} e^{ax} \frac{1}{\sigma \sqrt{2\pi}} e^{(x-\mu)^2/2\sigma^2} dx$$

$$= e^{+(\mu a + a^2 \sigma/2)} \int_{-\infty}^{+\infty} \frac{1}{\sigma \sqrt{2\pi}} e^{-(1/2\sigma^2)[x-(\mu+a\sigma^2)]^2} dx$$

The integral is merely the area under a shifted normal density function, which is unity. Therefore

$$E(e^{ax}) = e^{\mu a + a^2 \sigma^2/2} \tag{8.82}$$

In the case of the constant-hazard reliability, $\lambda$ is the variable and $a = -t$. Thus substitution into Eq. (8.82) yields

$$E[R(t)] = E(e^{-\lambda t}) = e^{-(\hat{\lambda}t - \hat{\lambda}^2 t^2/2n)} \tag{8.83}$$

where the quantities $\mu$ and $\sigma$ have been replaced by their MLEs $\hat{\lambda}$ and $\hat{\lambda}/\sqrt{n}$.

If instead of computing the $E[R(t)]$ one computes $\hat{R}(t)$, the result is $e^{-\hat{\lambda}t}$ because of the previously stated theorem on functions of an MLE. Note that for small $t$ or large $n$, Eq. (8.83) also reduces to $e^{-\hat{\lambda}t}$. Equa-

[1] Joan R. Rosenblatt, Confidence Limits for the Reliability of Complex Systems, in M. Zelen (ed.) "Statistical Theory of Reliability," p. 115, The University of Wisconsin Press, Madison, Wis., 1963.

tion (8.83) is valid only for fairly large $n$, say $n > 10$.† To compute the variance of $R(t)$, one must compute $E(e^{2ax})$. Substitution of $2a$ for $a$ in Eq. (8.82) yields

$$E(e^{2ax}) = e^{2a^2\sigma^2+2a\mu}$$
$$\text{var } e^{ax} = E(e^{2ax}) - E^2(e^{ax}) = e^{2a^2\sigma^2+2a\mu} - (e^{a^2\sigma^2/2+a\mu})^2$$
$$= E^2(e^{ax})(e^{a^2\sigma^2} - 1) \tag{8.84}$$

Substitution into Eq. (8.84) yields

$$\sigma[R(t)] = e^{-(\hat{\lambda}t - \hat{\lambda}^2 t^2/2n)}(e^{-t^2\lambda^2/n} - 1) \tag{8.85}$$

For small $t$ or large $n$, Eq. (8.85) can be approximated by

$$\sigma[R(t)] = e^{-\hat{\lambda}t}(\lambda t/\sqrt{n})$$

If one were to construct a confidence interval $E[R(t)] \pm 2\sigma[R(t)]$, the result would be a band extending on either side of $E[R(t)]$, which would constitute a confidence band. Such a confidence band is shown in Fig. 8.12. If the transformed distribution were normal (actually it is not), the confidence coefficient would be 95 percent (see Table 2.7). If

† If $n$ is small, the assumption that $\lambda$ is normally distributed is no longer valid. Also the normal-distribution model for $\lambda$ assumes that $\lambda$ can become negative, i.e., the left-hand tail of the distribution trails off along the $-\lambda$ axis. Physically $\lambda$ must be positive; therefore, to minimize this effect, one chooses $\sigma < \mu/3$ so that the negative tail is out $3\sigma$ units and represents only about $\frac{1}{2}$ percent area. Since $u \sim \lambda$ and $\sigma \sim \hat{\lambda}/\sqrt{n}$, $n > 10$.

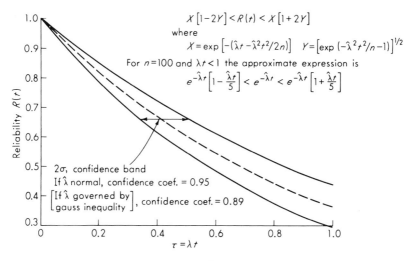

Fig. 8.12   Confidence band for $R(t) = e^{-\hat{\lambda}t}$.

only the Gauss inequality held, it would be 89 percent. The actual distribution probably yields a confidence coefficient which lies somewhere between these two.

The case of a Weibull distribution is somewhat more complex. The quantity $\hat{R}(t) = \exp[-\hat{K}t^{\hat{m}+1}/(\hat{m}+1)]$ is easily computed, but attempts to find the transformed density function or $E[R(t)]$ are difficult because of the complex manner in which the two parameters are involved. One technique is to assume that $\hat{m}$ and $\hat{K}$ have distributions entirely concentrated between maximum and minimum values; that is, $K_{min} < \hat{K} < K_{max}$, and $m_{min} < \hat{m} < m_{max}$. Then for any fixed time $t_1$, $R(t_1)_{max}$ and $R(t_1)_{min}$ are functions of $K_{min}$, $K_{max}$, $m_{min}$ and $m_{max}$. For small $t_1$

$$R(t_1)_{min} = \exp\left(-\frac{K_{max}}{m_{min}+1} t_1{}^{m_{min}+1}\right)$$

$$R(t_1)_{max} = \exp\left(-\frac{K_{min}}{m_{max}+1} t_1{}^{m_{max}+1}\right) \qquad t_1 < (m+1)^2 \qquad (8.86)$$

and for $t_1$ large

$$R(t_1)_{min} = \exp\left(-\frac{K_{max}}{m_{max}+1} t_1{}^{m_{max}+1}\right)$$

$$R(t_1)_{max} = \exp\left(-\frac{K_{min}}{m_{min}+1} t_1{}^{m_{min}+1}\right) \qquad t_1 > (m+1)^2 \qquad (8.87)$$

It seems reasonable to use $\hat{K} \pm \sigma_K$ for $K_{max}$ and $K_{min}$ and $\hat{m} \pm \sigma_m$ for $m_{max}$ and $m_{min}$. However, all one can say is that $R(t_1)$ probably lies between the respective values of $R(t_1)_{min}$ and $R(t_1)_{max}$. Since the statistics are unknown, no confidence coefficient can be stated for this situation. This discussion should be compared with the discussion of worst-case analysis in Chap. 7. If the reader is dissatisfied with the above solution to Weibull reliability confidence intervals, he can solve numerically for the transformed density function of $E[R(t)]$ and var $R(t)$.

## PROBLEMS

8.1 Assume that a 200-volt filter capacitor is placed across a 100-volt power source. Assume that the capacitor voltage (dielectric strength) is normally distributed with a standard deviation of 20 volts. Assume that the distribution of surge voltages on the line has a normal distribution with a mean of 100 volts and a standard deviation of 10 volts. Also the rate of occurrence of surges is 1 per month. Use Eqs. (8.3) and (8.8) to calculate the MTTF for this capacitor and sketch the reliability function.

8.2 Repeat Problem 8.1 if a capacitor with a mean dielectric strength of 400 volts and a standard deviation of 40 volts is used.

8.3 Assume that a resistor is operated at a temperature stress of 100°F. The strength density is assumed to have a Rayleigh density. The Rayleigh parameter is assumed to increase exponentially, as governed by the relation

$$K = 10^{-6} \exp 10^{-5}t$$

Use Eqs. (8.10) and (8.15) to compute the reliability.   Compute the MTTF and sketch the reliability and hazard functions.

8.4   Repeat Prob. 8.3 assuming that the strength has a Weibull distribution with $m = 2$, and use Eqs. (8.23) and (8.24).

8.5   Assume an accelerated-test result of the form

$$t_1 = \left(\frac{x_2}{x_1}\right)^n t_2$$

If a 1 percent experimental error occurs in each of the parameters, namely, $t_2$, the ratio $x_2/x_1$, and the exponent $n$, compute the error in $t_1$.   Sketch this error vs. $n$.

*The following four problems are extensions of Probs. 4.1 to 4.4.*

8.6   Using the data in Prob. 4.1,
   (a)   Compute a least-squares estimate of the hazard parameters.
   (b)   Compute a moment estimate of the hazard parameters.
   (c)   Compute MLE for the hazard parameters.
   (d)   Compute the standard deviation of the hazard parameters.

8.7   Repeat Prob. 8.6 for the data given in Prob. 4.2.

8.8   Repeat Prob. 8.6 parts c and d for the data given in Prob. 4.3.

8.9   Repeat Prob. 8.6 parts c and d for the data given in Prob. 4.4.

8.10   Compute the MLE of the parameter $K$ in a Rayleigh distribution for a test *with replacement*.

8.11   Compute the variance of $K$ in Prob. 8.10.

8.12   Comment on the trade-off between costs and accuracy for tests with and without replacement.   Base your discussion on the results derived in the text for $\lambda$ and var $\lambda$ for the exponential distribution and Prob. 8.10 and 8.11 for the Rayleigh distribution.

8.13   Suppose that a life test involving $n$ items is terminated when the first failure occurs at $T$ hr.   What is the estimator for $\hat{\lambda}$?   var $\hat{\lambda}$?   Comment.   Do you think that the formula for var $\hat{\lambda}$ has much meaning in this case?

8.14   Suppose that a life test on $n$ items is terminated after $T$ hr and that no failures have occurred.   Can you compute $\hat{\lambda}$?   Can you suggest a bound to be used in this case?

8.15   Prepare a summary table for exponential and Rayleigh distributions listing the MLE of the parameter and the standard deviation of the estimated parameter.   Include both ordinary and truncated tests as well as test with and without replacements (four combinations for each distribution.)

8.16   Preliminary data indicate that a certain component has a constant hazard rate of $10^{-3}$ per hr.   If 100 items are placed on test, use the MTTF to estimate how many hours $T$ would elapse before the first failure occurred.   Use the estimated density function $10^{-3} \exp 10^{-3}t$ and the binomial distribution to predict the number of failures in the same time period $T$ and compare them.

8.17   The var $\hat{\lambda}$ would be large in the test described in Prob. 8.16.   Keeping the same 100 test items, redesign the test length $T$ so that

$$\frac{2 \sqrt{\text{var } \hat{\lambda}}}{\hat{\lambda}} = 10\%$$

8.18 Repeat Prob. 8.17 keeping the same test time $T$ but increasing the number of items on test.

8.19 Sketch a curve of test hours along the $x$ axis and number of items on test along the $y$ axis, using the results of Probs. 8.17 and 8.18. Also sketch the curves for $2\sqrt{\mathrm{var}\,\hat{\lambda}}/\hat{\lambda} = 25$ and 1 percent.

How do these curves change if $\hat{\lambda}$ changes? Can you normalize these curves for any $\lambda$?

8.20 Plot a reliability function and a 95 percent confidence band for the motors tested in Prob. 4.2.

# *A*

# *analog computation*

An analog computer is a physical device which is constructed so that its output response to an input is governed by certain mathematical laws. If one can design the physical device so that its laws of behavior are identical with a particular mathematical equation, then the computer response is the solution to the mathematical problem. Analog computation is most simply described for the case of linear constant-coefficient differential equations and then extended to the solution of nonlinear and time-varying equations. To solve a linear constant-coefficient differential equation the analog computer must have devices which integrate (and/or differentiate), add and subtract, and multiply by a constant.

The first analog computers[1] were mechanical and used ball and disk devices for integration, differential gears for addition and subtraction, and gear ratios to multiply by constants. Modern analog computers are electronic[2] and use transistor amplifiers (the older versions used vacuum tubes) and feedback to perform integration and summation and simple adjustable potentiometers to achieve multiplication by a constant. For a number of practical reasons it is easier to integrate than to differentiate;

---

[1] One of the earliest mechanical analog computers was constructed by Vannevar Bush at M.I.T. in the 1930s.

[2] The chopper stabilization feedback circuit invented by E. Goldberg of RCA in 1948 made possible the first accurate, low-drift, vacuum-tube analog computers.

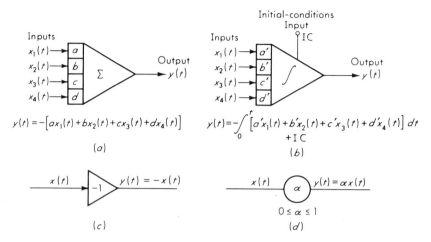

**Fig. A-1**   Basic electronic analog-computer components.   (*a*) Amplifier summer; (*b*) amplifier integrator; (*c*) inverter amplifier (sign changer); (*d*) multiplication by a constant (potentiometer).

therefore, equations are always manipulated so as to require only integration for solution.[1]

The basic electronic analog-computer components are shown in Fig. A-1.   Note that the components shown in Fig. A-1*a* to *c* are all built using electronic amplifiers and feedback networks, and by nature of their operation always multiply the output by $-1$.   The unit shown in Fig. A-1*d* is simply a very accurate potentiometer with a calibrated dial, which allows one to set the constant $\alpha$ to three-place accuracy.   The amplifier summer and amplifier integrator are built in two ways, depending on the manufacturer.

In the first arrangement one is supplied with packaged amplifiers with convenient input, output, and feedback plug-in terminals and a supply of accurate plug-in feedback resistors and capacitors.   A summer is formed from an amplifier unit by plugging in feedback resistors to form an appropriate circuit.   An amplifier integrator uses the same basic amplifier units but uses an appropriate plug-in circuit of resistors and capacitors.   This allows flexibility in the choice of the gains $a$, $b$, $c$, $d$, $a'$, $b'$, $c'$, $d'$, which depend on the resistor and capacitor values.

In the second arrangement, which is slightly less flexible and slightly more convenient, the manufacturer preselects the $R$ and $C$ values and builds them into the unit.   This discussion will assume that the packaged

[1] When one cannot avoid differentiation, one often incorporates a low-pass filter with the differentiator to alleviate some of the noise problems associated with a differentiation.

units already contain the resistors and capacitors and that the manufacturer has chosen the gains to be $a = b = 10$, $c = d = 1$, and

$$a' = b' = c' = d' = 1$$

Further details on the construction of electronic analog-computing components, often called operational amplifiers, can be found in the references.

The sign changer can be a separate unit or an amplifier summer in which we feed the single input signal into the unity gain input ($c$ or $d = 1$). The sign inverter is used to achieve subtraction by changing the sign and then adding and also to compensate for the inherent sign change of the amplifier summer or amplifier integrator when necessary. All variables are represented by electric voltages, and the computer has associated voltmeters and multitrack chart recorders for instantaneous monitoring and recording of the variables. The scheme used to solve constant-coefficient differential equations is illustrated below.

In order to solve an $n$th-order differential equation one needs $n$ integrations, $n$ coefficient potentiometers, and a few sign changers. As an example consider the third-order differential equation

$$\dddot{y} + c_2 \ddot{y} + c_1 \dot{y} + c_0 y = f(t) \tag{A-1}$$

with the initial conditions $\ddot{y}(0)$, $\dot{y}(0)$, $y(0)$. Because we are committed to using only integrators and no differentiators, we start our solution scheme by first solving for the highest derivative

$$\dddot{y} = -c_2 \ddot{y} - c_1 \dot{y} - c_0 y + f(t) \tag{A-2}$$

We assume that $\dddot{y}$ is known and compute its three integrals as shown in Fig. A-2$a$. Equation ($A$-2) tells us that $\dddot{y}$ is actually the sum of the four signals on the right-hand side of the equation, therefore the input to the $\dddot{y}$ summer must be a properly weighted combination of the four input signals, as shown in Fig. A-2$b$. Note that the product of the potentiometer gains and the $\dddot{y}$ integration input gains must satisfy Eq. (A-2). If any of the potentiometer settings turn out to be larger than unity, one inserts an amplifier (and sign changer if needed) to boost the gain. The initial conditions appear as a separate set of inputs, and their polarity must be adjusted as shown to correspond with the sign of the output. The input signal $f(t)$ can be obtained using conventional signal generations or special-purpose equipment. The initial-condition signals are obtained from a built-in accurate dc source and a potentiometer. Control relays are provided which automatically insert the initial conditions and the input signal when the problem start button is pressed at $t = 0$. (Thus, the dc source really supplies steps which can be integrated to give ramps or other functions which may serve as input signals.)

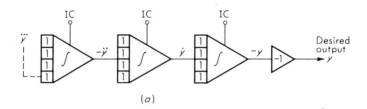

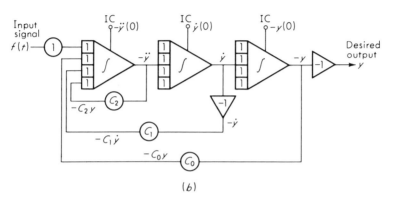

**Fig. A-2**  Analog-computer diagram for the third-order equation (A-1). (a) Generation of $-\ddot{y}$, $\dot{y}$, $-y$, from $\dddot{y}$ by three integrations; (b) solution of the equality by closing the loops around part (a).

Using the same techniques as described above, the following two coupled differential equations may be solved simultaneously:

$$\ddot{y}_1 + c_1\dot{y}_1 + c_2 y_1 = f(t) + c_3 y_2 \qquad \dot{y}_1(0), \; y_1(0)$$
$$\dot{y}_2 + c_4 y_2 = c_5\dot{y}_1 \qquad y_2(0) \tag{A-3}$$

The analog-computer diagram is given in Fig. A-3.

Nonlinear differential equations can be solved on an analog computer if the appropriate nonlinear function blocks can be made. The most fundamental nonlinear component block is the multiplier, which produces the product of two time signals, and this is the only one which will be mentioned here. The multiplier symbol is simply a circle with a times sign written inside with two input arrows and one output arrow. The following example illustrates how a multiplier can be used to solve many nonlinear and/or time-varying equations

$$\ddot{y} + \underset{\substack{\text{Time-varying} \\ \text{term}}}{f_1(t)\dot{y}} + \underset{\substack{\text{Nonlinear} \\ \text{term}}}{c_0\ddot{y}y} = f_2(t) \qquad \dot{y}(0), \; y(0) \tag{A-4}$$

The analog-computer diagram is given in Fig. A-4. A separate multi-

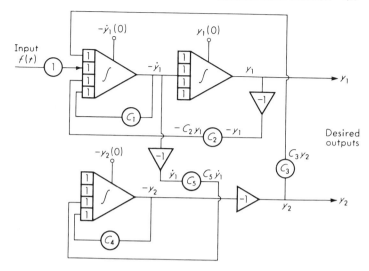

**Fig. A-3**  Analog-computer diagram for equations (A-3).

plier is required for the time-varying term and the nonlinear term.  In this problem two signals must be generated, $f_1(t)$ and $f_2(t)$.

This discussion has only hinted at some of the more sophisticated uses of the analog computer and is intended only to provide sufficient background so that the reader not previously acquainted with analog computers can understand their use in the solution of reliability problems.

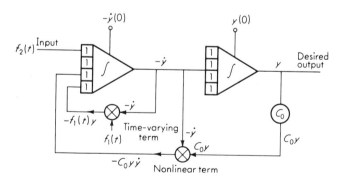

**Fig. A-4**  Analog-computer solution of a nonlinear and time-varying equation.

# numerical
# analysis
# and digital
# computation

A digital computer, like an analog computer, is built from many small elementary components. In the digital computer the building blocks are much simpler, but a large number are organized in an intricate fashion such that the digital computer is capable of much more sophisticated tasks. The first digital computers were vacuum-tube units.[1] Modern equipment is transistorized or uses integrated circuits and is capable of much higher computation speeds, yielding a tremendous increase in computational capacity per cubic foot.

The basic operations are addition and storage, which are simple to mechanize in terms of a binary or binary-coded decimal number system, which most computers use. Many other algebraic operations are possible by combination of addition and storage. The great flexibility and sophistication of the digital computer is realized by the interconnection of the simple blocks.

The set of sequential instructions which organize the computer operation is called the *program*. In order to simplify programming, certain simple algebraic operations are built-in, such as addition, subtraction, multiplication, division, raising to a power, logarithms, trigonometric functions, etc. Also in order to organize the computations efficiently it is

[1] The first digital computers were built in the 1940s at the University of Pennsylvania and Harvard University.

necessary to establish a certain set of control operations, e.g., place the decimal point; read the parameter values from data cards; perform a certain sequence of steps $n$ times, skipping certain steps; examine a number to see whether it is greater than, less than, or equal to zero; print out certain answers; stop. In early computers, the programming instructions were written in a symbolism called *machine language*. It was always necessary to convert from the algebraic or logical statement of the problem to machine language to write the program for the problem. Much effort has been placed on developing programming languages which are close to the algebraic statement of the problem. In the early 1960s program languages such as Fortran, Algol, Basic, etc., were developed to speed up the task of programming. In such cases the computer must compile (translate) between the program language and machine language. Thus, one pays a little extra computer time to use a simpler program language. The examples which follow will all be written in terms of the Basic language, since it is perhaps the simplest to explain. The following section discusses how one prepares a problem for programming.

If a problem simply involves computation of a formula involving algebraic, trigometric, or logarithmic terms, the formula is simply transcribed into program language. One merely substitutes the program-language notation for the respective algebraic symbols. If some special function, e.g., a Bessel function, is required, it can be computed by evaluating sufficient terms in the series expansion to obtain the required accuracy. Integration and differentiation require special treatment, however, which is discussed below. In order to solve differential and integral equations, derivatives and integrals must be approximated by algebraic manipulations. This general topic is called *numerical analysis*. There are many techniques employed in numerical analysis, but only the simplest are considered here.

To approximate the $\int_a^b f(t)\, dt$ one returns to the fundamental definition of the integral as the summation of infinitesimal area elements. One divides the range $b - a$ into $n$ small elements $\Delta t = (b - a)/n$ and computes

$$\int_a^b f(t)\, dt \sim \sum_{k=0}^{n-1} f(a + k\, \Delta t)\, \Delta t \tag{B-1}$$

of course as $n \to \infty$, $\Delta t \to 0$, and the summation converges to the integral.

Similarly, if one wishes to approximate the derivative $df(t)/dt$ over the range $a \le t \le b$, one divides the range into small elements $\Delta t = (b - a)/n$ and computes the derivative as

$$\frac{df(t)}{dt} \sim \frac{f(t + \Delta t) - f(t)}{\Delta t} \tag{B-2}$$

again as $n \to \infty$, $\Delta t \to 0$, and we have the definition of the derivative as a limit.    For the second derivative we compute

$$\frac{d}{dt}\frac{df(t)}{dt} = \frac{\dfrac{df(t + \Delta t)}{dt} - \dfrac{df(t)}{dt}}{\Delta t}$$

$$= \frac{\dfrac{f(t + 2\Delta t) - f(t + \Delta t)}{\Delta t} - \dfrac{f(t + \Delta t) - f(t)}{\Delta t}}{\Delta t}$$

$$= \frac{f(t + 2\Delta t) - 2f(t + \Delta t) + f(t)}{\Delta t^2} \tag{B-3}$$

As an example of the use of a digital computer in reliability work some simple reliability examples will be programmed on the GE data net computer using Basic computer language.

*Example*    If we consider a two-element system, there are three possible reliability configurations of interest.    If both elements must operate for the system to operate, the elements are in series

$$R = P(AB)$$

For independent units

$$R = P(AB) = P(A)P(B)$$

If both units have the same exponential failure distribution $f(t) = \lambda e^{-\lambda t}$, $P$ (no failure) $= e^{-\lambda t}$

$$R_1(t) = e^{-\lambda t}e^{-\lambda t} = e^{-2\lambda t} \tag{B-4}$$

If the system operates when either of the two units is working, the structure is a parallel structure, and

$$R = P(A + B) = P(A) + P(B) - P(AB)$$

Assuming identical independent units with an exponential failure law

$$R_2(t) = 2e^{-\lambda t} - e^{-2\lambda t} \tag{B-5}$$

for a two-element standby system the reliability function is [see Eqs. (2.32) and (2.33)]

$$R_3(t) = (1 + \lambda t)e^{-\lambda t} \tag{B-6}$$

We wish to compute a table of values of $R_1(t)$, $R_2(t)$, and $R_3(t)$ for several values of $t$ and compare the results.

The problem will be solved on the GE data net computer, a large computer which is time-shared by 40 different users.    The central computer is located in New York City and is connected by telephone lines to teletype consoles at each user's installation.   The Basic language (one of three which can be employed on this computer), as its name implies, is a rudimentary language which is ideal for people first learning how to use digital computers.   (It only takes 1 to 2 hr to learn the language and the teletype keyboard, which can be done simultaneously.)   Two features of Basic which make for great simplicity are that the computer automatically places decimal points and automatically spaces output data in appropriate columns.   The Basic language variables are coded by assigning to each one a name consisting of a single capital letter followed by a single decimal digit.[1]   (Subscripts and superscripts cannot be used in the conventional sense.)   Some of the algebraic symbols which are used in this language system are given in Table B-1.

Using the notation in Table B-1, we can define computational variables and rewrite Eqs. (B-4) through (B-6) as

$$E = LT$$
$$P = EXP(-LT) = EXP(-E)$$
$$R1 = P{\uparrow}2$$
$$R2 = 2{*}P - P{\uparrow}2$$
$$R3 = (1 + E){*}P$$

Since there are no Greek letters in this language, λ was changed to L.

The above sequence of variables was used in the program which appears in Table B-2, along with the introducing address to the computer.   The

[1] The decimal digit may be omitted if desired.

**Table  B-1  Algebraic  operations  in Basic computer language**

| Algebraic statement | Basic statement |
|---|---|
| $A + B$ | $A + B$ |
| $A - B$ | $A - B$ |
| $A \times B$ | $A{*}B$ or $(A)(B)$ |
| $A \div B$ | $A/B$ |
| $A^N$ | $A{\uparrow}N$ |
| $e^A$ | $EXP(A)$ |

**Table B-2    Computer program for reliability problem**

```
HELLO
TIME—16:07
USER NUMBER—N12661
SYSTEM—BASIC
NEW OR OLD—NEW
NEW PROBLEM NAME—RELCOM
READY.

10 PRINT "RELIABILITY COMPUTATION FOR TWO ELEMENT"
11 PRINT "SERIES, PARALLEL, AND STANDBY SYSTEMS"
20 PRINT "R1 = SERIES = EXP(−2LT)"
21 PRINT "R2 = PARALLEL = 2EXP (−LT)−EXP(−2LT)"
22 PRINT "R3 = STANDBY=(1 + LT) EXP(−LT)"
30 INPUT L
40 LET X = L/10
50 FOR T= 0 TO L   STEP X
60 LET E = L*T
70 LET P = EXP(−E)
80 LET R1 = P↑2
90 LET R2 = 2*P − P↑2
100 LET R3 = (1 + E)*P
110 PRINT "L="L
120 PRINT "T= "T, "R1 = "R1, "R2 ="R2, "R3= "R3
130 NEXT T
140 END
```

first seven lines, HELLO to READY, represent a dialog between the
computer and the operator to establish certain basic facts.   The program
is composed of statements 10 to 140.   Statements 10, 11 and 20 to 22
merely serve to label the program, for as far as the computer is concerned,
the only label is RELCOM.   The PRINT instruction tells the computer
to type whatever is within the quotation marks.   The label was broken
into five lines with five separate print instructions, since the computer
needs a new command each time the teletype carriage is returned to the
left margin.   Instruction 30 says that L is a datum which must be
inserted each time the program is run.   The computer will ask for it
when needed.   This allows us to run the program over and over again
for different values of L, the failure rate.   Instruction 40 defines X, the
time interval between our computations, to be L/10.   Instruction 50 is a
key one, which defines the sequence of time values T which will be used
in the computation.   In other words T advances sequentially from 0
to L in steps of X = L/10.   The LET instructions 60, 70, 80, 90, 100
tell the computer our sequence of computations in terms of the variable
names already decided on.   Instructions 110 and 120 print out the data
table labels as well as the computed values.   The material in quotes is

**Table B-3   Three runs of the program given in Table B-2**

```
RUN
WAIT

RELCOM      16:37 NY THU 07/07/66

RELIABILITY COMPUTATION FOR TWO ELEMENT SERIES,
   PARALLEL, AND STANDBY SYSTEMS
R1 = SERIES = EXP [−2LT]
R2 = PARALLEL = 2EXP[−LT] − EXP[−2LT]
R3 = STANDBY = [1 + LT]EXP[−LT]
?1
L = 1
T = 0       R1 = 1            R2 = 1            R3 = 1
L = 1
T = .1      R1 = .818731      R2 = .990944      R3 = .995321
L = 1
T = .2      R1 = .67032       R2 = .967141      R3 = .982477
L = 1
T = .3      R1 = .548812      R2 = .932825      R3 = .963064
L = 1
T = .4      R1 = .449329      R2 = .891311      R3 = .938448
L = 1
T = .5      R1 = .367879      R2 = .845182      R3 = .909796
L = 1
T = .6      R1 = .301194      R2 = .796429      R3 = .878099
L = 1
T = .7      R1 = .246597      R2 = .746574      R3 = .844195
L = 1
T = .8      R1 = .201897      R2 = .696761      R3 = .808792
L = 1
T = .9      R1 = .165299      R2 = .64784       R3 = .772482
L = 1
T = 1.      R1 = .135335      R2 = .600424      R3 = .735759

TIME:  2 SECS.
```

**Table B-3   Three runs of the program given in Table B-2** *(Continued)*

RUN
WAIT.

RELCOM 16:47   NY THU 07/07/66

RELIABILITY COMPUTATION FOR TWO ELEMENT SERIES,
 PARALLEL, AND STANDBY SYSTEMS
R1 = SERIES = EXP [−2LT]
R2 = PARALLEL = 2FXP [−LT] − EXP [−2LT]
R3 = STANDBY = [1 + LT] EXP [−LT]
?2

| | | | |
|---|---|---|---|
| L = 2 | | | |
| T = 0 | R1 = 1 | R2 = 1 | R3 = 1 |
| L = 2 | | | |
| T = .2 | R1 = .449329 | R2 = .891311 | R3 = .938448 |
| L = 2 | | | |
| T = .4 | R1 = .201897 | R2 = .696761 | R3 = .808792 |
| L = 2 | | | |
| T = .6 | R1 = .090718 | R2 = .51167 | R3 = .662627 |
| L = 2 | | | |
| T = .8 | R1 = 4.07622 E−2 | R2 = .363031 | R3 = .524931 |
| L = 2 | | | |
| T = 1. | R1 = 1.83156 E−2 | R2 = .252355 | R3 = .406006 |
| L = 2 | | | |
| T = 1.2 | R1 = 8.23000 E−3 | R2 = .173206 | R3 = .308441 |
| L = 2 | | | |
| R = 1.4 | R1 = 3.69786 E−3 | R2 = .117922 | R3 = .231078 |
| L = 2 | | | |
| T = 1.6 | R1 = 1.66156 E−3 | R2 = 7.98629 E−2 | R3 = .171201 |
| L = 2 | | | |
| T = 1.8 | R1 = 7.46586 E−4 | R2 = 5.39009 E−2 | R3 = .125689 |
| L = 2 | | | |
| T = 2. | R1 = 3.35463 E−4 | R2 = 3.62958 E−2 | R3 = 9.15782 E−2 |

TIME:   3 SECS.

**Table B-3   Three runs of the program given in Table B-2** *(Continued)*

RUN
WAIT.

RELCOM 16:50 NY THU 07/07/66

RELIABILITY COMPUTATION FOR TWO ELEMENT SERIES,
    PARALLEL, AND STANDBY SYSTEMS
R1 = SERIES = EXP[−2LT]
R2 = PARALLEL = 2 EXP[−LT] − EXP[−2LT]
R3 = STANDBY = [1 + LT]EXP[−LT]
?0.5
L = .5

| | | | |
|---|---|---|---|
| T = 0 | R1 = 1 | R2 = 1 | R3 = 1 |
| L = .5 | | | |
| T = .05 | R1 = .951229 | R2 = .99939 | R3 = .999693 |
| L = .5 | | | |
| T = .1 | R1 = .904837 | R2 = .997621 | R3 = .998791 |
| L = .5 | | | |
| T = .15 | R1 = .860708 | R2 = .994779 | R3 = .997324 |
| L = .5 | | | |
| T = .2 | R1 = .818731 | R2 = .990944 | R3 = .995321 |
| L = .5 | | | |
| T = .25 | R1 = .778801 | R2 = .986193 | R3 = .992809 |
| L = .5 | | | |
| T = .3 | R1 = .740818 | R2 = .980598 | R3 = .989814 |
| L = .5 | | | |
| T = .35 | R1 = .704688 | R2 = .974226 | R3 = .986362 |
| L = .5 | | | |
| T = .4 | R1 = .67032 | R2 = .967141 | R3 = .982477 |
| L = .5 | | | |
| T = .45 | R1 = .637628 | R2 = .959404 | R3 = .978182 |
| L = .5 | | | |
| T = .5 | R1 = .606531 | R2 = .951071 | R3 = .973501 |

TIME:  2 SECS.
BYE
***OFF AT 16:52.

simply printed.   For the variables L, T, R1, R2, R3 not in quotes, the computer looks into its memory for the most recent numerical value of that variable and prints it out.   Instruction 130 refers back to instruction 50 and moves the sequence back to 50 to go through the computation for another value of T.   Instructions 50 and 130 form what is called a *program loop*.   After the last step T = L, instruction 130 recognizes that instruction 50 is completed, and the program skips to 140, which indicates completion.

The program was run for L = 1.0, 2.0, and 0.5, and the results are given in Table B-3.   The instruction RUN signals the computer to process the program which has been composed, and the WAIT reply simply means another user is computing.   Waiting time is seldom more than a few seconds thanks to the great computer speed.   Print instructions 10 to 22 produced the five-line title.   The question mark in the ninth line is the computer's response to our number 30 input instruction. The reply immediately following is 1, meaning L = 1.   Notice how the computer has automatically spaced the data table to account for the number of digits.   The computer running time was 2 sec.   The time following the program name RELCOM is merely clock time, which allows one to calculate how long the telephone tie line was in use.   The second run is for L = 2.   Notice that for T = 0.8, R1 = 4.07622E − 2, which means R1 = $4.70622 \times 10^{-2}$.   The 3-sec running time must have been caused by the smaller values of reliability which were involved. The third run was for L = 0.5.   The command BYE disconnects the user from the system.

In retrospect when we examine the program, we see that if instruction 110 had been deleted and inserted as instruction 35, the PRINT statements L = 1, 2, 0.5 would have been moved outside the FOR-NEXT loop and would therefore have been printed only once as column headings.

The foregoing material should allow the reader who is unfamiliar with digital-computer computations to understand the programs used in this text.

# some useful integrals

This appendix tabulates some useful definite and indefinite integrals which constantly occur in reliability work. In most cases the integrand is an exponential function or the product of an exponential function and some other simple function.

These integrals are taken from one of the following three references:

W. Gröbner and N. Hofreiter: "Integraltafel," vols. 1 and 2, Springer-Verlag OHG, Vienna, 1957 (abbreviated [1]).
H. B. Dwight: "Tables of Integrals and Other Mathematical Data," The Macmillan Company, New York, 1961 (abbreviated [2]).
D. R. Cox: "Renewal Theory," John Wiley & Sons, Inc., New York, 1962 (abbreviated [3]).

The number given in the final column is the original number used in the source.

**Table of Integrals**

| No. | Integral | Source | Page | No. |
|-----|----------|--------|------|-----|
| 1 | $\int x e^{ax}\, dx = e^{ax}\left(\dfrac{x}{a} - \dfrac{1}{a^2}\right)$ | [2] | 134 | 567.1 |

**Table of Integrals** *(Continued)*

| No. | Integral | Source | Page | No. |
|---|---|---|---|---|
| 2 | $\int x^2 e^{ax}\, dx = e^{ax}\left(\dfrac{x^2}{a} - \dfrac{2x}{a^2} + \dfrac{2}{a^3}\right)$ | [2] | 134 | 567.2 |
| 3 | $\int x^3 e^{ax}\, dx = e^{ax}\left(\dfrac{x^3}{a} - \dfrac{3x^2}{a^2} + \dfrac{6x}{a^3} - \dfrac{6}{a^4}\right)$ | [2] | 134 | 567.3 |
| 4 | $\int x^n e^{ax}\, dx = \dfrac{x^n e^{ax}}{a} - \dfrac{n}{a}\int x^{n-1} e^{ax}\, dx$ | [2] | 134 | 567.8 |
|  | $= e^{ax}\left[\dfrac{x^n}{a} - \dfrac{nx^{n-1}}{a^2} + \dfrac{n(n-1)x^{n-2}}{a^3}\right.$ |  |  |  |
|  | $\left. - \cdots + (-1)^{n-1}\dfrac{n!x}{a^n} - (-1)^n \dfrac{n!}{a^{n+1}}\right]$ |  |  |  |
|  | for $n \geq 0$ | [2] | 134 | 567.9 |
| 5 | $\int x e^{-x^2}\, dx = -\tfrac{1}{2}e^{-x^2}$ | [1] | 109 | 3c |
| 6 | $\int x^n e^{-x^2}\, dx = -\tfrac{1}{2}x^{n-1}e^{-x^2} + \dfrac{n-1}{2}\int x^{n-2}e^{-x^2}\, dx$ | [1] | 109 | 3a |
| 7 | $\int (x-\alpha)^n e^{-h^2(\alpha-\beta)^2}\, dx$ |  |  |  |
|  | $= \displaystyle\sum_{\nu=0}^{n}\binom{n}{\nu}\dfrac{(\beta-\alpha)^{n-\nu}}{h^{\nu+1}}\int y^\nu e^{-y^2}\, dy$ | [1] | 109 | 4 |
| 8 | $\int F(x)e^{\lambda x}\, dx = e^{\lambda x}\displaystyle\sum_{\nu=0}^{N}\dfrac{(-1)^\nu}{x^\nu+1}F^{(\nu)}(x)$ |  |  |  |
|  | $\qquad + \dfrac{(-1)^{N+1}}{\lambda^{N+1}}\int F^{(N+1)}(x)e^{\lambda x}\, dx$ |  |  |  |
|  | where |  |  |  |
|  | $F^{(\nu)}(x) = \dfrac{d^\nu}{dx^\nu}F(x) \qquad F^{(0)}(x) = F(x)$ | [1] | 108 | 5a |
| 9 | $\int F(x)e^{\lambda x}\, dx = e^{\lambda x}\displaystyle\sum_{\nu=0}^{N}(-1)^\nu\lambda^\nu F_{\nu+1}(x)$ |  |  |  |
|  | $\qquad + (-1)^{N+1}\lambda^{N+1}\int F_{\nu+1}(x)e^{\lambda x}\, dx$ |  |  |  |
|  | where |  |  |  |
|  | $F_{\nu+1}(x) = \displaystyle\int F_\nu(x)\, dx \qquad F_0(x) = F(x)$ | [1] | 108 | 5b |

**Table of Integrals** *(Continued)*

| *No.* | *Integral* | *Source* | *Page* | *No.* |
|---|---|---|---|---|
| 10 | $\displaystyle\int R(x)e^{-(ax^2+2bx+c)}\,dx$ | | | |
| | $\displaystyle = \frac{1}{\sqrt{a}}\,e^{(b^2-ac)/a}\int R\left(\frac{\sqrt{a}\,y-b}{a}\right)e^{-y^2}\,dy$ | | | |
| | with | | | |
| | $\displaystyle y = \sqrt{a}\left(x+\frac{b}{a}\right)$    for $a > 0$ | [1] | 109 | 2 |
| 11 | $\displaystyle F(x)=\int_0^x \frac{\rho(\rho y)^{a-1}e^{-\rho y}}{(a-1)!} = 1 - \sum_{r=0}^{a-1}\frac{e^{-\rho x}(\rho x)^r}{r!}$ | [3] | 15, 20 | — |
| | (Erlangian density and distribution function) | | | |
| 12 | $\displaystyle\int_0^\infty e^{-ax}\,dx = \frac{1}{a}$ | [2] | 200 | 861.1 |
| 13 | $\displaystyle\int_0^\infty x^n e^{-ax}\,dx$ | | | |
| | $\displaystyle = \begin{cases} \dfrac{\Gamma(n+1)}{a^{n+1}} & \text{for } n > -1,\, a > 0 \\[2mm] \dfrac{n!}{a^{n+1}} & \text{for } n = \text{positive integer},\, a > 0 \end{cases}$ | [2] | 200 | 861.2 |
| 14 | $\displaystyle\int_0^\infty e^{-a^2x^2}\,dx = \frac{\sqrt{\pi}}{2a}$    $a > 0$ | [2] | 200 | 861.3 |
| 15 | $\displaystyle\int_0^\infty x e^{-x^2}\,dx = \tfrac{1}{2}$ | [2] | 200 | 861.4 |
| 16 | $\displaystyle\int_0^\infty x^2 e^{-x^2}\,dx = \frac{\sqrt{\pi}}{4}$ | [2] | 200 | 861.5 |
| 17 | $\displaystyle\int_0^\infty x^{2a} e^{-px^2}\,dx = \frac{1(3)(5)\,\cdots\,(2a-1)}{2^{a+1}p^a}\sqrt{\frac{\pi}{4}}$ | [2] | 200 | 861.7 |
| 18 | $\displaystyle\int_0^\infty e^{-x^p}\,dx = \frac{1}{p}\Gamma\left(\frac{1}{p}\right)$    $p > 0$ | [2] | 201 | 861.8 |
| 19 | $\displaystyle\int_0^\infty x^k e^{-\lambda x^2}\,dx = \tfrac{1}{2}\lambda^{-(K+1)/2}\Gamma\left(\frac{K+1}{2}\right)$ | | | |
| | for $K > -1,\, \lambda > 0$ | [1] | 64 | 2 |
| 20 | $\displaystyle\int_0^\infty x^{2n+1} e^{-\lambda x^2}\,dx = \frac{n!}{2\lambda^{n+1}}$ | | | |
| | for $\lambda > 0,\, n = 0, 1, 2, \ldots$ | [1] | 65 | 2b |

## Table of Integrals (Continued)

| No. | Integral | Source | Page | No. |
|---|---|---|---|---|
| 21 | $\int_0^\infty f(x)e^{-(ax^2+2bx+c)}\,dx$ $= \dfrac{1}{\sqrt{a}}\,e^{(b^2-ac)/a}\int_{b/\sqrt{a}}^\infty e^{-y^2}f\left(\dfrac{y}{\sqrt{a}} - \dfrac{b}{a}\right)dy$ $\text{for } a > 0$ | [1] | 65 | 5a |
| 22 | $\int_0^\infty f(x)e^{-\lambda x^m}\,dx$ $= \dfrac{1}{m(\lambda)^{1/m}}\int_0^\infty e^{-y}f\left(\sqrt[m]{\dfrac{y}{\lambda}}\right)y^{-(1-1/m)}\,dy$ $\text{for } m > 0, \lambda > 0$ | [1] | 67 | 13 |
| 23 | $\int_0^\infty x^K e^{-\lambda x^m}\,dx = \dfrac{1}{m}\,\lambda^{-(K+1)/m}\Gamma\left(\dfrac{K+1}{m}\right)$ $\text{for } K > -1,\, m > 0,\, \lambda > 0$ | [1] | 67 | 14 |
| 24 | $\int_0^\infty e^{-\lambda x^m} = \dfrac{\Gamma(1/m)}{m\lambda^{1/m}}\qquad \text{for } m > 0,\, \lambda > 0$ | [1] | 67 | 14a |
| 25 | Gamma-function identities $\quad(a)\quad \Gamma(n) = (n-1)\Gamma(n-1)$ $\quad(b)\quad \Gamma(n) = (n-1)!\quad$ for positive integer values $\qquad\qquad$ of $n$ $\quad(c)\quad \Gamma(\tfrac{1}{2}) = \sqrt{\pi}$ | | | |

# *number of Monte Carlo trials*

In Sec. 5.10.4 Monte Carlo methods were discussed, and it was pointed out that one of the major drawbacks is the large number of trials required in certain cases. A graph which allows one to estimate the required number of trials is given in Fig. 5.19. The purpose of this appendix is to discuss the basis of that graph.

One can view the outcomes of all the Monte Carlo trials as a set of experimental data. We are trying to estimate probabilities when we use Monte Carlo techniques in reliability work. Since each trial has a certain probability of success $p$, a probability of failure $q = 1 - p$, and the trials are independent, the trials have a binomial distribution. A good point estimate for the parameter $p$ (the required probability) is given as the ratio of success to total number of trials. When we ask for a confidence-interval estimate, the problem becomes more complex. We now must compute how many trials are needed to achieve a certain confidence coefficient. The problem is complicated, since the variance of the sampling distribution is a function of the probability to be estimated and also the binomial is a discrete distribution. A graphical solution to this problem is discussed in the references.[1]

---

[1] I. Miller and J. Freund, "Probability and Statistics for Engineers," chap. 10, Prentice-Hall, Inc., Englewood Cliffs, N.J., 1965; A. Mood and F. Graybill, "Introduction to the Theory of Statistics," p. 260, McGraw-Hill Book Company, New York, 1963; N. Roberts, "Mathematical Methods in Reliability Engineering," p. 72, McGraw-Hill Book Company, New York, 1964.

If the number of trials is large (as is generally the case in Monte Carlo analysis), one can make use of the nomial approximation to the binomial (see Sec. 2.6.8) for $p \leq 0.5$ and $np \geq 5$ or $p > 0.5$ and $nq > 5$. Since Fig. 5.19 deals with the high-reliability region, we are interested in how large $n$ must be for the normal approximation to hold. The most critical regions in Fig. 5.19 is for $p = 0.999$, $N = 40,000$ and for $p = 0.9$ and $N = 500$. At these two points $nq = 40$ and $50$, respectively, which clearly satisfies the approximation criteria. Using the normal approximation, we write the following probability statement with a 95 percent confidence coefficient

$$P(-2\sigma < x - \mu < +2\sigma) = 0.95 \tag{D-1}$$

where $x$ is the number of failures. If we substitute for $\mu$ and $\sigma$ in terms of the binomial parameters,

$$P(-2\sqrt{npq} < x - nq < +2\sqrt{npq}) = 0.95 \tag{D-2}$$

Dividing by $n$, we have

$$P\left(-2\sqrt{\frac{pq}{n}} < \frac{x}{n} - q < 2\sqrt{\frac{pq}{n}}\right) = 0.95 \tag{D-3}$$

where $q$ is the true probability, which is a parameter in the binomial distribution, and $x/n$ is the outcome ratio of the Monte Carlo experiment, which we take to be the predicted probability. Since $x$ is the number of experimental failures, $x/n$ and $p$ are failure probabilities.

Thus, we can write the percentage error (difference between actual probability and experimental outcome) as

$$\epsilon\% = \frac{x/n - q}{q} 100\% \tag{D-4}$$

Combining Eqs. (D-3) and (D-4), we obtain

$$\epsilon\% = 200\sqrt{\frac{p}{nq}} \tag{D-5}$$

For example, if $n = 10,000$ and $q = 0.01$, Eq. (D-5) yields

$$\epsilon\% = 200\sqrt{\frac{199}{10^4 \times 0.01}} \approx 20\%$$

This value of course agrees with Fig. 5.19.

# bibliography

## CHAPTER 1

The following list of references contains those cited in the chapter as well as 20 books on the subject of reliability. Various research journals which are solely devoted to reliability research are listed, as well as other references of a historic nature or of broad significance.

Aeronautical Radio, Inc.: "Reliability Engineering," Prentice-Hall, Inc., Englewood Cliffs, N.J., 1964.

Annual Reliability and Maintainability Conference Volumes, SAE, New York.

Balaban, M. S.: A Selected Bibliography on Reliability and Quality Control, *IRE Trans. Reliability Quality Control*, July, 1962.

Barlow, R., and F. Proschan: "Mathematical Theory of Reliability," John Wiley & Sons, Inc., New York, 1965.

Bazovsky, I.: "Reliability Theory and Practice," Prentice-Hall, Inc., Englewood Cliffs, N.J., 1961.

Boden, E. H.: *IRE Trans. Reliability Quality Control*, vol. PGRQC-13, July, 1958.

Calabro, S. R.: "Reliability Principles and Practices," McGraw-Hill Book Company, New York, 1962.

Chorafas, D. N.: "Statistical Processes and Reliability Engineering," D. Van Nostrand Company, Inc., Princeton, N.J., 1960.

Cox, D. R.: "Renewal Theory," John Wiley & Sons, Inc., New York, 1962.

Dummer, G., and N. Griffin: "Electronic Equipment Reliability," John Wiley & Sons, Inc., New York, 1960.

—— and ——: "Reliability Calculations and Design," Pergamon Press, New York, 1966.

Getting to Work and Back, *Consumer Repts.*, February, 1965.

Goldman, A., and T. Slattery: "Maintainability: A Major Element of System Effectiveness," John Wiley & Sons, Inc., New York, 1964.

"Handbook of Reliability Engineering," Bureau of Naval Weapons Handbook, NAVWEPS 100-65-502, 1964.

Haviland, R. P.: "Engineering Reliability and Long Life Design," D. Van Nostrand Company, Inc., Princeton, N.J., 1964.

Henney, K., et al.: "Reliability Factors for Ground Electronic Equipment," McGraw-Hill Book Company, New York, 1956.

*IEEE Proc. Ann. Symp. Reliability.*

*IEEE Trans. Reliability.*

IRE, Inc.: "Reliability Training Text," New York, 1959.

Ireson, W. G.: "Reliability Handbook," McGraw-Hill Book Company, New York, 1966.

Levenback, G. J.: System Reliability and Engineering Statistical Aspects, *Am. Scientist*, September, 1965.

Lloyd, D., and M. Lipow: "Reliability: Management, Methods, and Mathematics," Prentice-Hall, Inc., Englewood Cliffs, N.J., 1961.

Myers, R., et al.: "Reliability Engineering for Electronic Systems," John Wiley & Sons, Inc., New York, 1964.

Myers, R. H.: Which Road to Satellite Reliability, *Ann. Conv. Trans., Am. Soc. Quality Control,* 1961.

Nalos, E. J., and R. B. Schulz: Reliability and Cost of Avionics, *IEEE Trans. Reliability,* October, 1965.

Pierce, W.: "Failure Tolerant Computer Design," D. Van Nostrand Company, Inc., Princeton, N.J., 1966.

Pieruschka, E.: "Principles of Reliability," Prentice-Hall, Inc., Englewood Cliffs, N.J., 1963.

Redler, W. M.: Parts Reliability Problems in Aerospace Systems, *IEEE Proc. Sixth Ann. New York Conf. Electron. Reliability,* May, 1965.

*Reliability Abstracts and Technical Reviews*, NASA, Scientific and Technical Information Division, Washington, D.C.

Reliability of Military Electronic Equipment, Advisory Group on Reliability of Electronic Equipment (AGREE), Office of the Asst. Secretary of Defense, Washington, D.C., June 4, 1957.

Roberts, N.: "Mathematical Methods in Reliability Engineering," McGraw-Hill Book Company, New York, 1964.

Sandler, G.: "System Reliability Engineering," Prentice-Hall, Inc., Englewood Cliffs, N.J., 1963.

Weiss, G. H.: A Survey of Mathematical Models in the Theory of Reliability, in M. Zelen (ed.), "Statistical Theory of Reliability," The University of Wisconsin Press, Madison, Wis., 1963.

Zelen, M.: "Statistical Theory of Reliability," The University of Wisconsin Press, Madison, Wis., 1963.

## CHAPTER 2

The following textbooks are selected from among the many good reference works available on probability and statistics. For a reading guide to these and other probability texts, see the bibliography in Drake.

Bean, H. S.: "Differential Equations," Addison-Wesley Publishing Company, Inc., Reading, Mass., 1962.

Burington, R., and D. May: "Handbook of Probability and Statistics with Tables," McGraw-Hill Book Company, New York, 1953.

Courant, R.: "Differential and Integral Calculus," vol. 2, John Wiley & Sons, Inc., New York, 1964.

Drake, A.: "Fundamentals of Applied Probability Theory," McGraw-Hill Book Company, New York, 1967.

Fischer, R. A.: "Contributions to Mathematical Statistics," John Wiley & Sons, Inc., New York, 1950.

Franklin, P.: "Treatise on Advanced Calculus," Dover Publications, Inc., New York, 1964.

Freeman, H.: "Introduction to Statistical Inference," Addison-Wesley Publishing Company, Inc., Reading, Mass., 1963.

Freund, J.: "Mathematical Statistics," Prentice-Hall, Inc., Englewood Cliffs, N.J., 1962.

Hildebrand, F. B.: "Advanced Calculus for Engineers," Prentice-Hall, Inc., Englewood Cliffs, N.J., 1949.

Hoel, P.: "Introduction to Mathematical Statistics," John Wiley & Sons, Inc., New York, 1955.

Lloyd, D. K., and M. Lipow: "Reliability: Management, Methods, and Mathematics," Prentice-Hall, Inc., Englewood Cliffs, N.J., 1962.

Meyer, P. L.: "Introductory Probability and Statistical Applications," Addison-Wesley Publishing Company, Inc., Reading, Mass., 1965.

Miller, I., and J. Freund: "Probability and Statistics for Engineers," Prentice-Hall, Inc., Englewood Cliffs, N.J., 1965.

Molina, E.: "Poisson's Exponential Binomial Limit," D. Van Nostrand Company, Inc., Princeton, N.J., 1942.

Mood, A., and F. Graybill: "Introduction to the Theory of Statistics," McGraw-Hill Book Company, New York, 1963.

Munroe, M. E.: "Theory of Probability," McGraw-Hill Book Company, New York, 1951.

Owen, D.: "Handbook of Statistical Tables," Addison-Wesley Publishing Company, Inc., Reading, Mass., 1962.

Papoulis, A.: "Probability, Random Variables, and Stochastic Processes," McGraw-Hill Book Company, New York, 1965.

Pearson, K.: "Tables of the Incomplete Gamma Function," Cambridge University Press, New York, 1922.

"Tables of the Binomial Probability Distribution," National Bureau of Standards, Washington, D.C., 1950.

Thomas, H. B.: "Calculus and Analytic Geometry," 3d ed., Addison-Wesley Publishing Company, Inc., Reading, Mass., 1965.

Wadsworth, G. A., and J. G. Bryan: "Introduction to Probability and Random Variables," McGraw-Hill Book Company, New York, 1960.

## CHAPTER 3

Most of the techniques of this chapter are clear extensions of basic probability theory. The theoretical basis for the cut-set and tie-set approach is discussed by Essary and Proschan. A transformation-of-random-variables approach, not discussed in this chapter, is treated by Papoulis.

Barlow, R., and F. Proschan: "Mathematical Theory of Reliability," John Wiley & Sons, Inc., New York, 1965.
Bazovsky, I.: "Reliability Theory and Practice," Prentice-Hall, Inc., Englewood Cliffs, N.J., 1961.
Essary, J., and F. Proschan: Coherent Structures of Non-identical Components, *Technometrics*, vol. 5, no. 2, pp. 191–209, 1963.
Goldman, S.: "Information Theory," Prentice-Hall, Inc., Englewood Cliffs, N.J., 1953.
Messinger, M., and M. Shooman: Reliability Approximations for Complex Structures, *IEEE Proc. Ann. Symp. Reliability, New York*, 1967.
Papoulis, A.: "Probability, Random Variables, and Stochastic Processes," p. 193, example 7-6, McGraw-Hill Book Company, New York, 1965.
Shooman, M.: Reliability—Mathematics and Concepts, *Sperry Gyroscope Co. Tech. Mem.*, October, 1956.
——: Probability Theory Applied to Reliability, *Sperry Gyroscope Co. Tech. Mem.*, November, 1956.
——: A General Consideration of Multiple Failures, *Sperry Gyroscope Co. Tech. Mem.*, April, 1957.

## CHAPTER 4

The hazard function, which is the central theme of this chapter, was first used in actuarial work (see "Standard Mathematical Tables"). A classical reference to the hazard function is Carhart's report. The Weibull distribution (named after Weibull) represents a contribution by the reliability field to the field of probability.

Carhart, R. R.: A Survey of the Current Status of the Reliability Problem, *Rand Corp. Res. Mem.* RM-1131, Aug. 14, 1953.
"Failure Rate Data Handbook (FARADA)," Bureau of Naval Weapons, U.S. Naval Fleet Missile Systems Analysis and Evaluation Group, Corona, Calif.
Golant, A. S.: Comparison of MIL-HDBK-217A and MIL-HDBK-217, *IEEE Proc. Ann. New York Symp. Reliability*, Jan. 10, 1967.
Gunther, P.: Techniques for Statistical Analysis of Life Test Data, *General Electric Co., Advanced Tech. Lab. Rept.* 56GL278, Nov. 23, 1956.
Hoel, P. G.: "Introduction to Mathematical Statistics," sec. 4.2, John Wiley & Sons, Inc., New York, 1955.
Horn, R., and G. Shoup: Determination and Use of Failure Patterns, *IEEE Proc. Eighth Natl. Symp. Reliability Quality Control*, January, 1962.
Lloyd, D. K., and M. Lipow: "Reliability: Management, Methods, and Mathematics," Prentice-Hall, Inc., Englewood Cliffs, N.J., 1962.
"Reliability Stress and Failure Rate Data," Department of Defense, MIL-HDBK-217, August, 1962, and MIL-HDBK-217A, December, 1965.
"Standard Mathematical Tables," pp. 399 and 407, Chemical Rubber Publishing Co., Cleveland, Ohio, 1954.
Sturges, H. A.: The Choice of a Class Interval, *J. Am. Statist. Assoc.*, vol. 21, pp. 65–66, 1926.
Weibull, W.: A Statistical Distribution Function of Wide Application, *J. Appl. Mech.*, vol. 18, pp. 293–297, 1951.
Zelen, M.: "Statistical Theory of Reliability," The University of Wisconsin Press, Madison, Wis., 1963.

## CHAPTER 5

The most significant new topic introduced in this chapter is the Markov model, which is introduced in Sandler and treated in more depth in Kenemy and Muth. The dependent-probability and compound-probability methods, which are valid in situations where the Markov method fails, are discussed briefly in Bazovsky and the Aeronautical Radio book and in more detail by Messinger.

Aeronautical Radio, Inc.: "Reliability Engineering," Prentice-Hall, Inc., Englewood Cliffs, N.J., 1964.

"A Million Random Digits," The Free Press of Glencoe, New York, 1966.

Bazovsky, I.: "Reliability Theory and Practice," Prentice Hall, Inc., Englewood Cliffs, N.J., 1961.

Chambers, R. P.: Random Number Generation on Digital Computers, *IEEE Spectrum*, p. 48, February, 1967.

Drenick, R. F.: The Failure Law of Complex Equipment, *J. Soc. Ind. Appl. Math.*, vol. 8, no. 4, December, 1960.

Hammersley, J. M., and D. C. Handscomb: "Monte Carlo Methods," John Wiley & Sons, Inc., New York, 1964.

Jolley, L. B. W.: "Summation of Series," Dover Publications, Inc., New York, 1961.

Kart, J.: Effects of Thermal Proximity on Transistor Reliability, M.S. project Department of Electrical Engineering, Polytechnic Institute of Brooklyn, New York, June, 1965.

Kenemy, J., and J. Snell: "Finite Markov Chains," D. Van Nostrand Company, Inc., Princeton, N.J., 1960.

Messinger, M.: Models, Analysis, and Approximations for System Reliability and Availability, Ph.D. dissertation in system science, Polytechnic Institute of Brooklyn, New York, June, 1967.

———— and M. Shooman: Exponential and Weibull Approximations for Chain Structures, *IEEE Proc. Ann. Reliability Symp.*, New York, 1968.

Monte Carlo Method, *Natl. Bur. Std. Appl. Mech. Ser.* 12, June, 1951.

Muth, E.: Stochastic Theory of Repairable Systems, Ph.D. dissertation in system science, Polytechnic Institute of Brooklyn, New York, June, 1967.

Sandler, G.: "System Reliability Engineering," Prentice-Hall, Inc., Englewood Cliffs, N.J., 1963.

Shooman, M.: Models for Systems with Dependent Failures, *Proc. Twelfth Natl. Symp. Reliability Quality Control*, January, 1966.

Thomas, G. B.: "Calculus and Analytic Geometry," 3d ed., Addison-Wesley Publishing Company, Inc., Reading, Mass., 1965.

## CHAPTER 6

This chapter contains a wide variety of techniques for improving system reliability. Two of the most interesting areas are digital redundancy (see Pierce, von Neumann, and Moore) and repairable systems (see Cox and Muth).

Barlow, R. E., and L. C. Hunter: Reliability Analysis of a One Unit System, *J. Operations Res. Soc. Am.*, vol. 9, no. 2, March–April, 1961.

Chu, Y.: "Digital Computer Design Fundamentals," McGraw-Hill Book Company, New York, 1962.

Cole, G., et al.: Study of Pilot-Controller Integration for Emergency Conditions,

R7D-7DR-63-4092, *Wright-Patterson Air Force Base Tech. Doc. Rept.*, January, 1964.

Cox, D. R.: "Renewal Theory," John Wiley & Sons, Inc., New York, 1962.

Geissler, W., and R. P. Gillooly: "The Gemini Attitude and Maneuvering Control Systems," McDonnell Aircraft Co., St. Louis, Mo., 1963.

Grisamone, N.: Calculation of Circuit Reliability by Use of von Neumann Redundancy Logic Analysis, *IEEE Proc. Fourth Ann. New York Conf. Electron. Reliability*, October, 1963.

"Handbook for Systems Applications of Redundancy," U.S. Naval Applied Science Laboratory, August, 1966.

"How Effective Are Dual Brakes?" *Consumer Repts.*, August, 1965, p. 410.

Ireson, W. G.: "Reliability Handbook," McGraw-Hill Book Company, New York, 1966.

Knox-Seith, J. K.: A Redundancy Technique for Improving the Reliability of Digital Systems, *Stanford Electron. Lab. Tech. Rept.* 4816-1, December, 1963.

McRuer, D., et al.: Human Pilot Dynamics in Compensatory Systems, *Wright-Patterson Air Force Base Tech. Rept.* AFFD2-TR-65-15, July, 1965.

Messinger, M., and M. Shooman: Models, Analysis, and Approximations for System Reliability and Availability, Ph.D. dissertation in system science, Polytechnic Institute of Brooklyn, New York, June, 1967.

Miller, E.: Reliability Aspects of the Variable Instruction Computer, *IEEE Trans. Elect. Comp.*, vol. EC-16, no. 5, October, 1967, p. 596.

Moore, E. F., and C. E. Shannon: Reliable Circuits Using Less Reliable Relays, *J. Franklin Inst.*, pt. 2, October, 1956.

Muth, E.: "Stochastic Theory of Repairable Systems," Ph.D. dissertation in system science, Polytechnic Institute of Brooklyn, New York, June, 1967.

Neuman, J. von: Probabilistic Logics and the Synthesis of Reliable Organisms from Unreliable Components, in C. Shannon and K. McCarthy (eds.), "Automata Studies," Princeton University Press, Princeton, N.J., 1956.

Pearson, K.: "Tables of the Incomplete Gamma Function," Cambridge University Press, New York, 1922.

Pierce, W. H.: "Failure Tolerant Computer Design," D. Van Nostrand Company, Inc., Princeton, N.J., 1966.

————: Improving the Reliability of Digital Systems by Redundancy and Adaption, *Stanford Electron. Lab. Tech. Rept.* 1552–3, July, 1961.

Redler, W. M.: "Parts Reliability Problems in Aerospace Systems," *Proc. Sixth Ann. New York Conf. Electron Reliability*, May, 1965.

"Reliability Stress and Failure Rate Data," Department of Defense, MIL-HDBK-217, August, 1962.

Roberts, N.: "Mathematical Methods in Reliability Engineering," McGraw-Hill Book Company, New York, 1964.

Sandler, G.: "System Reliability Engineering," Prentice-Hall, Inc., Englewood Cliffs, N.J., 1963.

Shooman, M. L.: "Comparison of Component Redundancy with Unit Redundancy," *Sperry Gyroscope Co. Tech. Mem.* 3280, April 18, 1957.

"A Study of the Feasibility of Using Artificial Neurons to Develop More Reliable Flight Control Systems," *Wright-Patterson Air Force Base Tech. Rept.* ASD-TDR-63–143, April, 1963.

Takacs, L.: "On Certain Sojourn Time Problems in the Theory of Stochastic Processes," *Acta. Math. Hung.*, 1957, p. 169.

Tsien, H.: "Engineering Cybernetics," McGraw-Hill Book Company, New York, 1954.

Wolf, J.: Notes on Coding for Course EE115, Department of Electrical Engineering, Polytechnic Institute of Brooklyn, New York, September, 1966.

Young, L., and R. Winblade: M.I.T.–NASA Working Conference on Manual Control, *IEEE Spectrum*, November, 1966, p. 88.

## CHAPTER 7

In some ways the subject of this chapter is merely an application of the techniques of transformation of a random variable. This subject is well covered in the probability texts which are cited. Another theoretical treatment in terms of network and control-system sensitivity functions can be found in Belove and Truxal, respectively. The engineering approximations necessary to solve many practical problems are discussed in some of the other references.

Belove, C.: The Sensitivity Function in Variability Analysis, *IEEE Trans. Reliability*, vol. R-15, no. 2, 1966.

Connor, J.: R. M. Myers et al. (eds.), chap. 4 in "Reliability Engineering for Electronic Systems," John Wiley & Sons, Inc., New York, 1964.

Final Report on Prediction of Circuit Drift Malfunctions of Satellite Systems, *IBM FSD Space Guidance Center, ASTIA* 276044, September, 1961.

Freeman, H.: "Introduction to Statistical Inference," Addison-Wesley Publishing Company, Inc., Reading, Mass., 1963.

Freund, J.: "Mathematical Statistics," Prentice-Hall Inc., Englewood Cliffs, N.J., 1962.

Hoel, P.: "Introduction to Mathematical Statistics," John Wiley & Sons, Inc., New York, 1954.

Menon, M. V.: Problems Arising in Considering the Distribution of Equivalent Resistance, *IBM Gen. Prod. Develop. Lab. TR*02.163, *Tech. Rept.* June, 1961.

Munroe, M. E.: "Theory of Probability," McGraw-Hill Book Company, New York, 1951.

Papoulis, A.: "Probability, Random Variables, and Stochastic Processes," McGraw-Hill Book Company, New York, 1965.

Shooman, M.: "Stability Analysis of Two Parameter Systems," D.E.E. dissertation, Polytechnic Institute of Brooklyn, New York, June, 1961.

————: Determination of Variations in System Performance Resulting from Component Variations, *Sperry Gyroscope Co. Tech. Mem.* 314034, July, 1957.

————: Mathematical Models for Drift Failure Analysis, *Eleventh Natl. Sym. Reliability Quality Control*, vol. R-15, no. 2, 1966.

Taylor, N. H.: Designing for Reliability, *Proc. IRE*, June, 1957.

Truxal, J. G.: "Control Engineer's Handbook," p. 4-47, McGraw-Hill Book Company, New York, 1958.

Wadsworth, G., and J. Bryan: "Introduction to Probability and Random Variables," McGraw-Hill Book Company, New York, 1960.

Wall, H.: Circuit Analysis by Computer, *Electro-Technology*, November, 1966.

## CHAPTER 8

The first half of this chapter on reliability physics is a new area in reliability (and for that matter the physical sciences). For an idea of the diversity of ideas see the book edited by Goldberg (listed under Levinson). The second half treats some of the life-test aspects of reliability. Most of the work concerning the exponential distribution was done by Epstein. Freund's books give a good introduction to this area of statistics from a broader viewpoint.

Aranoff, S.: "Derivation of a Stress-Strength Reliability Model for Electronic Components with Application to Life Tests," M.S. thesis, Polytechnic Institute of Brooklyn, New York, June, 1968.

Blakemore, G. J.: On the Use of Weibull Sampling Plans, *Proc. Conf. Reliability Assurance Tech. Semicond. Specifications*, Washington, D.C., 1961.

Cole, G., et al: Study of Pilot-Controller Integration for Emergency Conditions, *Wright-Patterson Air Force Base Tech. Doc.* Rept. RTD-TDR-63-4092, January, 1964.

Disney, R. L., C. Lipson, and N. J. Sheth: The Determination of the Probability of Failure by Stress/Strength Interference Theory, *IEEE Symp. Reliability*, January, 1968.

Epstein, B.: Tests for the Validity of the Assumption That the Underlying Distribution of Life Is Exponential, *Dept. of Defense Tech. Rept.*, November, 1960.

Freund, J.: "Mathematical Statistics," Prentice-Hall, Inc., Englewood Cliffs, N.J., 1962.

Glasstone, S., K. Laidler, and H. Eyring: "The Theory of Rate Processes," McGraw-Hill Book Company, New York, 1941.

Haviland, R. P.: "Engineering Reliability and Long Life Design," D. Van Nostrand Company, Inc., Princeton, N.J., 1964.

Hoel, P. G.: "Introduction to Mathematical Statistics," John Wiley & Sons, Inc., 1954.

Kao, J. H. K.: A Summary of Some New Techniques for Failure Analysis, *Proc. Sixth Natl. Symp. Reliability*, Washington, D.C., January, 1960, p. 193.

Kornblum, S.: Serial Choice Reaction Time: Inadequacies of the Information Hypothesis, *Science*, vol. 159, no. 3813, p. 432, January, 1968.

Levinson, D. W., and R. G. Pohl: Failure Physics, in M. F. Goldberg (ed.), "Physics of Failure in Electronics," Spartan Books, Inc., Baltimore, 1963.

Lloyd, D. K., and M. Lipow: "Reliability: Management, Methods, Mathematics," Prentice-Hall, Inc., Englewood Cliffs, N.J., 1962.

Miller, I., and J. Freund: "Probability and Statistics for Engineers," Prentice-Hall, Inc., Englewood Cliffs, N.J., 1965.

Pieruschka, E.: "Principles of Reliability," chap. 14, Prentice-Hall, Inc., Englewood Cliffs, N.J., 1963.

Rosenblatt, J. R.: Confidence Limits for the Reliability of Complex Systems, in M. Zelan (ed.), "Statistical Theory of Reliability," The University of Wisconsin Press, Madison, Wis., 1963.

Schwartz, M.: "Information Transmission, Modulation, and Noise," McGraw-Hill Book Company, New York, 1959.

Young, L., and R. Winblade: M.I.T.-NASA Working Conference on Manual Control, *IEEE Spectrum*, November, 1966, p. 88.

# *name index*

# subject index

*Numbers in parentheses that follow page references, indicate "Problems."*